Jonathan Lytton

Annual Review of
Biophysics and
Biomolecular Structure

ANNUAL REVIEW OF BIOPHYSICS AND BIOMOLECULAR STRUCTURE

VOLUME 29, 2000

ROBERT M. STROUD, *Editor*
University of California, San Francisco

WILMA K. OLSON, *Associate Editor*
Rutgers, The State University of New Jersey

MICHAEL P. SHEETZ, *Associate Editor*
Duke University, Durham

www.AnnualReviews.org   science@AnnualReviews.org   650-493-4400

ANNUAL REVIEWS
4139 El Camino Way • P.O. Box 10139 • Palo Alto, California 94303-0139

ANNUAL REVIEWS
Palo Alto, California, USA

International Standard Serial Number: 1056-8700
International Standard Book Number: 0-8243-1829-3
Library of Congress Catalog Card Number: 79-188446

TYPESET BY TECHBOOKS, FAIRFAX, VA
PRINTED AND BOUND IN THE UNITED STATES OF AMERICA

CONTENTS

ANNUAL REVIEWS is a nonprofit scientific publisher established to promote the advancement of the sciences. Beginning in 1932 with the *Annual Review of Biochemistry*, the Company has pursued as its principal function the publication of high-quality, reasonably priced *Annual Review* volumes. The volumes are organized by Editors and Editorial Committees who invite qualified authors to contribute critical articles reviewing significant developments within each major discipline. The Editor-in-Chief invites those interested in serving as future Editorial Committee members to communicate directly with him. Annual Reviews is administered by a Board of Directors, whose members serve without compensation.

Annu. Rev. Biophys. Biomol. Struct. 2000. 29:1–26

MEASURING THE FORCES THAT CONTROL PROTEIN INTERACTIONS

Deborah Leckband

*Department of Chemical Engineering and the Center for Biophysics and Computational
Biology, University of Illinois at Urbana-Champaign, Urbana, Illinois 61801;
e-mail: leckband@uiuc.edu*

Key Words   molecular forces, force probes, receptor, intermolecular potentials,
unfolding

■ **Abstract**   Although the force fields and interaction energies that control protein
behavior can be inferred indirectly from equilibrium and kinetic measurements, recent
developments have made it possible to quantify directly (*a*) the ranges, magnitudes, and
time dependence of the interaction energies and forces between biological materials;
(*b*) the mechanical properties of isolated proteins; and (*c*) the strength of single receptor-
ligand bonds. This review describes recent results obtained by using the atomic force
microscope, optical tweezers, the surface force apparatus, and micropipette aspiration
to quantify short-range protein-ligand interactions and the long-range, nonspecific
forces that together control protein behavior. The examples presented illustrate the
power of force measurements to quantify directly the force fields and energies that
control protein behavior.

CONTENTS

1056-8700/00/0610-0001$14.00   1

INTRODUCTION

Protein interactions with ligands, other proteins, or surfaces are controlled by a complex array of intermolecular and intersurface forces. Soluble antibody binding to cell surface antigens, for example, involves specific, lock-and-key interactions, which are mediated by multiple hydrogen bonds, van der Waals interactions, and hydrophobic and steric contacts within the antibody-binding site. To focus on only the binding site, however, neglects the important influence of several nonspecific electrostatic, van der Waals, and steric forces that operate outside the binding pocket between the antibody surface and the target membrane. These forces are superimposed on the lock-and-key interaction and can alter not only the binding kinetics but also the equilibrium distribution of receptor-ligand bonds. This interplay of specific and nonspecific forces controls all protein interactions ranging from bimolecular collisions in solution to adhesion between cells.

The forces that control protein behavior and their physical chemical origins are typically inferred indirectly from equilibrium binding and kinetic measurements or are calculated with molecular models. From changes in association rates caused by site-directed mutations, for example, one might infer the contribution of charged amino acids to the long-range receptor-ligand forces. Alternatively, calculated energies are used to identify the role of physical chemical interactions in protein function and behavior. Although detailed calculations are feasible for small molecules, such calculations become prohibitive with the increasing size and complexity of biological macromolecules and their state of aggregation, the number of solvent molecules involved, and the range of the interactions.

Time-dependent forces between soft or mobile species add yet another degree of complexity. Because of the importance of dynamics in biology, static models of intermolecular or intersurface interactions do not describe the full range of parameters that influence biological behavior. Some computational approaches such as Brownian dynamics simulations do address these issues, but they are subject to the accuracy of the force fields used and have limited applications. A goal of many biophysical studies is to determine the molecular forces that control biological interactions and to use this information to rationally manipulate, for example, protein function. This capability is currently limited by our inability to quantitatively link molecular architecture, composition, and dynamics to the force fields that govern the behavior of complex biological molecules such as proteins.

Force measurements provide powerful means of directly quantifying the complex interactions that determine the properties of biological molecules and biomaterials. With the recent, rapid development of several force probes, one can now measure directly (*a*) the ranges, magnitudes, and time dependence of the interaction energies and forces between materials; (*b*) the mechanical properties of isolated proteins; and (*c*) the strength of single receptor-ligand bonds. The combination of these measurement techniques with (*a*) structural information, (*b*) the ability to construct well-defined model systems, and (*c*) computer simulations has made it possible to establish quantitatively how the composition, architecture, and dynamics govern interactions in biology.

Biological force measurements encompass many different measurement techniques. This review focuses, in particular, on approaches that (*a*) quantify directly the ranges, magnitudes, and dynamics of forces in protein interactions and (*b*) elucidate the detailed relationships between chemistry, molecular structure, physical chemistry of bond formation or rupture, and bond energetics. We first consider measurements of the specific and the nonspecific forces that together control protein behavior. The review then focuses on force measurements of single proteins and the theoretical developments that recently clarified how such forces relate to the protein bond chemistry. The final section addresses multivalent protein interactions and the use of force measurements to establish how these interactions differ from those of single, isolated protein-ligand bonds. Together, the examples presented illustrate the power of direct measurements to identify the fundamental forces that control protein interactions.

FORCES IN BIOLOGICAL INTERACTIONS

Nonspecific Interactions

Electrostatic Double-Layer Force   The electrostatic double-layer force between charged particles is one of the principal long-range forces that govern biological interactions. In aqueous solutions, the charges on the particle surface are balanced by an electrical double layer of ions in solution. This layer increases the ion concentration in the gap between the interacting particles relative to the bulk solution. The resulting osmotic pressure between the surfaces is the basis of the repulsive (or attractive) "double-layer" force (32). Except at small separations, it decays exponentially with the distance D as $e^{-\kappa D}$, where κ^{-1} is the Debye screening length. The latter depends on the solution dielectric constant and the ion concentration (32). The surface charge density determines the counterion concentration near the surface and hence the magnitude of the double-layer force. This force also depends on geometry. For example, between a spherical probe tip and a flat surface, the magnitude scales with the tip radius R (32).

Van der Waals Force   The van der Waals force is the second important long-range interaction in biology. Between atoms and small molecules, the force decays as $1/D^7$. However, between a larger sphere of radius R and a flat surface, for example, the force is $F = -\frac{AR}{6D^2}$, and it is longer ranged (32). One consequence of this longer range is that the nonspecific van der Waals force between the tip of a force probe and the sample can contribute to the apparent forces between molecules bound to those surfaces.

In the above expression, A, the Hamaker constant, scales the magnitude of the force between the materials (32). This parameter depends on the polarizability of atoms and on the refractive indices and the dielectric constants of the interacting materials, as well as the medium between them. Therefore, depending on the media, the van der Waals force can be attractive or repulsive (32). Its exact distance dependence does depend on geometry, and between a sphere and a flat surface, the magnitude also scales with the radius of the sphere (32).

"Steric" Forces   Repulsive forces between surface-anchored polymeric materials operate at intermediate separations, that is, 1–10 nm, the range of which is generally determined by the molecular weight and grafting density of the polymer. Cell surfaces and some biomaterials are coated with a dense layer of water-soluble polymers, which present a repulsive barrier that prevents the close approach of two particles or the diffusion of soluble molecules to the underlying surface. These forces are entropic in origin and depend on temperature but not ionic strength.

Steric repulsion operates at short intermolecular separations. This force is caused by the overlap of electron clouds, and the resulting repulsion is a consequence of the Pauli exclusion principle (32). There is no theoretically defined distance dependence for this force. However, the dimensions of the interacting species determine the range, and the decay is described empirically by a $1/D^{12}$ power law. This distance dependence is independent of temperature and of the ionic strength.

Specific Interactions

Specific interactions refer to a particular class of highly complementary, noncovalent bonds between molecules. Crystal structures of protein-ligand complexes exhibit the high degree of shape and chemical complementarity typical of molecular recognition. Owing to the multiple van der Waals, hydrogen-bonding, and hydrophobic contacts that stabilize the interaction, the binding free energy can be large. However, these interactions are determined by the local geometry, and they typically lock in when the ligands are docked, that is, within 1–2 nm. There are examples in which the electrostatic potential fields caused by charges in the binding sites extend over much larger distances (70). In general, however, the potential may be deep relative to the thermal energy kT, but the width tends to be narrow and the interaction short ranged.

Net Interaction Profiles—The Principle of Superposition

Any protein interaction will be governed by a superposition of some or all of these different forces. The net interaction force profile (or potential) can therefore be a complicated function with multiple minima and maxima (Figure 1). The distance dependence and magnitudes of the force profiles govern both protein association kinetics and the equilibrium-binding behavior. In terms of the corresponding energies, the deepest minimum determines the thermodynamic stability of complexes, and the potential profile at larger separations modulates the association rates (29).

Protein interactions are clearly not determined solely by their specific binding sites. However, both the magnitudes and distance dependencies of the force (or energy) profiles are required to identify the different interactions responsible for protein behavior. These factors can be determined by measuring directly the distance-dependent force profiles between the materials of interest. One can further

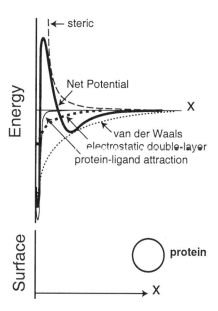

Figure 1   Hypothetical interaction potential between a soluble protein and a surface. The net potential profile (*bold solid line*) is a superposition of the van der Waals potential (*dotted line*), attractive or repulsive double-layer potential (*bold dashed line*), steric repulsion (*long dashed line*), and specific, short-range interactions (*solid line*). The relative ranges and magnitudes of these interactions can give rise to complicated potentials that exhibit multiple minima and energy barriers.

identify the contributing interactions by measuring changes in the profiles caused by changes in temperature and solution conditions (29, 32).

Some of the techniques discussed in this review can measure distance-dependent force (or energy) profiles. Other techniques lack the requisite distance resolution but are sufficiently sensitive to quantify single bond strengths. With the best distance resolution of ± 0.1 nm, the fine structure of short-ranged lock-and-key potentials still cannot be mapped directly. It is possible to quantify changes in bond rupture kinetics in response to applied stress. Additionally, a recent strategy enabled investigators to detect energy barriers along the unbinding pathway of a ligand in the binding site of a protein. These methodologies offer a comprehensive toolbox with which to probe the variety of forces and energies that govern protein function.

TECHNIQUES FOR PROBING MOLECULAR FORCES

With the current force probes, one can now quantify forces between biological materials that range from 0.01 pN to 10 nN. The principal techniques used to investigate proteins are the atomic force microscope (AFM) (Figure 2a) (90), surface force apparatus (SFA) (Figure 2b) (31), bioforce probe (BFP) (Figure 2c) (18), and optical tweezers (OT) (Figure 2d) (71, 77).

In addition to the direct force probes shown in Figure 2a–d, shear flow detachment assays have been used to determine the strengths of protein bonds and the dynamic responses of bonds to stress (1, 37, 79). With this approach, one measures the fluid shear stress required to detach a cell or beads from a chemically modified substrate. From the determined force, the geometry of the cell or sphere, and the receptor density, one can determine the average strength of the adhesive bonds.

Atomic Force Microscope and Optical Tweezers

The AFM uses a silicon nitride probe mounted on a soft cantilever spring to measure the force between the probe tip with a radius of $\sim$10–50 nm and a second surface. This instrument has been used extensively to image soft biological materials with a lateral resolution of ± 1 nm. As the tip approaches the test material, the cantilever deflects under the influence of the net force between the surfaces, and forces of 1–1000 pN can be measured. The position of a laser beam reflected off the cantilever surface tracks the relative movements of the probe within ± 0.1 nm and records the spring deflection. The sample separation is inferred indirectly from the cantilever displacement relative to the apparent position of steric, that is, hard wall contact between the materials.

The OT uses the radiation pressure focused on a 1- to 2-μm bead to exert very small forces (1–200 pN) against molecules or materials interacting weakly with the bead (71, 77). The bead is visualized in the optical trap, and the substrate or a second bead to which it is bound is moved relative to the trap position. By varying the force exerted on the optically trapped bead, one can determine the

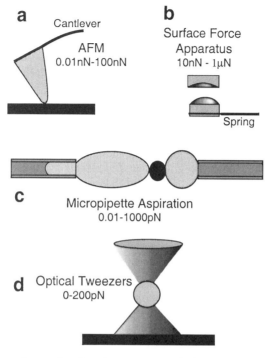

Figure 2 Force probes used to directly measure protein interaction forces. *a*. The atomic force microscope, showing the probe tip attached to the cantilever force transducer. *b*. The surface force apparatus, showing the crossed cylinders (2-cm radii) of the apparatus and the force-transducing spring. *c*. The bioforce probe, consisting of a membrane capsule aspirated into a pipette. A bead (*center*) is attached to one membrane (*left*), and the force between the bead and a second capsule or glass bead (*right*) is exerted by aspirating the (*left*) membrane into the pipette. *d*. Optical tweezers. The bead is held in the optical trap, and the radiation pressure exerted on the bead opposes adhesive contacts between materials on the bead and surface.

force necessary to break the weak bonds. Although force-distance profiles cannot be measured accurately, OTs—because of their sensitivity—have been used to measure the force-extension profiles of soft, entropic springs such as titin (38, 81), as well as the force-velocity relationships of molecular motors (71).

Surface Force Apparatus

With the SFA (31), one measures the force as a function of the separation distance between materials bound to two crossed cylinders with 1- to 2-cm radii of curvature. This approach differs from many others because the probed regions are large, for example, 1–5 μm^2, and typically reflect an average of >10,000 molecular interactions. These interactions collectively give rise to a sufficiently large force to be measured with a sensitive leaf spring that supports one of the samples. An important point is that this geometry in fact allows one to measure the free energy between the materials directly. This consequence results from the Derjaguin approximation, which relates the force between materials on two crossed cylinders to their interaction energy (29, 32). The interaction energy—not the force—determines equilibrium protein behavior. With the SFA, one measures this energy directly. Whereas the force resolution of ±10 nN is lower than that of the other instruments (see below), weak interactions caused by, for example, van der Waals forces are routinely measured.

An advantage of this method is the optical interferometric technique used to measure the intersurface distances. The sample materials are within the resonant cavity of an interferometer, so that changes in the distance between the materials shift the wavelengths of the interference fringes. From the wavelength shifts, one determines in situ the surface separations with a resolution of ±0.1 nm. This resolution is independent of surface deformations or the compression of soft materials between the layers. The shapes of the fringes also reflect the shape of the contact region, and local surface deformations are visualized in situ. During measurements, one can therefore determine distance between samples, extent of surface contact, shape of the contact region, and lateral heterogeneity with ±1-μm resolution in the surface topology (31). With the SFA, one obtains the most accurate force-distance profiles of the current measurement techniques.

Micropipette Aspiration/Bioforce Probe

The micropipette aspiration technique is used to measure the force between a membrane bag, for example, an erythrocyte, and giant vesicles, cells, or, more recently, functionalized beads (18). The adhesion between the membranes is determined from micromechanical analyses of the global deformations of the membrane capsules, which are held in contact by suction at the tips of opposed micropipettes. The force transducers are soft membrane capsules rather than mechanical springs, and the membrane tension controls the transducer stiffness. With a measurable range of from 0.01 pN to $\sim$1000 pN, this approach can probe the widest range of forces accessible with a single instrument.

The more recent configuration, the BFP, uses reflectance interference contrast microscopy to determine the distances between the bead and substrate, with a resolution of $\sim$5 nm (18). The use of a bead attached to the erythrocyte transducer (Figure 2c) made distance measurements possible, and it significantly expanded the number of systems accessible for study with this approach.

MAPPING THE ELECTROSTATIC PROPERTIES OF PROTEIN SURFACES

In solution, the long-range electrostatic forces between proteins and other molecules are important determinants of protein behavior. In particular, the distribution of charges on protein surfaces and the resulting asymmetric electrostatic fields are believed to modulate ligand association rates, catalytic rates, and redox potentials (21, 28, 41, 85). The electrostatic fields are thought to enhance association rates by preorienting charged reactants. For example, DNA-binding proteins, such as the processivity factor of *Escherichia coli* DNA polymerase III, are net negatively charged, but the DNA-binding domain contains a localized patch of positive charge (45).

Although difficult to measure directly, electrostatic surface potentials of proteins can be calculated by using mean field approaches and the crystal structures of the macromolecules (28, 53, 85). These methods have been extremely valuable for interpreting biochemical data in terms of the influences of structure on protein function. Calculated protein electrostatic potentials are also used in Brownian dynamics simulations to model protein association kinetics (28, 53). However, the simulation results depend on the electrostatic models used and on the underlying assumptions of these models. The calculated intermolecular potentials often involve adjustable parameters such as solvation energies, the protein dielectric constants, and the variation of the solvent dielectric with the intermolecular distances (53, 85). Given these uncertainties, recent efforts have focused on developing scanning-probe methods for obtaining electrostatic maps of protein surfaces by direct measurements.

AFM images of charged patches on patterned surfaces demonstrated the feasibility of mapping charge distributions at high resolution (26). The repulsive forces between a charged molecule or surface and the AFM tip are caused by both steric repulsion and the electrostatic double-layer force between the surfaces. The variation of the tip-sample repulsion reflects the surface topography with a lateral resolution of ± 1 nm.

Steric forces are ionic strength independent, and one can, in principle, quantify the double-layer force based on salt-dependent changes in the repulsive forces. Two groups thus mapped the relative spatial variations of the local charge densities on protein surfaces from differences in the force contours measured at various ionic strengths (26, 57). From the measured changes in the repulsive forces with changes in the salt concentration, they obtained a qualitative map of the protein surface charge density. The ability to obtain accurate quantitative data is, however, limited by the uncertainty in the distance between the probe tip and the protein surface and in the curvature of the probe tip, which scales the force (32).

An alternative approach used the SFA to probe protein electrostatics. Rather than resolving lateral features on the protein surface, the investigators manipulated the orientation of the immobilized protein so that all proteins in a monolayer exposed the identical surface. The average electrostatic surface properties of the monolayer and of the adjacent electrostatic double-layer are then determined primarily by the outermost charged amino acid residues. Fits of the measured double-layer force between the protein monolayer and a "test surface" of known charge to solutions of the Poisson-Boltzmann equation yield the average electrostatic potential of the outer protein surface (46, 48). The optical interferometric technique of the SFA made possible accurate determinations of the protein-probe surface separation (± 0.2 nm), the local radius of curvature of the probe, and hence the measured, average charge density of the exposed protein surface (31).

Such surface force measurements performed with immobilized, oriented Fab' fragments of monoclonal, antifluorescein antibodies demonstrated that a cluster of positive charges surrounding the binding site attracts the negatively charged antigen fluorescein (46). These qualitative results provided direct evidence for the role of charge clusters in guiding ligand-docking trajectories, despite the net negative charges on both molecules.

Recently, Sivasankar et al (76) used the SFA to quantify the pH-dependent charge density on a single face of immobilized, oriented streptavidin. To do this, they measured the average charge density of the exposed protein surface as a function of the solution pH. The measured point of zero charge differed by ~ 1.5 pH units from the isoelectric point of the soluble protein. This finding confirmed that the measured double-layer force reflects local electrostatic fields on the exposed surface of the macromolecule and not the overall protein charge.

The comparison of these results with mean field electrostatic calculations, which accounted for these pH-dependent changes, verified that the measured charge densities on the streptavidin surface exhibited the predicted pH dependence. The surface-averaged charge densities, determined from the calculated three-dimensional electrostatic potential distribution, agreed quantitatively with results from the force measurements (76). These experimental and computational results show therefore that coarse-grained electrostatic potential maps of the protein exterior can be determined directly using (*a*) surface force measurements and (*b*) the controlled manipulation of the immobilized protein orientation.

FORCES CONTROLLING THE RECOGNITION OF IMMOBILIZED RECEPTORS

Nonspecific forces also affect recognition events at interfaces. In many examples, such as hormone binding to cell surface receptors and drug targeting, the surface microenvironment can alter the apparent kinetics and/or thermodynamics of protein recognition events. In such cases, the force profiles that control receptor binding are a superposition of specific receptor-ligand interactions and nonspecific forces between the soluble ligand and the substrate (cf Figure 1). Changes in the net force (or potential) profile can perturb the distribution of bound and free states; the rates of ligand binding (2); and, in cell adhesion, both the contact area and the membrane separation at equilibrium (5, 80). Direct measurements of the force-distance curves can identify the different forces that govern protein interactions at surfaces. Such studies have been used to quantify, for example, the impact of grafted polymers and polymer dynamics on these events.

Short-Range Steric Barriers and the Accessibility of Immobilized Receptors

Close to surfaces ($D < 2$ nm), short-range forces can affect the recognition of small, surface-bound molecules. In particular, near hydrated bilayers, repulsive forces caused by out-of-plane lipid fluctuations, the motion of chemical groups, and adsorbed water can extend ≤ 1–2 nm (32, 33). This range is often comparable with both the dimensions of small, tethered receptors and the depth of the protein-binding sites. As a result, these repulsive forces can counter the specific bonds between the bound receptors and soluble ligands. This interference can be avoided by tethering receptors via long spacers, which position the receptors beyond most steric surface barriers and allow them to fully penetrate the protein-binding pockets.

With the SFA, Leckband et al (46) quantified the effect of short-range hydration/fluctuation forces on binding between the Fab' fragment of an antifluorescein antibody and membrane-bound fluorescein. They related reductions in the receptor-ligand adhesion directly to measured changes in the ranges of short-ranged repulsive surface barriers. By immobilizing the fluorescein antigen with spacers of different lengths, these investigators used the tethers as molecular rulers to control the distance between the receptor and the surface (46). Although the antibody-binding pocket is 1.8 nm deep, to achieve the maximum adhesion, they required at least a 2.3- to 2.5-nm tether (46). The additional 0.5–0.7 nm needed was attributed to the repulsive hydration/fluctuation forces, which decreased the effective spacer length. The measured 0.7 ± 0.1-nm range of these repulsive forces confirmed this interpretation.

Polymer Surface Barriers and Selective Binding

Longer-ranged surface forces (1–10 nm) caused by surface-bound polymers prevent or modulate the binding of soluble molecules to immobilized receptors. Absent direct protein binding to cell surface carbohydrates or to polymers, the latter large molecules can prevent protein access to surface-bound molecules (a) by resisting the compression of the chains or (b) by preventing protein penetration of the layers. Investigations of the influence of such barriers on protein adsorption have focused on synthetic, water-soluble polymers owing to their biotechnological importance. Nevertheless, although there are important differences between them, synthetic, linear polymers and cell surface carbohydrates are expected to hinder molecule or particle interactions with surfaces by qualitatively similar mechanisms.

The energy penalty for compressing end-anchored polymers (brushes) by soluble proteins was first modeled by Jeon et al (36). This scenario can occur when the distance between chain-anchoring sites is less than the protein radius (25). Direct measurements of the forces between streptavidin monolayers and end-grafted polyethylene oxide (PEO) chains tested this model directly. Of particular interest are the dependencies of the ranges and magnitudes of the steric barriers on the polymer molecular weight and grafting density. Sheth & Leckband (72) found that the range and distance dependence of the repulsion were as predicted by theories for polymer brushes (36). They also measured weak attraction between the protein and the PEO (72), the outcome of which was in contrast to expectations. It is important that, although they did show that simple polymer theories describe some properties of this polymer, these direct measurements (*a*) identified deviations from ideal behavior and (*b*) revealed the limitations of simple theories for describing the full range of PEO interactions with proteins. Such investigations are not limited to PEO but can be conducted with other polymers and proteins.

Soluble proteins can also penetrate polymer layers when the spacing between the chain-anchoring sites exceeds the protein diameter. In this case, the osmotic penalty for protein insertion into the layer opposes its diffusion through the chains (25, 78). Using micropipette aspiration, Noppl-Simson & Needham (59) quantified the osmotic barrier for avidin binding to biotin receptors beneath grafted polymers. They used polyethylene oxide bound to large, unilamellar vesicles, which also contained lipid-anchored biotin. From the work to induce adhesion between the latter vesicles and avidin-coated vesicles, they determined that the osmotic penalty for avidin penetration of the polymer film was roughly consistent with that estimated with the polymer surface density and protein size (25, 59, 78).

Grafted chains also sterically impede particle aggregation and receptor-mediated cell adhesion. Coating blood-borne drug carriers with PEO, for example, prevents their rapid uptake by the liver and prolongs their circulation time (61). Kennedy and coworkers (39) showed similarly that, by tuning the balance of the streptavidin-biotin attraction and polymer repulsion between vesicles, they could control the vesicle aggregation rates and the aggregate structures that formed. In cell adhesion studies, the degree of cell spreading on surfaces displaying adhesion peptides could be tuned by adjusting the length of the surrounding grafted polymers (13). Chan & Springer (7) similarly showed that increasing the length of the lymphocyte function-associated antigen-3 adhesion protein increased the attachment efficiency of lymphocytes displaying the adhesion protein CD2 onto lymphocyte function-associated antigen-3–transfected cells.

In these examples the balance between protein-ligand attraction and steric repulsion between membrane-anchored polymers determines the net intermembrane adhesion. Determination of the magnitudes and ranges of the forces exerted provides mechanistic information regarding the forces that determine the biological behavior. Alternatively, to manipulate the interactions, we need to know how the range and the magnitude of the repulsion depend on the polymer identity, molecular weight, and surface density (43). Again, direct-force measurements can directly test whether simple theories for grafted chains accurately predict the properties of real polymers.

To investigate the mechanism of vesicle stabilization by grafted PEO, for example, the distance dependence of the repulsive forces between lipid bilayers with grafted chains was quantified by two different approaches (43, 58). The results confirmed that the polymer barrier sterically stabilizes the vesicles. Further, by showing that simple polymer theories describe the repulsion between PEO brushes, the measurements also confirmed that, with PEO, such theories can be used to generate design criteria for stabilizing vesicles or tuning receptor-mediated cell adhesion (13).

Extending these measurements to cell surface carbohydrates should similarly clarify the role of these biopolymers in regulating biological activity. For example, the posttranslational modification of the neural cell adhesion molecule by polysialic acid, a linear polyelectrolyte, has been linked to neural plasticity in the early stages of development (67). Force measurements between neural cell adhesion molecule monolayers with and without polysialic acid would quantify the impact of this modification on the protein function and directly test various models for the biological activity of this carbohydrate.

Long-Range Electrostatic Forces

Force probes have similarly been used to quantify the effects of long-range electrostatic forces on biological interactions. In particular, these tests have determined (*a*) the forces responsible for the altered affinities of immobilized receptors (87, 88) and (*b*) the ranges and magnitudes of competing receptor-ligand attraction and electrostatic repulsion (46, 48). Shear detachment studies also demonstrated the effects of electrostatics on receptor-ligand bond formation and rupture in cell adhesion (68).

Dynamic Properties of Surface-Bound Receptors

In previous sections, we treated the surface-bound molecules as static structures. They are, however, soft materials that undergo thermally excited fluctuations. The lateral mobility of molecules on fluid cell surfaces can also lead to time-dependent intermembrane potentials. For example, using the SFA, Leckband et al (48) measured the time dependence of nonequilibrium forces between membranes that were associated with the dynamics of lateral receptor diffusion and ligand-receptor binding.

Tethered receptors bound via longer anchors can undergo large fluctuations, which can be quantified by similar time-dependent measurements of force-distance profiles. Such receptors are common in biology, in cases where the binding sites of cell surface molecules extend away from the bilayer surface and the glycocalyx. In addition, polymer conjugates are used to anchor receptors to drug-delivery agents such as liposomes. The flexible anchors can undergo thermally excited fluctuations. As a result, the receptor-ligand potential is distributed over a continuum of states that are a function of the parameters that control the tether mobility. The resultant intersurface potential, or the potential of mean force, is then an ensemble-averaged distortion of the intrinsic receptor-ligand potential. The ligand mobility thus smears the potential over a much greater range than would be exhibited by the rigidly bound molecule.

Surface force measurements between tethered biotin and an immobilized, oriented streptavidin monolayer (Figure 3) demonstrated directly the effects of such ligand dynamics on intersurface potentials (86). When bound via a flexible PEO tether, the distribution of biotin near the surface was determined by the large

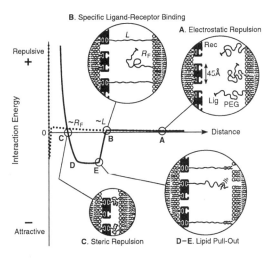

Figure 3   Interaction potential between tethered biotin and streptavidin. At A, the surfaces experience electrostatic repulsion. The protein and ligand lock in at B, as a result of the large fluctuations of the tethered biotin, and then jump in to C. Upon separation, the streptavidin and biotin remain bound (C, D, and E) until the polymer is stretched, and the lipids anchoring the polyethylene oxide pull out of the membrane (E). The *dotted line* shows the interaction potential between streptavidin and biotin anchored directly to the membrane. Reproduced from reference 86 with permission.

fluctuations of the chain. Although the average thickness of the polymer brush was 3.5 nm, the tethered biotin end-groups can undergo large, rapid excursions from the mean polymer thickness. Using the SFA, these investigators measured the distance dependence and the dynamics of the intersurface interactions. In contrast to the short-range attraction measured between streptavidin and lipid-anchored biotin (Figure 3) (27, 48), PEO-tethered biotin bound streptavidin readily at distances up to two thirds of the fully extended polymer chain length (Figure 3) (86). The increased range of the biotin-streptavidin potential is a direct consequence of the thermal fluctuations of the PEO tether. Without both the distance and the force resolution, these measurements would not be possible. These studies open up exciting possibilities for exploring the impact of chain stiffness, polymer molecular weight, and grafting density both on the polymer fluctuations and on receptor-ligand potentials.

MEASURING THE STRENGTHS OF RECEPTOR-LIGAND BONDS

Theoretical Interpretation of the Forces to Rupture Single Bonds

The measured nonspecific forces considered thus far are well understood theoretically, but the potential energy surfaces that govern specific recognition are less well characterized. The recent use of force probes to rupture single receptor-ligand bonds suggested that such measurements might in fact be used to probe the details of protein-ligand potentials. One expects that the forces to induce bond failure can be readily interpreted in terms of certain properties of the bonds. Bell, over 20 years ago (4), first proposed a relationship between the bond rupture forces and both the intermolecular potentials of stressed bonds and the kinetics of bond failure. Applying the kinetic theory of the strength of solids to receptor-ligand bond failure, he predicted that the external force applied to the bond would increase the detachment rate and that the bond strength would depend on the gradient of the binding free energy (4).

The effect of an applied mechanical force f on the potential $E(x)$ of an unstressed bond is illustrated in Figure 4. Owing to ambient thermal noise, there is a finite probability that the unperturbed bonds (Figure 4a) will acquire sufficient energy to overcome the activation barrier $E(x_{ts})$ at the transition state x_{ts} and will dissociate spontaneously. However, the application of a force f at an angle θ relative to the bond axis distorts the net potential by $-f \cos \theta$ (Figure 4a). This distortion lowers the activation barrier relative to kT at x_{ts}, increases the probability of barrier crossings, and thereby increases the frequency of bond rupture.

Measurements of cell detachment kinetics as a function of the shear stress on attached cells first demonstrated the decrease in bond lifetimes with increasing

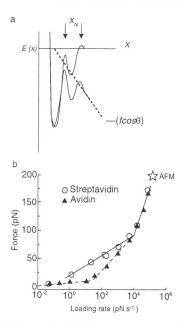

Figure 4 Effect of applied mechanical force on receptor-ligand unbinding. a. The application of a mechanical potential $-f \cos \theta$ on the receptor-ligand potential $E(x)$ tilts the potential and lowers the activation energy $E(x_{ts})$ at the transition state x_{ts}. b. The different slopes of the streptavidin- and avidin-biotin rupture force vs the logarithm of the loading rate. Reproduced with permission from reference 55.

applied load. Alon et al (1) showed that the rupture of bonds between glycoproteins on activated neutrophils and immobilized selectins increased with increasing fluid shear stress. A similar approach was used to study the lifetimes of bonds between receptor-coated beads and ligand coated substrates (61, 62). The dissociation rate both of antibody-antigen and of CD2-CD48 (T-cell adhesion proteins) bonds also increased with increasing shear stress (61, 62).

Recently, Evans & Ritchie expanded on Bell's model in a rigorous theoretical model of induced bond failure (16). This analysis makes the important point that the apparent bond rupture force is the force to induce bond failure in a defined time interval. They used Kramers' rate theory (42) to describe the detachment of mechanically stressed receptor-ligand bonds. Their analysis predicts an increased rupture frequency with the applied load, and the dependence of the apparent rupture force on the observation time. Within this framework are three dynamic unbinding regimes, which are defined by the relative loading and intrinsic bond dissociation rates. First, in the slow-loading regime, the rate at which the bonds are stressed is slower than the intrinsic dissociation rate. The linkages will break spontaneously before any appreciable force is applied, and the force to induce bond failure tends to zero. In the intermediate regime, the force relaxation rate is of the same order of magnitude as the intrinsic relaxation rate of the bond, and the apparent bond strength varies with the loading velocity. In both of the latter cases, receptor-ligand unbinding is thermally activated. In the forced-unbinding regime, however, the applied load reaches the maximum bond strength faster than spontaneous dissociation occurs, and the rupture force reflects the maximum bond strength.

Using the BFP and two unrelated proteins, Merkel et al (55) and Simson et al (74) verified the predictions of the Evans & Ritchie model. With avidin and biotin, Merkel et al (55) showed that the apparent bond strength indeed varies with the loading velocity (Figure 4b). At rapid loading rates, the analysis also predicts the crossover between spontaneous and force-induced unbinding. With avidin and biotin, the force vs loading-rate curves did not reach the maximum bond strength $F_b = E_b / X_{ts}$. This may be because the experimental methods cannot achieve the rapid rates required (16, 18). Recent studies of the breakage of immunoglobulin G (IgG)-protein A bonds did exhibit crossover from spontaneous to force-activated unbinding (74).

The Tensile Strengths of Single Bonds Depend on the Activation Energy for Unbinding

The model proposed by Evans & Ritchie (16) predicts that the bond rupture kinetics are controlled by the activation energy for unbinding. By contrast, Bell's analysis assumed that the applied mechanical potential must overcome the binding free energy ΔG. Later arguments similarly proposed that the rupture force would depend logarithmically on the affinity (12). Indeed, measurements of antibody-antigen bond strengths, determined by using shear flow detachment assays, exhibited the predicted logarithmic dependence on affinity (44).

The first AFM studies of the forces to break bonds between streptavidin and different biotin analogs did not, however, correlate with the binding free energy ΔG (49, 56). Instead they varied linearly with the equilibrium enthalpy of the bond ΔH (56). A later, elegant study with streptavidin mutants demonstrated that the critical force to break the streptavidin-biotin linkage depends on the activation enthalpy $\Delta H^{\ddagger}$ for unbinding (9). In this case, the energy barrier for unbinding and hence the rupture force is determined primarily by the activation enthalpy. The activation entropy $\Delta S^{\ddagger}$, which is related to the width of the potential and the distribution of bound states (22, 35), may contribute in other systems, but it is apparently negligible for streptavidin-biotin bond rupture.

The groups using the AFM analyzed receptor-ligand unbinding in terms of the transition state theory for reaction rates (19, 49, 56). This approach is not inconsistent with the theoretical model proposed by Evans & Ritchie (16). Although there are important distinctions between transition state theory and Kramers' rate theory, both approaches describe the reactions in terms of an activation barrier with a finite width (22, 35, 42). Kramers' theory reduces to transition state theory in the low viscosity limit—that is, when the viscous drag on the ligand is small (42).

The dependence of the rupture forces on the activation energy for unbinding suggests the possibility of mapping the energy landscapes of receptor-ligand potentials. The BFP studies with avidin detected three different dynamic regimes of the rupture force (Figure 4b). These regimes were attributed to the three major energy barriers along the unbinding trajectory that were identified in prior molecular dynamics simulations (Figure 4a) (16, 34). As the mechanical force tilts the net potential surface, the outer barriers are lowered to $<kT$, and each of the inner barriers emerges in succession to dominate the unbinding kinetics (Figure 4a). Detecting all three barriers, however, required measurements at loading rates that spanned 5–6 orders of magnitude (55)!

Force probes have already been used to detect qualitative changes in protein interactions caused by site-directed mutagenesis or cofactor binding. For example, AFM measurements detected changes in protein interactions that alter insulin crystallization behavior after site-directed mutagenesis (89). Differences in protein interactions with the chaperone GroEL were also measured in the presence and absence of ATP (83). The challenge now is to determine how such changes affect the potential energy surfaces mapped by dynamic force measurements.

Mechanical Properties of Proteins

There are many reports of force probe measurements of the mechanical properties of proteins. The majority of them address the mechanico-chemical transduction of motor proteins and the relationship between structure, catalysis, and force transduction. Several excellent reviews have been written that describe this body of work (40, 54, 71, 77), and we do not duplicate those efforts here. However, we focus on the recent use of force probes to investigate both the structural and the functional aspects of force-induced distortions of protein structure. Proteins are stabilized by multiple noncovalent interactions, and the disruption of these bonds by either mechanical or chemical means induces protein unfolding. Direct measurements have therefore been used to investigate the forces that stabilize protein structures and to determine how they affect the mechanical properties of isolated proteins.

The first investigations of mechanically induced unfolding were done with titin (38, 65, 66, 81). This protein is a scaffold for thick-filament formation, and it determines the elasticity of relaxed, striated muscle. It comprises multiple, tandem repeats of IgG- and fibronectin III-like domains, and its force-extension profiles were measured both with the AFM and with OT (38, 65, 66, 81). The AFM measurements exhibited periodic spikes in the force-extension curve that were attributed to the reversible unfolding transitions of the individual domains (65) (Figure 5). The sharpness of the peaks suggested that the protein unfolded by a two-state mechanism (65).

The force curves alone cannot identify the chemical mechanisms responsible for the peaks, that is, transition states in the extension profiles. However, molecular dynamics simulations (see below) suggest that the rupture of hydrogen bonds between two antiparallel strands of the beta sheet of the Ig domains generates the force to induce domain unfolding and hence the peaks in the force-extension curves (50, 51). Differences between the AFM and laser tweezers data suggest that the force-extension profiles depend on both the unfolding chemistry and the measurement method, that is, the sample history (38, 65, 81). Whereas the AFM curves display a sequence of periodically spaced peaks, the tweezers data exhibit a broad, extensible region from which domain unraveling was inferred (38). This difference was recently rationalized in terms of the different loading rates. An extension of the earlier model of Evans & Ritchie (16) described

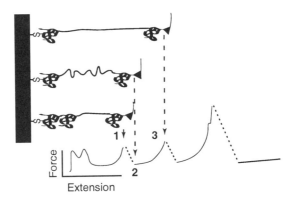

Figure 5   Forced unfolding of titin. The successive unfolding of titin domains gives rise to the corresponding peaks and valleys in the force-extension profile measured with the atomic force microscope (*bottom*). Reproduced with permission from reference 65.

the rupture of bonds attached to soft tethers and accounted for these differences in terms of the intrinsic unfolding reaction rates relative to the loading dynamics (17).

The dependence of bond rupture characteristics on loading rates was used to test whether the transition state in the forced unfolding pathway was the same as for protein unfolding in solution. By changing the rate of pulling, Carrion-Vazquez and coworkers (6) estimated the unfolding kinetics of a polypeptide consisting of multiple Ig domains in tandem. Comparing the measured kinetics to Monte Carlo simulations gave the unfolding rate in the absence of force. The quantitative agreement between the rates thus determined and those measured in solution strongly supports the hypothesis that the events that generate the peaks in the force curve are the same as those responsible for the transition state in the unfolding pathway of the soluble protein (6).

Although there are only a few molecular mechanics investigations of known structural proteins, recent reports suggest that forced protein deformations may play a broader role in biology. The molecular dynamics simulation of forced fibronectin unfolding suggests that the resulting encryption of the RGD sequence may act as a mechanical recognition switch (50, 51). That this function may regulate the biological activity of extracellular matrix proteins is suggested by studies that show differential fibronectin activities on different substrata (20). In addition, a recent study of the chaperone protein GroEL suggests that the latter may actually facilitate protein folding by stretching misfolded or partially folded proteins (73).

Simulations of Forced Unbinding—Relating Rupture Forces to Bond Chemistry

Supercomputers have made it possible to simulate the unbinding trajectories of ligands as they are pulled over the rugged energy landscape of the binding pocket. The first such study sought to identify the physical chemical interactions that determine the unbinding force for avidin-biotin bond rupture. Simulations of the forced rupture of the bond between biotin and a monomer of the tetrameric protein streptavidin reproduced quantitatively the measured detachment force (23).

The natural tendency would be to use such steered molecular dynamics (SMD) simulations to interpret single-bond detachment data in terms of the chemical interactions and simulated energy barriers that control unbinding. The obstacle to such quantitative comparisons lies in the different time scales on which intermolecular dissociation is induced in the experimental versus the computational approaches (3, 34). Experimentally measured dissociation events occur on millisecond time scales and are thermally activated. By contrast, the nanosecond time scales used in molecular dynamics simulations are fast relative to the intrinsic relaxation time of the bond. To induce bond dissociation in the simulations, very large forces must be applied rapidly to overcome all potential barriers on such short time scales. Under these conditions, there is a substantial frictional contribution to the pull-off force that scales with the detachment velocity. This term is large relative to the applied load, and for this reason, the simulations overestimate the experimental values significantly (3, 34). Not only do the frictional terms differ in these two limits, but the rupture force also scales differently with the applied load (3).

The amount of irreversible work performed in the simulations is the principle obstacle to quantitative comparisons between SMD results and force probe measurements. The error in the potential surface reconstructed from simulations is related to the irreversible work performed during bond rupture (3). Potential surfaces cannot be reconstructed quantitatively from force probe measurements, which record thermally activated events (3). Recent theoretical developments suggest that the results from these two approaches can be bridged through a potential of mean force (24). The latter can be constructed through time-series analyses of the position and applied force data obtained from calculated SMD trajectories (24). The thus determined potential of mean force can then be used to interpret force probe measurements in terms of the energy peaks and valleys that control receptor-ligand unbinding.

Simulated unbinding trajectories already identified key molecular interactions that prevent protein unfolding and limit the escape or determine the binding pathways of ligands. They provided important information regarding, for example, retinal binding to bacterio-opsin (30) and the forced unfolding of proteins (50, 51). Other results guided the interpretation of experimental measurements of avidin-biotin bond rupture (55). These examples illustrate the value of combining theoretical approaches and force probe measurements. SMD promises to be a powerful tool for interpreting bond rupture measurements.

INTERACTIONS INVOLVING MULTIPLE INTERMOLECULAR BONDS

Multiple Bonds in Parallel

Biological adhesion is not typically mediated by single, high-affinity interactions, but by many weak contacts. The advantage of the latter is that weak interactions allow for plasticity in adhesive junctions, the formation of dynamic contacts, and cell motility (11, 14, 15, 52, 60). Because low-affinity bonds are believed to exhibit short lifetimes and low rupture forces, adhesion requires multiple such interactions (62, 82).

To investigate how the rupture of multiple contacts might differ from single-bond failure, Vijayendran and associates (84) used the adhesive dynamics algorithm (8) to simulate the adhesion between receptor-linked surfaces in surface force measurements. At equilibrium, there will be a distribution of bound and free states, and the average bond strength will be less than that of isolated cross bridges. However, the materials remain pinned in close proximity by the unbroken, neighboring cross bridges, and broken bonds can reform. Because of this, the time-averaged tension on each bond during the junction rupture can approach and even exceed the critical rupture force of the individual bonds. This effect will be most prevalent when the intrinsic breakage and reformation rates are faster than the loading rate (84). Such behavior will not be observed in single-bond measurements because the surfaces jump out of contact when the cross bridges fail. The adhesive dynamics simulations thus show that, with multiple contacts in parallel, the adhesion is determined by the unbinding kinetics, the loading rate, and the reassociation kinetics.

The Rupture of Bonds in Series

Adhesive interactions can also involve several bonds in series. For example, receptor-mediated cell-cell contacts that involve cytoskeletal interactions may involve five or more bonds in series. One predicts that the average strength of such linkages would be lower than any of the individual linkages. If the binding probability of each of two different bonds in series is less than unity, then the probability that both bonds will exist simultaneously is the product of the probabilities of each of the constitutive bonds. The overall likelihood of simultaneous binding will then be less than that of either individual bond (69).

This hypothesis was confirmed by radial flow detachment assays of cross-bridges formed by two low-affinity bonds. These studies showed that the average bond rupture force was 2- to 10-fold smaller than that of the weakest bond in the series (69). On the other hand, with linkages comprising four high-affinity bonds, surface force measurements demonstrated that the bond with the lowest rupture force failed first (47). The force-extension curves of titin suggest similarly that the domains with the lowest activation barrier to unfolding unravel first (65). The affinities do influence the adhesion by determining the probability of cross-bridge formation. However, the force to rupture the existing cross bridges is determined (*a*) by the bond in the series with the lowest activation barrier to unbinding and (*b*) by the loading dynamics relative to the intrinsic unbinding rates (16).

Multivalent Protein Interactions

Other proteins such as fibronectin may bind more than one ligand simultaneously or have multiple binding sites for single ligands. Many cell adhesion molecules contain large, multidomain extracellular segments (10), and some exhibit multiple contacts with their corresponding ligands (64). Whereas multiple interactions may contribute to binding, their implications for protein-mediated adhesion have not been explored.

A recent study identified one possible consequence of such interactions. The extracellular domain of an adhesion protein cadherin consists of five homologous domains in tandem and binds to identical proteins on opposing cell surfaces. With the force apparatus, Sivasankar et al (75) found that cadherin extracellular domains bind in at least two antiparallel configurations. By controlling the distance between two cadherin monolayers, they identified two discrete protein separations at which the proteins adhere. The force-distance profile generated during protein detachment suggests that the sequential rupture of these bonds may hinder the abrupt failure of the cadherin junctions (75).

Whether other adhesion proteins undergo similar multidomain interactions or bind in more than one configuration remains to be determined. In addition, the functional consequences of such interactions have yet to be explored. Direct force measurements will be essential tools for quantifying the tensile strengths of the linkages and determining the mechanisms by which the proteins bind and resist adhesive failure.

ACKNOWLEDGMENTS

I thank A Halperin, K Schulten and S Sivasankar for their helpful comments. This work was supported by NIH GM51338 and NSF BES 9503045 CAREER.

Visit the Annual Reviews home page at www.AnnualReviews.org

LITERATURE CITED

1. Alon R, Hammer DA, Springer TA. 1995. Lifetime of the P-selectin-carbohydrate bond and its response to tensile force in hydrodynamic flow. *Nature* 374:539–42
2. Balgi G, Leckband D, Nitsche JM. 1995. Transport effects on the kinetics of protein-surface binding. *Biophys. J.* 68:2251–60
3. Balsera M, Stepaniants S, Izrailev S, Oono Y, Schulten K. 1997. Reconstructing potential energy functions from simulated force-induced unbinding processes. *Biophys. J.* 73:1281–87
4. Bell GI. 1978. Models for the specific adhesion of cells to cells. *Science* 200:618–27
5. Bell GI, Dembo M, Bongrand P. 1984. Cell adhesion: competition between nonspecific repulsion and specific bonding. *Biophys. J.* 45:1051–64
6. Carrion-Vazquez M, Oberhauser AF, Fowler SB, Marszalek PE, Broedel SE, et al. 1999. Mechanical and chemical unfolding of a single protein: a comparison. *Proc. Natl. Acad. Sci. USA* 96:3694–99
7. Chan P, Springer TA. 1992. Effect of lengthening lymphocyte function associated antigen 3 on adhesion to CD2. *Mol. Biol. Cell* 3:157–76
8. Chang K-C, Hammer DA. 1996. Influence of direction and type of applied force on the detachment of macromolecularly-bound particles from surfaces. *Langmuir* 12:2271–82
9. Chilkoti A, Boland T, Ratner BD, Stayton PS. 1995. The relationship between ligand-binding thermodynamics and protein-ligand interaction forces measured by atomic force microscopy. *Biophys. J.* 69:2125–30
10. Chothia C, Jones EY. 1997. The molecular structure of cell adhesion molecules. *Annu. Rev. Biochem.* 66:823–62
11. Davis MM. 1995. Serial engagement proposed. *Nature* 375:104
12. Dembo M, Torney DC, Saxman K, Hammer D. 1988. The reaction-limited kinetics of membrane-to-surface adhesion and detachment. *Proc. R. Soc. London Ser. B* 234:55–83
13. Dori Y, Bianco-Peled H, Satija SK, Fields GB, McCarthy JB, Tirrell M. 2000. Ligand accessibility as a means to control cell response to bioactive bilayer membranes. *Langmuir.* Submitted
14. Dustin ML. 1997. Adhesive bond dynamics in contacts between T lymphocytes and glass-supported planar bilayers

reconstituted with the immunoglobulin-related adhesion molecule CD58. *J. Biol. Chem.* 272:15782–88

15. Dustin ML, Golan DE, Zhu D-M, Miller JM, Meier W, et al. 1997. Low-affinity interaction of human or rat T cell adhesion molecule CD2 with its ligand aligns adhering membranes to achieve high physiological affinity. *J. Biol. Chem.* 272:30889–98

16. Evans E, Ritchie K. 1997. Dynamic strength of molecular adhesion bonds. *Biophys. J.* 72:1541–55

17. Evans E, Ritchie K. 1999. Strength of a weak bond connecting flexible polymer chains. *Biophys. J.* 76:2439–47

18. Evans E, Ritchie K, Merkel R. 1995. Sensitive force technique to probe molecular adhesion and structural linkages at biological interfaces. *Biophys. J.* 68:2580–87

19. Florin E-L, Moy VT, Gaub HE. 1994. Adhesion forces between individual ligand-receptor pairs. *Science* 264:415–17

20. Garcia A, Vega MD, Boettinger D. 1999. Modulation of cell proliferation and differentiation through substrate-dependent changes in fibronectin conformation. *Mol. Biol. Cell* 10:785–98

21. Getzoff E, Cabelli D, Fisher C, Parge H, Viezzoli M, et al. 1992. Faster superoxide dismutase mutants designed by enhancing electrostatic guidance. *Nature* 358:347–51

22. Glasstone S, Laidler K, Eyring H. 1941. *The Theory of Rate Processes.* New York: McGraw-Hill

23. Grubmüller H, Heynman B, Tavan P. 1996. Ligand binding: molecular mechanics calculation of the streptavidin-biotin rupture force. *Science* 271:997–99

24. Gullingsrud JR, Braun R, Schulten K. 1999. Reconstructing potentials of mean force through time series analysis of steered molecular dynamics simulations. *J. Comput. Physics* 151:190–211

25. Halperin A. 1999. Polymer brushes that resist adsorption of model proteins. *Langmuir* 15:2525–33

26. Heinz WF, Hoh JH. 1999. Relative surface charge density mapping with the atomic force microscope. *Biophys. J.* 76:528–38

27. Helm CA, Knoll W, Israelachvili JN. 1991. Measurement of ligand-receptor interactions. *Proc. Natl. Acad. Sci. USA* 88:8169–73

28. Honig B, Nicolls A. 1995. Classical electrostatics in biology and chemistry. *Science* 268:1144–49

29. Hunter R. 1989. *Foundations of Colloid Science.* Oxford, UK: Oxford Univ. Press

30. Isralewitz B, Israilev S, Schulten K. 1997. Binding pathway of retinal to bacterio-opsin: a prediction by molecular dynamics simulations. *Biophys. J.* 73:2972–79

31. Israelachvili J. 1992. Adhesion forces between surfaces in liquids and condensable vapours. *Surf. Sci. Rep.* 14:110–59

32. Israelachvili J. 1992. *Intermolecular and Surface Forces.* New York: Academic

33. Israelachvili J. Wennerström H. 1996. Role of hydration and water structure in biological and colloidal interactions. *Nature* 379:219–25

34. Izrailev S, Stepaniants S, Balsera M, Oono Y, Schulten K. 1997. Molecular dynamics study of unbinding of the avidin-biotin complex. *Biophys. J.* 72:1568–81

35. Jencks WP. 1987. *Catalysis in Chemistry and Enzymology.* Mineola, NY: Dover

36. Jeon SI, Lee IH, Andrade JD, De Gennes PG. 1991. Protein-surface interactions in the presence of polyethylene oxide I: simplified theory. *J. Colloid Interface Sci.* 142:149–58

37. Kaplanski G, Famarier C, Tissot O, Pierres A, Benoliel AM, et al. 1993. Granulocyte-endothelium initial adhesion: analysis of transient binding events mediated by E-selectin in a laminar shear flow. *Biophys. J.* 64:1922–33

38. Kellermayer M, Smith SB, Granzier HL, Bustamante C. 1997. Folding-unfolding transitions in single titin molecules characterized with laser tweezers. *Science* 276:1112–15

39. Kennedy MT, Kisak E, Trommeshauser D,

Zasadzinski JA. 2000. Self-limiting aggregation by controlled ligand-receptor stoichiometry. Submitted

40. Khan S, Sheetz MP. 1997. Force effects on biochemical kinetics. *Annu. Rev. Biochem.* 66:785–805

41. Koppenol W, Margoliash E. 1982. The asymmetric distribution of charges on the surface of horse heart cytochrome c. *J. Biol. Chem.* 257:4426–37

42. Kramers HA. 1940. Brownian motion in a field of force and the diffusion model of chemical reactions. *Physica* 7:284–304

43. Kuhl T, Leckband DE, Lasic DD, Israelachvili JN. 1995. Modulation of interaction forces between bilayers exposing short-chained ethylene oxide headgroups. *Biophys. J.* 66:1479–88

44. Kuo SC, Lauffenburger DA. 1993. Relationship between receptor/ligand binding affinity and adhesion strength. *Biophys. J.* 65:2191–200

45. Kuriyan J, O'Donnell M. 1993. Sliding clamps of DNA polymerases. *J. Mol. Biol.* 234:915–25

46. Leckband DE, Kuhl TL, Wang HK, Müller W, Ringsdorf H. 1995. 4-4-20 Anti-fluorescyl IgG Fab' recognition of membrane bound hapten: direct evidence for the role of protein and interfacial structure. *Biochemistry* 34:11467–78

47. Leckband D, Müller W, Schmitt F-J, Ringsdorf H. 1995. Molecular mechanisms determining the strength of receptor-mediated intermembrane adhesion. *Biophys. J.* 69:1162–69

48. Leckband D, Schmitt F-J, Israelachvili J, Knoll W. 1994. Direct force measurements of specific and nonspecific protein interactions. *Biochemistry* 33:4611–24

49. Lee GU, Kidwell DA, Colton RJ. 1994. Sensing discrete streptavidin-biotin interactions with atomic force microscopy. *Langmuir* 10:354–57

50. Lu H, Isralewitz B, Krammer A, Vogel V, Schulten K. 1998. Unfolding of titin immunoglobulin domains by steered molec-

ular dynamics simulation. *Biophys. J.* 75:662–71

51. Lu H, Isralewitz B, Krammer A, Vogel V, Schulten K. 1998. Unfolding of titin immunoglobulin domains by steered molecular dynamics simulation. *Proc. Natl. Acad. Sci. USA* 75:662–71

52. Matsui K, Boniface JJ, Reay PA, Hansjörg S, Fazekasde de St. Groth B, Davis MM. 1991. Low-affinity interaction of peptide-MHC complexes with T-cell receptors. *Nature* 254:1788–91

53. McCammon AJ. 1998. Theory of biomolecular recognition. *Curr. Opin. Struct. Biol.* 8:245–49

54. Mehta A, Rief M, Spudich JA, Smith DA, Simmons RA. 1999. Single-molecule biomechanics with optical methods. *Science* 283:1689–95

55. Merkel R, Nassoy P, Leung A, Ritchie K, Evans E. 1999. Energy landscapes of receptor-ligand bonds explored with dynamic force spectroscopy. *Nature* 397:50–53

56. Moy VT, Florin E-L, Gaub HE. 1994. Intermolecular forces and energies between ligands and receptors. *Science* 266:257–59

57. Müller DJ, Engel A. 1997. The height of biomolecules measured with the atomic force microscope depends on electrostatic interactions. *Biophys. J.* 73:1633–44

58. Needham D, McIntosh TJ, Lasic D. 1992. Repulsive interactions and mechanical stability of polymer-grafted lipid membranes. *Biochim. Biophys. Acta* 1108:40–48

59. Noppl-Simson DA, Needham D. 1996. Avidin-biotin interactions at vesicle surfaces: adsorption and binding, cross-bridge formation, and lateral interactions. *Biophys. J.* 70:1391–401

60. Palecek S, Loftus JC, Ginsberg MH, Lauffenburger DA, Horwitz AF. 1997. Integrin-ligand binding properties govern cell migration speed through cell-substratum adhesiveness. *Nature* 385:537–40

61. Papahadjopolous D, Allen T, Gabizon A, Mayhew E, Matthay K, et al. 1991.

Sterically stabilized liposomes: improvements in pharmacokinetics and antitumor therapeutic efficacy. *Proc. Natl. Acad. Sci. USA* 88:11460–64

62. Pierres A, Benoliel AM, Bongrand P. 1995. Measuring the lifetime of bonds made between surface-linked molecules. *J. Biol. Chem.* 270:26586–92

63. Pierres A, Benoliel AM, Bongrand P, Van Der Merwe AP. 1996. Determination of the lifetime and force dependence of interactions of single bonds between surface-attached CD2 and CD48 adhesion molecules. *Proc. Natl. Acad. Sci. USA* 93:15114–18

64. Rao Y, Wu X-F, Gariepy J, Rutishauser U, Siu C-H. 1992. Identification of a peptide sequence involved in homophilic binding in the neural cell adhesion molecule NCAM. *J. Cell Biol.* 118:937–49

65. Rief M, Gautel M, Oesterhelt F, Fernandez JM, Gaub HE. 1999. Reversible unfolding of individual titin immunoglobulin domains by AFM. *Science* 276:1109–12

66. Rief M, Pascual J, Saraste M, Gaub HE. 1999. Single molecule force spectroscopy of spectrin repeats: low unfolding forces in helix bundles. *J. Mol. Biol.* 286:553–61

67. Rutishauser U. 1996. Polysialic acid and the regulation of cell interactions. *Curr. Opin. Cell Biol.* 8.679–84

68. Sabri S, Pierres A, Benoliel AM, Bongrand P. 1995. Influence of surface charges on cell adhesion: difference between static and dynamic conditions. *Biochem. Cell Biol.* 73:411–20

69. Saterbak A, Lauffenburger DA. 1996. Adhesion mediated by bonds in series. *Biotechnol. Prog.* 12:682–99

70. Sharp KA, Honig B. 1990. Electrostatic interactions in macromolecules: theory and applications. *Annu. Rev. Biophys. Biophys. Chem.* 19:302–32

71. Sterbe RE, Sheetz M. 1998. Basic laser tweezers. *Methods Cell Biol.* 55:29–41

72. Sheth SR, Leckband D. 1997. Measurements of attractive forces between proteins and end-grafted poly(ethylene glycol) chains. *Proc. Natl. Acad. Sci. USA* 94:8399–404

73. Shtilerman M, Lorimer GH, Englander W. 1999. Chaperonin function: folding by forced unfolding. *Science* 284:822–24

74. Simson DA, Strigl M, Hohenadl M, Merkel R. 1999. Statistical breakage of single protein A-IgG bonds reveals crossover from spontaneous to force-induced bond dissociation. *Phys. Rev. Lett.* 83:652–55

75. Sivasankar S, Brieher W, Lavrik N, Gumbiner B, Leckband D. 1999. Direct molecular force measurements of multiple adhesive interactions between cadherin ectodomains. *Proc. Natl. Acad. Sci. USA* 96:11820–24

76. Sivasankar S, Subramaniam S, Leckband D. 1998. Direct molecular level measurements of the electrostatic properties of a protein surface. *Proc. Natl. Acad. Sci. USA* 95:12961–66

77. Svoboda K, Block SM. 1994. Biological applications of optical forces. *Annu. Rev. Biophys. Biomolec. Struct.* 23:247–85

78. Szleifer I. 1997. Protein adsorption on surfaces with grafted polymers: a theoretical approach. *Biophys. J.* 72:595–12

79. Tees DF, Coenen O, Goldsmith HL. 1993. Interaction forces between red cells agglutinized by antibody. IV. Time and force dependence of break up. *Biophys. J.* 65:1318–34

80. Torney DC, Dembo M, Bell GI. 1986. Thermodynamics of cell adhesion. II. Freely mobile repellers. *Biophys. J.* 49:501–7

81. Tskhovrebova L, Trinick J, Sleep JA, Simmons RM. 1999. Elasticity and unfolding of single molecules of the giant muscle protein titin. *Nature* 387:308–12

82. Van Der Merwe PA, Brown MH, Davis S, Barclay NA. 1993. Affinity and kinetic analysis of the interaction of the cell adhesion molecules rat CD2 and CD48. *EMBO J.* 12:4945–54

83. Vinckier A, Gervasoni P, Zaugg F, Ziegler

U, Lindner P, et al. 1998. Atomic force microscopy detects changes in the interaction forces between GroEL and substrate proteins. *Biophys. J.* 74:3256 63

84. Vijayendran R, Hammer D, Leckband D. 1998. Simulations of the adhesion between molecularly bonded surfaces in direct force measurements. *J. Chem. Phys.* 108:7783–93

85. Warshel A, Papazyan A. 1998. Electrostatic effects in macromolecules: fundamental concepts and practical modeling. *Curr. Opin. Struct. Biol.* 8:211–17

86. Wong JY, Kuhl TL, Israelachvili JN, Mullah N, Zalipsky S. 1997. Direct measurement of a tethered ligand-receptor interaction potential. *Science* 275:820–22

87. Yeung C, Leckband D. 1997. Molecular-level characterization of microenvironmental influences on the properties of immobilized proteins. *Langmuir* 13:6746–54

88. Yeung C, Purves T, Kloss A, Sligar S, Leckband D. 2000. Cytochrome c recognition of immobilized, orientational variants of cytochrome b5: direct force and equilibrium binding measurements. *Langmuir.* In press

89. Yip CM, Yip CC, Ward MD. 1998. Direct force measurements of insulin monomer-monomer interactions. *Biochemistry* 37:5439–49

90. Zhifeng S, Mou J, Czaijkowsky DM, Yang J, Yuan JY. 1996. Biological atomic force microscopy: what is achieved and what is needed. *Adv. Physics.* 45:1–86

Annu. Rev. Biophys. Biomol. Struct. 2000. 29:27–47

STRUCTURE AND FUNCTION OF LIPID-DNA COMPLEXES FOR GENE DELIVERY

S. Chesnoy and L. Huang

Laboratory of Drug Targeting, Department of Pharmacology,
University of Pittsburgh School of Medicine, Pittsburgh, Pennsylvania 15261;
e-mail: Leafh+@pitt.edu, Chesnoy+@pitt.edu

Key Words   plasmid DNA, cationic lipid, transfection, X-ray diffraction, toxicity

■ **Abstract**   Owing to the rapid development of in vivo applications for non-viral gene delivery vectors, it is necessary to have a better understanding of how the structure-activity relationships of these lipid-DNA complexes are affected by their environment. Indeed, research in gene therapy first focused on in vitro cell culture studies to determine the mechanisms involved in the delivery of DNA into the cell. New biophysical techniques such as electron microscopy and X-ray diffraction have been developed to discern the structure of the lipid-DNA complex. However, further studies have revealed discrepancies between optimal lipid-DNA formulations for in vitro transfection and for in vivo administration of these vectors. Furthermore, some immune stimulatory effects have been associated with in vivo lipid-DNA administration. This review summarizes the current state of knowledge on in vitro and in vivo lipid-DNA complex transfections. New prospects of vectors for in vivo gene transfer are also discussed.

CONTENTS

INTRODUCTION

During the past 10 years, there has been keen interest in the design of novel non-viral systems for gene transfer. The first nonviral DNA vector developed was a complex of a cationic lipid and DNA (lipoplex). A cationic lipid can be used alone or with a helper lipid, usually neutrally charged. These nonviral vectors are very promising because they are easy to mass-produce and less immunogenic than the viral vectors. However, their level of gene transfer efficiency is not as high as that of viral vectors. Some very recent findings suggest that the low efficiency of these vectors could be related to a nonspecific immunogenic response (30, 62). Moreover, these vectors are unstable in the presence of serum, which creates difficulties for in vivo application. Tremendous effort has recently been devoted to solving this problem, including the continuous synthesis of new cationic lipids and the search for new formulations that have reduced interactions with serum proteins.

New techniques have been developed to better characterize these complexes, such as X-ray diffraction and electron microscopy. The most recent X-ray diffraction analyses have revealed very interesting structures in lipid-DNA complexes. Indeed, it appears that DNA and cationic lipids form very well-organized multilamellar structures (25, 41, 45). The structure of lipid-DNA complexes exposed to serum still remains to be elucidated.

The biological fate of lipid-DNA complexes inside the cell involves a complex mechanism comprising several steps: binding of DNA to the cell, escape of DNA into the cytoplasm, and entry of DNA into the nucleus. The role of cationic lipids in this process has been found to be very important, and some correlations have been established between the lipid-DNA structure and its transfection efficiency in vitro (22). However, it has been reported recently that in vitro studies are not predictive of in vivo studies, which emphasizes the importance of the biological environment in the structure-activity relationship of such complexes.

It is beyond the scope of this review to summarize all of the recent findings in lipidic gene delivery. Instead, this review is a general clarification of the structure and function of the lipid-DNA complex for in vitro and in vivo gene delivery.

STRUCTURE AND PHYSICAL PROPERTIES OF CATIONIC LIPIDS

All cationic lipids are composed of three parts: a hydrophobic anchor, a linker, and a head group (Figure 1).

Hydrophobic Anchor

Hydrophobic anchors represent the nonpolar hydrocarbon moieties of the cationic lipids and can be grouped into three categories—single-chain hydrocarbons, double-chain hydrocarbons, and cholesterol.

Single-Chain Hydrocarbons   Single-chain hydrocarbons are better known as surfactants because of their ability to form micelles in solution. Their use in

Oleoyl
O
Oleoyl
O
N+
Hydrophobic anchor
Linker
Head group

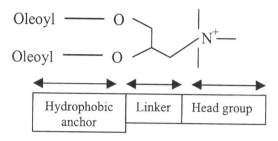

Figure 1 Graphic example of a cationic lipid.

gene therapy has been very restricted because of their toxicity against the cells (37).

Double-Chain Hydrocarbons Double-chain hydrocarbons represent the majority of cationic lipids synthesized so far (Figure 2). Oleoyl chain (C18:1) is the most frequently observed unsaturated acyl chain, whereas C14, C16, and C18 are the commonly observed saturated hydrocarbon chains. The importance of the

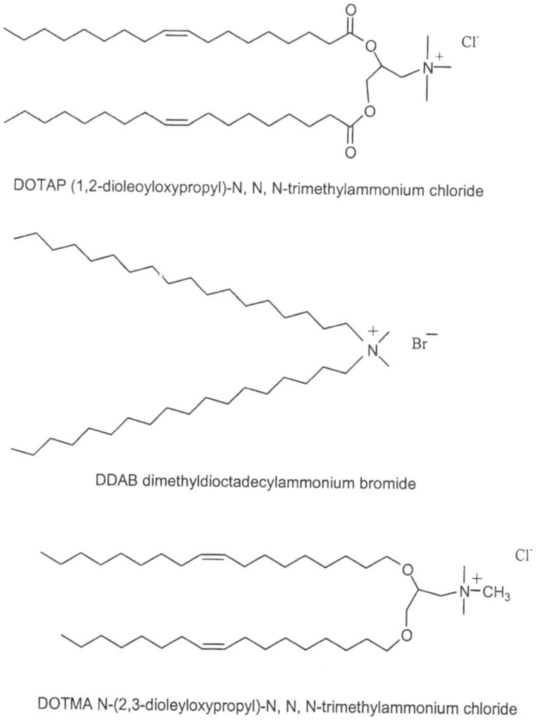

Cl⁻
DOTAP (1,2-dioleoyloxypropyl)-N, N, N-trimethylammonium chloride
Br⁻
DDAB dimethyldioctadecylammonium bromide
Cl⁻
N-CH3
DOTMA N-(2,3-dioleyloxypropyl)-N, N, N-trimethylammonium chloride

Figure 2 Double-chain cationic lipids.

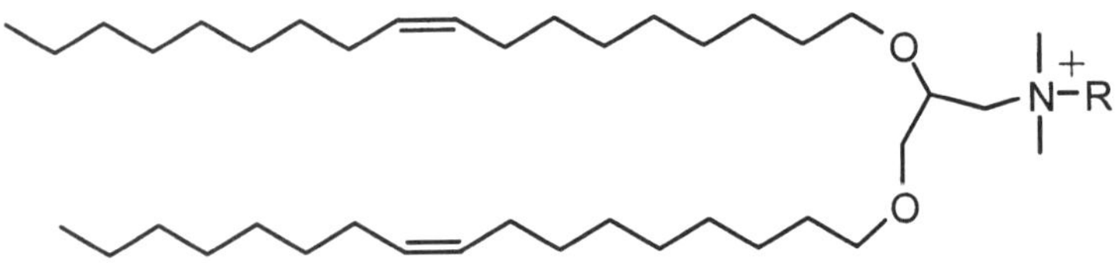

R

DOTMA	CH_3
DORIE	$HO(CH_2)_2$
DORIE-HP	$HO(CH_2)_3$
DORIE-HB	$HO(CH_2)_4$
DORIE-HPe	$HO(CH_2)_5$

Figure 3   Double-chain cationic lipids synthesized by Felgner et al (12). DOTMA: 1,2-dioleyloxypropyl-3-trimethyl ammonium bromide; DORIE: 1,2-dioleyloxypropyl-3-dimethyl-hydroxyethyl ammonium bromide; DORIE-HP: 1,2-dioleyloxypropyl-3-dimethyl-hydroxypropyl ammonium bromide; DORIE-HB: 1,2-dioleyloxypropyl-3-dimethyl-hydroxybutyl ammonium bromide; DORIE-HPe: 1,2-dioleyloxypropyl-3-dimethyl-hydroxypentyl ammonium bromide.

alkyl chain length in transfection activity in vitro was studied by Felgner et al (12), who varied the alkyl chain length in a homologous series of hydroxyethyl quaternary ammonium derivatives (Figure 3). They observed that the alkyl chain length can influence the transfection activity (C14:0 > C18:1 > C16:0 > C18:0). Usually, double-chain hydrocarbons are capable of forming liposomes by themselves, but they are often used with a helper phospholipid in cationic lipid transfection formulations.

Cholesterol   The hydroxyl at position 3 was used for derivatization (10, 54). Such compounds are usually mixed with double-chain amphiphiles to form stable cationic liposome formulations (Figure 4).

Linker

The linker represents any chemical part between the hydrophobic anchor and the head group. The linker is important in ensuring optimal contact between the cationic head group and the negatively charged phosphates of the DNA. In cationic lipids containing double-chain hydrocarbons, a three-carbon skeleton of glycerol is used as the linker [e.g. *N*-(2,3-dioleoyloxypropyl)-*N,N,N*-trimethylammonium chloride (DOTMA); (1,2-dioleoyloxypropyl)-*N,N,N*-trimethylammonium chloride (DOTAP); etc]. For cholesterol derivatives, a spacer of ~3–6 atoms between the amino group and linker is optimal for activity (10). Furthermore, cholesterol

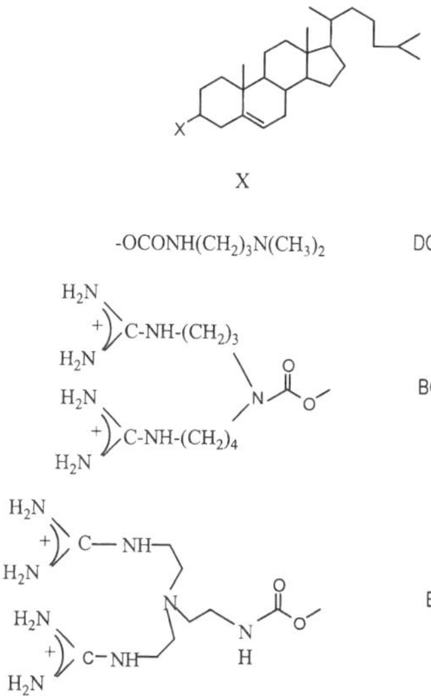

DC-chol

BGSC Bis-guanidinium-spermidine-cholesterol

BGTC Bis-guanidinium-tren-cholesterol

Figure 4 Cholesterol derivatives. DC-chol: 3-β-[N-(N′, N′-dimethyl-ethane) carbamoyl] cholesterol.

derivatives containing nondegradable ether bonds are generally more toxic than those containing biodegradable linker bonds such as ester, amide, and carbamoyl bonds (10). Comparing the activities of DOTMA and DOTAP for in vivo gene transfer, Liu et al (31) concluded that stable ether bonds may be more beneficial than the less stable ester bonds.

Head Group

The number of charges on the head group determines whether the cationic lipid will be monovalent or multivalent. In monovalent lipids, the head group consists of either tertiary or quaternary ammonium groups. Chemical modifications of the head group were evaluated by Felgner et al (12), who synthesized a series of 2,3-dialkyloxy quaternary ammonium compounds containing a hydroxyl moiety on the quaternary amine (Figure 3). Those compounds are more efficient in transfection compared with DOTMA, which lacks a hydroxyl group on the quaternary amine. It was suggested that the hydroxyl group could improve the compaction of DNA by several mechanisms. DNA can form hydrogen bonds with the lipid, and the hydroxyl group can enhance the membrane hydration. In their study, Felgner et al (12) varied the chain length of the hydroxyalkyl moiety, while keeping the remaining structure unchanged, and observed that the activity of lipid decreased with an increase in the hydroxyalkyl chain length. It was speculated that an increase in the number of carbon atoms in the hydroxyalkyl chain, providing more flexibility to the terminal hydroxyl group, could lead to an inefficient interaction with DNA, which is responsible for the less observed transfection activity. High levels of transfection were also obtained with -N-(3-aminopropyl)-N, N-dimethyl-2, 3-bis (dodecyloxy)-1-propanaminium (GAP-DLRIE) (56), which contains a primary amine appended to the quaternary ammonium group in the polar head region. This primary amine, protonated at physiological pH, increases the hydrophilic character of the lipid, which may result in optimal cationic lipid-DNA interaction and lipid-DNA packing.

To design lipids containing a head group well adapted for interactions with phosphate groups of DNA, Vigneron et al (54) synthesized divalent cationic cholesterol derivatives bis-guanidinium cholesterol (Figure 4), which are able to form hydrogen bonds with nucleic acid bases. These compounds are very efficient for transfection for a variety of mammalian cell lines.

Multivalent cationic lipids known as lipopolyamines or lipospermine were synthesized by Behr et al (2). Remy et al (42) tested a series of lipopolyamines by varying the number, nature, and location of charges on the head group. They found that increasing the charge on the molecule containing an identical backbone and spacer [lipids $(C_{18})_2GlySper^{3+}$, $(C_{18})_2GlyOrn^{2+}$, and $(C_{18})_2Gly^+$] increased the efficacy of transfection (Figure 5).

Most of the structure-function relationship studies performed on cationic lipids have been realized in vitro, but very few are done in vivo. Solodin et al (47), who studied imidazolinium compounds, reported that in vitro efficiency is not predictive of in vivo efficiency. Indeed, short, saturated alkyl chain length compounds were the most effective for in vitro transfection, whereas long, unsaturated alkyl chain length compounds were the most effective in vivo.

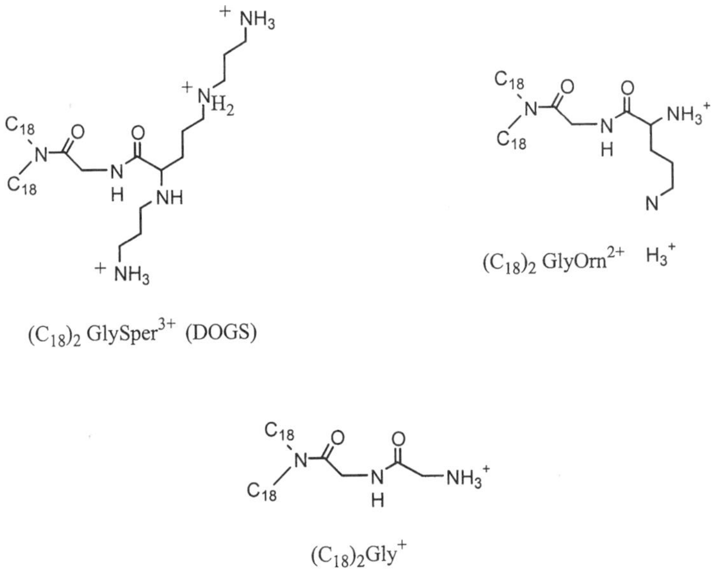

Figure 5   Double-chain multivalent lipids.

In another study, Balasubramaniam et al (1) reported that a cationic lipid containing a hydroxyethylammonium moiety in the polar head group improved in vivo gene delivery to the lung. In contrast, cationic lipids containing a trimethylammonium moiety in the polar head group, such as DOTAP, were less effective. In another study, Song et al (49) compared double-chain amphiphilic cationic lipid with cholesterol-based cationic lipid and observed a better activity of the cationic lipids with alkyl chains for in vivo lung cell transfection.

In summary, the definition of a good cationic lipid for in vitro experiments is not necessarily the same as that of a good cationic lipid for in vivo experiments. Furthermore, the development of systemic lipid-DNA complexes requires that the DNA be efficiently compacted and that particles are small enough to undergo extravasation into target tissues. From this point of view, multivalent cationic lipids are more likely to be the most efficient in compacting DNA. However, small particles have been obtained from new formulations involving monovalent cationic lipids and phospholipids (3, 19). Synthesis of efficient cationic lipids and improvement of current formulations should help define the ideal vector for in vivo administration.

STRUCTURE OF THE LIPID-DNA COMPLEX

Characterization of the structure of the lipid-DNA complex is gaining more interest, based on the idea that a better understanding of the molecular assembly of DNA and cationic lipids should help to establish correlations with their biological activity. Indeed, the transfection efficiency of a given lipid-DNA complex highly depends on its structural and physicochemical properties.

Electron microscopy was the first technique to visualize the structure of a lipid-DNA complex. Sternberg et al (50) used freeze-fracture electron microscopy to study cationic liposomes composed of 3-β-[N-(N',N'-dimethyl-ethane) carbamoyl] cholesterol (DC-chol) and dioleoylphosphatidylethanolamine (DOPE) mixed with plasmid DNA, and they observed several different kinds of structures, depending on incubation time of the complex and DNA concentration. At low lipid-DNA ratios and after short incubation times, semifused liposomes were observed. When the lipid-DNA ratio was increased and the incubation time prolonged, DNA appeared to be covered by a single bilayer of lipids connected to the liposomes, forming "spaghetti and meatball structures." Tubular spaghetti-like structures and spherical meatball-like aggregates were also observed for DOTMA liposome-DNA complexes. A similar study performed by Gustafsson et al (16) by cryotransmission electron microscopy on cationic liposomes composed of DOTAP or dimethyldioctadecylammonium (DDAB) and DOPE mixed with plasmid DNA revealed entrapment of DNA into aggregated multilamellar structures at low lipid-DNA ratios. When the amount of DNA was increased, free plasmid DNA was found to be associated on the surface of the complexes. In another study, Smyth Templeton et al (46) observed, through cryotransmission

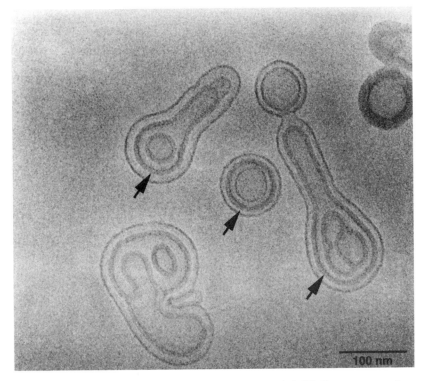

Figure 6 Cryoelectron micrographs of liposomes and DNA-liposome complexes. DOTAP-cholesterol liposomes (5 mM) were mixed with 150 μg of DNA [reprinted with permission from Smyth Templeton N, Lasic DD, Frederik PM, Strey HH, Roberts DD, et al. 1997. Improved DNA:liposome complexes for increased systemic delivery and gene expression. *Nat. Biotechnol.* 15:647 (46)].

electron microscopy, a unique feature of the liposome-DNA complex in which DNA was internalized within liposomes composed of DOTAP and cholesterol (Figure 6).

Recent cryotransmission electron microscopy studies performed in collaboration with P Frederik (University of Limburg, Maastricht, the Netherlands) on liposome-protamine-DNA complex (lipopolyplex) revealed double-ring structures, suggesting that the protamine-DNA condensed core is surrounded by a lipid bilayer (Figure 7).

Visualization of DNA incorporated into emulsion was also studied by freeze-fracture electron microscopy, and it seems that the DNA is condensed in the oil droplets (Figure 8) by means of formation of a hydrophobic complex between the DNA and cationic lipids (17).

Recently the use of synchrotron radiation combined with optical microscopy has given new insights into the structure of the lipid-DNA complex. Small-angle X-ray

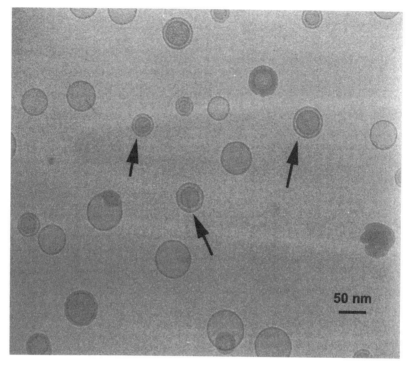

Figure 7 Cryoelectron micrographs of liposome-protamine-DNA complex from Song Li (Lab of Drug Targeting, University of Pittsburgh, unpublished results).

scattering experiments carried out by Radler et al (41) on liposomes composed of dioleoylphosphatidylcholine (DOPC) and DOTAP (1:1) mixed with plasmid DNA revealed that liposomes and DNA are rearranged in a multilamellar structure, with DNA intercalated between the bilayers (Figure 9). The interlayer spacing is in the range of 65.1 ± 2 Å and represents the lipid membrane thickness plus one monolayer of B-DNA (diameter ~20 Å), including a hydration shell. These authors demonstrated that the DNA interhelical spacing varied as a function of the total lipid-DNA ratio for isoelectric complexes, in which the number of cationic lipids equals the number of phosphate groups on the DNA. Their results showed that the interaxial distance between two helixes of DNA in the multilayers increased with lipid dilution, from being essentially closely packed at 24.5 Å to being significantly diluted at 57.1 Å. The intercalation of DNA between lipid bilayers can be explained as replacement of DNA counterions by cationic lipid. In the absence of DNA, lipidic membranes formed by the mixture of DOPC and DOTAP exhibit strong long-range interlayer electrostatic repulsions. DNA interacting with the cationic lipids effectively screens the electrostatic interactions between the lipid bilayers, resulting in the appearance of the condensed multilayers with intercalated

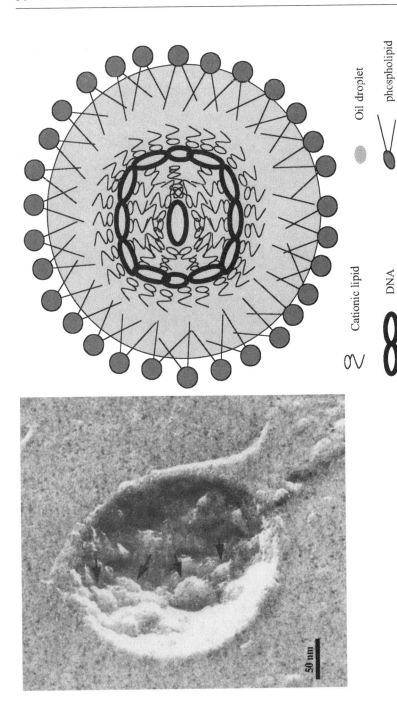

Cationic lipid

DNA

Oil droplet

phospholipid

Figure 8 Freeze-fracture electron microscopy of hydrophobized DNA incorporated into an emulsion, from Sophie Chesnoy (Lab of Drug Targeting, University of Pittsburgh, unpublished results). *Left:* Freeze fracture electron microscopy of hydrophobized DNA incorporated into an emulsion. *Right:* Schematic representation of DNA coated by cationic lipids in an oil droplet. The oil droplet incorporating the DNA is coated by phospholipids to form the emulsion.

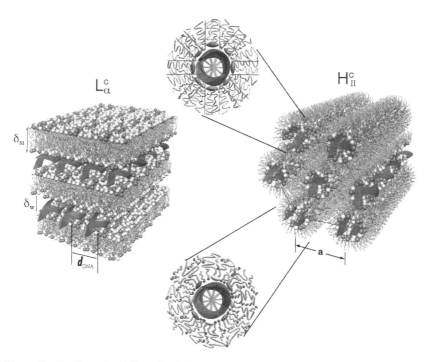

Figure 9   Condensed multilamellar lipids incorporating DNA and hexagonal arrangement of lipids with DNA [reprinted (abstracted/excerpted) with permission from Koltover I, Salditt T, Radler JO, Safinya CR. 1998. An inverted hexagonal phase of cationic liposome-DNA complexes related to DNA release and delivery. *Science* 281:78]. Copyright © 1998 Am. Assoc. Advance. Sci. L_α^C: lamellar phase; H_{II}^C: columnar inverted hexagonal phase; a: unit cell spacing; δ_m: bilayer thickness; δ_w: water gap; d_{DNA}: interaxial DNA-DNA spacing.

planar DNA rod lattices. The same conclusions were reached by Lasic et al (25), who investigated the structure of dioctadecylammonium bromide/Chol-DNA complexes.

A completely different structure was found when Koltover et al replaced DOPC in DOPC/DOTAP liposomes by DOPE (22). These authors demonstrated that, when the weight fraction of DOPE/(DOPE + DOTAP) is between 0.7 and 0.85, the internal structure of the complex undergoes a structural transition from a lamellar gel-condensed phase to a 2-dimensional columnar, inverted hexagonal structure (Figure 9). In this structure, the lipids are arranged in a hexagonal phase II structure in excess water with the water space inside the lipid micelle filled with DNA.

Formation of a lipid DNA lamellar or inverted hexagonal phase depends on the shape of the lipid molecule. For example, a mixture of DOPC and DOTAP forms lamellar structures characterized by zero natural curvature. Replacement of

DOPC by DOPE gives rise to an inverted hexagonal phase because of the intrinsic conelike shape of DOPE.

For multivalent cationic lipids, lamellar and micellar conformations of lipid-DNA complex have been reported recently (4, 38, 39, 63).

In conclusion, it seems that the formation of a condensed lamellar gel phase is the main structural feature reported at this time on mixtures of monovalent and multivalent cationic lipids with DNA. However, when the cationic lipid is mixed with a helper lipid, other structures can be formed upon mixing with DNA, which are dependent primarily on the intrinsic shape of the helper lipid.

FUNCTION OF THE LIPID-DNA COMPLEX

Interaction with Cells In Vitro

Interaction of a lipid-DNA complex with cells can be divided into three steps: binding and internalization of DNA by the cells, escape of DNA into the cytoplasm, and entry of DNA into the nucleus.

Binding of DNA to the Cell   The cell membrane is negatively charged owing to its high content of glycoproteins and glycolipids containing negatively charged sialic acid residues that can display, depending on the function of the cell, various types of receptors and antigens. As a direct consequence of the general structure of the cell membrane, the mechanism by which a lipid-DNA complex interacts with the cell will depend primarily on the presence of a specific ligand as well as the overall charge content of the vector.

In the absence of a targeting ligand, the driving force for the binding of the lipid-DNA complex to the cell membrane is electrostatic. Heparansulfate proteoglycan molecules may be involved in the capture of a lipid-DNA complex, especially in vivo (35). The main differences in binding efficiency between various lipid-DNA systems are most likely related to their physical properties, such as size, stability, and charge density.

The charge ratio between cationic lipids and DNA is an important parameter for transfection efficiency. A lipid-DNA complex with a high charge ratio $(+/-)$, in which the number of positive charges is in excess, is more efficient in vitro than a lipid-DNA complex with a charge ratio near neutrality.

In a recent study, Ross & Hui (44) found that lipid-DNA size is a major determinant of in vitro transfection efficiency. They showed that the size of positively charged lipid-DNA complexes incubated in the presence of a polyanionic medium was significantly increased and resulted in a higher transfection efficiency in CHO cells.

Several electron microscopic studies (24, 66) of lipid-DNA complex-to-cell interactions have clearly shown that the internalization of the lipid-DNA complex occurs mainly through endocytosis. However, there is a size limit for particles to be taken up by the cells through endocytosis. To explain why even large lipid-DNA complexes can be taken up by cells in vitro through endocytosis, Ross & Hui (44) proposed that small lipoplexes incubated in a polyanionic medium enlarged and formed granules on the surface of the cells. The granules then entered cells by membrane-directed movement. Zabner et al (64) and Van der Woude et al (53) also showed that the duration of incubation is an important parameter; they observed that more lipid-DNA complexes were taken up by an endocytic process as incubation time increased. In another study, Hui et al (21) compared the effects of phosphatidylethanolamine and phosphatidylcholine as helper lipids for gene transfer in vitro. They obtained higher transfection efficiencies with phosphatidylcholine than with phosphatidylethanolamine and attributed this effect to the fact that phosphatidylcholine-containing complexes form granules very slowly in transfection medium compared with phosphatidylethanolamine-containing complexes.

So it can be concluded that an optimal lipid-DNA formulation will be determined both by a critical ratio between cationic lipid and DNA and by the structure of the helper lipid, to provide a maximal complex-cell interaction with no toxicity.

Escape of DNA into the Cytoplasm   For the gene to be expressed, DNA has to be dissociated from lipids. Using microinjection, Zabner et al (64) clearly demonstrated that DNA cannot be expressed when complexed with lipids.

Zhou & Huang (66) and Friend et al (13) studied the intracellular processing of cationic lipid-DNA complexes by electron microscopy and observed that DNA is released into the cytoplasm from an early endosomal compartment, possibly by disruption of the endosomal membrane. In another study, Wattiaux et al (55) investigated, in vitro, how the endosomal membrane could be affected by cationic lipids (DOTAP). They concluded that destabilization of an endosomal membrane depends on interaction between cationic lipids and anionic molecules present in the membrane. According to Xu & Szoka (59), destabilization could be explained by a flip-flop of anionic lipids from the cytoplasmic facing monolayer of the endosomal membrane and subsequent formation of charge-neutral ion pairs with cationic lipids. Depending on the structure of the hydrophobic part of the cationic lipid, differences in the frequency of endosomal membrane disruption will occur. For example, El Ouahabi et al (9) and Balasubramaniam et al (1) observed that lipids with short alkyl chains may be more efficient in interlipid mixing than longer-chain analogs.

To facilitate disruption of the endosomal membrane, fusogenic lipid molecules such as phosphatidylethanolamine are often used as helper lipids (10, 12, 27, 64). A surprising observation is that this fusion process requires the endocytic pathway to occur and does not seem to occur directly at the plasma membrane (58). Indeed these authors demonstrated that binding to the cell surface is insufficient for lipid-DNA fusion. Furthermore, Farhood et al (10) and Legendre & Szoka (27) demonstrated that the lysosomotropic agent chloroquine inhibited the activity of the cationic liposome containing DOPE. However, as mentioned above, the binding to cell surface for phosphatidylethanolamine-containing complexes could be relatively inefficient owing to their rapid aggregation upon incubation in the transfection medium (21). Thus, although the endocytic pathway remains the primary mechanism for DNA transfer inside cells, spontaneous fusion between cationic liposome and plasma membrane cannot be ruled out (9).

Entry of DNA into the Nucleus   Entry of DNA into the nucleus after its release into the cytosol is necessary for gene expression. The precise mechanism of the nuclear delivery of the lipid-DNA complex is unknown but is believed to be an inefficient process. The aqueous channels of the nuclear pore complex allow the free diffusion of small macromolecules ($\leq$70 kDa), but the transport of larger macromolecules requires an active process (8). Remy et al (43) formulated a virus-like particle containing lipospermine as the cationic lipid and a lipid bearing a head group of nuclear localizing signal peptide, but they did not notice any improvement in transfection. Zabner et al (64) showed that intact lipid-DNA complex microinjected into the cytoplasm of *Xenopus* oocytes has little transfection activity. Thus it can be concluded that DNA has to be freed from lipids to enter the nucleus. Even so, the efficiency of entry is very low. Another drawback to the nuclear transport of plasmid DNA is its instability in the cytoplasm. Lechardeur et al (26) demonstrated that the half-life of naked plasmid DNA after direct injection is very short (1–2 h) and could be attributed to the action of cytosolic nucleases. However, Zanta et al (65) reported that a single nuclear-localization signal peptide linked to one end of a gene is sufficient to promote up to 1000-fold–higher transfection levels compared with naked plasmid DNA lacking the single nuclear-localization signal peptide.

Several studies (11, 34) reported that a correlation exists between mitotic activity and transfection by the cationic lipid-DNA complex. The exact mechanism by which cell proliferation results in gene transfer increase has not been elucidated, yet the breakdown of the nuclear membrane during mitosis could facilitate entry of plasmid DNA into the nucleus.

To overcome the inefficient nuclear transport of plasmid DNA, a cytoplasmic expression system was developed by using a reporter gene driven by a bacteriophage T7 promoter (6, 14). Expression of this gene is dependent on codelivery of T7 RNA polymerase, which remains largely in the cytoplasm owing to the absence of a nuclear localizing signal. Rapid and transient expression of a CAT reporter gene, pT7*cat*, has been reported when codelivered with T7 RNA polymerase and a T7 RNA polymerase regeneration system (15). Recently Brisson et al (5) developed a new T7 RNA polymerase autogene for cytoplasmic expression, which induces a higher and more sustained level of reporter gene expression. This new autogene consists of the T7 RNA polymerase gene driven by both cytomegalovirus and T7 promoters. The cytomegalovirus promoter is used to drive the first round of synthesis of T7 RNA polymerase. The endogenous T7 RNA polymerase produced from the cytomegalovirus promoter could then act on the T7 promoter of the new autogene in an autocatalytic fashion.

Interaction with Serum Components

In comparison with viral vectors, a major problem of cationic liposomes is their relatively low transfection efficiency. One of the reasons for this drawback is that the transfection efficiency is strongly inhibited by the presence of serum. This shortcoming limits the application of a cationic liposome for systematic gene delivery in vivo.

Several studies have been carried out to determine how the physicochemical properties of cationic liposome-DNA complexes can be affected in the presence of serum. Yang & Huang (61) investigated the role of the charge ratio of DC-chol liposome to DNA in inhibition of transfection by serum. They found that the inhibitory effect of serum can be overcome by increasing the charge ratio of cationic liposome to DNA. One possible explanation is that, for a higher charge ratio, the neutralizing effect of serum is saturated by excess lipids, allowing some cationic liposome-DNA complexes to bind to the cell surface. In another study, the same authors reported that serum sensitivity of the cationic liposome-DNA complex can also be overcome by prolonging the incubation time of the complex (60). In this study, a DNA–DC-chol liposome complex was incubated for different lengths of time after mixing liposome with DNA. At the end, fetal bovine serum was added to the complex immediately before this mixture was added to murine melanoma BL6 cells. The results showed that, as the incubation time increased, the sensitivity to serum decreased, which indicates that the lipid-DNA complex had undergone a maturation process resulting in a total resistance to serum.

Usually, DOPE is used as a helper lipid in the composition of cationic liposome. Crook et al (7) included cholesterol with DOTAP liposomes instead of DOPE and obtained significant levels of in vitro transfection in serum concentrations of ≤80%. These authors suggested that the inclusion of cholesterol in the membrane could create a highly ordered crystalline state, which would increase the stability of lipid-DNA complexes when exposed to serum. Smyth Templeton et al (46) and Liu et al (31) reported good protection and effective delivery to tissue of DNA mixed with DOTAP:cholesterol liposome, after systemic administration into mice.

In a more recent study by Li et al (29), a correlation between the rate of disintegration of lipidic vectors exposed to serum and their in vivo transfection efficiency in the lung was established. Vectors containing DOPE as a helper lipid were characterized by a rapid rate of disintegration, resulting in poor retention of these vectors in the lung and poor transfection efficiency. In contrast, cholesterol-containing vectors had a slower disintegration rate and were highly efficient in transfecting lung cells in vivo.

To increase the stabilization of cationic liposome-DNA complexes in vivo, Hong et al (20) included a small amount of polyethylene glycol phospholipid conjugate in their cationic liposome-DNA complexes to prevent their aggregation upon contact with serum.

In summary, DNA in complex with cationic liposomes has a strong tendency to form large aggregates over time and is unstable when in contact with serum. By changing the helper lipid in the composition of liposomes, increased serum stability of the vectors is obtained.

Biodistribution and Toxicity

In all of the reported studies on intravenous administration of lipid-DNA and lipid-protamine-DNA complexes, gene expression appeared in all major organs, including heart, lung, liver, spleen, and kidney (28, 32, 33, 46, 48, 52). The lung is always the organ with the highest level of gene expression, and endothelial cells are the major cell type transfected. Intravenous administration of DNA incorporated in emulsion showed that the liver was the organ with the highest level of gene expression (17). However, only transient expression occurred, and repeated injections of cationic liposome-DNA complexes were ineffective at frequent intervals. In a very recent study, Li et al (30) suggested that inactivation in lung endothelial cells might be caused by a nonspecific immune response. Substantial amounts of interferon γ and tumor necrosis factor α were induced after intravenous injection of liposome-protamine-DNA complexes, but methylation of plasmid DNA significantly decreased the level of cytokine production. Interferon γ and tumor necrosis factor α have been reported as potential inhibitors of gene expression (40). In a recent review, Krieg (23) explained that most microbial-plasmid DNAs, owing to their high content of unmethylated "CpG motifs," are responsible for triggering rapid activation of B cells, monocytes, macrophages, dendritic cells, and natural killer cells. A specific sequence motif has been identified as highly stimulatory (GACGTT). In another study based on cationic lipid-DNA complexes, Yew et al (62) have shown that the CpG motifs induce immune response in a dose-dependent manner. In our laboratory, oligodeoxynucleotides were used to further elucidate the inhibitory role of CpG in lipid-mediated intravenous gene delivery (51). It has been reported that cytokine production is mainly mediated by unmethylated CpG sequences present in the oligodeoxynucleotides. Interestingly, reversal of CG to GC almost completely abolished the immunostimulatory effect. Furthermore, it appeared from this study that the nucleotides flanking CpG are very important in the induction of the immune stimulatory effect. Finally, the degree of immune stimulation was correlated with the degree of inhibition of transgene expression in the lung.

Considerable effort has been spent in reducing the cytokine production after in vivo administration of lipid-DNA complexes. The reduction of CpG-stimulatory motifs in bacterial DNA is one possible way to inhibit cytokine secretion (30, 62).

Another possible approach is the introduction of CpG-neutralizing sequences (23). The use of immunosuppressive drugs can help to improve transgene expression (51).

FUTURE DIRECTIONS

A promising area of research is the design of targeted lipid-DNA complexes. It is clear that the physicochemical properties of lipid-DNA complexes are very important in the design of the ideal lipidic vector. The requirements for such an ideal vector can be summarized as follows. The particles should be small enough to be taken up by organs and surface protected by polyethylene glycol, to avoid protein interaction in the serum and thus extend their circulation lifetime into the blood. Furthermore, the addition of a targeting ligand is necessary to allow specific recognition by target cells. The DNA should be condensed and protected from nuclease degradation. Finally, DNA should be sufficiently inert to the immune cells to avoid a high level of cytokine production.

Recently several new methods were used to form small and stable lipid-DNA particles. Small and negatively charged particles were obtained by Blessing et al (3), but, because of their negative charge content and their lack of a targeting ligand, these particles are not active in transfection. In another study, Wheeler et al (57) described a detergent dialysis method to form small lipid-DNA particles coated by polyethylene glycol. These particles showed variable degrees of in vitro transfection efficiency depending on the acyl chain length of the polyethylene glycol-conjugated lipid.

Besides the use of cationic lipid, polycations are extensively studied for in vitro and in vivo gene transfer. Several studies have already reported transfer and gene expression via the strategy of receptor-mediated gene transfer (18, 36), using a polycation-DNA complex, but no efficient transfection in vivo has been reported at this time with targeted lipid-DNA complexes.

ACKNOWLEDGMENTS

We would like to thank *Nature Biotechnology* and Nancy Smyth Templeton for their permission to print the photograph showing cryoelectron micrographs of liposomes and DNA-liposome complexes. We would also like to thank *Science* and Cyrus Safinya for their permission to print the schematic representation of lamellar and hexagonal phases of lipid-DNA complexes.

The work of this laboratory is supported by the following grants: Targeted Genetics Corporation, NIH 1R001DK54225-01, NIH R01 CA 74918-01A2, NIH P01 DK44935-06A1, NIH AR 45925-01, Muscular Dystrophy of America, NIH CA 64654-05A1.

Visit the Annual Reviews home page at www.AnnualReviews.org

LITERATURE CITED

1. Balasubramaniam RP, Bennett MJ, Aberle AM, Malone JG, Nantz MH, et al. 1996. Structural and functional analysis of cationic transfection lipids: the hydrophobic domain. *Gene Ther.* 3:163

2. Behr JP, Demeneix B, Loeffler JP, Mutul JP. 1989. Efficient gene transfer into mammalian primary endocrine cells with lipopolyamine-coated DNA. *Proc. Natl. Acad. Sci. USA* 86:6982

3. Blessing T, Remy JS, Behr JP. 1998. Monomolecular collapse of plasmid DNA into stable virus-like particles. *Proc. Natl. Acad. Sci. USA* 95:1427

4. Boukhnikachvili T, Aguerre-Chariol O, Airiau M, Lesieur S, Ollivon M, et al. 1997. Structure of in-serum transfecting DNA-cationic lipid complexes. *FEBS Lett.* 409:188

5. Brisson M, He Y, Li S, Yang JP, Huang L. 1999. A novel T7 RNA polymerase autogene for efficient cytoplasmic expression of target genes. *Gene Ther.* 6:263

6. Chen X, Li Y, Xiong K, Kie Y, Aizicovici S, et al. 1995. A nonviral cytoplasmic gene expression system and its implications in cancer gene therapy. *Cancer Gene Ther.* 2:281

7. Crook K, Stevenson BJ, Dubouchet M, Porteous DJ. 1998. Inclusion of cholesterol in DOTAP transfection complexes increases the delivery of DNA to cells in vitro in the presence of serum. *Gene Ther.* 5:137

8. Dowty ME, Williams P, Zhang G, Hagstrom J, Wolff JA. 1995. Plasmid DNA entry into postmitotic nuclei of primary rat myotubes. *Proc. Natl. Acad. Sci. USA* 92:4572

9. El Ouahabi A, Thiry M, Pector V, Fuks R, Ruysschaert JM, et al. 1997. The role of endosome destabilizing activity in the gene transfer process mediated by cationic lipids. *FEBS Lett.* 414:187

10. Farhood H, Serbina N, Huang L. 1995. The role of dioleoyl phosphatidylethanolamine in cationic liposome mediated gene transfer. *Biochim. Biophys. Acta* 1235:289

11. Fasbender A, Zabner J, Zeiher BG, Welsh MJ. 1997. A low rate of cell proliferation and reduced DNA uptake limit cationic lipid-mediated gene transfer to primary cultures of ciliated human airway epithelia. *Gene Ther.* 4:1173

12. Felgner JH, Kumar R, Sridhar CN, Wheeler CJ, Tsai YJ, et al. 1994. Enhanced gene delivery and mechanism studies with a novel series of cationic lipid formulations. *J. Biol. Chem.* 269:2550

13. Friend DS, Papahadjopoulos D, Debs RJ. 1996. Endocytosis and intracellular processing accompanying transfection mediated by cationic liposomes. *Biochim. Biophys. Acta* 1278:41

14. Gao X, Huang L. 1993. Cytoplasmic expression of a reporter gene by co-delivery of T7 RNA polymerase and T7 promoter sequence with cationic liposomes. *Nucleic Acids Res.* 68:2867

15. Gao X, Jaffurs D, Robbins PD, Huang L. 1994. A sustained, cytoplasmic transgene expression system delivered by cationic liposomes. *Biochem. Biophys. Res. Commun.* 200:1201

16. Gustafsson J, Arvidson G, Karlsson G, Almgren M. 1995. Complexes between cationic liposomes and DNA visualized by cryo-TEM. *Biochim. Biophys. Acta* 1235:305

17. Hara T, Tan Y, Huang L. 1997. In vivo gene delivery to the liver using reconstituted chylomicron remnants as a novel nonviral vector. *Proc. Natl. Acad. Sci. USA* 94:14547

18. Hisayasu S, Miyauchi M, Akiyama K, Gotoh T, Satoh S, et al. 1999. In vivo targeted gene transfer into liver cells

mediated by a novel galactosyl-D-lysine/D-serine copolymer. *Gene Ther.* 6:689

19. Hofland HEJ, Shepard L, Sullivan SM. 1996. Formation of stable cationic lipid/DNA complexes for gene transfer. *Proc. Natl. Acad. Sci. USA* 93:7305

20. Hong K, Zheng W, Baker A, Papahadjopoulos D. 1997. Stabilization of cationic liposome-plasmid DNA complexes by polyamines and poly(ethylene glycol)-phospholipid conjugates for efficient in vivo gene delivery. *FEBS Lett.* 400:233

21. Hui SW, Langner M, Zhao YL, Ross P, Hurley E, et al. 1996. The role of helper lipids in cationic liposome-mediated gene transfer. *Biophys. J.* 71:590

22. Koltover I, Salditt T, Radler JO, Safinya CR. 1998. An inverted hexagonal phase of cationic liposome-DNA complexes related to DNA release and delivery. *Science* 281:78

23. Krieg AM. 1999. Direct immunologic activities of CpG DNA and implications for gene therapy. *J. Gene Med.* 1:56

24. Labat-Moleur F, Steffan AM, Brisson C, Perron H, Feugeas O, et al. 1996. An electron microscopy study into the mechanism of gene transfer with lipopolyamines. *Gene Ther.* 3:1010

25. Lasic DD, Strey H, Stuart MCA, Podgornik R, Frederik PM. 1997. The structure of DNA-liposome complexes. *J. Am. Chem. Soc.* 119:832

26. Lechardeur D, Sohn KJ, Haardt M, Joshi PB, Monck M, et al. 1999. Metabolic instability of plasmid DNA in the cytosol: a potential barrier to gene transfer. *Gene Ther.* 6:482

27. Legendre JY, Szoka FC Jr. 1992. Delivery of plasmid DNA into mammalian cell lines using pH-sensitive liposomes: comparison with cationic liposomes. *Pharm. Res.* 9 (10):1235

28. Li S, Rizzo MA, Bhattacharya S, Huang L. 1998. Characterization of cationic lipid-protamine-DNA (LPD) complexes for intravenous gene delivery. *Gene Ther.* 5:930

29. Li S, Tseng WC, Beer Stolz D, Wu SP, Watkins SC, et al. 1999. Dynamic changes in the characteristics of cationic lipidic vectors after exposure to mouse serum: implications for intravenous lipofection. *Gene Ther.* 6:585

30. Li S, Wu SP, Whitmore M, Loeffert EJ, Wang L, et al. 1999. Effect of immune response on gene transfer to the lung via systemic administration of cationic lipidic vectors. *Am. J. Physiol.* 276:L796

31. Liu F, Qi H, Huang L, Liu D. 1997. Factors controlling the efficiency of cationic lipid-mediated transfection in vivo via intravenous administration. *Gene Ther.* 4:517

32. Liu Y, Mounkes LC, Liggitt HD, Brown CS, Solodin L, et al. 1997. Factors influencing the efficiency of cationic liposome-mediated intravenous gene delivery. *Nat. Biotechnol.* 15:167

33. Mahato RI, Anwer K, Tagliaferri F, Meaney C, Leonard P, et al. 1998. Biodistribution and gene expression of lipid/plasmid complexes after systemic administration. *Hum. Gene Ther.* 9:2083

34. Mortimer I, Tam P, MacLachlan I, Graham RW, Saravolac EG, et al. 1999. Cationic lipid-mediated transfection of cells in culture requires mitotic activity. *Gene Ther.* 6:403

35. Mounkes LC, Zhong W, Cipres-Palacin G, Heath TD, Debs RJ. 1998. Proteoglycans mediate cationic liposome-DNA complex-based gene delivery in vitro and in vivo. *J. Biol. Chem.* 40:26164

36. Ogris M, Brunner S, Schuller S, Kircheis R, Wagner E. 1999. Pegylated DNA/transferrin-PEI complexes: reduced interaction with blood components, extended circulation in blood and potential for systemic gene delivery. *Gene Ther.* 6:595

37. Pinnaduwage P, Schmitt L, Huang L. 1989. Use of quaternary ammonium detergent in liposome mediated DNA transfection of mouse L-cells. *Biochim. Biophys. Acta* 985:33

38. Pitard B, Aguerre O, Airiau M, Lachages AM, Boukhnikachvili T, et al. 1997. Virus-sized self-assembling lamellar complexes between plasmid DNA and cationic micelles promote gene transfer. *Proc. Natl. Acad. Sci. USA* 94:14412

39. Pitard B, Oudrhiri N, Vigneron JP, Hauchecorne M, Aguerre O. 1999. Structural characteristics of supramolecular assemblies formed by guanidinium–cholesterol reagents for gene transfection. *Proc. Natl. Acad. Sci. USA* 96:2621

40. Qin L, Ding Y, Pahud DR, Chang E, Imperiale MJ, et al. 1997. Promoter attenuation in gene therapy: interferon-gamma and tumor necrosis factor-alpha inhibit transgene expression. *Hum. Gene Ther.* 8:2019

41. Radler JO, Koltover I, Salditt T, Safinya CR. 1997. Structure of DNA-cationic liposome complexes: DNA intercalation in multilamellar membranes in distinct inter-helical packing regimes. *Science* 275:810

42. Remy JS, Sirlin C, Vierling P, Behr JP. 1994. Gene transfer with a series of lipophilic DNA-binding molecules. *Bioconjugate Chem.* 5:647

43. Remy JS, Kichler A, Mordvinov V, Schuber F, Behr JP. 1995. Targeted gene transfer into hepatoma cells with lipopolyamine-condensed DNA particles presenting galactose ligands: a stage toward artificial viruses. *Proc. Natl. Acad. Sci. USA* 92:1744

44. Ross PC, Hui SW. 1999. Lipoplex size is a major determinant of in vitro lipofection efficiency. *Gene Ther.* 6:651

45. Salditt T, Koltover I, Radler JO, Safinya CR. Two-dimensional smectic ordering of linear DNA chains in self-assembled DNA-cationic liposome mixtures. *Phys. Rev. Lett.* 79:2582

46. Smyth Templeton N, Lasid DD, Frederik PM, Strey HH, Roberts DD, et al. 1997. Improved DNA:liposome complexes for increased systemic delivery and gene expression. *Nat. Biotechnol.* 15:647

47. Solodin I, Brown CS, Bruno MS, Chow CY, Jang EH, et al. 1995. A novel series of amphiphilic imidazolinium compounds for in vitro and in vivo gene delivery. *Biochemistry* 34:13537

48. Song Y, Liu F, Chu SY, Liu DX. 1997. Characterization of cationic liposome-mediated gene transfer in vivo by intravenous administration. *Hum. Gene Ther.* 8:1585

49. Song YK, Liu F, Liu D. 1998. Enhanced gene expression in mouse lung by prolonging the retention time of intravenously injected plasmid DNA. *Gene Ther.* 5:1531

50. Sternberg B, Sorgi FL, Huang L. 1994. New structures in complex formation between DNA and cationic liposomes visualized by freeze-fracture electron microscopy. *FEBS Lett.* 356:361

51. Tan Y, Li S, Pitt BR, Huang L. 1999. The inhibitory role of CpG immunostimulatory motifs in cationic lipid vector-mediated transgene expression in vivo. *Gene Ther.* In press

52. Thierry AR, Rabinovich P, Peng B, Mahan LC, Bryant JL, et al. 1997. Characterization of liposome-mediated gene delivery: expression, stability and pharmacokinetics of plasmid DNA. *Gene Ther.* 4:226

53. Van der Woude I, Willy Visser H, Ter Beest MBA, Wagenaar A, Ruiters MHJ, et al. 1995. Parameters influencing the introduction of plasmid DNA into cells by the use of synthetic amphiphiles as a carrier system. *Biochim. Biophys. Acta* 1240:34

54. Vigneron JP, Oudrhiri N, Fauquet M, Vergely L, Bradley JC, et al. 1996. Guanidinium-cholesterol cationic lipids: efficient vectors for the transfection of eukaryotic cells. *Proc. Natl. Acad. Sci. USA* 93:9682

55. Wattiaux R, Jadot M, Warnier-Pirotte MT, Wattiaux-De Coninck S. 1997. Cationic lipids destabilize lysosomal membrane in vitro. *FEBS Lett.* 417:199

56. Wheeler CJ, Fegner PL, Tsai YJ, Marshall J, Sukhu L, et al. 1996. A novel cationic lipid greatly enhances plasmid DNA

delivery and expression in mouse lung. *Proc. Natl. Acad. Sci. USA* 93:11454

57. Wheeler JJ, Palmer L, Ossanlou M, MacLachlan I, Graham RW, et al. 1999. Stabilized plasmid-lipid particles: construction and characterization. *Gene Ther.* 6:271

58. Wrobel I, Collins D. 1995. Fusion of cationic liposomes with mammalian cells occurs after endocytosis. *Biochim. Biophys. Acta* 1235:296

59. Xu Y, Szoka FC. 1996. Mechanism of DNA release from cationic liposome/DNA complexes used in cell transfection. *Biochemistry* 35:5616

60. Yang JP, Huang L. 1998. Time-dependent maturation of cationic liposome-DNA complex for serum resistance. *Gene Ther.* 5:380

61. Yang JP, Huang L. 1997. Overcoming the inhibitory effect of serum on lipofection by increasing the charge ratio of cationic liposome to DNA. *Gene Ther.* 4:950

62. Yew NS, Wang KX, Przybylska M, Bagley RG, Stedman M. 1999. Contribution of plasmid DNA to inflammation in the lung after administration of cationic lipid:DNA complexes. *Hum. Gene Ther.* 10:223

63. Yoshikawa Y, Emi N, Kanbe T, Yoshikawa K, Saito H. 1996. Folding and aggregation of DNA chains induced by complexation with lipospermine: formation of a nucleosome-like structure and network assembly. *FEBS Lett.* 396:71

64. Zabner J, Fasbender AJ, Moninger T, Poellinger KA, Welsh MJ. 1995. Cellular and molecular barriers to gene transfer by a cationic lipid. *J. Biol. Chem.* 270:18997

65. Zanta MA, Belguise-Valladier P, Behr JP. 1999. Gene delivery: a single nuclear localization signal peptide is sufficient to carry DNA to the cell nucleus. *Proc. Natl. Acad. Sci. USA* 96:91

66. Zhou X, Huang L. 1994. DNA transfection mediated by cationic liposomes containing lipopolylysine: characterization and mechanism of action. *Biochim. Biophys. Acta* 1189:195

67. Zhu N, Liggitt D, Liu Y, Debs R. 1993. Systemic gene expression after intravenous delivery DNA delivery into adult mice. *Science* 261:209

Annu. Rev. Biophys. Biomol. Struct. 2000. 29:49–79

SIGNALING AND SUBCELLULAR TARGETING BY MEMBRANE-BINDING DOMAINS[1]

James H. Hurley and Saurav Misra

Laboratory of Molecular Biology, National Institute of Diabetes and Digestive and Kidney Diseases, National Institutes of Health, Bethesda, Maryland 20892-0580; e-mail: jh8e@nih.gov

Key Words C1 domain, C2 domain, FYVE domain, PH domain, subcellular localization

■ **Abstract** Protein kinase C homology-1 and -2, FYVE, and pleckstrin homology domains are ubiquitous in eukaryotic signal transduction and membrane-trafficking proteins. These domains regulate subcellular localization and protein function by binding to lipid ligands embedded in cell membranes. Structural and biochemical analysis of these domains has shown that their molecular mechanisms of membrane binding depend on a combination of specific and nonspecific interactions with membrane lipids. In vivo studies of green fluorescent protein fusions have highlighted the key roles of these domains in regulating protein localization to plasma and internal membranes in cells.

CONTENTS

---

[1]The US government has the right to retain a nonexclusive, royalty-free license in and to any copyright covering this paper.

49

PERSPECTIVES AND OVERVIEW

Subcellular targeting of proteins is a fundamental control mechanism in eukaryotic cells. Localization to different cell compartments is often brought about by protein-protein interaction domains (70, 100). Another major class of subcellular targeting domains binds specifically to lipid ligands in cell membranes. The best known members of this group are the protein kinase C (PKC) homology-1 (C1) (54, 111) and -2 (C2) domains (89, 110), the pleckstrin homology (PH) domain (8, 34, 73, 109), and the FYVE domain (34, 42, 141). Although some C1, C2, and PH domains interact with proteins in addition to—or instead of—lipids, their best known roles are in lipid binding. This review emphasizes the membrane-binding mechanisms of these domains and their role in cell signaling.

These are exciting times for research on signal transduction domains. Studies of green fluorescent protein fusions with signaling proteins are yielding quantitative kinetic information in living cells. The three-dimensional structures of the C1, C2, FYVE, and PH domains have all been solved at high resolution by X-ray crystallography, and they have also been studied by nuclear magnetic resonance (NMR) and electron paramagnetic resonance (EPR). Site-directed mutagenesis, fluorescence, and surface pressure studies have made critical contributions to understanding how these proteins interact with membranes. Databases such as SMART (115; http://www.coot.embl-heidelberg.de/SMART) and Pfam (6; http://www.sanger.ac.uk/Software/Pfam) provide the most comprehensive census yet of signal-transducing domains. With the rapid growth of interest in membrane targeting as a mechanism for signal transduction, these developments are due for review.

C1 DOMAINS

The C1 domain is a compact zinc-containing motif of ~50 amino acid residues, formerly known as a "cysteine-rich" domain (Figure 1*a*). The C1 domain was discovered as a conserved region responsible for the allosteric activation of PKC isozymes (PKCs) by diacylglycerol and phorbol esters. C1 domains are now known to occur not only in PKCs but in >200 different proteins in the nonredundant

(a)

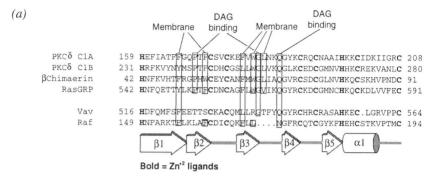

(b)

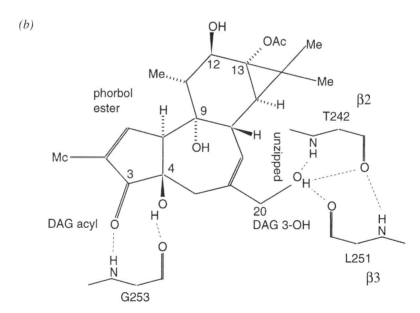

Figure 1 *a*. Alignment of C1 domains. Zn^{2+}-liganding residues are shown in bold. Membrane-interacting and diacylglycerol-binding-site residues are boxed. Vav and Raf represent atypical C1 domains that do not bind diacylglycerol and lack the crucial boxed residues. *b*. Schematic of the typical C1 phorbol ester-binding site (modified from Reference 146).

sequence databases [these numbers, obtained from the SMART database (115), are higher than quoted elsewhere owing both to new discoveries and to the inclusion of orthologs]. Some of these proteins, including PKCs, the chimaerins, Unc-13 (54, 111), and RasGRP (24, 111), are effectors of diacylglycerol. However, many of the known C1 domains do not bind diacylglycerol. This group of C1 domains is referred to as "atypical," and they are implicated in interactions with small G-proteins and membrane lipids other than diacylglycerol.

Structure of the C1 Domain

C1 domains contain two small β sheets and a short C-terminal α-helix that are built around two 3-Cys–1-His Zn^{2+}-binding clusters (52, 146; Figure 2a—see color insert). The Zn^{2+} ions are an integral part of the structure. The diacylglycerol- and phorbol ester-binding site is formed at one tip of the domain, where part of the second β sheet unzips. The linked ring structures of phorbol are inserted lengthwise into the narrow groove at the tip of the C1 domain. The 3- and 20-oxygens of phorbol interact with main-chain groups exposed by unzipping two β strands (Figure 1b). One of the acyl group oxygens and the 3-hydroxyl of diacylglycerol are believed to occupy the same sites, whereas it is less clear how the second acyl group oxygen interacts.

Diacylglycerol-Promoted Membrane Association

One entire end of the C1 domain surrounding the binding groove is almost completely hydrophobic (Figure 2a). The region adjoins a basic ring that circumscribes the midsection of the domain surface. NMR studies in short-chain lipid micelles (145) and surface pressure analysis of C1 domain mutants of PKCα (84) confirmed the prediction that the hydrophobic region penetrates into the membrane interior while the basic ring contacts the membrane surface (146). There is an exceptionally strong synergism between diacylglycerol or phorbol ester binding and membrane binding (86), and the presence of diacylglycerol or phorbol ester is required for targeting of C1 domains to membranes. The monomeric phorbol ester head group binds 10^4-fold more weakly than tetradecanoyl phorbol acetate presented in mixed micelles (63). The synergistic binding is explained by the two types of binding surfaces: a stereospecific diacylglycerol-phorbol ester-binding site in a groove surrounded by a nonstereospecific membrane-binding site. Binding of either diacylglycerol or bulk membrane to its site alone leaves interactions with other sites unsatisfied; hence simultaneous binding is favored.

C1 domains from PKCγ can translocate from the cytosol to the plasma membrane within a few seconds after addition of diacylglycerol (95). Free fatty acids can stimulate PKC translocation to a variety of different cell compartments depending on the isozyme (117), yet specific binding to PKC C1 and C2 domains has not been documented. Free fatty acids could modulate the nonspecific interactions of PKC-C1 or PKC-C2 with membranes.

Predicting C1 Domain Function from Sequence

The structure of the C1-phorbol ester complex and its nonspecific membrane-binding surface depend on the conservation of a number of amino acids in the group of "typical" C1 domains that do bind diacylglycerol and phorbol ester (Figure 1*a*). The typical C1 domains conserve both the large hydrophobic residues that form the nonspecific binding surface and three structural residues (a Pro, Gly, and Gln) involved in the stabilization of the binding groove (64, 146). Counting from the first conserved His, the consensus motif for the typical C1 domains begins at Pro-11:PXArCX$_2$CX$_2$Hy$_3$GX$_{0-1}$HyX$_2$QG, where X is any amino acid; Ar is Phe, Trp, or Tyr; Hy is any hydrophobic residue; and residues involved in groove formation or membrane penetration are shown in bold (64, 146). This signature is inconsistent with the properties of synthetic peptide models for PKC C1 domains (58), although the motif has been largely successful in predicting the properties of naturally occurring and recombinant C1 domain-containing proteins. For example, this motif is present in the most recently discovered C1 domain, that of RasGRP (24). RasGRP is targeted to cell membranes in response to diacylglycerol via its C1 domain (131), revealing a new pathway from diacylglycerol to Ras signaling.

Atypical C1 domains occur in two large groups of proteins: the diacylglycerol kinases (DAGKs) (132) and effectors and regulators of small G-proteins. The function of the DAGK C1 domains is mysterious. None of these kinases is known to bind phorbol ester, and the C1 domains of DAGKα are dispensable for catalytic activity (113, 132). The atypical C1 domain of Raf is involved in allosteric regulation of this protein kinase by activated Ras, although the primary binding site for Ras lies elsewhere, on the Raf-RBD domain. Several regions on the surface of the Raf-C1structure (87) appear to be involved in autoinhibitory interactions in the inactive conformation of Raf (18, 19). At least one epitope, comprising Lys-144 and Leu-160 of c-Raf-1, overlaps with the phorbol ester-binding site on the typical C1 domains and probably has direct interactions with Ras (19).

Multi-C1-Domain Proteins: the Contribution of Context

In most of the PKCs and DAGKs, C1 domains occur in pairs. The function of individual C1 domains depends on their context in the larger protein, as illustrated by the interdependent allosteric activation of PKC by various lipids (93, 119). The diacylglycerol-binding sites on the C1 domains of PKCγ are obstructed in the inactive cytosolic form of the enzyme, as judged by translocation kinetics in vivo (94). Diacylglycerol binding to the C1 domain is believed to be coupled to a large-scale conformational change that alters the interactions of the C1 domains with the kinase catalytic domains, thereby allosterically activating the enzyme (53, 93, 94). PKCδ and PKD/PKCμ both contain two C1 domains, C1A and C1B. For these isozymes, the C1B contributes to phorbol ester–stimulated translocation by an order of magnitude more than the C1A (57, 128). It remains to be seen whether other PKCs follow this pattern.

C2 DOMAINS

C2 domains are $\sim$120-residue domains that were originally discovered as a conserved sequence motif in the Ca^{2+}-dependent PKCs. There are now $\sim$600 C2 domains identified in >400 different proteins (see above regarding numbers taken from the SMART database). Much of the intense interest in these domains arises from the roles of C2 domain proteins not only in signal transduction, but also in inflammation, synaptic vesicle trafficking and fusion, and many other cell processes (89, 110). Many, but not all, C2 domains bind phospholipid membranes in the presence of Ca^{2+}. Some C2 domains bind membranes constitutively and do not bind Ca^{2+} at all. Other C2 domains bind proteins instead of membranes, using both Ca^{2+}-dependent and -independent mechanisms. Still other C2 domains bind soluble inositol polyphosphates, usually in a Ca^{2+}-independent manner.

Structure of the C2 Domain

Structures of five different C2 domains are now known: the C2A domain of synaptotagmin I (SytI) (126) and the C2 domains of PKC-β (126) and PKC-δ (98) and of phospholipases A_2 (cPLA$_2$) (21, 102, 144) and C-δ1 (PLCδ1) (27, 44). The structure of the C2 domain is a β sandwich related to the immunoglobulin fold (45). Two permutations of the C2 fold occur, known as types I (S-type) and II (P-type), in which the sequence starts at a position in the β sheet offset by a single strand in one as compared with the other (Figure 3a). The Ca^{2+}-binding sites are formed by three loops at one tip of the structure. The loops, known as the Ca^{2+}-binding regions (CBRs), correspond structurally to the antigen-binding complementarity-determining regions of antibody Fabs. In addition to forming the Ca^{2+}-binding sites of the Ca^{2+}-dependent class of C2 domains, the CBRs are involved in phospholipid specificity and probably in other ligand-binding interactions.

Figure 3   *a.* Structure-based alignment of C2 domains. Membrane-binding residues and specific Ca^{2+}-binding residues are boxed. Residues that bind Ca^{2+} through the backbone are not indicated. The Ca^{2+} sites in which the ligands participate are marked by Roman numerals. All of the ligands for a given Ca^{2+} site must be present in a given sequence for the site to be functional. Two permuted C2 secondary structures are shown above and below the alignment. The three calcium-binding loops (CBRs) are bracketed. The atypical PKCδ-C2 domain does not bind Ca^{2+}. *b.* Schematic of the Ca^{2+}-binding sites in C2 domains. Site I is occupied in cPLA$_2$ (cp) and PLCδ1 (pl); site II is occupied in all Ca^{2+}-binding C2 domains; and sites III and IV are known or predicted to be bound in PLCδ1, SytI-C2A (sy), and PKCβ (pb). MES, 2-[N-morpholino]ethanesulfonic acid.

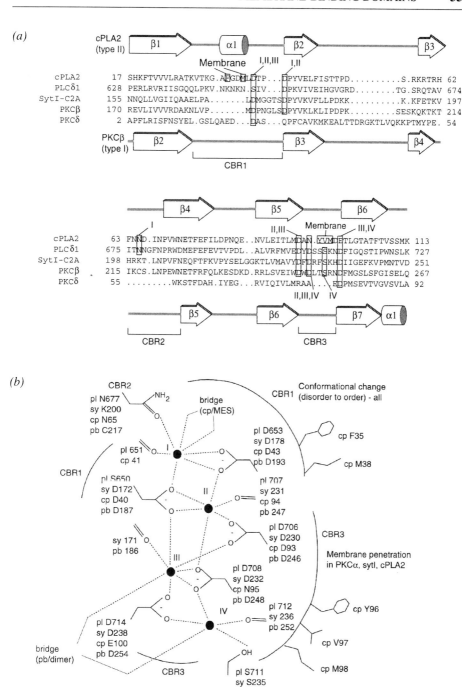

(a)

cPLA2 (type II)   β1   α1   β2   β3

Membrane   I,II,III   I,II

```
cPLA2      17  SHKFTVVVLRATKVTKG.AEGDMLDTP...DPYVELFISTTPD..........S.RKRTRH  62
PLCδ1     628  PERLRVRIISGQQLPKV.NKNKN.SIV...DPKVIVEIHGVGRD.......TG.SRQTAV  674
SytI-C2A  155  NNQLLVGIIQAAELPA......LDMGGTSDPYVKVFLLPDKK..........K.KFETKV  197
PKCβ      170  REVLIVVVRDAKNLVP......MDPNGLSDPYVKLKLIPDPK........SESKQKTKT  214
PKCδ        2  APFLRISFNSYEL.GSLQAED...DAS...QPFCAVKMKEALTTDRGKTLVQKKPTMYPE.  54
```

PKCβ (type I)   β2   β3   β4

CBR1

β4   β5   β6   Membrane   III,IV

I   II,III

```
cPLA2      63  FNND.INPVWNETFEFILDPNQE..NVLEITLMDAN.YVMDETLGTATFTVSSMK  113
PLCδ1     675  ITNNGFNPRWDMEFEFEVTVPDL..ALVRFMVEDYDSSSKNDFIGQSTIPWNSLK  727
SytI-C2A  198  HRKT.LNPVFNEQFTFKVPYSELGGKTLVMAVYDFDRFSKHDIIGEFKVPMNTVD  251
PKCβ      215  IKCS.LNPEWNETFRFQLKESDKD.RRLSVEIWDWDLTSRNDFMGSLSFGISELQ  267
PKCδ       55  .........WKSTFDAH.IYEG...RVIQIVLMRAA...\.EDPMSEVTVGVSVLA  92
```

II,III,IV   IV

β5   β6   β7   α1

CBR2   CBR3

(b)

CBR2

pl N677   NH₂
sy K200
cp N65
pb C217

bridge (cp/MES)

CBR1   Conformational change (disorder to order) - all

pl D653
sy D178
cp D43
pb D193

cp F35

cp M38

CBR1

pl 651
cp 41   I

pl S650
sy D172
cp D40
pb D187

pl 707
sy 231
cp 94
pb 247   II

pl D706
sy D230
cp D93
pb D246

CBR3

Membrane penetration in PKCα, sytI, cPLA2

sy 171
pb 186   III

pl D708
sy D232
cp N95
pb D248

pl 712
sy 236
pb 252

cp Y96

pl D714
sy D238
cp E100
pb D254   IV

cp V97

bridge (pb/dimer)

CBR3

pl S711
sy S235
pb S251

cp M98

Ca^{2+}-Binding Sites

Ca^{2+}-binding affinities are strongly dependent on the presence of phospholipid or other ligands. cPLA$_2$-C2 binds two Ca^{2+} in the presence or absence of membrane (Figure 3*b*) (92, 102, 144). SytI-C2A and PKCβ-C2 bind three ions, although binding to the third site is immeasurably weak in the absence of an exogenous acidic ligand (125, 134). PLCδ1-C2 binds three ions in the absence of ligands (28, 46). A hypothetical fourth site exists on PLCδ1-C2, corresponding to the very low-affinity third site on SytI, but this has not been confirmed. The individual Ca^{2+} sites within a C2 domain have distinct functions in binding and enzyme activation (7, 83).

Membrane-Binding Sites

There is an emerging consensus on the membrane-docking modes of Ca^{2+}-dependent membrane-binding C2 domains (Figure 2*b*). The structures of the PLCδ1-C2 and cPLA2-C2 are known in the context of the larger enzyme (21, 27, 44). The presence of the phospholipase active sites in the same structure provides a powerful constraint on the orientation of the C2 domain with respect to the bilayer, which led to a detailed model of C2-membrane docking (44). The membrane-docked PLCδ1-C2 placed the CBR3 region closest to the membrane and juxtaposed the Ca^{2+}-binding sites with the membrane surface. In this model, the concave face of the C2 structure and strand β3 in particular face the membrane surface across a distance of 5–10 Å. The overall orientation is similar for cPLA$_2$-C2, but this C2 domain has a larger and more hydrophobic CBR1 than that of PLCδ1-C2 (21, 102, 144).

The inferences from structures have been confirmed and elaborated on by functional studies. Trp residues incorporated into the SytI-C2A and cPLA$_2$-C2 domains as fluorescent reporters reveal membrane penetration by SytI-C2A's CBR1 (13) and both CBR1 and CBR3 of cPLA$_2$-C2 (90, 103). NMR of SytI-C2A (12) and NMR and EPR studies of cPLA$_2$-C2 support this picture (4, 144). Scanning mutagenesis and surface pressure measurements on PKCα (84) and cPLA$_2$ (7) came to similar conclusions. NMR suggests that residues on the concave face of cPLA$_2$-C2 sense an altered environment when bound to the membrane (144). However, mutagenesis of the concave faces of PKCβII-C2 (61) and cPL A$_2$-C2 (7) show that this region does not contribute substantially to membrane binding even though it is oriented toward the membrane surface.

Phospholipid Specificity and Subcellular Localization

Most Ca^{2+}-dependent C2 domains bind acidic phospholipids (89, 110), and PLCδ1-C2 was most recently added to this group (81). cPLA$_2$-C2, in contrast, seems to prefer neutral membranes, especially phosphatidylcholine (PC) (91). cPLA$_2$ also binds phosphatidylmethanol, and it has been suggested that small head groups promote binding by favoring the bilayer insertion of cPLA$_2$-C2 (51). The differences in specificity correlate with the structures of the CBRs and with the ionic strength dependence of the interaction. The CBR3 of SytI and many other acidic phospholipid-binding C2 domains contains basic residues, whereas hydrophobic residues predominate in cPLA$_2$. cPLA$_2$ also contains a helix in its CBR1 that inserts part of its hydrophobic surface into the membrane (4, 7, 90, 102, 103, 144). This helix is not present in the acidic phospholipid binders. Consistent with these ideas, SytI-C2/membrane binding is attenuated by >500 mM NaCl, the signature of an electrostatic interaction, whereas cPLA$_2$-C2 binding is not (20). An aromatic cluster specific to the cPLA$_2$-C2 structure is predicted to form a choline head group-binding site that may explain the preference for PC over other zwitterionic lipids (144).

Subcellular localization of C2 domains correlates with their phospholipid specificity. PKCα–C2 (16) and PKCγ (94) translocate to the plasma membrane, rich in the acidic phospholipid phosphatidylserine (PS), when free [Ca^{2+}] increases. This is vividly illustrated by the plasma membrane translocation of PKCγ coincident with Ca^{2+} oscillations (94). In contrast, increased cytoplasmic [Ca^{2+}] induces intact cPLA$_2$ and cPLA$_2$-C2 to translocate to the PC-rich nuclear envelope and endoplasmic reticulum (43, 103).

Mechanism of Ca^{2+}-Dependent Membrane Binding

Three mechanisms by which Ca^{2+} could promote membrane binding by C2 domains have been widely discussed. The first is the "Ca^{2+} bridge" model. The second model invokes a conformational change in which the structure of the CBRs is altered by Ca^{2+} binding such that their ability to bind membranes is increased. The third is the "electrostatic switch" mechanism. These three mechanisms are not necessarily mutually exclusive, nor do they exhaust the possibilities.

The Ca^{2+} Bridge Model In the Ca^{2+} bridge model, Ca^{2+} ions are specifically coordinated by functional groups provided by both the C2 domain and by phospholipids. The annexins provide a precedent (127). The membrane-docked position of the C2 domain tip at the bilayer surface is consistent with a Ca^{2+} bridge. All efforts at forming specific Ca^{2+}-bridged complexes between C2 domains and short-chain phospholipids have thus far disappointed. However, a structure of a Ca^{2+}-bridged complex between the cPLA$_2$-C2 and the sulfonate moiety of a morpholineethanesulfonic acid buffer ion has been reported (21; Figure 3*b*). The 10 Å between the putative choline site and Ca^{2+} site I suggests that a single PC molecule would be unlikely to both coordinate Ca^{2+} and occupy the choline pocket. The crystal structure of the PKCβ-C2 (125) reveals a Ca^{2+}-bridged protein dimer that provides a different model for chelation in the putative phospholipid complex (Figure 3*b*). This model would position the phosphodiester $\sim$8 Å nearer to the membrane center (or the protein 8 Å farther from it) than would be suggested by the cPLA$_2$-C2 [N-morpholino]ethanesulfonic acid complex. Arguing against a bridge mechanism, cPLA$_2$-C2 is capable of Ca^{2+}-dependent partitioning to pure

Triton micelles (20). It appears that Ca^{2+} bridging is an important contributing factor but cannot on its own serve as a general explanation for all Ca^{2+}-dependent membrane binding by C2 domains.

Ca^{2+} Induced Conformational Changes   The structure of a truncated PLCδ1 has been determined in two different crystal forms, cubic and triclinic. In the "apo-" form of the triclinic crystal, CBR1 is almost completely invisible in electron density owing to disorder. Ca^{2+} analog binding in the triclinic form induces a disorder-to-order conformational change in which CBR1 adopts a well-defined conformation (44). In the cubic-crystal form, CBR1 is ordered in both apo- and bound structures (28). CBR1 in the cubic form interacts extensively with crystal packing contacts, explaining the apparent lack of a conformational change. Movement of the CBR1 in the triclinic form is much less restricted. With the exception of PLCδ1, all crystallized Ca^{2+}-dependent C2 domains have been grown only in a single Ca^{2+} ligation state. SytI-C2A was crystallized as an apodomain, but it can bind one Ca^{2+} ion in the crystal (126). Binding of additional ions shatters the SytI-C2A crystals, strongly suggesting a conformational change. Comparison of the crystal structures of closely related apo-SytI-C2A (126) and Ca^{2+}-saturated PKCβ-C2 (125) reveals that the CBR1 moves 1–2 Å and its mobility relative to the rest of the domain decreases fourfold, again consistent with an increase in order in the bound state. Taken together these data reveal a consistent pattern of Ca^{2+} effects on C2 domain conformation.

Fluorescence spectroscopy of the SytI (13) and cPLA$_2$-C2 (92) domains indicates substantial Ca^{2+}-induced conformational changes that extend some distance from the binding site. Chemical modification of cPLA$_2$-C2 with TID increases several-fold on Ca^{2+} binding (20), consistent with a conformational change that exposes more hydrophobic surface area, although ANS binding does not increase. NMR of SytI-C2A reveals many CBR NOEs in the bound state that decrease or disappear in the apostructure, consistent with a disorder-to-order conformational change upon Ca^{2+} binding (116). NMR of cPLA2-C2 reveals large Ca^{2+}-induced chemical-shift perturbations that are greatest for the CBRs but extend beyond them (144). There is now overwhelming evidence that conformational changes do occur in C2 domains when they bind Ca^{2+}, despite statements to the contrary (110). It is still not clear how much these conformational changes contribute to Ca^{2+}-dependent membrane binding.

Electrostatic Interactions with Membranes

The electrostatic switch model is based on the change in electrostatic potential at the tip of the C2 domain from negative to positive upon Ca^{2+} binding (110, 148). The electrostatic switch model is not general because it cannot explain the neutral lipid-specific C2 domains exemplified by cPLA$_2$. There is no doubt that electrostatic interactions are involved in the membrane binding of acidic phospholipid-specific C2 domains, because the interaction can be abolished by increasing ionic strength (20, 148). The key question is whether a nonspecific electrostatic inter-action is both necessary and sufficient for binding, as opposed to a necessary role for specific interactions with Ca^{2+} ions. A charge reversal mutant that increases the net charge in the CBRs of PKCβII-C2 by +4 severely impairs Ca^{2+}-dependent binding but does not confer Ca^{2+}-independent binding (26). This result rules out the electrostatic switch model as applied to the anionic lipid-binding class of C2 domains (26).

A little discussed but potentially important model invokes a decrease in Born repulsion after Ca^{2+} binding (D Murray, B Honig & S McLaughlin, personal com-munication). Born repulsion is the force that keeps ions out of the low dielectric medium of membrane and protein interiors. There is a substantial Born energy penalty for bringing ions near a low dielectric medium even if they do not enter it. By nearly neutralizing the net negative charge on the tip of the C2 domain, this penalty might be reduced. No experiments specifically designed to test this idea have been reported to date. The failure of the PKCβII-C2 charge reversal mutant (26) to bind membranes rules this mechanism out for the conventional PKC-like acidic lipid-specific C2 domains, but it has yet to be tested for cPLA$_2$-C2. In short, no single mechanism can account for all of the Ca^{2+}-dependent C2 domains. Con-ventional PKCs, SytI-C2A, and many similar proteins probably rely heavily on the Ca^{2+} bridge mechanism, whereas cPLA$_2$ may depend more on the conformational change or Born mechanisms or both.

Ca^{2+}-Independent C2 Domains

Not all C2 domains bind Ca^{2+} ions. Little is known of the function of these C2 domains. The Ca^{2+}-independent C2 domains of the AplII PKC (101) and PI3K-C2β (3) bind phospholipids with low affinity and little specificity. There are enough structural data on C2 domains to predict which domains will bind and which will not. The sequences of the Ca^{2+}-independent class show that most or all Ca^{2+} ligands are absent. The structure of the Ca^{2+}-independent PKCδ-C2 confirms the expected absence of the usual acidic pocket (98). The CBRs in the PKCδ-C2 are in sharply different conformations from those in other C2 domains. This suggests that more is required to create a Ca^{2+}-independent membrane-binding site than the mere removal of the Ca^{2+}-binding Asp residues.

Interdomain Interactions

The structures of PLCδ1 and cPLA$_2$ show differing degrees of interaction between C2 and the rest of the protein. The PLCδ1-C2 interacts extensively with the cat-alytic and EF hand domains of the enzyme, although the CBRs are not occluded (27, 44). The extensive contact surfaces of the PLCδ1-C2 suggest that it may con-tribute to structural stabilization. In contrast, cPLA$_2$-C2 has almost no interactions with the catalytic domain and can pivot through an angle of $\geq 10°$ (21). Kinetics suggest that the PKCγ-C2, like the other two, is oriented in an "outside-out" man-ner such that its CBRs are not occluded by the rest of the protein (94). Despite the "outside-out" orientation, Ca^{2+} binding to particular subsites within the C2 domain appears able, directly or indirectly, to trigger activating long-range conformational changes in $PKC\alpha$ and in $cPLA_2$ (7, 83).

FYVE DOMAINS

The FYVE domains, so far identified in ~60 proteins (see above regarding numbers taken from the SMART database), are the mostly recently characterized addition to the family of membrane-binding modules. FYVE domains are ~70- to 80-residue domains containing 8 Cys or 1 His and 7 Cys residues that coordinate two Zn^{2+} atoms (42, 123, 141). FYVE domains are involved in endosomal localization of proteins crucial for membrane trafficking in yeast (141) and mammals (118, 123). The current fascination with FYVE domains was triggered by the 1998 discovery that effectors of class III phosphatidylinositol (PI) 3-kinases are localized by binding PI 3-phosphate (PI3P) via their FYVE domains (10, 41, 99). FYVE domains bind PI3P but not more highly phosphorylated phosphoinositides (10, 41, 99).

FYVE Domain Structure, Ligand Binding, and Specificity

The crystal structure of the FYVE domain from Vps27p (85), a protein involved in endosomal maturation in yeast, reveals a compact core consisting of two small double-stranded β sheets and a C-terminal α-helix (Figure 2c). The structure is distantly similar to that of the C1 domain. The Zn^{2+}-chelating Cys/His residues are located in pairs such that the first and third pairs bind one zinc atom, while the second and fourth pairs bind the other zinc atom. The surface of Vps27p-FYVE contains a relatively large basic region contributed by the conserved RKHHCR motif located near and on $\beta 1$ and by a conserved arginine from the $\beta 4$ strand (Figure 4a,b). Mutagenesis of the RKHHCR motif results in loss of PI3P binding (10). The sequence (R/K)(R/K)HHCR is present in all known PI3P-binding FYVE domains, although there are structurally similar domains that lack this motif (97). The basic region is divided into two subsites consisting of the first two and the last four residues of the RKHHCR motif. PI3P can be modeled so that its 1-phosphate interacts with the first two residues of the motif, while the 3-phosphate interacts with a tight pocket formed by the last three basic motif residues and the Arg

$\longrightarrow$

Figure 4 *a.* Structure-based alignment of FYVE domains and the related rabphilin Zn^{2+}-binding domain. Zn^{2+}-binding residues are shown in bold. PI3P binding and membrane interacting residues are boxed. The rabphilin Zn^{2+}-binding domain is structurally similar to FYVE domains but does not have the boxed PI3P-binding residues and is predicted not to bind PI3P. *b.* Schematic of the PI3P-binding site of the FYVE domain. The phosphoinositide is intentionally drawn as an oversimplified achiral molecule to emphasize the pseudo-twofold relationship between PI3P and PI5P. Equivalent residues from the Vps27p (*black*) and EEA1 (*gray*) FYVE domains are shown. Trp170/1348 does not bind PI3P, but helps to buttress His191/1372 and the ligand-binding site.

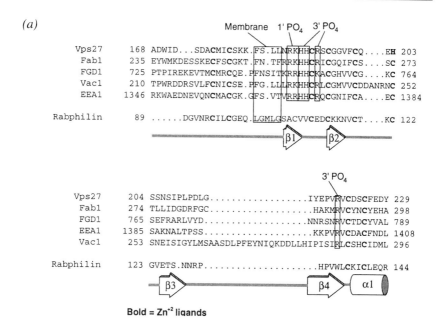

Bold = Zn⁺² ligands

(b)

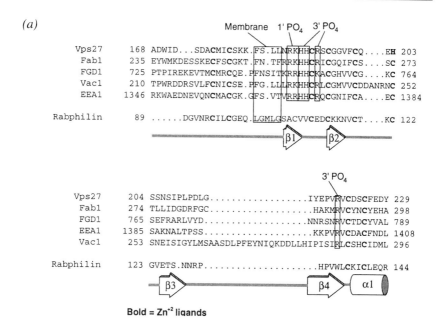

contributed by $\beta 4$. In support of this model, the chemical shifts of the corresponding residues in early endosomal antigen-1 (EEA-1) exhibit the largest perturbations upon titration with a water-soluble PI3P (71).

FYVE domains are specific for PI3P, showing negligible affinity for PI4P, polyphosphorylated phosphoinositides, or other phospholipids (10, 41, 99). Specificity is probably controlled by the distance between the two phosphate-binding subsites. This distance appears too short to tolerate binding of the 1- and 4-phosphate groups of PI4P to their respective sites simultaneously. The 3-phosphate binding pocket is too occluded to permit binding of polyphosphorylated phosphoinositides such as those that bind to PH domains. EEA1-FYVE binds to PI5P but probably too weakly to be meaningful in vivo (71). The basic phosphate-binding residues are sufficiently well conserved that it seems likely most of the as-yet-uncharacterized FYVE domains will have similar ligand specificity. It is also possible that other FYVE domains could have higher affinities for PI5P than EEA1.

FYVE Domain Binding to Membranes

The FYVE domain binds to PI3P-containing membranes such that the tip of the N-terminal loop penetrates into the bilayer (Figure 2c). This part of Vps27p-FYVE has two successive Leu residues that form an exposed hydrophobic protrusion at one end of the domain (85). The NMR resonances from the corresponding region from EEA1-FYVE disappear upon binding to PI3P-containing micelles (71), suggesting that the residues penetrate the micelle. In addition, mutation of two of these residues (Val and Thr) eliminates endosomal localization in vivo (71). This region contains two or more hydrophobic residues in most FYVE domains. The hydrophobic protrusion is also present in the FYVE-like Ze^{2+}-binding domain of rabphilin-3A, suggesting a function for this domain in nonspecific membrane binding. In Vps27p, several lysines not involved in PI3P binding are located at the base of the protrusion (85). These lysines are poorly conserved and do not show main-chain chemical shift perturbations by micelles (71), but other sequences contain positively charged residues that map to similar parts of the domain surface. It appears likely that the hydrophobic protrusion penetrates into membranes, whereas the basic residues at the base of the protrusion interact nonspecifically with the membrane.

FYVE domain-containing proteins and FYVE domains localize to endosomal membranes containing PI3P (10, 41, 96, 99, 118, 123, 133). Endosomal localization can be blocked when PI3-kinase is inhibited with wortmannin. Although isolated FYVE domains can bind to PI3P-containing membranes, the membrane avidity of FYVE-domain containing proteins may be increased by dimerization (11, 71). EEA1-FYVE has limited ability to dimerize. However, FYVE domain-GST fusions form dimers that exhibit increased binding to PI3P-containing liposomes (71). The full-length EEA1 protein is predicted to homodimerize by forming a parallel coiled coil, so that the two C-terminal EEA1-FYVE domains are located near each other at one end of the dimer (11).

PLECKSTRIN HOMOLOGY DOMAINS

PH domains have been found in >500 cell regulatory proteins (see above regarding numbers taken from the SMART database). Most PH domains bind phosphoinositides, albeit with varying degrees of specificity (8, 34, 48, 73, 109). As such, they respond directly to free phosphoinositide levels regulated by phosphoinositide kinases, phosphatases, and phospholipases. The discovery over the past 3 years that signaling through PI3-kinases depends on PH domain-containing effectors has led to intense and renewed interest in these domains (34, 72). PH domains also participate in protein-protein interactions with such partners as $G\beta\gamma$ subunits and PKC-C1 domains; this aspect of PH domains has been extensively reviewed elsewhere (8, 73, 109).

Structure of the PH Domain

Structures are now known for PH domains from eight different proteins: pleckstrin (49, 143), spectrin (55, 82, 147), dynamin (23, 30, 38, 130), PLCδ1 (31), son of sevenless 1 (Sos1) (69, 151), β-adrenergic receptor kinase (βArk) (39), Bruton's tyrosine kinase (Btk) (5, 56), and insulin receptor substrate 1 (IRS-1) (22). The PH domain structure contains two orthogonal antiparallel β sheets of three and four strands (Figure 2d). These are followed by a C-terminal α helix. The β sheets curve in a tight barrel-like conformation, while the C-terminal helix folds in to cover one end of the barrel. This fold is also found in the protein-binding phosphotyrosine binding (PTB) (25, 149, 152), enabled/VASP homology (EVH) (106), and Ran binding (RanBD) (138) domains and as a substructure within the protein- and phospholipid-binding 4.1, ezrin, radixin, and moesin (FERM) domain (M Pearson, D Reczek, A Bretscher, PA Karplus, submitted for publication). The interstrand loops are involved in ligand binding and vary substantially in sequence and structure between PH domains. The membrane-binding face of the domain contains basic residues that assist in ligand binding.

Inositol Phosphate-Binding Subsites

The structures of complexes of PLCδ1-PH with Ins(1,4,5)P$_3$ (31) and Btk-PH with Ins(1,3,4,5)P$_4$ (5) define four different phosphate-binding subsites that participate in high-affinity specific phosphoinositide binding (Figure 5a). The general outlines of the binding site are the same for PH domains of pleckstrin (48, 49), dynamin (114, 150), Sos1 (151), and βArk (39), based on NMR chemical-shift perturbations. In both structures, the β1/β2 and β3/β4 loops of the first β sheet

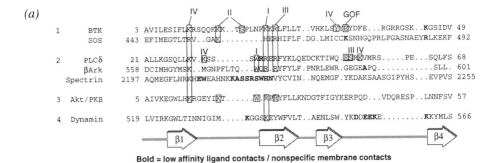

(a)

1	BTK	3	AVILESIFL**K**RSQQK**K**K..T**S**PLNF**KK**R**L**FLLT..VHKLS**Y**M**E**YDFE...RGRRGSK..**K**GSIDV	49
	SOS	443	EFIMEGTLT**R**V..GA**K**........**H**E**R**HIFLF.DG.LMICC**K**SNHGQPRLPGASNAEYRLKEKF	492
2	PLCδ	21	ALLKGSQLL**K**V.**K**SS......S**W**R**R**E**R**FYKLQEDCKTIWQ.**E**S**R**K**V**MRS.....PE...SQLFS	68
	βArk	558	DCIMHGYMS**K**..MGNPFLTQ...**W**Q**R**.**R**YFYLF.PNRLEWR.GEGE**A**PQ...........SLL.	601
	Spectrin	2197	AQMEGFLNR**K**H**EW**EAHNK**KASSRSWHN**VYCVIN..NQEMGF.YKDAKSAASGIPYHS...EVPVS	2255
3	Akt/PKB	5	AIVKEGWLH**K**RGEYI**K**T......**W**.**R**H**R**YFLLKNDGTFIGYKERPQD...VDQRESP..LNNFSV	57
4	Dynamin	519	LVIRKGWLTINNIGIM.....**K**GGS**K**EYWFVLT..AENLSW.YKDD**EEKE**.........**K**KYMLS	566

Bold = low affinity ligand contacts / nonspecific membrane contacts

(b)

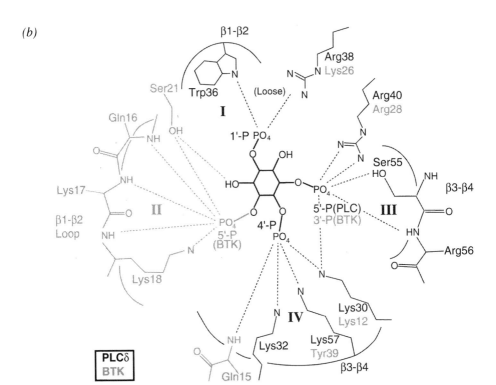

Figure 5 *a*. Structure-based alignment of PH domains (there is no structure available of the Akt-PH, which has been aligned by sequence homology). Examples of each of the four provisional PH domain groups (34, 107) are shown. Residues that interact nonspecifically with the membrane or with ligands are shown in bold. Residues that interact directly with ligands are boxed. *"GOF"* designates the Btk and PLCδ1 E → K mutants that increase membrane affinity. Phosphate-binding subsites are marked with Roman numerals. Conservation of residues in all four subsites suggests, but does not prove, membership in group 1. Group 3 sequences are similar to group 1 but with fewer basic residues in the site II (β1/β2 loop) region. The absence of sites II–IV suggests membership in group 4. *b*. Schematic of the high-affinity phosphoinositide-binding site of PLCδ1-PH and Btk-PH. Structural elements found only in Btk are drawn in gray. Elements found in PLCδ1only or in both PH domains are drawn in black. The bound phosphoinositide is intentionally drawn as an oversimplified achiral molecule, as in Figure 4*b*, to emphasize the pseudo-twofold relationship between the PI(4,5)P$_2$- and PI(3,4,5)P$_3$-binding modes.

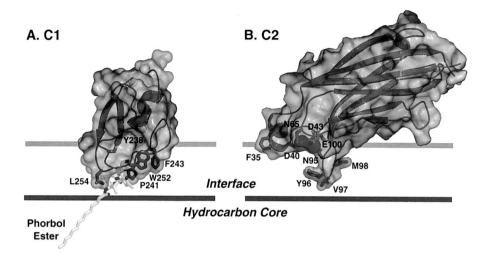

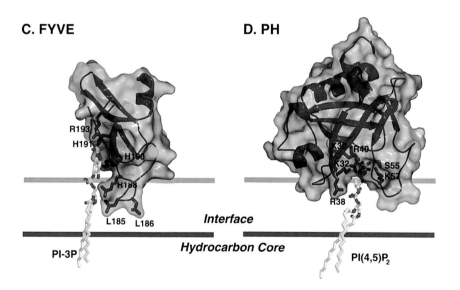

Figure 2 Membrane-docked structures of (*a*) PKCδ-C1B phorbol ester complex with the myristoyl tail modeled (146), (*b*) cPLA$_2$-C2 Ca^{2+} complex (102), (*c*) Vps27p-FYVE with PI3P modeled (85), and (*d*) PLCδ1-PH complex with Ins (1, 4, 5) P$_3$, with dimyristoyl group modeled (31). The secondary structure and molecular surface of each domain are shown. Surface colors indicate the underlying residue type: hydrophobic (*green*) or basic (*blue*). Selected specific- and nonspecific-contact residues are shown. Domains are positioned so that known membrane-interacting residues penetrate the membrane and basic patches are proximal to the membrane surface. The membrane leaflet is divided into an interfacial zone and a hydrophobic core (each ~15 Å thick) and is drawn to scale. The two bound zinc ions in parts *a* and *c* are shown in *cyan*. The two bound Ca^{2+} ions in part *b* are shown in *blue*.

form most of the key interactions. In PLCδ1-PH, Ins(1,4,5)P$_3$ is buried between the 2 loops and forms 12 hydrogen bonds to 9 different amino acids of the domain. Interactions are even more extensive in Btk-PH, involving 18 hydrogen bonds. This is consistent with the higher affinity of the latter for its cognate ligand, 40 nM (36), as compared with 210 nM for PLCδ1-PH (74).

The 1- and 4-phosphates of Ins(1,4,5)P$_3$ and Ins(1,3,4,5)P$_3$ bind to equivalent subsites (denoted I and IV in Figure 5a) in PLCδ1-PH and Btk-PH. Subsite I is relatively solvent exposed and poorly defined. Subsite IV is buried and makes at least three close interactions with the 4-phosphate in both structures. Subsite IV is more positively charged in PLCδ1-PH compared with Btk-PH. There is one dramatic difference between the two structures; the inositol ring of the ligand is rotated about the axis defined by the 1- and 4-carbons of the inositol ring. Thus the 3-phosphate of Ins(1,3,4,5)P$_4$ bound to Btk-PH occupies the subsite (III) belonging to the 5-phosphate of Ins(1,4,5)P$_3$ bound to PLCδ1-PH. The critical Arg-28 of Btk participates in subsite III and is conserved in PLCδ1. The 5-phosphate of Ins(1,3,4,5)P$_4$ occupies a subsite (II) that is created by a unique loop conformation in Btk-PH. Subsite II is missing in PLCδ1-PH.

Two modes of low-affinity phosphoinositide binding have been defined by the structure of the spectrin-PH-Ins(1,4,5)P$_3$ complex (55) and by a secondary Ins(1,3,4,5)P$_4$-binding site in the Btk gain-of-function mutant E41K (5). The Ins(1,4,5)P$_3$ interacts with spectrin-PH via the β5/β6 loop and the opposite side of the β1/β2 loop from the PLCδ1-PH domain complex. The second Ins(1,3,4,5)P$_4$ binds to the β3/β4 loop of Btk-PH E41K close to subsite I of the high-affinity binding site. The low-affinity sites are more solvent exposed and involve fewer contacts than those described above. Although they do not overlap, both low-affinity sites are on the membrane-binding face of the PH domain and are consistent with the overall picture of PH domain/membrane interactions inferred from other studies.

Phosphoinositide Specificity

PH domain binding to different phosphoinositide polyphosphates and inositol polyphosphates has been systematically examined (59, 62, 107), revealing a wide range of ligand affinity and specificity. Rameh et al (107, 120) subdivide PH domains into four groups, which provides a useful working classification scheme. PH domains are so divergent that sequence-based classification may not be conclusive for every case. Even classification based on in vitro function is complicated by the variety of soluble inositol polyphosphate- and phosphoinositide-binding assays in use.

Group 1   PI(3,4,5)P$_3$-binding PH domains include those of Btk (36, 68, 107, 114), Grp1 (62, 65, 66), ARF nucleotide site opening (ARNO) (137), cytohesin-1 (88), Son-of-sevenless (Sos) (107), Tiam-1 N-terminal domain (107), Gap1^{IP4BP}

(17, 79), Gap1^m (37, 80), Vav (47), and several newly identified members (59). They are highly specific for PI(3,4,5)P$_3$, which they typically prefer over PI(4,5)P$_2$ by ~100-fold. Their sequences have more positively charged residues (6–11 residues, including histidines) in the $\beta 1/\beta 2$ strands and loop than group 2 (Figure 5b). In Btk-PH, these additional positive residues contribute to the unique site II, which binds the 5-phosphate. Positive charges predominate in the $\beta 1/\beta 2$ loop in other group 1 PH domains, suggesting that the binding mode observed in Btk-PH may be general to this group. Subsite IV has fewer charged interactions with the 4-phosphate than in group 2, consistent with the weaker binding of group 1 PH domains to PI(4,5)P$_2$.

Group 2 The members of the second group have high affinities for PI(4,5)P$_2$ and PI(3,4,5)P$_2$ and include PLCδ1 (15, 40, 62, 74), βArk (62, 104, 107), β-spectrin (62, 107), RasGAP (62), the N-terminal domain of pleckstrin (62, 129), DAGKδ (62, 129), oxysterol-binding protein (OSBP) (75, 107), IRS-1 (22), and others (62, 107). Group 2 domains do not discriminate substantially between PI(4,5)P$_2$ and PI(3,4,5)P$_3$ in vitro (62, 107). Preferential binding to PI(4,5)P$_2$ in vivo may be more a function of the greater abundance of this lipid than discrimination against 3-phosphoinositides. PLCδ1-PH binds PI(4,5)P$_2$ and PI(3,4,5)P$_2$ with high affinity compared with other acidic lipids (73, 109), but other group 2 PH domains are less specific. In these group 2 domains, unlike PLCδ1-PH, strong binding to PI(4,5)P$_3$ may depend more on the high negative charge on this lipid than on stereospecific recognition. This is consistent with the imperfect conservation of some of the key PLCδ1-PH basic side chains in group 2 domains.

Group 3 A third group, including Akt (also known as PKB) (32, 33, 59, 60, 62) and PDK1 (1, 124), binds PI(3,4)P$_2$ as well as PI(3,4,5)P$_3$. The only other reported member of this group is an expressed sequence tag (EST)-encoded protein of unknown function (62). Group 3 PH domains vary somewhat in their relative affinities for PI(3,4)P$_2$ vs PI(4,5)P$_2$ and PI(3,4,5)P$_3$ in different reports. The $\beta 1/\beta 2$ loops of group 3 PH domains contain fewer basic residues than many of the group 1 domains, but the structural basis for specificity still is not entirely clear, pending the structure determination of a group 3 PH domain.

Group 4 and Others Group 4 members, which include dynamin and the C-terminal PH domain of TIAM-1, exhibit relatively low binding affinity for the ligands mentioned above. The high-affinity phosphate subsites are absent or incompletely formed in these PH domains. Despite the low affinity of dynamin-PH monomers for PI(4,5)P$_2$, the physiological importance of this interaction for endocytosis is well established. The effective affinity is bolstered by oligomerization of dynamin (67). PLCβ1- and PLCβ2-PH bind nonspecifically to neutral and acidic phospholipids with low affinity (139). PLCγ-PH binds 3-phosphoinositides, including PI3P (29, 62). Neither its sequence nor its binding affinities conform to groups 1 or 3, so it may represent a new group.

Membrane-Binding Mechanisms

The positively charged face and loops of PH domains are poised to form nonspecific contacts with negatively charged phospholipids, in addition to the specific contacts already described (Figure 2d). The importance of nonspecific contacts is highlighted by the structure of the Btk-PH E41K gain-of-function mutant (5, 77). This mutation results in constitutive activation of the protein, probably owing to persistent membrane association (76). The corresponding mutation E54K in PLCδ1 produces a similar gain in enzyme function in vitro (9). The mutation does not increase the affinity for Ins(1,3,4,5)P$_4$ molecule to the binding pocket. In the crystal, a second Ins(1,3,4,5)P$_4$ molecule binds to the mutated lysine on the surface of the molecule near β-strands 3 and 4; three other (native) lysine residues complete this second binding site. The mutation increases the positively charged surface on this face of the domain (5), and it may enhance membrane association of the domain nonspecifically, either by generalized binding of negative membrane surface charge or by binding of phosphoinositide lipids other than PI(3,4,5)P$_3$ (136) at the second binding site.

A loss-of-function Btk mutant, K19E, maps to the β1/β2 loop but does not directly interact with Ins(1,3,4,5)P$_4$. This mutation does not affect specific ligand binding (5) but decreases the local positive electrostatic potential and nonspecific affinity for the membrane surface. Scanning mutagenesis of the positively charged residues in the PLCδ1-PH (142) shows that some of the surface residues are critical for membrane binding even though they are located outside the binding pocket. Their locations suggest that the β1/β2 and β3/β4 strands and loops interact substantially with the phospholipid head group region of the membrane (Figure 2d).

Differences in affinity for soluble inositol phosphates vs the cognate membrane-bound phosphoinositides are postulated to have important regulatory consequences. PLCδ1-PH binds to PI(4,5)P$_2$ in vesicles with micromolar affinity, but binds to the cognate Ins(1,4,5)P$_3$ with $K_d = 210$ nM (74). The high binding affinity of PLCδ1-PH to Ins(1,4,5)P$_3$ may be important in product inhibition of the enzyme (15, 74).

Localization to Cell Membranes

Stimulation of PLC causes repartitioning of green fluorescent protein-PLCδ1-PH from the plasma membrane to the cytosol (35, 50, 122, 135) concomitant with the hydrolysis of PI(4,5)P$_2$ in the membrane and the rise in soluble Ins(1,4,5)P$_3$ concentration. The relative contribution of the two factors to translocation is still under debate. Green fluorescent protein-PLCδ1-PH translocation has been used to visualize the coupled intracellular dynamics of Ca^{2+} and Ins(1,4,5)P$_3$ (50). OSBP-PH translocation to the Golgi depends on PI(4,5)P$_2$ and at least one other unknown factor (75). Plasma membrane localization of PH domains that bind 3-phosphorylated phosphoinositides has been similarly demonstrated. Examples include the PH domains of Btk (136), ARNO (137), GAP1^{IP4BP} (79), GAP1^m (80), PDK1 (2), and Akt (140). Wortmannin inhibition of PI3K blocks plasma membrane localization of these PH domains.

Roles of PH Domains Within Larger Proteins

PI(4,5)P$_2$ binding allosterically activates dynamin's GTPase activity (78). Since Ins(1,4,5)P$_3$ also has this capability (114), some effects of the PH domain on the rest of the protein seem to be independent of membrane binding. Dbl homology (DH) domain-containing proteins act as guanine nucleotide exchange factors for Rho-family GTPases. The DH domains are invariably followed by a PH domain, as for Sos and Vav proteins. A crystal structure of Sos DH-PH suggests that a putative GTPase-binding site is formed by both domains; the interface includes the negatively charged side of the PH domain (121). Ligand binding to the PH domain has been proposed to allosterically modulate the nucleotide exchange activity of Sos, perhaps via ligand-induced conformational changes in the β1-β2 loop. The PH domain of Sos is not required for membrane targeting (14). By the same token, the Rac GTP exchange factor Vav is allosterically activated by PI(3,4,5)P$_3$ (47).

Various appendages are required for the functioning of certain PH domains. The cytohesin PH domain is followed by a 17-residue polybasic sequence, which is required for high-affinity binding to PI(3,4,5)P$_3$ (88). The Btk PH domain is followed by a small Btk motif, which binds a single Zn^{2+} atom (56) and has no known role other than structural stabilization. G$\beta\gamma$ binds to the C-terminal helix of βArk-PH (104). The solution structure of βArk-PH reveals that this region belongs to an extension to the C-terminal helix (39), which protrudes past the core of the domain.

The activity of the Akt kinase is allosterically regulated by its PH domain, implying contacts between the PH and other domains. Phosphorylation of Akt by PDK1 is necessary for activation (1, 124). In addition to localizing Akt at the membrane, the PH domain directly regulates the susceptibility of Akt to phosphorylation. Deletion of the PH domain results in higher basal phosphorylation and activity of Akt (112). A working model postulates that the Akt-PH participates in autoinhibitory contacts with the catalytic domain of Akt that are broken upon PI(3,4)P$_2$ binding.

OTHER MEMBRANE-BINDING DOMAINS

The intensive analysis of data from genome-sequencing projects has probably left few important signaling domains undiscovered (6, 115). Of domains that have been recently identified by sequence analysis, the START domain stands out as a probable lipid-binding signaling domain (105). There are many important roles for basic and amphipathic sequences, often with covalent lipid modifications, although these sequences are not independently folded and do not qualify as domains. The catalytic domains of many enzymes involved in lipid metabolism contain membrane-interacting hydrophobic ridges and basic loops and patches that may help target them to membranes. Finally, certain SH2 and PTB domains can bind phospholipids (108, 152) in addition to their better known peptide-binding functions.

CONCLUDING REMARKS

Stereospecific and Nonspecific Interactions with Membranes

The unique interplay between specific and nonspecific interactions with membranes sets the lipid-directed class of signaling domains apart from all others. In all of the membrane-binding domains, the specific ligand-binding site is flanked by basic or hydrophobic side-chains, or both. This arrangement of specific and nonspecific binding sites has several profound consequences.

The nonspecific-interaction energy can add to the stereospecific interaction to greatly increase the net interaction energy. In practice, this can lead to $\leq 10^4$-fold–higher binding affinities. In the cell, this translates into a potent membrane-targeting mechanism. In other cases, the nonspecific component may be weak or even unfavorable. Some membrane-binding domains seem to have a dual life as receptors for mutually antagonistic membrane-bound and soluble second messengers.

Nonspecific membrane interactions can, in principle, augment the stereospecificity of the specific component of the interaction. The nonspecific membrane interaction makes an additional point of contact to define stereospecific interactions. Stereospecific recognition of a chiral lipid embedded in a membrane can be achieved with only two direct contacts between the protein and the lipid, provided that the protein makes an additional contact with the membrane. The degree of exposed hydrophobic surface on the protein dictates the depth to which it can penetrate the bilayer. The locations of known specific lipid-binding sites on domain structures closely match the expected distances of the lipid head groups as measured from the center of the bilayer. The relative positioning of the specific- and nonspecific-binding sites serves as a molecular ruler that has no counterpart among domains that recognize soluble ligands.

Biological Functions for Low-Affinity and Nonspecific Interactions

Many of the interactions described for membrane-targeting domains are of relatively low affinity. This complicates the problem of sorting out physiologically important interactions from artifacts. Many weak interactions are clearly important in cells and, indeed, appear to be weak "by design." Cooperativity can be achieved by the oligomerization of weakly interacting domains into an assembly that binds membranes strongly. Under physiological conditions, the stable interaction of many signaling proteins with membranes depends on ligand binding by two or more different domains, for instance the C1 and C2 domains of PKC. This arrangement allows proteins such as PKC to function as temporal coincidence detectors.

Targeting vs Allosteric Regulation

The current emphasis on the targeting roles of membrane-binding domains should not obscure their equally important roles in the allosteric regulation of enzymes that contain them. In an evolutionary economy, a given domain in a given protein often contributes to regulation at both levels. It is clear that many protein kinases and GTPase activating proteins are allosterically activated by engagement of their membrane-binding domains. For the best understood example, PKC, this is a multistep process in which membrane localization is necessary but not sufficient for PKC activation. In contrast, some GAPs can be activated when their PH domains bind soluble inositol phosphates, whereas GAP targeting requires a membrane-bound phosphoinositide.

Can Domain Studies Help Read Genome Sequences?

One of the great challenges to biologists in the postgenomic era will be the prediction of protein function from sequence. The concept of modular domains, developed over the past 15 years or so, is one of the most powerful tools available. The sophisticated use of domain data can contribute to predicting protein function. Clearly there is not a one-to-one correspondence between domain structure and function. Not all C1 domains bind diacylglycerol, not all C2 domains bind Ca^{2+}, and not all PH domains bind specifically to phosphoinositides. The attribution of such functions cannot be based solely on the presence of such a domain in a protein sequence.

Fortunately, structural and functional studies have allowed sequence motifs to be discovered whereby domains can be subdivided into "flavors" with common functions. These assignments may be very reliable when the sequence of interest has high identity to that of a well-characterized domain whose structure and binding specificity are known. Prediction is much less reliable for highly divergent sequences. A complete understanding of the sequence/function relationships of domains would be most valuable. A key direction for the bioinformatics of protein domains will be to systematize and automate the process of classifying domains into functional subgroups and to increase its scope and reliability.

ACKNOWLEDGMENTS

We thank T Balla, A Hickman, S McLaughlin, A Newton, and A Toker for comments on the manuscript. We apologize to the authors of many seminal papers, especially those predating 1994, that could not be cited for reasons of space.

Visit the Annual Reviews home page at www.AnnualReviews.org

LITERATURE CITED

1. Alessi DR, James SR, Downes CP, Holmes AB, Gaffney PR, et al. 1997. Characterization of a 3-phosphoinositide-dependent protein kinase which phosphorylates and activates protein kinase Bα. *Curr. Biol.* 7:261–69

2. Anderson KE, Coadwell J, Stephens LR, Hawkins PT. 1998. Translocation of PDK-1 to the plasma membrane is important in allowing PDK-1 to activate protein kinase B. *Curr. Biol.* 8:684–91

3. Arcaro A, Volinia S, Zvelebil MJ, Stein R, Watton SJ, et al. 1998. Human phosphoinositide 3-kinase C2β, the role of calcium and the C2 domain in enzyme activity. *J. Biol. Chem.* 273:33082–90

4. Ball A, Nielsen R, Gelb MH, Robinson BH. 1999. Interfacial membrane docking of cytosolic phospholipase A$_2$ C2 domain using electrostatic potential-modulated spin relaxation magnetic resonance. *Proc. Natl. Acad. Sci. USA* 96:6637–42

5. Baraldi E, Djinovic Carugo K, Hyvönen M, Lo Surdo P, et al. 1999. Structure of the PH domain from Bruton's tyrosine kinase in complex with inositol 1,3,4,5-tetrakisphosphate. *Structure* 7:449–60

6. Bateman A, Birney E, Durbin R, Eddy SR, Finn RD, Sonnhammer EL. 1999. Pfam 3.1: 1313 multiple alignments match the majority of proteins. *Nucleic Acids Res.* 27:260–62

7. Bittova L, Sumandea M, Cho W. 1999. A structure-function study of the C2 domain of cytosolic phospholipase A$_2$. Identification of essential calcium ligands and hydrophobic membrane binding residues. *J. Biol. Chem.* 274:9665–72

8. Bottomley MJ, Salim K, Panayotou G. 1998. Phospholipid-binding protein domains. *Biochim. Biophys. Acta* 1436:165–83

9. Bromann PA, Boetticher EE, Lomasney JW.

1997. A single amino acid substitution in the pleckstrin homology domain of phospholipase C-δ1 enhances the rate of substrate hydrolysis. *J. Biol. Chem.* 272:16240–46

10. Burd CG, Emr SD. 1998. Phosphatidylinositol(3)-phosphate signaling mediated by specific binding to RING FYVE domains. *Mol. Cell* 2:157–62

11. Callaghan J, Simonsen A, Gaullier J-M, Toh B-H, Stenmark H. 1999. The endosome fusion regulator early-endosomal autoantigen 1 (EEA1) is a dimer. *Biochem. J.* 338:539–43

12. Chae YK, Abildgaard F, Chapman ER, Markley JL. 1998. Lipid binding ridge on loops 2 and 3 of the C2A domain of synaptotagmin I as revealed by NMR spectroscopy. *J. Biol. Chem.* 273:25659–63

13. Chapman ER, Davis AF. 1998. Direct interaction of a Ca^{2+}-binding loop of synaptotagmin with lipid bilayers. *J. Biol. Chem.* 273:13994–4001

14. Chen RH, Corbalan-Garcia S, Bar-Sagi D. 1997. The role of the PH domain in the signal-dependent membrane targeting of Sos. *EMBO J.* 16:1351–59

15. Cifuentes ME, Delaney T, Rebecchi MJ. 1994. D-*myo*-inositol 1,4,5 trisphosphate inhibits binding of phospholipase C-δ1 to bilayer membranes. *J. Biol. Chem.* 269:1945–48

16. Corbalan-Garcia S, Rodrigues-Alfaro JA, Gomez-Fernandez JC. 1999. Determination of the calcium-binding sites of the C2 domain of protein kinase Cα that are critical for its translocation to the plasma membrane. *Biochem. J.* 337:513–21

17. Cullen PJ, Hsuan JJ, Truong O, Letcher AJ, Jackson TR, et al. 1995. Identification of a specific Ins(1,3,4,5)P$_4$ binding protein as a member of the GAP1 family. *Nature* 376:527–30

18. Cutler RE Jr, Stephens RM, Saracino MR, Morrison DK. 1998. Autoregulation of the Raf-1 serine/threonine kinase. *Proc. Natl. Acad. Sci. USA* 95:9214–19

19. Daub M, Jockel J, Quack T, Weber CK, Schmitz F, et al. 1998. The RafC1 cysteine-rich domain contains multiple distinct regulatory epitopes which control Ras-dependent Raf activation. *Mol. Cell. Biol.* 18:6698–710

20. Davletov B, Perisic O, Williams RL. 1998. Calcium-dependent membrane penetration is a hallmark of the C2 domain of cytosolic phospholipase A_2 whereas the C2A domain of synaptotagmin binds membranes electrostatically. *J. Biol. Chem.* 273:19093–96

21. Dessen A, Tang J, Schmidt H, Stahl M, Clark JD, et al. 1999. Crystal structure of human cytosolic phospholipase A_2 reveals a novel topology and catalytic mechanism. *Cell* 97:349–60

22. Dhe-Paganon S, Ottinger EA, Nolte RT, Eck MJ, Shoelson SE. 1999. Crystal structure of the pleckstrin homology-phosphotyrosine binding (PH-PTB) targeting region of insulin receptor substrate 1. *Proc. Natl. Acad. Sci. USA* 96:8378–83

23. Downing AK, Driscoll PC, Gout I, Salim K, Zvelebil MJ, Waterfield MD. 1994. 3-Dimensional solution structure of the pleckstrin homology domain from dynamin. *Curr. Biol.* 4:884–91

24. Ebinu JO, Bottorff DA, Chan EYW, Stand SL, Dunn RJ, Stone JC. 1998. RasGRP, a Ras guanylyl nucleotide-releasing protein with calcium- and diacylglycerol-binding motifs. *Science* 280:1082–86

25. Eck MJ, DhePaganon S, Trub T, Nolte RT, Shoelson SE. 1996. Structure of the IRS-1 PTB domain bound to the juxtamembrane region of the insulin receptor. *Cell* 85:695–705

26. Edwards AS, Newton AC. 1997. Regulation of protein kinase C βII by its C2 domain. *Biochemistry* 36:15615–23

27. Essen L-O, Perisic O, Cheung R, Katan M, Williams RL. 1996. Crystal structure of a mammalian phosphoinositide-specific phospholipase Cδ. *Nature* 380:595–602

28. Essen L-O, Perisic O, Lynch DE, Katan M, Williams RL. 1997. A ternary metal binding site in the C2 domain of phosphoinositide-specific phospholipase C-δ1. *Biochemistry* 36:2753–62

29. Falasca M, Logan SK, Lehto VP, Baccante G, Lemmon MA, Schlessinger J. 1998. Activation of phospholipase Cγ by PI 3-kinase-induced PH domain-mediated membrane targeting. *EMBO J.* 17:414–22

30. Ferguson KM, Lemmon MA, Schlessinger J, Sigler PB. 1994. Crystal structure at 2.2 Å resolution of the pleckstrin homology domain from human dynamin. *Cell* 79:199–209

31. Ferguson KM, Lemmon MA, Schlessinger J, Sigler PB. 1995. Structure of the high affinity complex of inositol trisphosphate with a phospholipase C pleckstrin homology domain. *Cell* 83:1037–46

32. Franke TF, Kaplan DR, Cantley LC, Toker A. 1997. Direct regulation of the Akt proto-oncogene product by phosphatidylinositol-3,4-bisphosphate. *Science* 275:665–68

33. Frech M, Andjelkovic M, Ingley E, Reddy KK, Falck JR, Hemmings BA. 1997. High affinity binding of inositol phosphates and phosphoinositides to the pleckstrin homology domain of RAC/protein kinase B and their influence on kinase activity. *J. Biol. Chem.* 272:8474–81

34. Fruman DA, Rameh LE, Cantley LC. 1999. Phosphoinositide binding domains: embracing 3-phosphate. *Cell* 97:817–20

35. Fujii M, Ohtsubo M, Ogawa T, Kamata H, Hirata H, Yagisawa H. 1999. Real-time visualization of PH domain-dependent translocation of phospholipase C-δ1 in renal epithelial cells (MDCK): response to hypo-osmotic stress. *Biochem. Biophys. Res. Commun.* 254:284–91

36. Fukuda M, Kojima T, Kabayama H, Mikoshiba K. 1996. Mutation of the pleckstrin homology domain of Bruton's

tyrosine kinase in immunodeficiency impaired inositol 1,3,4,5-tetrakisphosphate binding capacity. *J. Biol. Chem.* 271: 30303–6

37. Fukuda M, Mikoshiba K. 1996. Structure-function relationships of the mouse Gap1^m—determination of the inositol 1,3,4,5-tetrakisphosphate-binding domain. *J. Biol. Chem.* 271:18838–42

38. Fushman D, Cahill S, Lemmon MA, Schlessinger J, Cowburn D. 1995. Solution structure of the pleckstrin homology domain of dynamin by heteronuclear NMR spectroscopy. *Proc. Natl. Acad. Sci. USA* 92:816–20

39. Fushman D, Najmabadi-Haske T, Cahill S, Zheng J, LeVine H III, Cowburn D. 1998. The solution structure and dynamics of the pleckstrin homology domain of G protein-coupled receptor kinase 2 (β-adrenergic receptor kinase 1). *J. Biol. Chem.* 273:2835–43

40. Garcia P, Gupta R, Shah S, Morris AJ, Rudge SA, et al. 1995. The pleckstrin homology domain of phospholipase C-δ1 binds with high affinity to phosphatidyl-inositol 4,5-bisphosphate in bilayer membranes. *Biochemistry* 34:16228–34

41. Gaullier J-M, Simonsen A, D'Arrigo A, Biemnes B, Stenmark H. 1998. FYVE fingers bind PtdIns(3)P. *Nature* 394:432–33

42. Gaullier J-M, Simonsen A, D'Arrigo A, Bremnes B, Stenmark H. 1999. FYVE finger proteins as effectors of phosphatidyl-inositol 3-phosphate. *Chem. Phys. Lipids* 98:87–94

43. Gijon MA, Spencer DM, Kaiser AL, Leslie CC. 1999. Role of phosphorylation sites and the C2 domain in regulation of cytosolic phospholipase A2. *J. Cell Biol.* 145: 1219–32

44. Grobler JA, Essen L-O, Williams RL, Hurley JH. 1996. C2 domain conformational changes in phospholipase Cδ1. *Nat. Struct. Biol.* 3:788–95

45. Grobler JA, Hurley JH. 1997. Similarity between C2 domain jaws and im-

munoglobulin CDRs. *Nat. Struct. Biol.* 4:261–62

46. Grobler JA, Hurley JH. 1998. Catalysis by phospholipase C δ1 requires that Ca^{2+} bind to the catalytic domain, but not the C2 domain. *Biochemistry* 37:5020–28

47. Han J, Luby-Phelps K, Das B, Shu X, Xia Y, et al. 1998. Role of substrates and products of PI 3-kinase in regulating activation of Rac-related guanosine triphosphatases by Vav. *Science* 279:558–60

48. Harlan JE, Hajduk PJ, Yoon HS, Fesik SW. 1994. Pleckstrin homology domains bind to phosphatidylinositol (4,5) bisphosphate. *Nature* 371:168–70

49. Harlan JE, Yoon HS, Hajduk PJ, Fesik SW. 1995. Structural characterization of the interaction between a pleckstrin homology domain and phosphatidylinositol (4,5) bisphosphate. *Biochemistry* 34:9859–64

50. Hirose K, Kadowaki S, Tanabe M, Takeshima H, Iino M. 1999. Spatiotemporal dynamics of inositol 1,4,5-trisphosphate that underlies complex Ca^{2+} mobilization patterns. *Science* 284:1527–30

51. Hixon MS, Ball A, Gelb MN. 1998. Calcium-dependent and -independent interfacial binding and catalysis of cytosolic group IV phospholipase A2. *Biochemistry* 37:8516–26

52. Hommel U, Zurini M, Luyten M. 1994. Solution structure of a cysteine-rich domain of rat protein kinase C. *Nat. Struct. Biol.* 1:383–87

53. Hurley JH, Grobler JA. 1997. Protein kinase C and phospholipase C: bilayer interactions and regulation. *Curr. Opin. Struct. Biol.* 7:557–65

54. Hurley JH, Newton AC, Parker PJ, Blumberg PM, Nishizuka Y. 1997. Taxonomy and function of C1 protein kinase C homology domains. *Protein Sci.* 6:477–80

55. Hyvönen M, Macias MJ, Nilges M, Oschkinat H, Saraste M, Wilmanns M. 1995. Structure of the binding site for inositol phosphates in a PH domain. *EMBO J.* 14:4676–85

56. Hyvönen M, Saraste M. 1997. Structure of the PH domain and Btk motif from Bruton's tyrosine kinase: molecular explanations for X-linked agammaglobulinaemia. *EMBO J.* 16:3396–404

57. Iglesias T, Matthews S, Rozengurt E. 1998. Dissimilar phorbol ester binding properties of the individual cysteine-rich motifs of protein kinase D. *FEBS Lett.* 437:19–23

58. Irie K, Oie K, Nakahara A, Yanai Y, Ohigashi H, et al. 1998. Molecular basis for protein kinase C isozyme-selective binding: the synthesis, folding, and phorbol ester binding of the cysteine-rich domains of all protein kinase C isozymes. *J. Am. Chem. Soc.* 120:9159–67

59. Isakoff SJ, Cardozo T, Andreev J, Li Z, Ferguson KM, et al. 1998. Identification and analysis of PH domain-containing targets of phosphatidylinositol 3-kinase using a novel in vivo assay in yeast. *EMBO J.* 17:5374–87

60. James SR, Downes CP, Gigg R, Grove SJA, Holmes AB, Alessi DR. 1996. Specific binding of the Akt-1 protein kinase to phosphatidylinositol 3,4,5-trisphosphate without subsequent activation. *Biochem. J.* 315:709–13

61. Johnson JE, Edwards AS, Newton AC. 1997. A putative phosphatidylserine binding motif is not involved in the lipid regulation of protein kinase C. *J. Biol. Chem.* 272:30787–92

62. Kavran JM, Klein DE, Lee A, Falasca M, Isakoff SJ, et al. 1998. Specificity and promiscuity in phosphoinositide binding by pleckstrin homology domains. *J. Biol. Chem.* 273:30497–508

63. Kazanietz MG, Barchi JJ Jr, Omichinski JG, Blumberg PM. 1995. Low affinity binding of phorbol esters to protein kinase C and its recombinant cysteine-rich region in the absence of phospholipids. *J. Biol. Chem.* 270:14679–84

64. Kazanietz MG, Wang S, Milne GWA, Lewin NE, Liu HL, Blumberg PM. 1995. Residues in the 2nd cysteine-rich region of protein kinase C-δ relevant to phorbol ester binding as revealed by site-directed mutagenesis. *J. Biol. Chem.* 270.21852–59

65. Klarlund JK, Guilherme A, Holik JJ, Virbasius A, Czech MP. 1997. Signaling by phosphoinositide-3,4,5-trisphosphate through proteins containing pleckstrin and Sec7 homology domains. *Science* 275:1927–30

66. Klarlund JK, Rameh LE, Cantley LC, Buxton JM, Holik JJ, et al. 1998. Regulation of GRP1-catalyzed ADP ribosylation factor guanine nucleotide exchange by phosphatidylinositol 3,4,5-trisphosphate. *J. Biol. Chem.* 273:1859–62

67. Klein DE, Lee A, Frank DW, Marks MS, Lemmon MA. 1998. The pleckstrin homology domains of dynamin isoforms require oligomerization for high affinity phosphoinositide binding. *J. Biol. Chem.* 273:27725–33

68. Kojima T, Fukuda M, Watanabe Y, Hamazato F, Mikoshiba K. 1997. Characterization of the pleckstrin homology domain of Btk as an inositol polyphosphate and phosphoinositide binding domain. *Biochim. Biophys. Res. Commun.* 236:333–39

69. Koshiba S, Kigawa T, Kim J-H, Shirouzu M, Bowtell D, Yokoyama S. 1997. The solution structure of the pleckstrin homology domain of mouse son-of-sevenless 1 (mSos1). *J. Mol. Biol.* 269:579–91

70. Kuriyan J, Cowburn D. 1997. Modular peptide recognition domains in eukaryotic signaling. *Annu. Rev. Biophys. Biomol. Struct.* 26:259–88

71. Kutateladze TG, Ogburn KG, Watson WT, de Beer T, Emr SD, et al. 1999. Phosphatidylinositol 3-phosphate recognition by the FYVE domain. *Mol. Cell* 3:605–11

72. Leevers SJ, Vanhaesebroeck B, Waterfield MD. 1999. Signalling through phosphoinositide 3-kinases: The lipids take centre stage. *Curr. Opin. Cell. Biol.* 11:219–25

73. Lemmon MA, Falasca M, Ferguson KM, Schlessinger J. 1997. Regulatory

recruitment of signalling molecules to the cell membrane by pleckstrin-homology domains. *Trends Cell Biol.* 7:237–42

74. Lemmon MA, Ferguson KM, Sigler PB, Schlessinger J. 1995. Specific and high-affinity binding of inositol phosphates to an isolated pleckstrin homology domain. *Proc. Natl. Acad. Sci. USA* 92:10472–76

75. Levine TP, Munro S. 1998. The pleckstrin homology domain of oxysterol-binding protein recognises a determinant specific to Golgi membranes. *Curr. Biol.* 8:729–39

76. Li T, Rawlings DJ, Park H, Kato RM, Witte ON, Satterthwaite AB. 1997. Constitutive membrane association potentiates activation of Bruton tyrosine kinase. *Oncogene* 15:1375–83

77. Li T, Tsukada S, Satterthwaite A, Havlik MH, Park H, et al. 1995. Activation of Bruton's tyrosine kinase (BTK) by a point mutation in its pleckstrin homology (PH) domain. *Immunity* 2:451–60

78. Lin HC, Gilman AG. 1996. Regulation of dynamin I GTPase activity by G protein $\beta\gamma$ subunits and phosphatidylinositol 4,5-bisphosphate. *J. Biol. Chem.* 271:27979–82

79. Lockyer PJ, Bottomley JR, Reynolds JS, McNulty TJ, Venkateswarlu K, et al. 1997. Distinct subcellular localisations of the putative inositol 1,3,4,5-tetrakisphosphate receptors GAP1[IP4BP] and GAP1[m] result from the GAP1[IP4BP] PH domain directing plasma membrane targeting. *Curr. Biol.* 7:1007–10

80. Lockyer PJ, Wennstrom S, Kupzig S, Venkateswarlu K, Downward J, Cullen PJ. 1999. Identification of the Ras GTPase-activating protein GAP1[m] as a phosphatidylinositol 3,4,5-trisphosphate binding protein in vivo. *Curr. Biol.* 9:265–68

81. Lomasney JW, Cheng H-F, Roffler SR, King K. 1999. Activation of phospholipase C δ1 through C2 domain by a Ca^{2+}-enzyme-phosphatidylserine ternary complex. *J. Biol. Chem.* 274:21995–2001

82. Macias MJ, Musacchio A, Ponstingl H, Nilges M, Saraste M, Oschkinat H. 1994. Structure of the pleckstrin homology domain from β spectrin. *Nature* 369:675–77

83. Medkova M, Cho W. 1998. Mutagenesis of the C2 domain of protein kinase C-α. *J. Biol. Chem.* 273:17544–52

84. Medkova M, Cho W. 1999. Interplay of C1 and C2 domains of protein kinase C-α in its membrane binding and activation. *J. Biol. Chem.* 274:19852–61

85. Misra S, Hurley JH. 1999. Crystal structure of a phosphatidylinositol 3-phosphate-specific membrane targeting motif, the FYVE domain of Vps27p. *Cell* 97:657–66

86. Mosior M, Newton AC. 1996. Calcium-independent binding to interfacial phorbol esters causes protein kinase C to associate with membranes in the absence of acidic lipids. *Biochemistry* 35:1612–23

87. Mott HR, Carpenter JW, Zhong S, Ghosh S, Bell RM, Campbell SL. 1996. The solution structure of the Raf-1 cysteine-rich domain: a novel Ras and phospholipid binding site. *Proc. Natl. Acad. Sci. USA* 93:8312–17

88. Nagel W, Schilcher P, Zeitlmann L, Kolanus W. 1998. The PH domain and the polybasic c domain of cytohesin-1 cooperate specifically in plasma membrane association and cellular function. *Mol. Biol Cell* 9:1981–94

89. Nalefski EA, Falke JJ. 1996. The C2 domain calcium-binding motif: structural and functional diversity. *Protein Sci.* 12: 2375–90

90. Nalefski EA, Falke JJ. 1998. Location of the membrane-docking face on the Ca^{2+}-activated C2 domain of cytosolic phospholipase A_2. *Biochemistry* 37:17642–50

91. Nalefski EA, McDonagh T, Somers W, Seehra J, Falke JJ, Clark JD. 1998. Independent folding and ligand specificity of the C2 calcium-dependent lipid binding domain of cytosolic phospholipase A_2. *J. Biol. Chem.* 273:1365–72

92. Nalefski EA, Slazas MM, Falke JJ. 1997. Ca^{2+}-signaling cycle of a membrane-docking C2 domain. *Biochemistry* 36: 12011–18

93. Newton AC, Johnson JJ. 1998. Protein kinase C: a paradigm for regulation of protein functions by two membrane-targeting modules. *Biochim. Biophys. Acta Rev. Biomembr.* 1376:155–72

94. Oancea E, Meyer T. 1998. Protein kinase C as a molecular machine for decoding calcium and diacylglycerol signals. *Cell* 95:307–18

95. Oancea E, Teruel MN, Quest AFG, Meyer T. 1998. Green fluorescent protein (GFP)-tagged cysteine-rich domains from protein kinase C as fluorescent indicators for diacylglycerol signaling in living cells. *J. Cell Biol.* 140:485–98

96. Odorizzi G, Babst M, Emr SD. 1998. Fab1p PtdIns(3)P 5-kinase function essential for protein sorting in the multivesicular body. *Cell* 95:847–58

97. Ostermeier C, Brünger AT. 1999. Structural basis of Rab effector specificity: crystal structure of the small G protein Rab3A complexed with the effector domain of rabphilin-3A. *Cell* 96:363–74

98. Pappa H, Murray-Rust J, Dekker LV, Parker PJ, McDonald NQ. 1998. Crystal structure of the C2 domain from protein kinase C-δ. *Structure* 6:885–94

99. Patki V, Lawe DC, Corvera S, Virbasius JV, Chawla A. 1998. A functional PtdIns(3)P binding motif. *Nature* 394:433–34

100. Pawson T, Scott JD. 1997. Signaling through scaffold, anchoring, and adaptor proteins. *Science* 278:2075–80

101. Pepio AM, Fan XT, Sossin WT. 1998. The role of C2 domains in Ca^{2+}-activated and Ca^{2+}-independent protein kinase Cs in aplysia. *J. Biol. Chem.* 273:19040–48

102. Perisic O, Fong S, Lynch DE, Bycroft M, Williams RL. 1998. Crystal structure of a calcium-phospholipid binding domain from cytosolic phospholipase A$_2$. *J. Biol. Chem.* 273:1596–604

103. Perisic O, Paterson HF, Mosedale G, Lara-González S, Williams RL. 1999. Mapping the phospholipid-binding surface and translocation determinants of the C2 domain from cytosolic phospholipase A$_2$. *J. Biol. Chem.* 274:14979–87

104. Pitcher JA, Touhara K, Payne ES, Lefkowitz RJ. 1995. Pleckstrin homology domain-mediated membrane association and activation of the beta-adrenergic receptor kinase requires coordinate interaction with G beta gamma subunits and lipid. *J. Biol. Chem.* 270:11707–10

105. Ponting CP, Aravind L. 1999. START: a lipid-binding domain in StAR, HD-ZIP and signalling proteins. *Trends Biochem. Sci.* 24:130–32

106. Prehoda KE, Lee DJ, Lim WA. 1999. Structure of the Enabled/VASP homology 1 domain-peptide complex: a key component in the spatial control of actin assembly. *Cell* 97:471–80

107. Rameh LE, Arvidsson A-K, Carraway KL III, Couvillon AD, Rathbun G, et al. 1997. A comparative analysis of the phosphoinositide binding specificity of pleckstrin homology domains. *J. Biol. Chem.* 272:22059–66

108. Rameh LE, Chen CS, Cantley LC. 1995. Phosphatidylinositol (3,4,5)P$_3$ interacts with SH2 domains and modulates PI-3-kinase association with tyrosine-phosphorylated proteins. *Cell* 83:821–30

109. Rebecchi MJ, Scarlata S. 1998. Pleckstrin homology domains: a common fold with diverse functions. *Annu. Rev. Biophys. Biomol. Struct.* 27:503–28

110. Rizo J, Sudhof TC. 1998. C2 domains, structure and function of a universal Ca^{2+} binding domain. *J. Biol. Chem.* 273:15879–82

111. Ron D, Kazanietz MG. 1999. New insights into the regulation of protein kinase C and novel phorbol ester receptors. *FASEB J.* In press

112. Sable CL, Filippa N, Filloux C, Hemmings BA, Van Obberghen E. 1998. Involvement of the pleckstrin homology domain in the insulin-stimulated activation of protein kinase B. *J. Biol. Chem.* 273:29600–6

113. Sakane F, Kai M, Wada I, Imai S, Kanoh H. 1996. The C-terminal part of diacylglycerol kinase α lacking zinc fingers serves as a catalytic domain. *Biochem. J.* 318:583–90

114. Salim J, Bottomley MJ, Querfurth E, Zvelebil MJ, Gout I, et al. 1996. Distinct specificity in the recognition of phosphoinositides by the pleckstrin homology domains of dynamin and Bruton's tyrosine kinase. *EMBO J.* 15:6241–50

115. Schultz J, Milpetz F, Bork P, Ponting CP. 1998. SMART, a simple modular architecture research tool: identification of signalling domains. *Proc. Natl. Acad. Sci. USA* 95:5857–64

116. Shao XG, Fernandez I, Sudhof TC, Rizo J. 1998. Solution structures of the Ca^{2+}-free and Ca^{2+}-bound C2A domain of synaptotgamin I: Does Ca^{2+} induce a conformational change? *Biochemistry* 37:16106–15

117. Shirai Y, Kashiwagi K, Yagi K, Sakai N, Saito N. 1998. Distinct effects of fatty acids on translocation of γ- and ε-subspecies of protein kinase C. *J. Cell Biol.* 143:511–21

118. Simonsen A, Lippe R, Christoforidis S, Gaullier J-M, Brech A, et al. 1998. EEA1 links PI(3)K function to Rab5 regulation of endosome fusion. *Nature* 394:494–98

119. Slater SJ, Ho C, Kelly MB, Larkin JD, Taddeo FJ, et al. 1996. Protein kinase Cα contains two activator binding sites that bind phorbol esters and diacylglycerols with opposite affinities. *J. Biol. Chem.* 271:4627–31

120. Smith CIE, Driscoll PC, Waterfield MD, Panayotou G. 1996. Distinct specificity in the recognition of phosphoinositides by the pleckstrin homology domains of

dynamin and Bruton's tyrosine kinase. *EMBO J.* 15:6241–50

121. Soisson SM, Nimnual AS, Uy M, Bar-Sagi D, Kuriyan J. 1998. Crystal structure of the Dbl and pleckstrin homology domains from the human Son of Sevenless protein. *Cell* 95:259–68

122. Stauffer TP, Ahn S, Meyer T. 1998. Receptor-induced transient reduction in plasma membrane PtdIns(4,5)P2 concentration monitored in living cells. *Curr. Biol.* 8:343–46

123. Stenmark H, Asaland R, Toh B, D'Arrigo A. 1996. Endosomal localization of the autoantigen EEA1 is mediated by a zinc-binding FYVE finger. *J. Biol. Chem.* 271:24048–54

124. Stephens L, Anderson K, Stokoe D, Erdjument-Bromage H, Painter GF, et al. 1998. Protein kinase B kinases that mediate phosphatidylinositol 3,4,5-trisphosphate-dependent activation of protein kinase B. *Science* 279:710–14

125. Sutton RB, Sprang SR. 1998. Structure of the protein kinase Cβ phospholipid-binding C2 domain complexed with Ca^{2+}. *Structure* 6:1395–405

126. Sutton RD, Davletov BA, Berghuis AM, Sudhof TC, Sprang SR. 1995. Structure of the first C2 domain of synaptotagmin I; a novel Ca^{2+}/phospholipid binding fold. *Cell* 80:929–38

127. Swairjo MA, Concha NO, Kaetzel MA, Dedman JR, Seaton BA. 1995. Ca^{2+}-bridging mechanism and phospholipid head group recognition in the membrane-binding protein annexin V. *Nat. Struct. Biol.* 2:968–74

128. Szallasi Z, Bogi K, Gohari S, Biro T, Acs P, Blumberg PM. 1996. Non-equivalent roles for the first and second zinc fingers of protein kinase Cδ. *J. Biol. Chem.* 271:18229–301

129. Takeuchi H, Kanematsu T, Misumi Y, Sakane F, Konishi H, et al. 1997. Distinct specificity in the binding of inositol phosphates by pleckstrin homology

domains of pleckstrin, RAC-protein kinase, diacylglycerol kinase and a new 130 kDa protein. *Biochim. Biophys. Acta Mol. Cell Res.* 1359:275–85

130. Timm D, Salim K, Gout I, Guruprasad L, Waterfield M, Blundell T. 1994. Crystal structure of the pleckstrin homology domain from dynamin. *Nat. Struct. Biol.* 1:782–88

131. Tognon CE, Kirk HE, Passmore LA, Whitehead IP, Der CJ, Kay RJ. 1998. Regulation of RasGRP via a phorbol ester-responsive C1 domain. *Mol. Cell. Biol.* 18:6995–7008

132. Topham MK, Prescott SM. 1999. Mammalian diacylglycerol kinases, a family of lipid kinases with signaling functions. *J. Biol. Chem.* 274:11447–50

133. Tsukazaki T, Chiang TA, Davison AF, Attisano L, Wrana JL. 1998. SARA, a FYVE domain protein that recruits Smad2 to the TGF-β receptor. *Cell* 95:779–91

134. Ubach J, Zhang XY, Shao G, Sudhof TC, Rizo J. 1998. Ca^{2+} binding to synaptotagmin: How many Ca^{2+} ions bind to the tip of a C2 domain? *EMBO J.* 17:3921–30

135. Várnai P, Balla T. 1998. Visualization of phosphoinositides that bind pleckstrin homology domains: calcium- and agonist-induced dynamic changes and relationship to myo-$[^3H]$inositol-labeled phosphoinositide pools. *J. Cell Biol.* 143:501–10

136. Várnai P, Rother KI, Balla T. 1999. Phosphatidylinositol 3-kinase-dependent membrane association of the Bruton's tyrosine kinase pleckstrin homology domain visualized in single living cells. *J. Biol. Chem.* 274:10983–89

137. Venkateswarlu K, Oatey PB, Tavare JM, Cullen PJ. 1998. Insulin-dependent translocation of ARNO to the plasma membrane of adipocytes requires phosphatidylinositol 3-kinase. *Curr. Biol.* 8:463–66

138. Vetter IR, Nowak C, Nishimoto T, Kuhlmann J, Wittinghofer A. 1999. Structure of a Ran-binding domain complexed with Ran bound to a GTP analogue: implications for nuclear transport. *Nature* 398:39–46

139. Wang T, Pentyala S, Rebecchi MJ, Scarlata S. 1999. Differential association of the pleckstrin homology domains of phospholipases C-β1, C-β2, and C-δ1 with lipid bilayers and the βγ subunits of heterotrimeric G proteins. *Biochemistry* 38:1317–24

140. Watton SJ, Downward J. 1999. Akt/PKB localisation and 3' phosphoinositide generation at sites of epithelial cell-matrix and cell-cell interaction. *Curr. Biol.* 9:433–36

141. Wurmser AE, Gary JD, Emr SD. 1999. Phosphoinositide 3-kinases and their FYVE domain-containing effectors as regulators of vacuolar/lysosomal membrane trafficking pathways. *J. Biol. Chem.* 274:9129–32

142. Yagisawa H, Sakuma K, Paterson HF, Cheung R, Allen V, et al. 1998. Replacements of single basic amino acids in the pleckstrin homology domain of phospholipase C-δ1 alter the ligand binding, phospholipase activity, and interaction with the plasma membrane. *J. Biol. Chem.* 273:417–24

143. Yoon HS, Hajduk PJ, Petros AM, Olejniczak ET, Meadows RP, Fesik SW. 1994. Solution structure of a pleckstrin homology domain. *Nature* 369:672–75

144. Xu GY, McDonagh T, Yu H-A, Nalefski E, Clark JD, Cumming DA. 1998. Solution structure and membrane interactions of the C2 domain of cytosolic phospholipase A_2. *J. Mol. Biol.* 280:485–500

145. Xu RX, Pawelczyk T, Xia T-H, Brown SC. 1997. NMR structure of a protein kinase C-phorbol-binding domain and study of protein-lipid micelle interactions. *Biochemistry* 36:10709–17

146. Zhang G, Kazanietz MG, Blumberg PM, Hurley JH. 1995. Crystal structure of the Cys2 activator-binding domain of protein

kinase Cδ in complex with phorbol ester. *Cell* 81:917–24

147. Zhang P, Talluri S, Deng HY, Branton D, Wagner G. 1995. Solution structure of the pleckstrin homology domain of β-spectrin. *Structure* 3:1185–95

148. Zhang XY, Rizo J, Sudhof TC. 1998. Mechanism of phospholipid binding by the C2A domain of synaptotagmin I. *Biochemistry* 37:12395–403

149. Zhang ZT, Lee CH, Mandiyan V, Borg JB, Margolis B, et al. 1997. Sequence-specific recognition of the internalization motif of the Alzheimer's amyloid precursor protein by the X11 PTB domain. *EMBO J.* 16:6141–50

150. Zheng J, Cahill SM, Lemmon MA, Fushman D, Schlessinger J, Cowburn D. 1996. Identification of the binding site for acidic phospholipids on the PH domain of dynamin: implications for stimulation of GTPase activity. *J. Mol. Biol.* 255:14–21

151. Zheng J, Chen RH, Corbalan-Garcia S, Cahill D, Bar-Sagi D, Cowburn D. 1997. The solution structure of the pleckstrin homology domain of human SOS1. A possible structural role for the sequential association of diffuse B cell lymphoma and pleckstrin homology domains. *J. Biol. Chem.* 272:30340–44

152. Zhou MM, Ravichandran KS, Olejniczak EF, Petros AM, Meadows RP, et al. 1995. Structure and ligand recognition of the phosphotyrosine binding domain of Shc. *Nature* 378:584–92

Annu. Rev. Biophys. Biomol. Struct. 2000. 29:81–103

GCN5-RELATED N-ACETYLTRANSFERASES: A Structural Overview

Fred Dyda,[1] David C. Klein,[2] and
Alison Burgess Hickman[1]

[1]Laboratory of Molecular Biology, National Institute of Diabetes, Digestive,
and Kidney Diseases, National Institutes of Health, Bethesda, Maryland 20892;
e-mail: dyda@ulti.niddk.nih.gov, ahickman@helix.nih.gov
[2]Laboratory of Developmental Neurobiology, National Institute of Child Health
and Development, National Institutes of Health, Bethesda, Maryland 20892;
e-mail: klein@helix.nih.gov

Key Words   melatonin, histone acetylation, GNAT, aminoglycoside, acetyl
coenzyme A

■ **Abstract**   Hundreds of acetyltransferases exist. All use a common acetyl donor—
acetyl coenzyme A—and each exhibits remarkable specificity for acetyl acceptors,
which include small molecules and proteins. Analysis of the primary sequences of
these enzymes indicates that they can be sorted into several superfamilies. This review
covers the three-dimensional structures of members of one of these superfamilies,
now referred to in the literature as the GCN5-related N-acetyltransferases (GNAT),
reflecting the importance of one functional category, the histone acetyltransferases.
Despite the diversity of substrate specificities, members of the GNAT superfamily
demonstrate remarkable similarity in protein topology and mode of acetyl coenzyme
A binding, likely reflecting a conserved catalytic mechanism.

CONTENTS

1056-8700/00/0610-0081$14.00

INTRODUCTION

The transfer of an acetyl group from one molecule to another is a fundamental biochemical process. Several unrelated classes of enzymes catalyze such a reaction, and the focus of this review is the recent burst of three-dimensional structural information about one of these classes, the GCN5-related N-acetyltransferases (GNAT), which catalyze the transfer of the acetyl group from acetyl coenzyme A (AcCoA, the "donor") to a primary amine (the "acceptor"). Over the course of a twelve-month period spanning 1998–1999, eleven experimentally determined three-dimensional structures of GNAT superfamily members have been reported, elucidated both by single-crystal X-ray diffraction and by NMR spectroscopy (2, 7, 11, 12, 20, 34, 39, 43, 45). From the perspective of structural biology, the GNAT superfamily is a case study in how a common acetyltransferase domain evolved to serve a wide variety of functions. What makes this superfamily especially interesting is the large assortment of acceptor substrates carrying a primary amine that are capable of being acetylated, and which the different GNAT members have to interact with and recognize.

Even a cursory inspection of three-dimensional protein structures in the Protein Data Bank (http://www.rcsb.org/pdbl) reveals a large number of different ways in which AcCoA and CoA can be bound to protein molecules. In addition to the diverse binding modes, the protein subunits that are responsible for AcCoA binding also display high diversity in their folds (8). The GNAT superfamily adds yet other variations, both to AcCoA conformation and binding modes and to the variety of known protein folds. The polypeptide of the N-acetyltransferase domain that is responsible for AcCoA binding has a unique fold, as noted in the reports of the two first structures that were solved from the superfamily (7, 43). All the subsequent structure determinations have demonstrated nearly the same protein topology and AcCoA binding mode. There is no detectable similarity in either primary sequence or three-dimensional structure between enzymes in the GNAT superfamily and other AcCoA-dependent acetyltransferases such as chloramphenicol acetyltransferase (19) and dihydrolipoyl transacetylase (23). [To avoid confusion, it is important to keep this in mind, particularly since in the three-dimensional database SCOP (29), the family of CoA-dependent acetyltransferases contains only these two enzymes.]

Several years before three-dimensional structural information became available, two conserved sequence motifs (motifs A and B) were noticed between the yeast MAK3 protein and N-acetyltransferases (38); they were later identified in other N-acetyltransferases, including the arylalkylamine N-acetyltransferase (AANAT) family (3, 22). More recently, Neuwald & Landsman extended and generalized this observation to a large class of >140 related proteins, which they designated the GNAT superfamily (30). They also identified two additional motifs (motifs C and D) present in many GNAT members. The structures reviewed here represent three functional families within the GNAT superfamily and act on three general groups of substrates: histones, aminoglycosides, and arylalkylamines. Aspects of some of these structures have recently been reviewed elsewhere (28, 35).

Among the members of the GNAT superfamily, perhaps the most intense current interest swirls around a group of N-acetyltransferases involved in the acetylation of histones at specific lysine residues, a process that is required for transcriptional activation and that has been implicated in chromatin assembly and DNA replication (10, 27). Of the large number of histone N-acetyltransferase (HAT) enzymes, many turn out to be previously identified transcriptional activator proteins and most likely act in the context of large multiprotein assemblies. Probably the best studied group of HAT proteins are the members of the GCN5 family (indeed, the name of the superfamily derives from these prominent members), on which a wealth of biochemical and functional information is available.

Another important N-acetyltransferase activity is that contributing to the emergence of antibiotic resistance among pathogenic bacteria. N-acetylation of a particular amino group is one of the chemical modifications of aminoglycoside antibiotics that can result in decreased affinity of the drug for its target—a process therefore advantageous for the bacteria. These modifications are carried out by a class of bacterial aminoglycoside N-acetyltransferases (AAC) that can be divided into further subclasses depending on the regiospecificity of acetyl transfer.

Much recent attention has also focused on the arylalkylamine N-acetyltransferase (serotonin N-acetyltransferase, AANAT) family. Members of this family have been found only in vertebrates. AANAT catalyzes the penultimate step in the synthesis of the circadian neurohormone melatonin from serotonin (16). The circulating levels of melatonin are correlated with the light dark cycle, with high levels of melatonin occurring only at night. Melatonin plays an important role in the proper coordination of the sleep-wake cycle as well as in the adaptation to seasonal changes. There is special interest in AANAT because it exhibits a large light-dark rhythm in activity that controls the rhythm in circulating levels of melatonin. In addition, changes in active protein levels can be very rapid: Light exposure at night causes a decrease in AANAT activity with a half-life of only 3 min (17). AANAT activity has been found to be closely correlated with the amount of AANAT protein. This is regulated by control of proteasomal proteolysis and also by controlling synthesis through regulation of AANAT mRNA levels (9, 16).

Other members of the GNAT superfamily play a variety of anabolic and catabolic roles. For instance, an N-acetyltransferase has been identified that is essential in the synthesis of UDP-N-acetylglucosamine, an essential metabolite in both prokaryotes and eukaryotes (26). An example of catabolic involvement is spermidine/spermine N-acetyltransferase (22). Upon acetylation of the N^1 position of spermidine or spermine, the acetylated polyamines are excreted from the cell or subsequently metabolized by the FAD-requiring polyamine oxidase. This is by no means an exhaustive list of all the characterized N-acetyltransferases, and there are also several functionally uncharacterized proteins that are clearly members of the GNAT superfamily (3, 30). It is likely that as more sequence information becomes available, the already substantial functional diversity will expand even further.

Summary of Structures Determined to Date

As of mid-1999, there have been eleven reported three-dimensional structures of GNAT superfamily members. Protein particulars, constructs used for structure determination, structural resolution, and Protein Data Bank (PDB, http://www.rcsb. org/pdb/) ID codes are listed in Table 1.

Histone N-Acetyltransferases   Of the known structures, seven correspond to histone N-acetyltransferases, or HATs. The structure of Hat1 from *Saccharomyces cerevisiae* (yHat1) was determined complexed with AcCoA (7). The construct used to obtain well-diffracting crystals, despite missing 54 carboxy-terminal residues, is fully active in vitro. PCAF (p300/CBP-associating factor) is a transcriptional activator that can acetylate nucleosomal histone substrates, as well as other transcriptional activators such as p53 (21). Full-length human PCAF is an 832-residue molecule containing an N-terminal domain that interacts with transcriptional activators, a C-terminal bromodomain that can interact with acetylated lysine (for a recent NMR structure, see Reference 5), and a central HAT domain. The crystal

TABLE 1   Structurally characterized members of the GNAT superfamily

Protein[a]	Source	Residues in construct	Substrates	PDB ID	Resolution (Å)	Reference
AANAT	Ovine	28–201	—	1b6b	2.5	(11)
		28–201	Bisubstrate	1cjw	1.8	(12)
Hat1	Yeast	1–320	AcCoA	1BOB	2.3	(7)
GCN5	*Tetrahymena*	47–210	CoA	5GCN	b	(20)
		48–210	—	1QST	1.7	(34)
		48–210	AcCoA	1QSR	2.0	(34)
		48–210	CoA/peptide	1QSN	2.2	(34)
GCN5	Yeast	99–262	—	1ygh	1.9	(39)
PCAF	Human	493–658	CoA	1cm0	2.3	(2)
AAC(3)	*S. marcescens*	1–168	CoA	1bo4	2.3	(43)
AAC(6′)	*E. faecium*	1–182	AcCoA	1B87	2.7	(45)

[a]AANAT, arylalkylamine N-acetyltransferase; PCAF, p300/CBP-associating factor; Hat, histone N-acetyltransferase; AAC, aminoglycoside N-acetyltransferase.

[b]Structure determined by NMR.

structure of this ~200-residue HAT domain was solved in complex with CoA (2). Highly homologous with the PCAF HAT domain are the GCN5 proteins from various species. The crystal structure of the HAT domain of yeast GCN5 (yGCN5) was solved in absence of substrates (39), whereas the solution structure of the *Tetrahymena* GCN5 HAT domain (tGCN5) has been solved with NMR spectroscopy as a complex with CoA (20). Essentially the same version of tGCN5 was also used in a three-part crystallographic study in which the structure was solved in the uncomplexed form, complexed with AcCoA, and—most importantly—in a ternary complex with CoA and an 11-residue peptide centered around the reactive lysine of yeast histone H3 (34).

Aminoglycoside N-Acetyltransferases   The structures of two aminoglycoside N-acetyltransferases exhibiting different specificity for acetyl transfer to aminoglycoside antibiotics have been determined. 3-N-acetyltransferase [AAC(3)] from *Serratia marcescens* was solved complexed with CoA (43). Nine dispensable residues were truncated from the C terminus to obtain diffraction-quality cocrystals. Although no in vitro N-acetyltransferase activity could be demonstrated for this construct, in an in vivo experiment it was deemed sufficient to produce gentamicin resistance. Of all the known GNAT structures, this is the only one that forms a distinguishable dimer in the crystal lattice, with monomers related to each other by a nearly perfect twofold rotation axis. Although the surface area buried by this dimer is relatively large (880 Å^2), there is no direct experimental evidence to confirm that the biologically active species is indeed a dimer in solution, and the physiological significance of the observed dimer is unclear. The crystal structure of aminoglycoside 6'-N-acetyltransferase [AAC(6')] complexed with AcCoA was solved using the full-length protein (45), the only example within the group of currently available GNAT structures for which a nontruncated construct was used. Although analytical gel filtration data indicated that AAC(6') is a dimer in solution, it was not possible to select the biologically relevant oligomer from the large number of dimers that were created by the high (cubic) crystallographic symmetry. Considering the ambiguities regarding quaternary organization, or that in most cases the biologically relevant unit is a monomer, or that the structures solved involve only the catalytic domains of multidomain proteins, we do not further consider here the issue of oligomerization.

Serotonin N-Acetyltransferase   Serotonin N-acetyltransferase (AANAT) represents the third class of GNAT enzymes that have been structurally characterized, and the structure of ovine AANAT has been solved both in the uncomplexed form (11) and complexed with a bisubstrate analog (12). The full-length enzyme contains 207 amino acids but for successful crystallization was truncated at both termini, resulting in a fully active 28–201 construct. Together with the tGCN5 ternary complex, AANAT provides the most complete source of structural information to date, as the bisubstrate analog used in the cocrystallization is a very close chemical approximation of the intermediate that is present during the acetyl transfer. To date, among the GNAT complexes, this AANAT structure is the one solved at the highest resolution (1.8 Å), owing to the exceptional crystal quality resulting from the stabilizing effect of the bisubstrate compound.

A Structurally Related Cousin   Two recent structure determinations of N-myristoyltransferase, one of the uncomplexed enzyme (42) and the other of a ternary complex with myristoyl-CoA and a peptide (1), reveal a myristoyl-CoA binding domain with the same fold and mode of cofactor binding as those of the GNAT superfamily members. It seems likely that a common ancestral protein served as the precursor for both groups of enzymes, but further discussion of N-myristoyltransferase is beyond the scope of this review as it is not specifically an N-acetyltransferase.

Sequence and Structure-Based Alignment of GNAT Enzymes

With the several different three-dimensional structures representing three distinct families within the GNAT superfamily, we are now in a position to reexamine the N-acetyltransferase domain in light of this wealth of structural information. The aligned three-dimensional structures are shown in Figure 1 (see color insert) and the corresponding alignment of primary sequences in Figure 2 (see color insert). The four regions highlighted in both figures in the same colors correspond to the sequence motifs identified first by Tercero et al (38) and subsequently by Neuwald & Landsman (30). As a result of this two-step historical evolution, the order in which the conserved motifs follow each other in the primary sequences is C, D, A, and B. The most impressive conservation across the superfamily is in motifs A and B, whereas the weakest is in motif C. These four regions roughly comprise what we refer to as the N-acetyltransferase domain.

It is most remarkable to observe that, despite the functional variation across the superfamily, the protein topology is nearly identical. This is a clear example of the observation made by Petsko et al (31) that protein families seem to evolve from ancestral molecules that catalyze the necessary chemistry (in this case, transfer of an acetyl group from AcCoA), and that further mutations that do not change the topology will enable the protein to bind alternative substrates. As we shall see, deviations from the common topology of the GNAT superfamily members are most likely related to the need to accommodate a wide range of primary amine-carrying acceptor substrates, which varies from small compounds such as serotonin to large protein molecules such as histones.

DESCRIPTION OF THE STRUCTURE

Overview of the Structural Fold

From a topogical point of view, the N-acetyltransferase domain folds around a central, mixed β sheet that is largely built up of antiparallel strands; the only exception is a structurally conserved four-residue-long parallel stretch. The most common number of strands in the β sheet is six, although AAC(6′) has an extra C-terminal strand (45), whereas yHat1 has an additional strand at the N-terminal end of the domain (7). The absence of this N-terminal strand in the other proteins might be a result of the use of N-terminally truncated constructs or disorder in the crystal lattice that renders the electron density in this segment weaker than the noise level and therefore invisible. On the other hand, this additional strand is not present in AAC(6′), a full-length construct for which all the residues are resolved in the crystal structure (45). Given this fact, we start the strand numbering of the domain according to the first strand of AAC(6′), since this is the first common β strand in all the GNAT structures. (The numbering is shown in Figure 3, with the structure of the AANAT/bisubstrate analog complex serving as the representative structure for the superfamily.)

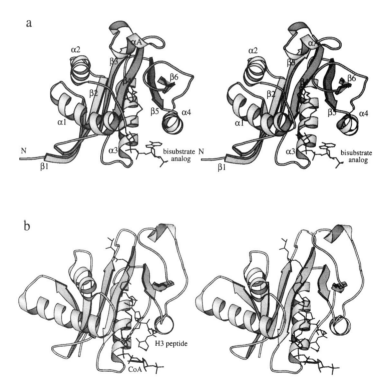

Figure 3 (*a*) Stereo view of serotonin N-acetyltransferase (AANAT) bound to a bisubstrate inhibitor. The common structural elements among the members of the GNAT superfamily are labeled and correspond to the elements shown in Figure 2. AANAT contains a unique insertion between strands $\beta3$ and $\beta4$, and the helix contained within this subdomain is labeled αA. (*b*) Stereo view of the tGCN5 ternary complex with CoA and an 11-residue H3 peptide, in the same orientation. The figure was prepared using MOLSCRIPT (18).

The N-Terminal Region and Motif C

The β sheet that forms the core of the N-acetyltransferase domain can be considered as being composed of two parts, one encompassing the first four strands that are nearly identical in all the structures and the second formed by the last two strands [or three, for AAC(6')]. Generally, in the loop connecting the first and the second strands, two helices run antiparallel to each other and nearly perpendicular to the direction of the first four strands. yHat1 is missing the second helix but not the first (Figure 1b), whereas AAC(3) has three helices in this region (Figure 1g). The absence of $\alpha 2$ in yHat1 might be due, in part, to the fact that the position of $\alpha 1$ of yHat1 is shifted with respect to the other GNAT structures, due to the proximity of an additional N-terminal domain (residues 1–111, not shown in Figure 1b) that is not present in the other structures (7). This ~ 4 Å shift in the direction of where $\alpha 2$ would be, as inferred from the rest of the structures, could destabilize its conformation to the extent that the helix is lost. (Note that this shift is also reflected in Figure 1b in the lack of alignment of $\alpha 1$ of yHat1 with the analogous helices in the other GNAT structures.) Unfortunately, as none of the other HATs was crystallized with regions other than the catalytic domain present, we will have to wait until such structures are elucidated to see if the absence of $\alpha 2$ in intact HAT proteins is a general feature of the family. A particularly important position on $\alpha 1$ is located on its last turn, represented by Phe-56 in AANAT. In all the structures, this is a large, hydrophobic side chain (Phe twice, Trp once, in two cases Leu and one Ile) that plays an important role in ensuring the characteristically bent conformation of AcCoA (discussed below).

There are an ample number of primarily (but not exclusively) hydrophobic interactions between helices $\alpha 1$ and $\alpha 2$ and the four-stranded sheet below. These very likely contribute to the rigidity of the first four strands of the β sheet and probably explain why this sheet is essentially unchanged from one molecule to another. Similarly, there are several (again, primarily hydrophobic) interactions between the two helices themselves. These sets of interactions, in conjunction with the hydrogen-bonding network between the four antiparallel strands, result in a rigid and compact subdomain in this region of the molecule.

It is obvious from the three-dimensional alignment of the different structures that there is a much better positional match between the first helices ($\alpha 1$) than between the second ones, where yHat1 can be regarded as sitting at the far end of the structural spectrum with $\alpha 2$ completely missing. It is not surprising, then, that sequence motif C includes the first helix. What is perhaps more interesting is that the HAT family, including the GCN5 enzymes, was initially thought to be missing this motif altogether (30). As shown in the sequence alignment in Figure 2, this may in part be due to the variable length of the turn (shown in light purple in Figure 1) between the first β strand and the first helix.

Where the second helix ($\alpha 2$) is present, it is generally shorter than $\alpha 1$ and shows more variation in position between the structures. Notably, it is significantly different in the two AANAT crystal structures (11, 12). In the uncomplexed form,

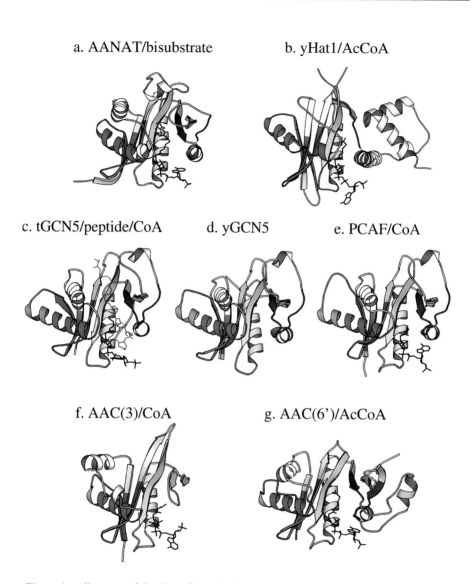

Figure 1 Alignment of the three-dimensional structures of GCN5-related N-acetyltransferases. *AANAT*, serotonin N-acetyltransferase; *PCAF*, p300/CBP-associating factor; *yHat*, histone N-acetyltransferase; *AAC*, aminoglycoside N-acetyltransferase. For AANAT (*a*), the complex with the bisubstrate analog is shown (indole ring in *blue*), while for tGCN5 (*c*), the ternary complex with CoA and an 11-residue peptide (in *blue*) is shown. The *black lines* indicate coenzyme A or acetyl coenzyme A. The four conserved motifs of the GNAT superfamily—C, D, A, and B—are shown in *purple*, *green*, *yellow*, and *red*, respectively. Structural elements that represent insertions into motifs C and B are shown in *lilac* and *pink*, respectively. Helix α1 of yHat1 is shown in *blue* to indicate the positional shift of this helix with respect to the other aligned structures. The figure was prepared using MOLSCRIPT (18).

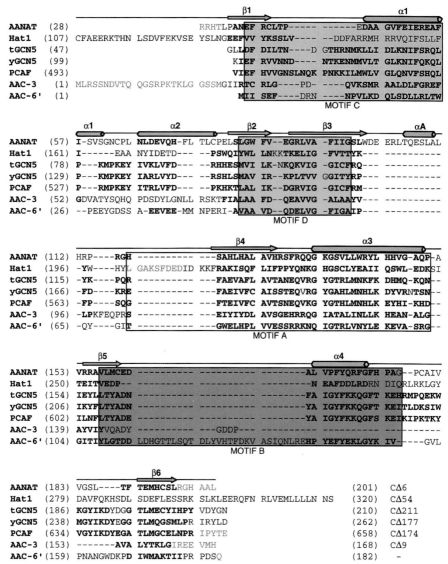

Figure 2 Primary sequences of structurally aligned GCN5-related N-acetyltransferases. Structures were optimally aligned to that of PCAF using "O" (13); residues whose Cα positions are within 3.8 Å of those of PCAF are shown in *bold* lettering. For AANAT, the bisubstrate-bound form was used, and for tGCN5, that of the ternary complex was used. The residues shown correspond to those present in the constructs used for structure determination, with the exception of yHat1, which had an additional N-terminal domain (residues 1–106). Residues in *blue* are disordered regions that could not be located in the electron density maps. The secondary structural elements of AANAT are shown above the aligned residues. The *colored boxes* correspond to the regions designated motifs C, D, A, and B by Neuwald & Landsman (30), and are shown in the same colors used in Figure 1. The final column indicates the number of residues truncated from the C terminus of each construct used for structure determination.

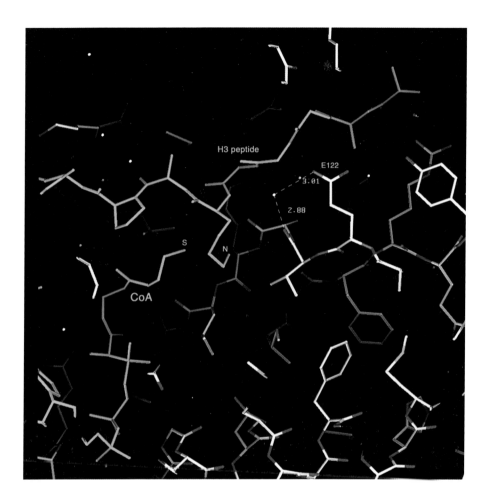

Figure 8 (*a*) The proton wire of serotonin N-acetyltransferase (AANAT). The crystallographically observed water molecules are shown as *white spheres*, the bisubstrate inhibitor in *blue*.

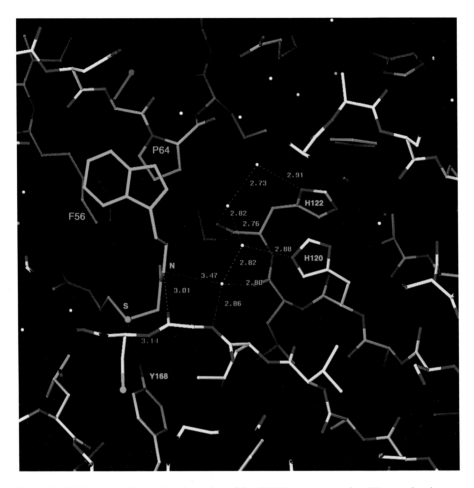

Figure 8 (*b*) Close-up of the active site region of the tGCN5 ternary complex. Water molecules are represented as *white spheres*, and the substrates are shown in *blue*.

a   b

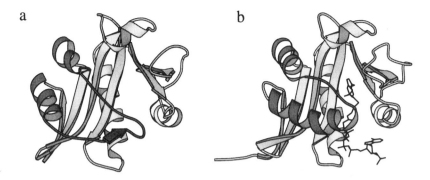

Figure 4   Comparison of the uncomplexed (*a*) and bisubstrate analog-bound (*b*) forms of serotonin N-acetyltransferase. Note the shorter helices $\alpha 1$ and $\alpha 2$, and the additional β strand in the uncomplexed form; the region of the conformational change is highlighted in dark gray. The figure was prepared using MOLSCRIPT (18).

both $\alpha 1$ and $\alpha 2$ are fairly short, whereas in the complex form of AANAT with the bisubstrate analog, both helices extend in length (Figure 4). The shorter helices in the uncomplexed form allow the polypeptide chain to assume a more extended conformation. Indeed, it reaches far enough out and down into the AcCoA binding site to form a short β strand that is not present in the complex form and that occupies part of the binding site. It is the binding of AcCoA that selects a conformational state in which the polypeptide has been reordered, creating the binding site for serotonin (12). This structural result is in good accord with earlier kinetic work that showed that AANAT binds its substrates in an ordered fashion, with AcCoA binding increasing the enzyme's affinity for serotonin substantially, and that a conformational change may be involved (4). The important observation is that, at least in the case of AANAT, this part of the molecule is clearly subject to conformational changes, and this change is a function of whether the AcCoA binding site is occupied or not.

Motifs D and A

The polypeptide chain after $\alpha 2$ completes the first four strands of the sheet, running through sequence motif D that includes most of strands $\beta 2$ and $\beta 3$, and turns into strand $\beta 4$ where motif A, the longest and most highly conserved motif, starts. Note that the regions corresponding to motifs C and D, despite their separation in the primary sequence, are located next to and interact with each other three-dimensionally, forming the rigid subdomain that comprises the first half of the molecule. Strand $\beta 4$ plays a crucial role in AcCoA binding and contains residues that are important for catalytic activity. In the region between strands $\beta 3$ and $\beta 4$, most of the structures contain a short turn. As can be seen in Figure 1, there are two exceptions. In yHat1, there is an $\sim$13-residue extension between $\beta 3$ and $\beta 4$ that cannot be aligned with the other structures; nine of these amino acids are disordered and therefore invisible in the crystal structure (7). In AANAT, there is also an $\sim$13-residue-long extension, but in this case, this region forms a small subdomain with a very well defined three-dimensional structure (11), folded around Trp-99, a conserved residue in AANATs. Mutation of Trp-99 to Ala results in a protein that is completely insoluble (AB Hickman, unpublished data), presumably because of gross folding problems. In AANAT, this subdomain contains a short two-turn helix, not seen in the other structures (labeled αA in Figure 3). This helix defines one side of the hydrophobic substrate binding pocket for serotonin and therefore likely plays a crucial role in determining substrate specificity. With the help of this short helix, AANAT manages to exclude the hydrophobic indole moiety of serotonin from solvent and surround it with an essentially entirely hydrophobic environment. In the other structures, the absence of such a subdomain leaves this part of the molecule more accessible to solvent, consistent with the larger-sized or more hydrophilic substrates (relative to serotonin) to be acetylated by the other GNAT enzymes.

Strand β4 and the structural element directly following it, α3, form the essence of the AcCoA binding site. Strand β4 starts with a four-residue stretch that runs parallel to β5, forming the only parallel β structure in the GNAT catalytic domain. Motif A begins just before the parallel stretch of β4 and extends to the carboxy end of α3. The parting of the two parallel strands results in a wedge-like opening in the center of the protein where AcCoA binds. A characteristic feature of the GNAT superfamily is a β bulge, located in the middle of β4, immediately following the short parallel strand segment. In a regular β strand, the peptide planes alternate in orientation from one residue to the next. This alternation projects each sequential main-chain carbonyl oxygen to opposite sides of the strand. This places the carbonyl groups in the appropriate location and register to form hydrogen bonds with similarly alternating main-chain amide groups of adjacent strands. A β bulge is an exception from this pattern, whereby two residues occupy the space in a β sheet normally occupied by one.

The "classic" β bulge (33) observed in β4 of GNAT enzymes is created by two residues that directly follow each other in the sequence turning their carbonyls to the same side of the β strand, in this case toward the cofactor binding site (shown in Figure 5 for AANAT). Correspondingly, the amides of these two adjacent residues point to the other side of the β strand, placed such that they can form a bifurcated hydrogen bond with a main-chain carbonyl from β3. Thus, the two strands remain held together albeit locally distorted. It is likely that the β bulge is a significant feature breaking the parallel segment between β4 and β5, and hence in the formation of the AcCoA binding site. Among the GNAT structures determined to date, there is one exception to this observation: AAC(6') has a Pro residue inserted at the analogous position in β4, resulting in a markedly different hydrogen-bonding pattern (45). Since the amide nitrogen of Pro is not available for hydrogen bonding, the introduction of a Pro into β4 results in an irregular hydrogen-bonding pattern between β3 and β4, with the two adjacent carbonyls from β4 now pointing toward β3. Since the α-carbon trace of AAC(6') is essentially identical to the others

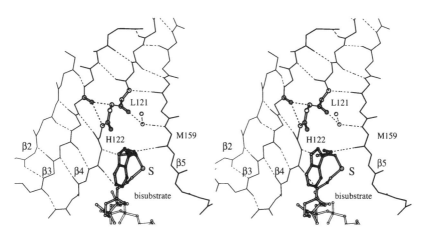

Figure 5 Stereo view of the β bulge region of serotonin N-acetyltransferase (AANAT). *Dashed lines* represent hydrogen bonds. The two *circles* represent the most deeply located water molecules in the proton wire. The figure was prepared using MOLSCRIPT (18).

in the region of the β bulge, insertion of a proline residue into β4 seems to be a different means of achieving essentially the same structural end.

Immediately downstream of the β bulge are three residues that form main-chain hydrogen bonds with the AcCoA substrate, starting with the amide of the residue immediately after the bulged residue. In the cases where the structures include AcCoA, this residue is directly hydrogen bonded to the carbonyl of the acetyl group. Indeed, AcCoA interacts with β4 much as if it were the next strand in a β sheet. The acetyl and pantetheine moieties of AcCoA project carbonyl and amide groups to both sides and are separated by the right distance to hydrogen bond with an adjacent β strand. (The structure of AcCoA is shown in Figure 6a.)

In addition to the β bulge, the second characteristic local structural feature of the GNAT superfamily in this region is the pyrophosphate binding pocket at the amino end of α3; this helix is part of a βαβ motif resembling the Rossman fold found in many nucleotide-binding proteins (32). Helix α3 is the longest helix in the structure, and the helix dipole must contribute significantly to phosphate binding. Indeed, it is quite impressive that among the different molecules, both substrate conformation and mode of pyrophosphate binding are essentially identical down to the most intimate details. (The overlain cofactor structures are shown in Figure 7, viewed from the same orientation as in Figure 1.) The only significant differences are seen in the NMR structure of the tGCN5/CoA complex (20), but since this is not consistent with the X-ray results for tGCN5 and the other members of the superfamily, we do not analyze this result further in this review.

One unusual feature of the coenzyme A binding mode is the lack of direct hydrogen bonds by Lys or Arg side chains to the phosphates, even though such salt bridges are frequently seen in other types of CoA-binding proteins (8). The

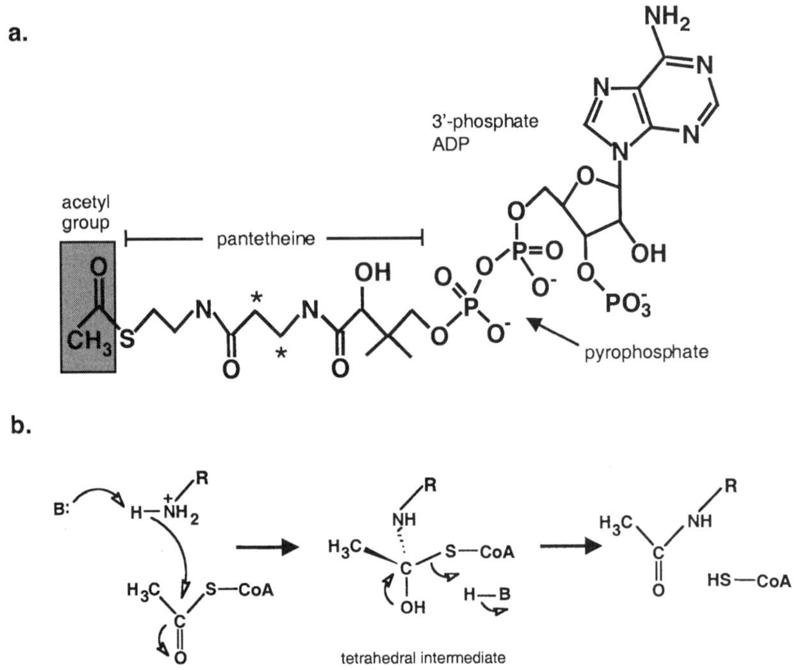

Figure 6 (*a*) The chemical structure of acetyl coenzyme A. The characteristic sharp bend observed in the bound forms of AcCoA and CoA in GNAT superfamily members is around the bond highlighted by the starred carbon atoms. (*b*) The general reaction catalyzed by GCN5-related N-acetyltransferases, showing the presumed tetrahedral intermediate that results from nucleophilic attack of a primary amine on the acyl carbon of the acetyl group.

pyrophosphate group is deeply buried, and with one exception, all the polar interactions between the phosphates and the protein involve main-chain amides. The amides of all the six residues that form the pyrophosphate binding pocket are hydrogen bonded to the phosphate oxygen atoms. Four of these bonds are direct, two are water mediated, and these water molecules are conserved in all the X-ray structures. This situation is somewhat reminiscent of that seen for succinyl-CoA synthetase in which the pyrophosphate is also hydrogen bonded to main-chain amides at the N-terminus of an α helix (44). In this case, however, the binding site for CoA is located between two adjacent protein subunits.

Among the GNAT structures, the only side-chain interaction with the pyrophosphate group is between the α-phosphate and the side-chain hydroxyl of a residue on the first turn of $\alpha 3$. With the exception of yGCN5, in the structures determined to date, this residue is either a Ser or a Thr and forms the same interaction with the phosphate. In yGCN5, the analogous residue is an Ala, but as this structure was solved without substrate (39), it is not yet clear how this affects phosphate binding. It should be noted that this residue is not conserved across the superfamily.

Figure 7 Stereo view of the superposition of all the observed conformations of bound coenzyme A–related substrates. The bisubstrate analog bound to AANAT is shown in the thickest line, and its indole moiety can be seen at the *upper left*; the thinnest line represents the conformation observed in the NMR structure (20). The view is the same as in Figure 1.

Motif B and the Completion of the AcCoA Binding Site

Helix α3, consisting of five turns, leads into β5, and the turn between these two structural elements is where motif A ends. Strand β5 starts by pairing up with β4 to form the short parallel segment of the β sheet, and subsequently parts from it to define the other side of the wedge-like AcCoA binding site. It is not surprising, therefore, that strand β5 is also where another highly conserved region, motif B, starts. With the exception of the main-chain carbonyl oxygen of one residue (Met-159 in AANAT; see Figure 5), there are no hydrogen-bond contacts at all between β5 and the substrates. However, this particular carbonyl is likely to play an important role in enzymatic action, as it is hydrogen bonded to the substrate amine in the AANAT/bisubstrate analog complex (12). The carbonyl of the analogous residue in tGCN5, Tyr-160, is in the appropriate position to do the same in the ternary complex of tGCN5 (34). Despite the lack of direct hydrogen bonds, β5 and the helix that follows it, α4, do make several interactions with the AcCoA substrate. In particular, there are several large hydrophobic residues located on helix α4 that contact either the substrate or side chains from β4, defining and stabilizing this bottom part of the donor substrate binding site. Another residue in α4 that appears to play a role in AcCoA binding is a highly conserved basic residue, corresponding to Arg-170 in AANAT (note this position is shifted downstream by one in yHat1). In some structures, this residue forms a salt bridge to the 3′ phosphate of AcCoA, whereas in other structures, it is in a position to potentially do so.

Another important position on α4 is that corresponding to Tyr-168 in AANAT. In all the aligned structures (allowing for a one-residue upstream shift in yHat1), this is a large hydrophobic residue, either Tyr or Phe. It contacts AcCoA from the direction of the protein interior and is likely to play an important role in the proper positioning of the acetyl group for the transfer reaction to occur (discussed below). In some cases, it may also have a role in the resolution of the reaction intermediate. Its importance was demonstrated in AANAT, where the Tyr-to-Phe mutation was shown to have a substantial negative effect on catalytic efficiency (12). Indeed, of all the point mutations that were made in the vicinity of the AANAT active site, the effect of this mutation was the most detrimental.

The one structure that deviates from the description above regarding $\alpha 4$ is AAC(3). Starting at the end of $\beta 5$, its secondary structure is significantly different from that of the other superfamily members (43). In particular, AAC(3) is completely missing $\alpha 4$. Instead, $\beta 5$ is immediately followed by a short antiparallel β strand (Figure 1f).

With the downstream end of $\alpha 4$, motif B ends as well, and from this point to the C-termini, the structures show more divergence than in the parts examined so far. This is probably due in part to the fact that the C-terminal region contains a loop of varying length and position. For example, in AAC(6$'$), there is a long insertion between $\beta 5$ and $\alpha 4$, whereas in the GCN5 enzymes, the loop follows $\alpha 4$ and contains 20 residues. In both the ternary complex form of tGCN5 (34) and in the AANAT/bisubstrate analog complex (12), this loop contacts the acceptor substrate. Consistent with the notion that this loop is a structural component of the binding site for acceptor substrates, in yGCN5, this region is where some of the most debilitating mutations were located (40). Thus, the structural diversity seen in this region may be a reflection of the variety of acceptor substrates that the different GNAT members have evolved to acetylate. A notable variation is yHat1 (7): after $\alpha 4$, the polypeptide does not return to the substrate binding surface but instead forms a helical bundle not seen in the other structures (Figure 1b). Given the lack of specific mutational data, the significance of this difference is not known. Finally, in the structures other than yHat1, the GNAT domain ends with a last β strand, $\beta 6$, that runs antiparallel to $\beta 5$.

SUBSTRATE BINDING

The Conformation of Bound AcCoA/CoA

As described earlier, AcCoA and CoA bind in the opening formed between the diverging strands $\beta 4$ and $\beta 5$, contacting protein atoms mainly from $\beta 4$ and $\alpha 4$, predominantly through main-chain interactions. Coenzyme A is bound in a characteristically sharply bent conformation (Figures 1, 7). This bend introduces an acute 65–70° angle between the two amide planes of the pantetheine group, and it seems to be the result of two specific hydrogen bonds to main-chain groups located on $\beta 4$ and of the steric influence of a large hydrophobic residue projecting from $\alpha 1$ (Phe-56 in AANAT). In the GNAT structures determined with co-crystallized AcCoA (or the bisubstrate analog for AANAT), in most cases the carbonyl of the acetyl group is hydrogen bonded to the main-chain amine of a residue just downstream of the β bulge on β4 (Leu-124 in AANAT). The one exception is AAC(6'), but in this case the crystallographic temperature factors at this end of AcCoA are significantly larger than those of the surrounding protein atoms (50–60 versus <5), so it is likely that the positional accuracy of the acetyl group is low (45). Apart from this variation, the conformation of AcCoA, up to and including the pyrophosphate group, is essentially identical in all the structures. In the CoA complexes, there is some variation in the position of the sulphur atom, but this is most likely due to the lack of the specific hydrogen bond stabilizing the position of the (missing) acetyl group.

In contrast, there is significant variation in the position and conformation of the ribose possessing the 3′ phosphate and the base. This correlates with the relatively few number of interactions in which this part of CoA engages with the protein. In some cases, the quality of the electron density is probably not sufficient for accurate determinations; nevertheless, in all the X-ray structures, the glycosidic bond is in the anti conformation, and the sugar pucker is the corresponding C2′ endo configuration.

Acceptor Substrate Binding

To date, only two structure determinations have been carried out that include the acceptor substrate. The first is the bisubstrate analog complex form of AANAT (12). In this case, a chemically stable compound was synthesized by covalently linking an N-acetylated substrate, tryptamine, to CoA (14). This bisubstrate analog, a close approximation of the presumed reaction intermediate (Figure 6b), is a potent inhibitor of AANAT ($IC_{50} \approx 150$ nM). More recently, tGCN5 was crystallized in a ternary complex form with CoA and a peptide containing the reactive lysine of histone H3 (34). These two cases reveal the essence of the situation: although the details of acceptor binding vary slightly, in both AANAT and tGCN5, the N-acetyltransferase domain utilizes the same regions to make key interactions with the amine-containing substrate (Figure 8, see color insert).

Critical for interaction are two loops mentioned earlier: one located between α1 and α2, and another just preceding the last β strand of the domain. The role of these two loops in acceptor substrate binding was initially suggested based on the uncomplexed structure of AANAT (11), and their importance was underscored by the alanine-scanning mutational work in yGCN5 in which a stretch of six residues just after α1 and a three-residue stretch just before β6 were demonstrated to be essential for its in vivo transcriptional function (40).

As discussed earlier, the upstream end of α2, including the loop between α1 and α2, plays an important role in the binding of the acceptor substrate. For example, in AANAT, Pro-64, an important residue that defines one side of the serotonin binding pocket (Figure 8a), is located in this region (12). Similarly, in the ternary complex of tGCN5, this same region spanning the connecting loop and most of α2 (Pro-78 to Val-88) makes numerous intimate contacts with the peptide substrate (34). In both proteins, the two loop regions are located on the same surface of the molecule and define a cleft located directly above the acetyl group of AcCoA. Both serotonin, the acceptor substrate of AANAT, and the histone H3 peptide substrate of yGCN5 lie in this cleft. In AANAT, the indole moiety of serotonin is almost entirely enclosed in the cleft whose "third wall" is contributed by the additional helix (αA), unique to AANAT, located between β3 and β4. In tGCN5, there is only a short turn between β3 and β4, and in this case the cleft is long and open on both ends, allowing the peptide to fit in such that all 11 residues are in contact with the protein (compare Figure 1a and c). Although the tGCN5-peptide interactions are about evenly distributed between van der Waals interactions and hydrogen bonds (interestingly, with the notable exception of the primary amine of the reactive Lys, these interactions mostly involve peptide main-chain groups), in AANAT, serotonin is held in place entirely by van der Waals–type contacts provided by residues in the three converging loops. Indeed, the indole ring is sandwiched between Pro-64 on one side and Phe-188 on the other. Since the NE1 nitrogen of the indole is hydrogen bonded to a water molecule, AANAT apparently does not exploit this group for substrate recognition. It should be noted, however, that in the experimental structure determination, tryptamine rather than serotonin is tethered to CoA. Tryptamine differs from serotonin in lacking the 5'-OH substitution on the indole, which—if present—would be in an ideal position to hydrogen bond to the side chain of Ser-60.

From the mapped acetylation sites of yGCN5, only two positions around the reactive lysine seem to be conserved, indicating a G-K-X-P consensus sequence for peptide recognition (34). Indeed, in the ternary complex, other than the reactive lysine, only this nearby Pro residue appears to be in extensive hydrophobic contact with the protein. Perhaps somewhat surprisingly, this proline residue also contacts the pantetheine moiety of AcCoA. It seems, therefore, that AcCoA contributes to peptide recognition and binding, or—stated another way—that the formation of a GCN5/AcCoA complex must be required prior to peptide binding. This is an interesting variation of what is observed for AANAT, where the binding of AcCoA introduces a major conformational change, resulting in the completion of the serotonin binding site, and only then in the binding of serotonin. In contrast, there are only modest movements of tGCN5 upon AcCoA binding (34).

CHEMICAL CATALYSIS

The Need for a General Base?

In considering catalytic mechanism, there are two distinct ways in which AcCoA-dependent acetyltransferases could catalyze the transfer of the acetyl group. In one, a ping-pong mechanism, the acetyl group is transiently transferred to a suitably located Cys residue of the enzyme, forming a covalently bound acetylated enzyme intermediate. The enzyme subsequently catalyzes the transfer of the acetyl group from the Cys residue to the acceptor substrate (see, for example, 6, 41). In the second possible mechanism, the acetyl group is transferred directly from AcCoA to the acceptor via direct nucleophilic attack by the primary amine on the acyl-carbon (Figure 6*b*). This second possibility obviously requires the formation of a ternary complex between the enzyme, AcCoA, and the acceptor substrate.

Several lines of biochemical data indicate that the GNAT superfamily members use the direct acetyl transfer mechanism. These include kinetic experiments (4, 37), the failure to identify covalently bound intermediates (7), and the inability to inactivate yGCN5 using reagents that block thiol groups (37). In addition, most of the structural work failed to identify suitably located Cys residues near the acetyl group of AcCoA, and the case for direct nucleophilic attack was further strengthened by the recent direct crystallographic evidence for the existence of ternary complexes (12, 34). Taken together, these data strongly favor direct acetyl transfer as the catalytic mechanism for the GNAT superfamily of enzymes.

For direct nucleophilic attack to occur, the primary amine must be in an uncharged form, and given the high pKa values [$\sim$10 for both arylalkylamines (24) and lysine (36)], it is very likely that GNAT enzymes must provide some mechanism of deprotonation, presumably involving an amino acid near the active site that can act as a general base. Further underscoring the need for a mechanism of proton removal, it was demonstrated for AANAT that the protonated form of the acceptor substrate preferentially binds to the enzyme (15). Extensive mutational work aimed at identifying the general base has been carried out in two systems, yGCN5 and AANAT. For yGCN5, the results strongly implicate Glu-173 as the general base (37), a residue that is conserved in the GCN5 family, including PCAF. The conservative replacement of Glu with Gln resulted in a 320-fold reduction of k_{cat}. Furthermore, pH profile experiments in the alkaline regime showed a decreased effect of this mutation, an expected result considering the increase in the relative concentration of the nonenzymatically deprotonated amine.

In contrast to the compelling evidence implicating Glu-173 as the general base in yGCN5, the results for AANAT are not as straightforward. Substitution of His-120 and His-122 in ovine AANAT, two residues previously suggested as possible catalytic residues (16), does not result in a significant decrease in k_{cat} (12). Looking at the three-dimensionally aligned structures, the situation becomes even more intriguing. His-120 of AANAT and Glu-122 of tGCN5 (the equivalent residue to Glu-173 of yGCN5) are in an identical location, just one residue upstream of the β bulge on β4. Although this position is clearly in the vicinity of the active site, it is still too far from the observed positions of the amine nitrogen for direct proton transfer to occur. In the bisubstrate analog complex form of AANAT, NE2 of His-120 is 7.5 Å away from the amine nitrogen, and in the ternary complex of tGNC5, the distance between the primary amine and OE1 of Glu-122 is >8 Å. For the other structurally characterized members of the GNAT superfamily, the situation regarding a general base is murky. While there is a Glu (Glu-72) in AAC(6$'$) at the analogous position, mutational data are not available. The corresponding residue in yHat1 is Lys-216, whereas in AAC(6$'$), it is Tyr-109. These residues are not likely to act as general bases. In yHat1, there are two Asp residues on $\beta 5$, located close to the acetyl group, one of which (Asp-255) appears well positioned for the task. However, it is also close to Lys-216, with which an interaction might interfere with a potential catalytic role. In AAC(3), there is a suitably located Asp (Asp-110) just one residue downstream of the β bulge, but again there are no mutational data available to support a catalytic role. Thus it appears that there is no conserved general base at the equivalent position in the active sites of these enzymes that would serve as a hallmark of catalysis.

The Role of Proton Wires in Amine Deprotonation

From a purely mechanistic point of view, the tGCN5 and AANAT complexes offer complementary—or dynamic—views of the catalytic process. The ternary complex of tGCN5 represents a snapshot of the reaction just prior to nucleophilic attack, since the system is frozen at this state due to the lack of the acetyl group on the donor substrate (34). In the AANAT complex, the snapshot is of the tetrahedral reaction intermediate, a consequence of the covalent linkage between the two substrates (12). It is reassuring that both structures offer a consistent view of how proton removal from the primary amine is likely to be effected by the enzyme.

In AANAT, there is an array of well-located water molecules, with low crystallographic temperature factors, that form a continuous chain or "proton wire" connecting the amine nitrogen both to internal exchangeable groups (including His-120 and His-122) and to the surrounding solvent (Figure 8). Such proton wires have been previously observed in biological systems (25). The first water molecule in the chain, located deepest in the protein interior, is coordinated by three hydrogen bonds: one to the carbonyl oxygen of Leu-121, the upstream residue of the β bulge on $\beta 4$; the second to the amide nitrogen of Met-159 on the adjacent strand, $\beta 5$; and the third to the next water molecule in the proton wire. In its observed location, this water molecule is well positioned to hydrogen bond to the primary amine of the substrate. In the experimentally determined structure, this hydrogen bond cannot exist, however, since the analog contains a secondary amine, already hydrogen bonded to the carbonyl oxygen of Met-159, a reflection of the fact that the analog is a representation of the chemistry after the initial nucleophilic attack by the primary amine. Nevertheless, this water molecule is obviously ideally suited to accept the extra proton and to channel it away to either of the two local imidazoles or to the open solvent through the chain of crystallographically visible water molecules. It is also worth noting that the two most deeply located water molecules of the proton wire are held in place by hydrogen bonds to the two carbonyl oxygens that are projected into the active site area by the β bulge (Figure 5), granting additional functional significance to this well-conserved structural feature.

In the ternary complex of tGCN5, a buried water molecule connects the location of the primary amine to the side chain of Glu-122 (34). This water molecule also has a low crystallographic temperature factor; thus its location is well determined (see Figure 8*b*). Its position is structurally identical to that of the first water molecule of the proton wire in the AANAT complex, and it is also held in place by a hydrogen bond to the carbonyl oxygen of the first β bulged residue. Allowing for the larger conformational flexibility permitted by the longer aliphatic side chain of lysine, this primary amine could donate its proton to this water molecule, which could subsequently transfer it to Glu-122. Thus, the two ternary complexes provide a structural alternative to direct proton abstraction by a catalytic general base: The water molecules observed in both structures most likely serve as a conduit for proton transfer away from the primary amine.

Substrate Positioning

In the absence of a conserved general base in the active sites of GNAT enzymes, what does seem to be conserved, on the other hand, is the relative positioning of the reactive groups (i.e. the primary amine and the acetyl group) by the enzyme. In the three-dimensionally aligned structures, the positions of the acyl carbons of AcCoA are nearly identical, maintained by virtue of an important hydrogen bond to a main-chain amide. In the case of the AANAT/bisubstrate complex, the primary amine of the "acceptor substrate" is perforce located close to the acyl group through covalent bonds. In the case of the tGCN5 ternary complex, the primary amine of the reactive Lys is not in precisely the same location as that of the amine of the bisubstrate. However, this may well be a consequence of experimental design: to trap a ternary complex prior to catalysis, CoA was used in place of AcCoA, and the hydrogen bond anchoring the acyl group in place cannot exist. Nevertheless, it is clear that only slight movements of the lysine side chain are required for the primary amine of the tGCN5 ternary complex to occupy the same position as the bisubstrate analog amine group in AANAT. Thus, despite the significant evolutionary distance between the different members of the GNAT superfamily, the positioning of the primary amine group is likely to be a conserved feature of catalysis. In this light, we note that the detrimental Tyr-168–to–Phe replacement in AANAT (discussed above) could affect this delicate positioning, and that this in turn could be responsible for the observed significant decrease in reaction rate (12).

Although there is no conserved catalytic base in the active sites of GNAT enzymes, it is not clear to what extent critical residues in the general vicinity of the acetyl group affect catalysis. Acetyl transfer from AcCoA to a primary amine in aqueous solution is energetically favorable as evidenced by measurable nonenzymatic background rates (37). The question remains to what extent the enzymatic rate acceleration can be attributed to appropriate substrate positioning.

Upon bringing the two substrates into the appropriate position for catalysis, the AANAT/bisubstrate complex offers insight into the next step in the reaction, the resolution of the tetrahedral intermediate. It is clear from chemical considerations that the resolution in the direction of the desired products could be facilitated by providing a proton to the sulfur of CoA since a negatively charged thiolate is not an ideal leaving group. In AANAT, Tyr-168 is located 3.1 Å from the sulfur in a position that would be ideal for donating a proton. Interestingly, there is a Tyr residue in an identical position in AAC(6′), although there are no mutational data available for this enzyme.

The final step in the catalytic cycle is product release. The environment around the primary amine is polar, and upon formation of acetylserotonin, the dramatic increase in hydrophobicity may serve to eject the acetylated product from the protein. The emptied indole binding pocket would lose its stability, leading to a conformational state that could effect the release of CoA. It is not clear, however, that hydrophobicity is necessarily the driving force across the superfamily of GNAT enzymes; for tGCN5, steric constraints have been invoked to explain product release (34).

SUMMARY

The three-dimensional structures determined for various members of three families of N-acetyltransferases of the GNAT superfamily demonstrate a remarkable consistency in protein topology. It appears that a central β sheet, which incorporates elements from all four conserved sequence motifs identifed prior to any structural information, serves as a scaffold to appropriately place residues to form two substrate binding sites. The binding site for the donor substrate, AcCoA, is remarkably conserved, and the same three-dimensionally aligned residues are involved in holding AcCoA in place. In particular, the crucial acyl group is hydrogen bonded in precisely the same manner among all the characterized members of the family, defining a conserved enzyme active site. The binding site for the acceptor substrate has been characterized in only two cases, but it is clear that the same regions of the protein are involved: two (or more) analogous loops of varying length and differing conformation are arrayed across the protein surface to create a substrate binding cleft that positions the reactive primary amine close to the acetyl group of AcCoA. The structural work to date provides intriguing glances into mechanisms of catalysis, unequivocably demonstrating that there is no universally conserved, general base to directly abstract a proton from the primary amine substrates, yet offering in its place a potential pathway for proton removal involving crystallographically located water molecules and a proton wire.

It is hoped that future work in this field will provide more information on modes of acceptor substrate binding, particularly for those members whose substrates differ from those characterized to date. It will also be instructive, from the point of view of regulation of activity, to obtain structures of the HAT domains, both in the context of their intact proteins and as part of the multiprotein complexes involved in transcriptional regulation.

LITERATURE CITED

1. Bhatnagar RS, Futterer K, Farazi TA, Korolev S, Murray CL, et al. 1998. Structure of N-myristoyltransferase with bound myristoylCoA and peptide substrate analogs. *Nat. Struct. Biol.* 5:1091–97

2. Clements A, Rojas JR, Trievel RC, Wang L, Berger SL, Marmorstein R. 1999. Crystal structure of the histone acetyltransferase domain of the human PCAF transcriptional regulator bound to coenzyme A. *EMBO J.* 18:3521–32

3. Coon SL, Roseboom PH, Baler R, Weller JL, Namboodiri MAA, et al. 1995. Pineal serotonin N-acetyltransferase: expression cloning and molecular analysis. *Science* 270:1681–83

4. De Angelis J, Gastel J, Klein DC, Cole PA. 1998. Kinetic analysis of the catalytic mechanism of serotonin N-acetyltransferase (EC 2.3.1.87). *J. Biol. Chem.* 273:3045–50

5. Dhalluin C, Carlson JE, Zeng L, He C, Aggarwal AK, Zhou M. 1999. Structure and ligand of a histone acetyltransferase bromodomain. *Nature* 399:491–96

6. Dupret J, Grant DM. 1992. Site-directed mutagenesis of recombinant human arylamine N-acetyltransferase expressed in *Escherichia coli. J. Biol. Chem.* 267:7381–85

7. Dutnall RN, Tafrov ST, Sternglanz R, Ramakrishnan V. 1998. Structure of the histone acetyltransferase Hat1: a paradigm for the GCN5-related N-acetyltransferase superfamily. *Cell* 94:427–38

8. Engel C, Wierenga R. 1996. The diverse world of coenzyme A binding proteins. *Curr. Opin. Struct. Biol.* 6:790–97

9. Gastel JA, Roseboom PH, Rinaldi PA, Weller JL, Klein DC. 1998. Melatonin production: proteolysis in serotonin N-acetyltransferase regulation. *Science* 279:1358–60

10. Grunstein M. 1997. Histone acetylation in chromatin structure and transcription. *Nature* 389:349–52

11. Hickman AB, Klein DC, Dyda F. 1999. Melatonin biosyntheses: the structure of serotonin N-acetyltransferase at 2.5 Å resolution suggests a catalytic mechanism. *Mol. Cell.* 3:23–32

12. Hickman AB, Namboodiri MAA, Klein DC, Dyda F. 1999. The structural basis of ordered substrate binding by serotonin N-acetyltransferase: enzyme complex at 1.8 Å resolution with a bisubstrate analog. *Cell* 97:361–69

13. Jones TA, Zou JY, Cowan SW, Kjeldgaard M. 1991. Improved methods for building protein models in electron density maps and the location of errors in these models. *Acta Crystallogr. A* 47:110–19

14. Khalil EM, Cole PA. 1998. A potent inhibitor of the melatonin rhythm enzyme. *J. Am. Chem. Soc.* 120:6195–96

15. Khalil EM, De Angelis J, Cole PA. 1998. Indoleamine analogs as probes of the substrate selectivity and catalytic mechanism of serotonin N-acetyltransferase. *J. Biol. Chem.* 273:30321–27

16. Klein DC, Coon SL, Roseboom PH, Weller JL, Bernard M, et al. 1997. The melatonin rhythm-generating enzyme: molecular regulation of serotonin N-acetyltransferase in the pineal gland. *Recent Prog. Horm. Res.* 52:307–58

17. Klein DC, Weller JL. 1972. Rapid light induced decrease in pineal serotonin N-acetyltransferase activity. *Science* 177:532–33

18. Kraulis PJ. 1991. MOLSCRIPT: a program to produce both detailed and schematic plots of protein structures. *J. Appl. Crystallogr.* 24:946–50

19. Leslie AGW, Moody PCE, Shaw VW. 1988. Structure of chloramphenicol

acetyltransferase at 1.75 Å resolution. *Proc. Natl. Acad. Sci. USA* 85:4133–37

20. Lin Y, Fletcher CM, Zhou J, Allis CD, Wagner G. 1999. Solution structure of the catalytic domain of GCN5 histone acetyltransferase bound to coenzyme A. *Nature* 400:86–89

21. Liu L, Scolnick DM, Trievel RC, Zhang HB, Marmorstein R, et al. 1999. p53 sites acetylated in vitro by PCAF and p300 are acetylated in vivo in response to DNA damage. *Mol. Cell. Biol.* 19:1202–9

22. Lu L, Berkey KA, Casero RA Jr. 1996. RGFGIGS is an amino acid sequence required for acetyl coenzyme A binding and activity of human spermidine/spermine N[1] acetyltransferase. *J. Biol. Chem.* 271:18920–24

23. Mattevi A, Obmolova G, Kalk KH, Westphal AH, de Kok A, Hol WGJ. 1993. Refined crystal structure of the catalytic domain of dihydrolipoyl transacetylase (E2p) from *Azotobacter vinelandii* at 2.6 Å resolution. *J. Mol. Biol.* 230:1183–99

24. *Merck Index.* 1976. p. 1095. Rahway, NJ: Merck & Co. 9th ed.

25. Meyer E. 1992. Internal water molecules and H-bonding in biological macromolecules: a review of structural features with functional implications. *Protein Sci.* 1:1543–62

26. Mio T, Yamada-Okabe T, Arisawa M, Yamada-Okabe H. 1999. *Saccharomyces cerevisiae* GNA1, an essential gene encoding a novel acetyltransferase involved in UDP-*N*-acetylglucosamine synthesis. *J. Biol. Chem.* 274:424–29

27. Mizzen CA, Allis CD. 1998. Linking histone acetylation to transcriptional regulation. *Cell. Mol. Life Sci.* 54:6–20

28. Modis Y, Wierenga R. 1998. Two crystal structures of N-acetyltransferases reveal a new fold for CoA-dependent enzymes. *Structure* 6:1345–50

29. Murzin AG, Brenner SE, Hubbard T, Chothia C. 1995. SCOP: a structural classification of proteins database for the investigation of sequences and structures. *J. Mol. Biol.* 247:536–40

30. Neuwald AF, Landsman D. 1997. GCN5-related histone *N*-acetyltransferases belong to a diverse superfamily that includes the yeast SPT10 protein. *Trends Biochem. Sci.* 22:154–55

31. Petsko GA, Kenyon GL, Gerlt JA, Ringe D, Kozarich JW. 1993. On the origin of enzymatic species. *Trends Biol. Sci.* 18:372–76

32. Rao ST, Rossman MG. 1973. Comparison of super-secondary structures in proteins. *J. Mol. Biol.* 76:241–56

33. Richardson JS. 1981. The anatomy and taxonomy of protein structure. *Adv. Protein Chem.* 34:167–330

34. Rojas JR, Trievel RC, Zhou J, Mo Y, Li X, et al. 1999. Crystal structure of *Tetrahymena* GCN5 with bound coenzyme-A and histone H3 peptide. *Nature* 401:93–98

35. Sternglanz R, Schindelin H. 1999. Structure and mechanism of action of the histone acetyltransferase Gcn5 and similarity to other *N*-acetyltransferases. *Proc. Natl. Acad. Sci. USA* 96:8807–8

36. Stryer L. 1988. *Biochemistry,* p. 21. New York: Freeman. 3rd ed.

37. Tanner KG, Trievel RC, Kuo M, Howard RM, Berger SL, et al. 1999. Catalytic mechanism and function of invariant glutamic acid 173 from the histone acetyltransferase GCN5 transcriptional coactivator. *J. Biol. Chem.* 274:18157–60

38. Tercero JC, Riles LE, Wickner RB. 1992. Localized mutagenesis and evidence for post-transcriptional regulation of MAK3. *J. Biol. Chem.* 267:20270–76

39. Trievel RC, Rojas JR, Sterner DE, Venkataramani RN, Wang L, et al. 1999. Crystal structure and mechanism of histone acetylation of the yeast GCN5 transcriptional coactivator. *Proc. Natl. Acad. Sci. USA* 96:8931–36

40. Wang L, Liu L, Berger SL. 1998. Critical residues for histone acetylation by Gcn5, functioning in Ada and SAGA complexes, are also required for transcriptional

function in vivo. *Genes Dev.* 12:640–53

41. Watanabe M, Sofuni T, Nohmi T. 1992. Involvement of Cys69 residue in the catalytic mechanism of *N*-hydroxyarylamine *O*-acetyltransferase of *Salmonella typhimurium. J. Biol. Chem.* 267:8429–36

42. Weston SA, Camble R, Colls J, Rosenbrock G, Taylor I, et al. 1998. Crystal structure of the anti-fungal target N-myristoyl transferase. *Nat. Struct. Biol.* 5:213–21

43. Wolf E, Vassilev A, Makino Y, Sali A, Nakatani Y, Burley SK. 1998. Crystal structure of a GCN5-related N-acetyltrans-

ferase: *Serratia marcescens* aminoglycoside 3-N-acetyltransferase. *Cell* 94:439–49

44. Wolodko WT, Fraser ME, James MNG, Bridger WA. 1994. The crystal structure of succinyl-CoA synthetase from *Escherichia coli* at 2.5 Å resolution. *J. Biol. Chem.* 269:10883–90

45. Wybenga-Groot LE, Draker K, Wright GD, Berghuis AM. 1999. Crystal structure of an aminoglycoside 6′-*N*-acetyltransferase: defining the GCN5-related *N*-acetyltransferase superfamily fold. *Structure* 7:497–507

Annu. Rev. Biophys. Biomol. Struct. 2000. 29:105–53

STRUCTURAL SYMMETRY AND PROTEIN FUNCTION

David S. Goodsell and Arthur J. Olson

Department of Molecular Biology, Scripps Research Institute, La Jolla, California 92037;
e-mail: goodsell@scripps.edu, olson@scripps.edu

Key Words oligomeric proteins, protein symmetry, protein structure/function relationships

■ **Abstract** The majority of soluble and membrane-bound proteins in modern cells are symmetrical oligomeric complexes with two or more subunits. The evolutionary selection of symmetrical oligomeric complexes is driven by functional, genetic, and physicochemical needs. Large proteins are selected for specific morphological functions, such as formation of rings, containers, and filaments, and for cooperative functions, such as allosteric regulation and multivalent binding. Large proteins are also more stable against denaturation and have a reduced surface area exposed to solvent when compared with many individual, smaller proteins. Large proteins are constructed as oligomers for reasons of error control in synthesis, coding efficiency, and regulation of assembly. Symmetrical oligomers are favored because of stability and finite control of assembly. Several functions limit symmetry, such as interaction with DNA or membranes, and directional motion. Symmetry is broken or modified in many forms: quasisymmetry, in which identical subunits adopt similar but different conformations; pleomorphism, in which identical subunits form different complexes; pseudosymmetry, in which different molecules form approximately symmetrical complexes; and symmetry mismatch, in which oligomers of different symmetries interact along their respective symmetry axes. Asymmetry is also observed at several levels. Nearly all complexes show local asymmetry at the level of side chain conformation. Several complexes have reciprocating mechanisms in which the complex is asymmetric, but, over time, all subunits cycle through the same set of conformations. Global asymmetry is only rarely observed. Evolution of oligomeric complexes may favor the formation of dimers over complexes with higher cyclic symmetry, through a mechanism of pre-positioned pairs of interacting residues. However, examples have been found for all of the crystallographic point groups, demonstrating that functional need can drive the evolution of any symmetry.

CONTENTS

1056-8700/00/0610-0105$14.00 **105**

INTRODUCTION

Symmetry has played an important role in science from its very origins. The Greeks, fascinated by the symmetry of vibrating strings, developed a quantitative understanding of pitch and harmony, and Kepler formulated a simple mathematical description of gravity that was based on the elliptical geometry of planetary orbits. Today, symmetry continues to permeate scientific thought. Physicists are looking for symmetries to unify an ever-growing menagerie of subatomic particles, and developmental biologists are discovering how the simple symmetries of molecular diffusion may combine to form complex body plans during embryogenesis. Some fields seem ripe for such symmetries, but when these fields are critically analyzed, the proposed symmetries never materialize. Kepler's attempt to rationalize the positions of the planets in the solar system based on Platonic solids is a historical case in point.

CA Coulson, a theoretical chemist and mathematician, described the utility and the seduction of symmetry in his own field: "It is when symmetry interprets facts that it serves its purpose; and then it delights us because it links our study of chemistry with another world of the human spirit—the world of order, pattern, beauty, satisfaction" (as quoted in 34). In the many studies, both proven and spurious, in which researchers have attempted to find symmetry, the assumption has been made implicitly that such unifying symmetries *do* exist—that Nature herself is built by symmetry from simpler components. Historically, many searches for symmetry were motivated by belief in a divine creator with aesthetic sensibilities similar to our own. Most modern researchers, however, see symmetry as an emergent feature of the general parsimony of our observed universe, resulting from the limited modes of interaction between a small number of building blocks as they assemble (or are assembled) into structures of greater complexity.

Symmetry has played a central role in biomolecular science since its earliest triumphs. The structure of DNA reported by Watson and Crick in 1953, with its direct relationship of double-helical symmetry to genetic function, set the stage and perhaps overshadowed all that has followed. Indeed, Kendrew is said to have been disappointed in the "visceral" nature of myoglobin at low resolution, a disappointment that was more than compensated for by the symmetrical spiral tubes of α-helices in the atomic-resolution structure. In this review, we explore the functional roles played by structural symmetry in macromolecules. For discussion of other types of symmetry in molecular processes, such as the inherent symmetry of reversible reactions, the reader might begin with the discussion by Garcia-Bellido (26).

THE SYMMETRY OF OLIGOMERIC PROTEINS

Symmetry is the rule rather than the exception for proteins. Most of the soluble and membrane-bound proteins found in living cells form symmetrical oligomeric complexes with two or more identical subunits, and nearly all structural proteins are symmetrical polymers of hundreds to millions of subunits. Svedberg has been credited with the idea that proteins are composed of discrete subunits (90). In 1967, Klotz presented a list of proteins presumed to form oligomers (48). This list was expanded to ~300 entries (primarily soluble enzymes) in a 1975 review (49), underscoring the prevalence of oligomeric proteins in cells. In that compilation, over half of the oligomeric proteins are homodimers or homotetramers, presumed to form symmetrical complexes, and only ~15% were heterooligomers of different chains. Klotz et al (49) also noted the relative scarcity of oligomers with odd numbers of subunits. Goodsell attempted to quantify the prevalence of oligomeric proteins in cells based on the concentration of soluble proteins in *Escherichia coli*, obtaining an average oligomerization state of about four (27), and a visual survey of soluble proteins in the Protein Data Bank (PDB) underscored the prevalence of symmetrical, oligomeric species (28). Jones & Thornton tabulated the multimeric states of proteins in the July 1993 release of the PDB (43), finding a predominance of monomers; of 970 total proteins, 66% were monomeric, 15% were dimeric, 12% were tetrameric, and the remainder adopted other oligomeric states. Jones & Thornton noted, however, that the PDB over-represents small monomers, owing to the difficulties involved in protein crystallization.

TABLE 1   Natural occurrence of oligomeric proteins in *Escherichia coli*[a]

Oligomeric state	Number of homooligomers	Number of heterooligomers	Percent
Monomer	72		19.4
Dimer	115	27	38.2
Trimer	15	5	5.4
Tetramer	62	16	21.0
Pentamer	1	1	0.1
Hexamer	20	1	5.6
Heptamer	1	1	0.1
Octamer	3	6	2.4
Nonamer	0	0	0.0
Decamer	1	0	0.0
Undecamer	0	1	0.0
Dodecamer	4	2	1.6
Higher oligomers	8		2.2
Polymers	10		2.7

[a]These data were compiled by using information at the SWISS-PROT annotated protein sequence database (on the World Wide Web at www.expasy.ch/sport), with search tools developed by Michel Sanner. The list of *Escherichia coli* K12 chromosomal entries (compiled by Amos Bairoch including release 35.0 of the database and updates to May 1998) was searched for entries with explicit "subunit" annotations, yielding 617 entries. This corresponds to 16% of the total list, or 30% if "hypothetical" proteins are omitted. These individual protein chains were then processed manually to create a list of 372 oligomeric species.

A survey of *E. coli* proteins in the SWISS-PROT annotated protein sequence databank is included in Table 1. This survey includes soluble proteins, membrane-bound proteins, and structural proteins. Monomers are in the minority, composing only about one fifth of the protein species. Dimers and tetramers are far more common. Homooligomers also predominate: 79% of oligomers with from 2 to 12 subunits are homooligomers, whereas only 21% form heterooligomeric complexes. As discussed in sections below, these homooligomeric complexes, when structures are known, associate by closed point group or helical symmetry. Asymmetric homooligomers are virtually unknown.

Characteristics and Natural Occurrence of Symmetry Groups

Early in the evolution of life, protein was selected as the basic material for building the cellular machinery. With this selection came a choice of "handedness"— choosing one chirality of the α carbon over the other. The reason for the choice of L-amino acids instead of D-amino acids, and chiral amino acids instead of an achiral analog, has been the subject of much scientific and philosophical discussion. One of the major consequences of the adoption of exclusively L-amino-acid proteins is that modern oligomeric proteins adopt only enantiomorphic symmetries; mirror and inversion symmetries are disallowed.

Examples of most of the low-copy-number enantiomorphic point groups have been observed in naturally occurring proteins. All of the crystallographic point groups have been used, as shown by the examples in Figure 1. The choice of a particular symmetry group can have a profound effect on the function and stability of the complex.

Cyclic Groups   The cyclic groups contain a single axis of rotational symmetry, forming a ring of symmetrically arranged subunits. C1 symmetry (monomeric proteins) and C2 symmetry (dimeric proteins) are common among proteins of diverse function. The higher cyclic groups are much more rare. Typically they are involved in functions that require directionality or sidedness, such as interaction with membranes or rotational motion, or functions that require formation of a hollow tube or chamber.

Dihedral Groups   The dihedral groups contain an axis of rotational symmetry and a perpendicular axis of two-fold symmetry. Dihedral symmetry is common among soluble cytoplasmic enzymes, particularly tetramers with D2 symmetry. Oligomers with dihedral symmetry have several different types of interface, including interfaces between oligomers related by the main rotational symmetry and dimeric interfaces related by the perpendicular two-fold axes. This provides a rich infrastructure from which to build allosteric control.

The choices for stability and interaction are potentially greater for dihedral oligomers than those available in cyclic oligomers with the same number of subunits. Cyclic groups of four-fold or greater symmetry limit contacts between subunits. In most cases, there will be few cross contacts in a cyclic group, and only neighboring subunits around the cyclic ring will be in contact. Imagine a C4 complex with subunits numbered sequentially around the ring. The nature of the symmetry makes difficult any contact between subunit 1 and subunit 3 and between subunits 2 and 4. In the dihedral group D2, however, these contacts are allowed (although observed less frequently than one might expect), and the complex is formed around three different dimeric interfaces, allowing many options for regulation of this interaction and giving more opportunity for contact between all subunits, thereby increasing stability. This problem is even worse in the higher symmetries, where even larger ring structures are formed.

Cubic Groups   Cubic symmetries contain three-fold symmetry combined with another, nonperpendicular rotational axis, with three possibilities: tetrahedral, with three- and two-fold axes; octahedral, with three- and four-fold axes; and icosahedral, with three- and five-fold axes. Cubic symmetries, with their exacting structural constraints, primarily play specialized roles in storage and transport. Crick & Watson (18, 19) first proposed that cubic symmetries, and icosahedral symmetry in particular, are uniquely suited to creation of hollow shells, such as the protein coats of simple spherical viruses.

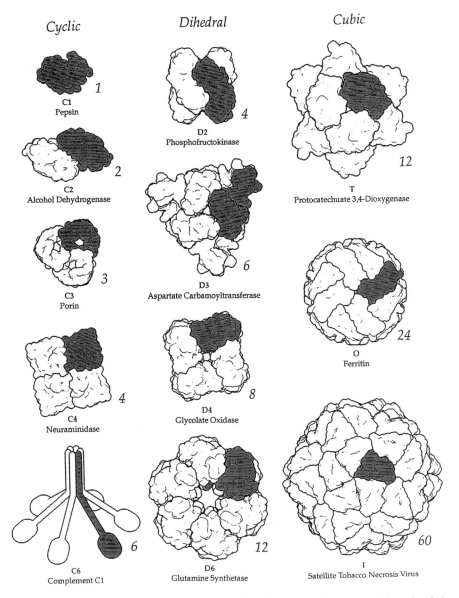

Figure 1 Crystallographic point group symmetries. Examples of proteins with each of the crystallographic point group symmetries have been found. Point group symbols are included below each protein structure (e.g. *C1* and *D2*), and the number of identical subunits in each group is included below and to the right of the structure (e.g. *24* in octahedral group *O*). One subunit is shaded in each example. Note that other noncrystallographic point groups are consistent with the enantiomorphic nature of proteins, including cyclic symmetries *C5* and *C7* or higher and dihedral symmetries *D5* and *D7* or higher. Protein Data Bank accession codes for all structures used in the figures (101) are accessible via the Internet (http://www.rcsb.org/pdb).

Line, Plane, and Space Groups   The addition of translational symmetry to rotational symmetries forms helical structures, symmetrical planes, and space-filling crystals. These symmetries are unbounded, in that they may be extended indefinitely until the organism runs out of room, runs out of subunits, or mechanically stops the growth.

Line symmetries combine rotation with translation along the rotation axis, forming a helix. A perpendicular two-fold rotation axis may also be incorporated, to form a double helix or higher-order intertwined helices. Helices formed of protein subunits are widely used as structural elements. Pauling proposed that a subunit with two complementary binding surfaces would form a hollow helical fibril (76). Structures from electron microscopy reveal this helical symmetry in, for example, microtubules, flagella, and tobacco mosaic virus. Helical interactions are also used to build tighter, narrower fibers, without the central hollow, by orienting the binding surfaces such that only a small number of subunits compose each turn. Examples of this include actin fibrils and intermediate filaments.

Plane symmetries are formed when translation is applied in two spatial directions and combined with rotational elements. Plane symmetries abound in decorative artwork; the elaborate tiling designs of MC Escher are prime examples. Plane arrays of proteins are found in biological membranes, such as connections at cellular gap junctions, which form a tight hexagonal array.

Space groups, although playing an indispensable role in protein structure determination, are relatively rare in vivo. Collagen forms a natural three-dimensional lattice in connective tissue fibers, and a mutation in hemoglobin favors the formation of long, fibrous three-dimensional lattices that distort red blood cells in sickle cell anemia. Small crystalline arrays may be found in hormone storage granules and in peroxisomes. Perhaps the rigid uniformity of three-dimensional lattices precludes their widespread use as biological motifs; life is built on a more malleable plan, allowing greater diversity of structure.

Structural Mechanisms of Oligomerization

The subunits in oligomeric proteins interact through highly specific contact surfaces. Monod et al identify two types of contact surfaces in oligomeric complexes: isologous (or homologous) contacts and heterologous contacts (72). They define isologous interfaces as those where identical surfaces on the two subunits interact and heterologous interfaces as those formed by different surfaces on the two subunits. As they mention, "In a heterologous association, the domain of bonding has no element of symmetry." They note that isologous interfaces are limited to dimeric associations, where a two-fold axis crosses through the middle of the interface, and all other associations between two subunits are necessarily heterologous. The major consequence of the type of an interface, isologous or heterologous, is for the evolution of the interface, as described below in the section on evolution. The terms isologous and heterologous have fallen out of use in recent years. This is perhaps owing to the discovery of many oligomeric proteins with noncontiguous interfaces, such as the β-subunit of the DNA polymerase III holoenzyme. Domain-swapped dimers, in particular, strain the definition; these interfaces are split into two discrete units, and often the flexibility of the linkers connecting the two domains may relax the strict two-fold symmetry of the entire split interface.

The structural features of protein-protein interfaces have received extensive study. Crane presented two ideas based on insights from physics, before atomic structures of proteins were known. "For a high degree of specificity, the contact or combining spots on the two particles must be *multiple* and *weak*. Furthermore, those on one particle must have a geometrical arrangement which is complementary to the arrangement of those on the other" (17). Chothia & Janin revealed, 25 years later, how these two principles were manifested in three protein structures: the insulin dimer, the trypsin-PTI complex, and the $\alpha\beta$ oxy-hemoglobin dimer (14). They noted that these three interfaces are complementary in shape and rely on the shielding of many hydrophobic groups for stabilization. Subsequent surveys, incrementally larger as more structures were available, honed these principles (see 60 and references therein).

Interfaces may be broken into two broad classes: interfaces between globular subunits and interlocked interfaces. Note that the line dividing these two classes is often fuzzy. Most interfaces are formed between globular subunits that presumably fold as single subunits and then associate to form the oligomer. Superoxide dismutase (Figure 2a) is an example of this type of complex; the two subunits are essentially squashed spheres, pressed together to form the dimer. Interlocked interfaces, the second type, are composed of subunits that adopt much of their folded structure only after forming the complex. Dimeric cytokines such as interleukin 10 (Figure 2b) are excellent examples; it is hard to imagine any structure in these subunits in the absence of the dimeric complex. The characteristics of these types of interfaces are quite distinct (60). Interfaces between globular subunits may or may not have hydrophobic cores, and most have a surprising amount of water scattered throughout the interface. Interlocked interfaces are indistinguishable from the interior of proteins: They often show β strands intercalated into sheets of their neighbors; together, the subunits form extensive hydrophobic cores; and buried water is relatively rare.

Interfaces that require extra stability may incorporate covalent attachments or metal sites. Antibodies use disulfide linkages to glue their two flexible halves together. Metal ions are particularly common at the center of cyclic and dihedral oligomers with three-fold or greater symmetry. These ions are typically coordinated to symmetry-related sidechains from each subunit, sitting directly on the rotational axis of symmetry. Examples include a zinc ion that stabilizes the insulin hexamer (2, 7) and divalent cations that stabilize viral capsids around three-fold axes (74).

WHY BUILD SYMMETRICAL PROTEINS?

Given that oligomeric proteins are very common, there must be some selective advantage driving the evolution of monomeric species into oligomers. This question has been discussed by many authors (see 49 and references therein) and was

(A)

(B)

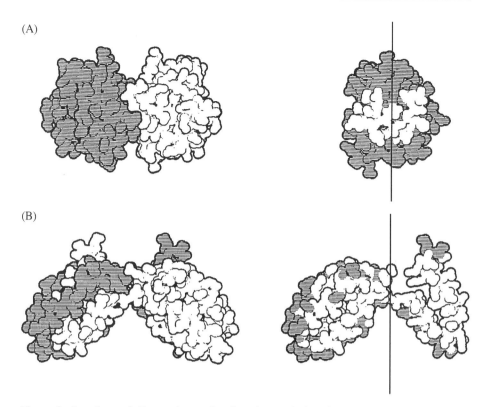

Figure 2   Interfaces of oligomeric proteins. Protein-protein interfaces are highly specific, being formed of several dozen amino acids on the surface of each subunit. They are typically complementary in shape and chemical nature. Interfaces are most commonly formed between two globular subunits, as in superoxide dismutase (A). On the left is the dimeric protein, with one subunit shaded. On the right is one subunit, rotated to show the interface region, with interface amino acids in white and solvent-exposed amino acids shaded. A minority of interfaces are formed by chains that interlock extensively, as in interleukin 10 (B). Again, the dimer is on the left and the single subunit, colored to show the interface, is on the right.

perhaps most succinctly answered by Monod, who considered the driving forces for formation of symmetrical oligomeric complexes to be "...finiteness, stability, and self-assembly" (71). The only major topic missing from this list is the novel functional possibilities presented by oligomers. We divide the problem into a series of questions: (*a*) Why build large proteins; (*b*) why build oligomeric proteins, and (*c*) why build *symmetrical*, oligomeric proteins?

The evolution of oligomeric proteins is bounded by two opposing forces. On one side, protein function typically drives evolution toward larger sizes. On the other hand, the mechanisms of protein synthesis tend to limit the length of polypeptide chains, favoring smaller proteins over larger ones. The typical size of 30,000–50,000 Daltons (87) is a compromise between these opposing forces.

Why Build Large Proteins?

Large proteins have many advantages over smaller ones:

1. *Morphological function* Many proteins have functions that require creation of very large, stable structures. These include long, thin structural elements and large, hollow capsids and rings. Other proteins simply need to be sterically large. These functions are described in detail in a later section.

2. *Cooperative function* Allostery and multivalent associations are other functions that create an evolutionary force selecting large proteins with several identical active sites rather than monomeric proteins with a single active site. These functions are described in detail in a later section.

3. *Stability against denaturation* Large proteins, with their extensive internal interactions, have more stable folded structures than very small proteins. Monod articulated this advantage: "...wherever order depends on very weak interactions, it must be bought at the price of increasing number of these interactions," where by "order," Monod referred to a stable, stereospecific globular protein that folded spontaneously to the active conformation (71). Protein stability involves a fine balance between the enthalpic stabilization by many weak nonbonded interactions and the competing effect of various entropic factors of conformational mobility and solvation (65). In small proteins, the enthalpic compensations of ordered structure are not sufficient to offset the entropic cost of conformational restriction. Proteins that are restrained to small sizes by their function (described below) thus use more extreme means to achieve stability, such as covalent disulfide linkages or specific metal sites.

4. *Reduction of surface area* In general, it is preferable to reduce the protein surface area that is exposed to solvent, by creating a large protein with several identical active sites, versus several individual proteins. This may be accomplished in several ways: by creating a long polyprotein of one chain with several functions, by creating an oligomer of several nonidentical subunits, or by creating a homooligomer of identical subunits.

   Reduction of surface area reduces the amount of solvent needed to hydrate proteins. A quick calculation can estimate the magnitude of this problem. Assume that the aqueous cytoplasm is composed entirely of 20,000-Dalton subunits and that all oligomers are spherical in shape. Thus a monomer would be a sphere of radius 1.8 nm, a dimer would have a radius of 2.2 nm, and so on. Assume that the cytoplasm is 20% protein (24) and that the bound water of hydration is ~1.4 g/g of protein (15) or a hydration shell ~0.6 nm thick. If the aqueous cytoplasm is composed entirely of monomers, the hydrated proteins occupy 47% of the total volume, over twice the 20% volume occupied by the protein alone. Assuming this same 0.6-nm layer of hydration, the volume of the hydrated protein drops to 40% for dimers, 35% for tetramers, and 30% for dodecamers. Thus, oligomerization can significantly reduce the amount of water bound to protein surfaces. However, this may not be a major evolutionary driving force, because Clegg has shown that many cells can lose over half of their water without adverse effects (15).

The reduced surface area provided by an oligomeric protein provides protection from degradation. Both insulin and proinsulin form hexamers in storage granules, stabilized by central zinc ions (7). In proinsulin, the outer surface is well covered by the connecting peptide, which is cleaved on maturation. The mature insulin, still in hexameric form, then forms a crystalline granule within the storage vesicle, further shielding the molecule from protease digestion. The crystallization also serves to enhance the conversion reaction, by removing mature insulin from the soluble pool. When released into the blood, dilution, reduced levels of zinc, and higher pH cause the hexamer to dissociate into the biologically active monomers, which are rapidly degraded.

Reduced surface area also has been postulated to improve the diffusion of substrates to enzyme active sites. Substrates are thought to perform a two-dimensional diffusive random walk along the surface upon encountering an enzyme, leading to more productive encounters with the active site than simple three-dimensional diffusive encounters. The process has been documented in simulations of superoxide dismutase, in which the surface around the active site forms a "funnel" that collects substrate (84). It has been postulated that the dimeric state of the protein serves to hide the "unproductive" side of the enzyme.

Proteins with conserved function but a nonconserved oligomerization state might be examples of evolutionary selection based simply on the advantages gained by reduction of surface area. For example, protocatechuate-3,4-dioxygenase contains a conserved $(\alpha\text{-}\beta\text{-}Fe^{3+})$ heterodimer core, but forms oligomeric complexes with 4, 5, or 12 $(\alpha\text{-}\beta)$ heterodimers in different species, all with no apparent cooperative interactions.

Why Build Oligomeric Proteins?

As noted above, many functions favor large proteins, requiring either one physically large protein or favoring one large protein with several identical active sites over many smaller proteins with individual active sites. These large proteins may be constructed in one of three ways: as long, single chains; as heterooligomers of several smaller chains; or as homooligomers of identical chains. As shown in Table 1, Nature favors the latter choice, most often constructing large proteins from many identical building blocks. Describing viral capsids, Crick & Watson write "...the virus, when in the cell, finds it easier to control the production of a large number of identical small protein molecules rather than that of one or two very large molecules to act as its shell" (18). Several reasons that homooligomers are favored have been proposed:

1. *Error control* By building a large complex from many small subunits, translation errors may be reduced by discarding subunits with defects, providing an extra step for proofreading. These errors have been characterized and quantified in prokaryotes (reviewed in 57, 75). Missense errors, which change an amino acid at a given position, have been estimated to occur at an average frequency of $\sim5 \times 10^{-4}$ per codon. Approximately one in four proteins of 500 amino acids have a substituted amino acid, and proteins with 2000 amino acids nearly always have an error. Missense errors, however, are fairly harmless; the vast majority of single-site mutations cause only a modest decrease in the protein's functionality. In a study of mutant bacteria with error-prone EF-Tu, a doubling of the missense error rate causes only a 10% decrease in bacterial growth rate.

   Processivity errors, in which translation is terminated prematurely to yield a truncated protein, have a more significant impact. The prokaryotic processivity error frequency has been estimated at an average of 3×10^{-4}/codon, so about one in seven proteins with 500 amino acids will be released before it is fully translated, and a protein with 3000 amino acids will only rarely be translated in full.

2. *Coding efficiency* Homooligomers provide a genetically compact way to encode the information needed to build a large protein: Association of many individual small subunits allows the creation of a large structure with a minimum of genetic space. Crick & Watson (19) proposed this idea and predicted that spherical plant virus capsids are composed of many identical subunits on these grounds. They argued that the amount of RNA in these small viruses—making the then-unproven assumption of a three-nucleotide codon—is insufficient to encode a capsid composed of a large, single protein; therefore, they went on to predict (correctly) that these capsids are composed of subunits arranged with icosahedral symmetry. However, the large amount of noncoding DNA in eukaryotic genomes argues against this being a major driving force in higher organisms (95).

3. *Regulation of assembly* Large assemblies built of many identical subunits have attractive regulatory properties, because they are subject to sensitive phase transitions. For instance, actin is involved in many dynamic processes at the cell surface. A collection of actin-binding proteins control the nucleation, growth, termination, and disassembly of actin filaments, allowing fine spatial and temporal control (88). Similarly, microtubules spontaneously switch between phases of growth and shrinkage, in a behavior termed "dynamic instability" (69). This dynamic regulation of microtubule length may have important physiological implications for mitosis (70).

Why Build Symmetrical Proteins?

The homooligomeric proteins found in modern cells are also highly symmetrical, with soluble oligomers forming closed complexes related by simple point groups, and extended polymers showing helical symmetry. Several features favor symmetrical complexes rather than asymmetric aggregates in the evolution of oligomeric proteins:

1. *Stability of association* Blundell & Srinivasan make an evocative comment in the proceedings of a recent symposium (8): "...generally, the lowest energy state of an assembly is a symmetrical one." This observation has been demonstrated in systems of identical particles, in which the particles interact by nondirectional forces. For instance, in clusters of noble gas atoms, certain highly symmetrical assemblies are favored (40). However, given that the symmetry of oligomeric proteins is under the control of evolution of function, this principle may not apply. For instance, if a nonsymmetrical protein is essential for function, a complex will evolve in which the nonsymmetric association is the lowest energy state. Just the same, many early analyses of quaternary structure tacitly assume that homooligomers adopt closed point group symmetries because they are optimally stable, with existence proofs as the justification (11, 49, 50, 72).

   Cornish-Bowden & Koshland performed a thermodynamic analysis of oligomeric proteins to justify the prevalence of point group symmetries (16). They arranged four subunits into a square and defined two binding surfaces on each subunit, denoted P and Q. Two planar point group symmetries are possible, one related by twofold axes in the plane of the page, with P-P interfaces and Q-Q interfaces, and one related by four-fold rotation, with all P-Q interfaces (Figure 3). Two asymmetric closed complexes are also possible by combining local two-fold axes with local 90° rotations, containing a mixture of P-P, P-Q, and Q-Q interfaces. By surveying many different values for the binding strength of P-P, P-Q, and Q-Q interfaces, Cornish-Bowden & Koshland were able to show that the symmetric arrangements are favored quite strongly, even given only modest differences in the binding energy between the three types of interface interaction. In reality, the difference in interaction energies will be very large, so that oligomers with mixed symmetries requiring the formation of two types of interactions, like the P-P and P-Q pairings, are rarely observed.

   The stability of closed, symmetrical oligomers is a consequence of two factors: (*a*) the specificity of protein-protein interfaces favors symmetrical complexes, and (*b*) the maximum numbers of intersubunit interactions are formed in closed complexes. The many structures of oligomeric proteins have revealed that protein-protein interaction sites, because they are composed of extended, complementary two-dimensional surfaces, are highly specific and directional. The directionality of protein-protein interfaces ensures that all homooligomers are symmetrical. A protein subunit is bound in one specific location and orientation relative to its mate; no relative rotation, slipping around this surface like a clutch, is allowed. This can be compared to the difference between carbon atoms in cycloalkanes and those in benzene. In cycloalkanes, the C-C bonds are relatively free to rotate, and most conformations of the molecule

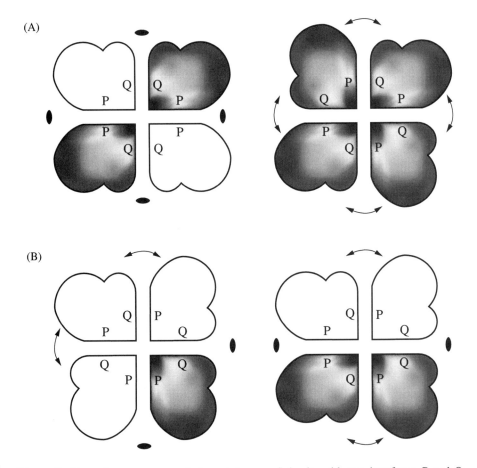

Figure 3 Four planar arrangements for a tetramer. Subunits with two interfaces, P and Q, may be arranged in a plane of the page in four unique conformations. Shaded subunits are flipped around two-fold axes in the plane compared with unshaded subunits. As described in the text, Cornish-Bowden & Koshland (16) used this model to validate the greater thermodynamic stability of the upper two symmetrical complexes over the lower two asymmetrical complexes.

are asymmetric. In benzene, however, delocalization over the C-C bonds disallows rotation, enforcing symmetry. The specificity and directionality of protein-protein interfaces ensures that each subunit will interact identically with its neighbors, limiting the transformations between neighbors to combinations of helical and cyclic (a special case with helical rise equal to zero) symmetries. (But, see the section on symmetry breaking below).

Given that homooligomers are symmetrical, with helical and cyclic symmetries, closed point group symmetries will give the maximal stability over the entire oligomer. Caspar (11) proposed that "Specific bonding between the [identical] units necessarily leads to a symmetrical structure, since there will be only a limited number of ways to form the maximum number of most stable bonds," where "bonds" refers to each unique protein-protein interaction surface. For instance, six subunits in an extended chain will have only five stabilizing interactions, with two less-stable subunits at the dangling ends, whereas a ring of six will have six protein-protein interfaces.

2. *Finite assembly* Proteins must avoid unwanted aggregation. Point group symmetry provides a method to create oligomers of defined copy number. Helical symmetries and other symmetries with translational elements are not bounded, however, and require special mechanisms to terminate growth. Several disease states seem to be the result of pathological aggregation of mutant proteins, such as sickle-cell anemia, Alzheimer's disease, and prion-related diseases.

3. *Folding efficiency* Wolynes has speculated that symmetric protein structures provide fewer kinetic barriers to folding than do asymmetric structures (95). Based on analogies with simple clusters of atoms, he argues that the energy landscape for folding of symmetric complexes may be smoother than that of completely asymmetric structures.

Functional Niches for Small Monomeric Proteins

In most cases, evolution appears to drive proteins to larger size and thus to symmetric, oligomeric complexes. In some specialized classes of proteins, however, functional considerations have the opposite effect, favoring small, monomeric proteins:

1. *Rapid diffusion* Cytochrome c, ferredoxin, plastocyanin, and other soluble electron transport proteins must be small and streamlined to diffuse rapidly to their sites of action in the crowded environment inside cells. Extracellular hydrolases, hormones, and many toxins are small for the same reason. These proteins are by and large monomeric, for the simple reason that it is difficult to create an oligomeric protein this small that can still fold to form a functional protein and remain stable under harsh environmental conditions.

2. *Stability at low concentrations* Oligomeric proteins are unstable at very low concentrations, so secreted proteins are commonly monomeric. Ricin is an interesting exception. It is a heterodimer, with a B chain that binds to the target cell surface and an A chain that inactivates eukaryotic ribosomes. The two subunits are connected by a disulfide bridge, but reduced ricin, if applied at concentrations at which the subunits associate, is even more toxic than the disulfide-linked complex (61). Apparently, the disulfide bridge serves primarily to hold the subunits together at the low concentrations found as the toxin diffuses to its target.

SYMMETRY AND COOPERATIVITY

Oligomerization of proteins provides the opportunity for cooperative interaction between subunits. Allosteric regulation and multivalent binding are two advantages exploited by proteins.

Allosteric Regulation

Allosteric regulation encompasses two classes: (*a*) *homotropic*, in which binding of a molecule to one subunit modulates the binding of the same type of molecule to the other subunits, and (*b*) *heterotropic*, in which binding of an effector molecule changes the conformation of the protein, modulating the binding of a second type of molecule. Hemoglobin is a familiar example of homotropic cooperativity, and enzymes such as phosphofructokinase and aspartate carbamoyltransferase are examples of heterotropic regulation by allostery. The structural basis of allosteric regulation has been the subject of several reviews (23, 63, 67, 79).

Symmetry arguments played a central role in the formulation of the concept of allosteric regulation. The original model of Monod et al postulated two states, the relaxed (R)-state and the tense (T)-state (72). These two states are different in conformation and in their affinity for substrates, but the subunits within a given state are related by perfect symmetry. In the model of Monod et al, the oligomer cycles between two symmetrical states, all R to all T, and by assuming strict symmetry, an attractively simple mathematical model may be used to describe the behavior of the system. Soon thereafter, Koshland et al proposed a sequential model in which one subunit at a time converts from the R to the T state, forming a series of asymmetric intermediates between the fully symmetrical all-R and all-T states (55). The mathematics are necessarily more complex with sequential models. It remains a surprise that the original two-state model of Monod et al worked so well and continues to be a reasonable first approximation in many cases.

Allosteric regulation requires a molecular geometry that allows the passing of messages from one subunit to the next or, better, from one subunit to all of the rest [although allosteric regulation in monomers has been proposed, based on slow conformational changes and "memory" of the enzyme for its product-bound state (81)]. Perutz noted that there are few a priori constraints on the possible motions, even if one requires identical symmetry for the T and the R states (79). As long as all subunits shift similarly relative to the point group symmetry axes, the overall symmetry will be preserved. Nonetheless, many of the cooperative enzymes that show allosteric motions use dihedral symmetry and show motions that are easily related to the dihedral axes.

Many allosteric enzymes are composed of two rigid rings of subunits, which then associate back-to-back around a perpendicular two-fold axis to form the dihedral complex. The allosteric regulation occurs by rotating these two rings in relation to one another about the cyclic axis and/or translating them along the axis. Fructose-1,6-bisphosphatase, a tetramer with D2 symmetry, shows a large motion

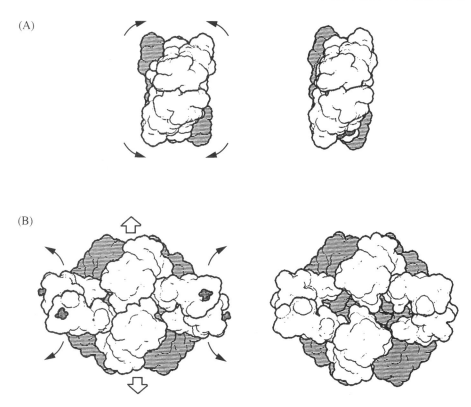

Figure 4   Allosteric motions. Two types of allosteric motion are common in oligomeric proteins. The first is a rotational motion, exemplified by fructose-1,6-bisphosphatase (A). The upper dimer rotates by 15° in the T-to-R transition. The second is a pincher motion, exemplified by aspartate carbamoyltransferase (B). Regulatory domains at the right and left of the complex flex open and separate the catalytic subunits at the center.

of this sort (Figure 4a). The tetramer is formed of two stable dimers, and the R-to-T transition involves a rotation of 15° around the two-fold axis, piercing the stable dimers. Lifting the requirement for identical subunits, hemoglobin also fits this model, with the two stable α-β pairs rotating independent units.

A second approach uses a "pincher" motion similar to the changes seen in bacterial repressors. In the repressors, the effector binds at the interface between two subunits in the dimer, causing the molecule to flex, repositioning the DNA-binding elements at the tips of the subunits. In allosteric proteins with dimeric symmetry, this type of motion is used for heterotropic regulation. The effector binds at or near the dimer interface, causing the two subunits to flex, and changes in conformation propagate to the active site, which may be quite distant from the effector site. Examples include glycogen phosphorylase (3) and chorismate mutase (89).

Allosteric enzymes with dihedral symmetry also show this type of pincher movement. Dimeric units within the complex perform a similar flexing upon effector binding. Often the active site is at the dimer interface that is remodeled in the transition. In aspartate carbamoyltransferase (29) with D3 symmetry, two trimers stack on one another and are connected by three pincher-type interactions at the points of a triangle. The regulatory motion separates and rotates the two trimers along the threefold-symmetry axis (Figure 4b). Bacterial L-lactate dehydrogenase (41) with D2 symmetry may be thought of as two dimers. Each dimer contains a single effector binding site that lies on a dimer axis. Binding of fructose-1,6-bisphosphate to this site effects a pincher-type motion between two subunits, shifting the orientation of one dimer relative to the next by ~6° (note that the binding of a single fructose-1,6,-bisphosphate molecule to a dimeric enzyme site is an example of symmetry mismatch and pseudosymmetry, as described below).

Other enzymes with more complex functions use less easily characterized motions. These enzymes still use dihedral symmetry, presumably because of the intimate nature of contacts possible, but they add intrasubunit-domain motions to increase the vocabulary of motion that may be used. GroEL, with 14 subunits in D7 symmetry, is an excellent example. The subunits within one ring show positive cooperativity in the binding of ATP, whereas the two rings show negative cooperativity, with ATP hydrolysis in one ring promoting ATP binding on the other. Large domain rotations have been observed both in ATP binding and in the binding of the protein effector GroES (97). Pyruvate kinase similarly shows extensive rearrangement of domains within each subunit during the allosteric transition (68).

Dihedral symmetries appear to be far more conducive to allosteric regulation than do the higher cyclic symmetries alone. The two solutions used by many allosteric enzymes—rotation of two rings around the highest symmetry axis in a dihedral group and pincherlike motions—are both consistent with dihedral symmetry, but not with cyclic symmetry alone. The rarity of allosteric proteins with exclusively cyclic symmetry may result from the relative inefficiency of information transfer; the allosteric transition must propagate one subunit at a time around the cyclic ring. Cyclic symmetries are used in allosteric proteins only when necessitated by the function. The gap junction is an example; an irislike motion regulates the diameter of the pore.

Multivalent Binding

Cross-linking proteins rely on two or more functional sites arranged to maximize their interaction with their targets. Structural cross-linkers have very specific shapes and symmetries that suit their function, and flexibility is often a key feature, allowing some latitude in the relative orientations of the objects linked together. Actin-binding proteins of several shapes are used to build different cellular structures (66). Actin-bundling proteins, such as α-actinin, are short rods with binding sites at each end. They link actin filaments into parallel bundles, for use in motility and the shaping of cellular membranes. Gelation proteins, on the other hand, are typically large, flexible molecules with several actin-binding sites, which link filaments into polyhedral networks and give cytoplasm its gell-like nature.

Multivalent binding also increases the binding strength of a molecule to a single target, when the target displays multiple sites for binding and the protein contains several discrete binding sites. The overall binding strength is improved by reduction of entropy. Once one site of the molecule has bound, the other sites are held in close proximity to the target, making binding far more likely. Immune recognition takes advantage of this cooperativity (20, 30). Immunoglobulin, complement C1, and C-lectin mannose-binding proteins are designed to recognize a bacterial or viral surface and thus search for targets with several sites of binding within a given distance.

This same type of "entropically favored" binding has been proposed as a possible means of inducing curvature in membranes (39). A polyvalent molecule binding to several sites on a membrane will induce a curvature concave towards the side of ligand binding. The energy of this interaction was estimated at about 0.1 kcal/mol for a divalent molecule, suggesting that an array of these interactions, such as the array of matrix proteins that mediate viral budding in retroviruses, would be needed for a biologically significant effect.

The functional roles of these molecules place severe restrictions on their shapes. For molecules that bind multivalently to large targets, such as antibodies to cell surfaces, the most efficient design has the binding sites oriented in a similar direction. In this way, the binding sites are arranged to bind to adjacent sites, and the "tail" of the complex is available for recognition by subsequent steps in immune recognition. The complement C1 protein is a case in point: It uses C6 symmetry to recognize bacterial surfaces. Given that the molecule will be built of six subunits, the C6 symmetry is far more effective than a D3 multipointed "jack." Thus, molecules of the immune system are often built with rotational symmetry, but not higher symmetries. Cross-linkers, on the other hand, are most efficient when formed of two or more oppositely oriented binding sites, and thus they often show dihedral symmetries. Thus, the S-lectins from plants are effective agglutinators, because their active sites point in opposite directions and bind to targets on different cells.

MORPHOLOGICAL FUNCTIONS OF SYMMETRY

Symmetrical oligomers of identical subunits are used for a wide range of morphological functions, in which the symmetrical shape of the complex is functionally useful.

Rulers, Rings, and Containers

Symmetry is often used to create objects of a given size, for use as rulers to measure nanoscale distances, rings to surround molecular targets, or containers to enclose objects of a given size.

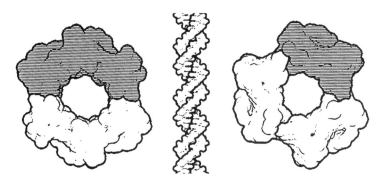

Figure 5   Sliding clamps of DNA polymerase. A ring of six average-sized subunits or domains is perfect for surrounding a DNA strand, shown at the center. Two methods of creating this ring have been discovered: The β subunit of bacterial DNA polymerase III (*left*) is a dimer, with three similar domains in each subunit, and the eukaryotic processivity factor PCNA (*right*) is a trimer with two domains in each subunit. A single subunit is shaded in each.

Repressors use cyclic two-fold symmetry to create allosteric "rulers" that accurately measure the repeat length of DNA. The two-fold symmetry makes allosteric regulation particularly straightforward; like a pair of calipers, the binding of an inducer or effector at the "hinge" can change the distance between the two functional "tips." These repressors carry with them the requirement for a palindromic DNA-binding site, matching the C2 symmetry of the repressor with the local C2 symmetry of DNA. A more detailed discussion of the restrictions imposed by DNA symmetry is included in a section below.

Three-fold and higher rotational axes of symmetry form pores or cavities that are often put to functional use. Kelman et al note that several proteins that encircle double-stranded DNA have six-fold rotational symmetry, with either six individual subunits or six similar domains (47). They argue that six-fold symmetry is the best compromise for the size of subunits (small enough to be economical and large enough to fold). The processivity factors of DNA polymerase (Figure 5) show approximate six-fold symmetry, with six average-sized domains arranged in a ring that clamps around the DNA strand. In the *Escherichia coli* β-subunit of polymerase III holoenzyme, two subunits assemble to form a ring, each with three domains (53). The eukaryotic processivity factor of DNA polymerase δ, on the other hand, adopts an identical ring shape, but is composed of three subunits, each with two domains (56). Perhaps a hexameric ring of single-domain subunits has yet to be discovered in another organism.

The size of the cavity may be estimated by using a simple approximation. First, the radius of the subunit (R_{SU}) is calculated (86):

$$R_{SU} = 3\sqrt{\frac{3vM}{4\pi N_A}} = 0.0665(nm)3\sqrt{M},$$

where v is the protein partial specific volume of 0.74 ml/g, M is the molecular mass in Daltons, and N_A is Avogadro's number. They then assume that these spheres just touch in the complex, yielding a cavity size (R_{cavity}):

$$R_{cavity} = R_{SU}\left(\frac{1}{\sin(\pi/n)} - 1\right),$$

where n is the number of subunits in the ring. This probably overestimates the size of the cavity. We use a second approximation, which simplifies the extension of the approximation to cubic symmetries. We sum the diameters of the n subunits and use the sum as the circumference of the oligomeric ring on which the subunit centers lie. The cavity size is then estimated as:

$$R_{cavity} = R_{SU}\left(\frac{n}{\pi} - 1\right).$$

This calculation yields smaller cavity sizes, particularly for rings with three to six subunits, and it approximates the extensive contact between subunits. In fact, the calculation for a trimer yields a nonphysical negative value, which is consistent with many observed trimeric structures such as porin, which have protein atoms extending to the three-fold axis.

Oligomeric rings are used as pores through lipid bilayers. Examples include the connexon, which forms a six-fold ring; the complement membrane attack complex and perforin, both of which form rings of variable size; and the nuclear pore, a large complex of proteins with eight-fold symmetry. Surprisingly, the trimeric bacterial porin does not use the oligomeric symmetry to form its pore—instead, each subunit forms a separate pore through the membrane, bounded by a large β-barrel. Rings are also important for the creation of rotary motors. The large flagellar motor complexes of *E. coli* and *Salmonella typhimurium* are examples of motors used to power rotary motion, and ATP synthase is an example that is used oppositely as a generator. As discussed below, rotary motors are limited to cyclic symmetry and lower symmetries. The trp RNA-binding attenuation protein, TRAP, may hold a surprise. It is a ring-shaped complex of 11 identical subunits, which, under control of tryptophan concentration, negatively regulates the trp genes by binding to RNA. Mutagenesis studies have suggested that the RNA wraps around the perimeter of the ring, rather than threading through the hole (98).

Approximate ring structures may be built with other symmetries. For example, human β-trypsin is a tetramer with approximate D2 symmetry, stabilized by binding to heparin, which forms a large pore along one of the two-fold axes (78). The active sites are oriented inwardly, opening onto the pore and limiting access. This has been proposed as the explanation for the resistance of β-trypsin to most endogenous protease inhibitors. The processivity factors of DNA polymerase, mentioned above, are another example, with approximate C6 symmetry.

Monomeric proteins are used to store and transport individual small molecules—for example, the bacterial periplasmic binding proteins and metallothioneins, but, for trapping and storing larger molecules or larger numbers of molecules,

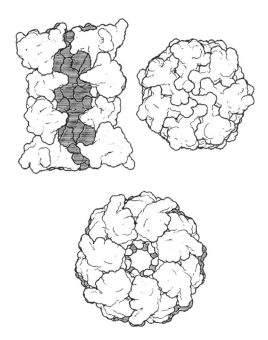

Figure 6 D7 symmetry to enclose a protein. Two proteins at opposite ends of the life of protein have similar symmetry. *Top*, the chaperone GroEL shows D7 symmetry, forming a protein-sized cavity that assists in the folding of nascent proteins. *Bottom*, the proteasome also shows D7 symmetry, forming a cavity that degrades obsolete proteins.

symmetrical oligomers are used. These containers have attractive properties; they may be built at a defined size to act as a "sieve," trapping only molecules of the proper size. They also may be built with defined chemical characteristics, creating a custom environment within the enclosed space.

The simplest solution is the use of cyclic symmetry to form a "cup," but, more commonly, two of these cups assemble back-to-back, using dihedral symmetry. Two proteins with identical symmetry but opposite function incorporate this motif (Figure 6). The bacterial chaperonin GroEL shows D7 symmetry, forming two cups that guide the folding of immature proteins (97). The bacterial proteosome also uses D7 symmetry, forming two cups that degrade obsolete proteins (64). Eukaryotic proteosomes use a similar overall morphology, but they are composed of a collection of similar proteins arranged in pseudo-D7 symmetry (32). The choice of this unusual symmetry group by both of these proteins is not as surprising as it might seem; it is dictated by two structural constraints: the need for a cavity of 40–50 Å to house the substrate protein and the need to build the cavity from typically sized proteins. From calculations like those above, we might expect that D6, D7, or D8 would be able to accommodate these functional constraints.

Cubic symmetry is used to build containers of even larger size. Ferritin (Figure 1) uses octahedral symmetry to build a container for iron ions (91), and virus capsids use icosahedral symmetry to create even larger containers. When more space is needed, quasisymmetry may be used (see below). The lumazine synthase-riboflavin synthase complex of *Bacillus subtilis* is a particularly unusual application of an icosahedral shell. The complex performs the two final reactions in the synthesis of riboflavin. The complex is composed of an icosohedral capsid of 60 β subunits, which carries out a condensation reaction that surrounds a trimer of α subunits, which then perform the final dismutation to form riboflavin (59).

The size of the cavity at the center of icosahedral capsids may be approximated as above, by summing the areas of a great circle through the center of the subunits and then calculating a sphere with similar overall surface area. The radius of the icosahedral cavity (R_{ico}) is then:

$$R_{ico} = R_{SU}\left(\sqrt{\frac{60T}{4}} - 1 \right),$$

where T is the triangulation number (described below). Calculated values for R_{ico} showed an rms error of $\sim 15\%$ over a test set of 22 crystallographically determined capsids (data not shown). Similarly, cavities for tetrahedral and octahedral complexes may be estimated by using values of 12 and 24 instead of 60 and using an appropriate triangulation number.

The Need to Be Large

Occasionally, the outer diameter of the complex may be functionally important. Koshland suggests that early cells needed large proteins to reduce loss through their leaky membranes (54). He postulates that early cells had not yet developed methods for active transport, so that large, primitive pores were the major method of transporting molecules into and out of the cell. Examples in modern organisms of the "need to be large" are difficult to find. The oxygen-carrying proteins of invertebrates, such as hemocyanin, form very large complexes. These proteins show allosteric control, but Perutz suggests that their high oligomerization state is to "prevent their passage through cell membranes," or perhaps to prevent loss at cellular junctions (79).

Structural Elements   Cells often use translational symmetries to build large structural elements from average-sized protein units. The most common method is the use of helical symmetry to construct filaments. Examples come in all sizes: thin filaments of actin, intermediate filaments of keratin and desmin, and thick filaments of tubulin. Filaments with simple helical symmetry are directional, in that one end may be distinguished from the other. This directionality is put to functional use in both actin and tubulin in their use as tracks for the molecular motors myosin and kinesin. Filaments that do not require directionality can incorporate two-fold symmetry perpendicular to the helical axis. For instance, intermediate filaments are formed of dimeric subunits that assemble in an approximate 4_2 helix, overlapping in a lap joint for maximal strength. Bacterial flagella are unusual cases; they form corkscrew-shaped superhelices, even though they are composed of a single type of flagellin subunit. As described below, a clever method of symmetry breaking is thought to be the mechanism.

One potential problem with helical symmetries is the lack of boundaries— how does the cell choose the proper length? For cytoskeletal elements, a complex series of initiation and termination proteins controls the assembly and disassembly of subunits. For tobacco mosaic virus, the solution is more direct. The RNA packaged in the virion acts as a "ruler," building a virion of defined length.

A remarkable exception to the use of modular helices as structural elements is the giant protein titin (58), the protein that limits the extension of muscle sarcomeres. With >27,000 amino acids and a molecular mass of 3 million Daltons, titin proteins extend over a micrometer in length. Because each one is a single protein, it is important as a ruler for defining the size of muscle sarcomeres. It also thought to contain a stretchable element, which adds elasticity to muscle cells.

FUNCTIONS THAT LIMIT SYMMETRY

Many biochemical functions limit the level of symmetry that is possible, working in opposition to the gains obtained from higher oligomerization and thus higher symmetry states. The result is an evolutionary tug of war, yielding the optimal state for a given functional niche.

Directional Motion

Directional linear motion places functional limits on the symmetry adopted by processive protein machinery. Polymerases and ribosomes perform a directional, asymmetric reaction and thus are themselves without point group symmetry. Note that individual subunits within these polymerases may have local symmetry, as for the sliding clamps mentioned above. The functions of these subunits, however, are nondirectional. Bacterial DNA polymerase III is an unusual exception to this observation; it is a large complex of enzymes that has, overall, approximately two-fold symmetry (37). The two polymerase subunits, one acting on the leading strand and one on the lagging strand, associate in the active complex, along with a helicase and several subunits that orchestrate the special needs of the lagging strand. This is an example of multivalent binding: The driving force for the dimerization of two polymerases is the advantage of having two enzymes tethered in one place, for acting on two strands of DNA that are guaranteed to be spatially close to one another.

For filaments used as tracks for molecular motors, simple helical symmetry is the highest that will allow unidirectional motion. Unidirectional motion along an intermediate filament or a double-stranded DNA helix is disallowed by symmetry. The motors themselves are also limited in symmetry; they cannot have symmetry elements that intersect with the helix axis. Similarly, rotary motors are limited to cyclic symmetry. Motors with dihedral symmetry would destroy the directionality of motion, leading to a frustrated random walk.

Interaction with DNA

One might speculate on the aspects of B-DNA structure that are not involved directly in its function. The helical symmetry of DNA is not specified by its function; it could adopt any form—left- or right-handed—and still transfer genetic information. The antiparallel orientation of the two strands, with local two-fold axes perpendicular to the helix axis at each base pair, is also not specified by function. Two strands in parallel, with a two-fold symmetry parallel with the helix axis, would also provide a mechanism for information transfer and would remove the need for discontinuous replication of the lagging strand (but might reduce the opportunities for control imposed by the helically wound antiparallel double helix). The B-DNA structure is an example of a design locked in at an early stage of evolution, perhaps not optimal, but unchangeable once incorporated.

The double-helical symmetry of DNA places limits on the symmetry of DNA-binding proteins. The sugar-phosphate backbones form a symmetrical double helix, but the local two-fold axes running through the center of each base pair, perpendicular to the helix axis, are broken at the atomic level by the nonidentity of bases in each pair. Thus, DNA-binding protein may interact at several levels. Proteins that bind nonspecifically to the backbone might be expected to show dimeric symmetry. In fact, however, this is relatively rare. Most non-base-specific functions use other symmetries: Nucleases are primarily monomeric, and remodeling proteins, such as the nucleosome, are complex oligomers. The dimeric symmetry of DNA is used primarily in the binding of bacterial repressors and restriction endonucleases, where the symmetry of the DNA backbone is mirrored in a self-complementary base sequence.

Alternatively, many monomeric proteins interact specifically with a given DNA site, binding directionally to the local sequence and ignoring the overall symmetry of the DNA backbone. Many eukaryotic transcription factors fall into this class. The TATA-binding protein is an interesting hybrid of the two approaches (44). At one level, it has two-fold pseudosymmetry, with two similar domains binding to symmetric DNA backbones. At another level, however, it recognizes and bends DNA in a sequence-specific and directional manner, initiating transcription in the proper direction from the TATA sequence.

Membrane Interactions

Biological membranes are nearly always asymmetric in function, separating "inside" from "outside." The functions of membrane proteins are also asymmetric.

Receptors must distinguish between extracellular and intracellular sides, and directional transport must be mediated by a protein that knows inside from outside. Thus the proteins interacting with these surfaces and those embedded in the membrane are nearly always limited to cyclic symmetries, with the cyclic axis perpendicular to the plane of the membrane.

A few functions do not require this specificity, and one might expect to find examples with higher symmetries. Channels that allow passive bidirectional transport might show dihedral symmetries. The gramicidin channel is one example, with two-fold symmetry such that the axis of symmetry is parallel to the surface instead of perpendicular. Thus far, larger protein channels such as aquaporins, have shown cyclic symmetry.

SYMMETRY BREAKING IN OLIGOMERIC PROTEINS

Biological molecules often break from perfect symmetry to accomplish specific functional goals. There are cases in which identical subunits adopt similar but different positions—this is termed quasisymmetry. Taken to extremes, identical subunits may be used to build several different structures, which is termed pleomorphic symmetry. On the other hand, there are cases in which similar but different subunits perform identical roles—this is termed pseudosymmetry. And finally, in large complexes, components with different symmetry may be fitted together, forming a symmetry mismatch locally at the interface.

Quasisymmetry

Most viruses require capsids that are larger than can be created by 60 identical, moderately–sized proteins in perfect icosahedral symmetry. Some viruses answer this need by creating capsids with multiple chains: For instance, poliovirus and rhinovirus capsids are composed of 60 copies of each of four different chains, all arranged in perfect icosahedral symmetry. Other viruses, however, have taken a more creative approach, using a single protein in several different quasiequivalent structural roles. In these viruses, each of the 60 symmetrically identical positions in the icosahedron is filled by a number of identical chains.

As quasisymmetry was originally conceived, these chemically identical chains adopt positions that are approximately identical in the local environment, and small elastic deformations of the subunits allow similar contacts to be formed between each. As stated by Klug: "... if each subunit in the final structure still forms the same types of sets of bonds with its neighbors, then, although the units are no longer exactly equivalently related, they may be said to be quasi-equivalently related" (51). Caspar & Klug described a method for tiling icosahedra with triangular networks, creating steadily larger capsids composed of quasiequivalent triangular subunits, thus introducing the concept of a "triangulation number" (12), as shown in Figure 7A and 7B. Using these triangular lattices, they showed that

A   **B**

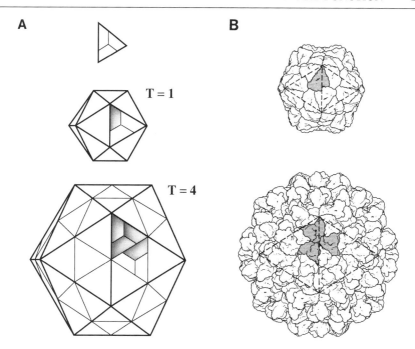

Figure 7   Triangulation number and quasisymmetry. *A*. With the basic triangular unit shown at top, composed of three subunits, a wide variety of quasisymmetrical icosahedral shells can be formed. The basic $T = 1$ icosahedron is the simplest. All subunits are identical—one subunit is shown shaded at center. A larger shell may be formed by creating an icosahedron with four triangular units tiled within each icosahedral face, as shown at the bottom. Then, each of the triangles is not identical, and there are four unique subunits (shown shaded) in different local environments. Many other triangulation numbers are possible, by tiling the triangular units differently within the icosahedral geometry. *B*. Two examples of viruses. *Top*, satellite tobacco necrosis virus, with $T = 1$ symmetry and a single subunit in the asymmetric unit; *bottom*, tomato bushy stunt virus, with $T = 3$ symmetry and three subunits in the asymmetric unit. Two faces of the underlying icosahedron are shown with *dotted lines*.

quasiequivalent lattices could be constructed for shells with $60T$ subunits, where $T = h^2 + hk + k^2$ and h and k are integers.

Some hint of the tolerances involved in assembly of large complexes from subunits that allow small local deformations is provided by the study of a bacteriophage portal protein (92). This protein forms 12- or 13-fold cyclical oligomers. It assembles sequentially, with subunits adding at an angle of 25.8° around the ring, just shy of the angle needed for a 14-fold ring. Apparently, small deviations in this angle allow the ring to close 40% of the time into 12-fold rings (30°/subunit) and 60% of the time into 13-fold rings (27.7°/subunit).

The structures of viral capsids have revealed that this ideal for quasiequivalence is only rarely achieved. Although the triangular-network model has been observed in nearly every icosahedral virus structure, the concept of minimal changes and elastic deformations in structure between different quasiequivalent subunits has fared less well (82). In reality, the viral protomers tend to show structural "switches," adopting two or more significantly different conformations that mediate the different quasiequivalent contacts. There is considerable literature describing the structural features used by viruses, as observed by electron micrograph reconstruction and X-ray crystallography. Based on these works, there has been a recent rebirth of interest in the field, as mutagenesis and computational chemistry are applied. We do not attempt to review this burgeoning field, but we do touch on a few interesting highlights. For more information, the reader might start with a recent review by Johnson & Speir (42).

Tomato bushy stunt virus (TBSV) is a classic example of a structural switch (Figure 8), allowing a single type of subunit to adapt to three different environments in a $T = 3$ quasisymmetrical capsid (35). The subunit is composed of an N-terminal shell domain located at the interior of the capsid, connected by a flexible linker to a C-terminal domain that projects from the capsid surface. An N-terminal region in the subunit undergoes an order-disorder transition based on the local symmetry environment, being ordered in subunits that associate around icosahedral two-fold axes and disordered in subunits that associate through quasisymmetrical twofold axes. The subunits make extensive contact with one another, and additional stability is obtained by the ordered N-terminal arms, which associate between three subunits at the quasi-six-fold axis.

Bluetongue virus (BTV) shows an interesting variation on quasisymmetry (Figure 9a). The virus is composed of several concentric protein shells (31). The outer shell adopts a $T = 13$ arrangement of surprising regularity, conforming closely to the quasisymmetrical ideal. The inner shell is more unusual. It adopts a $T = 1$ arrangement, but has two separate subunits in each equivalent position. These two subunits are bean shaped and are packed back-to-back in nonequivalent, asymmetric conformations. This arrangement is discussed in more detail below, under the heading of "Global Asymmetry."

———————————————————————————————→

Figure 8 Structural switch in tomato bushy stunt virus. The three subunits in the asymmetric unit of tomato bushy stunt virus adopt slightly different conformations to accommodate the geometric requirements of the quasisymmetrical positions. Two pairs of subunits are shown here, with the inside of the virion facing downward in each. Each subunit is composed of two domains, connected by a flexible linker. The C-terminal domain (at the top in each) forms a structure that protrudes from the spherical capsid, which is formed by the N-terminal domain (at the bottom in each). A, subunits arranged around the strict dimer axis that runs through each icosahedral edge, with ordered N-terminal arms extending from the bottom of the complex; B, subunits arranged around a quasisymmetrical two-fold axis that intersects the icosahedral face, with their disordered N-terminal arms. Notice the difference in the orientation of the N-terminal domains, forming a flatter capsid surface in A (shown by the lines) and a more curved surface in B.

A

B

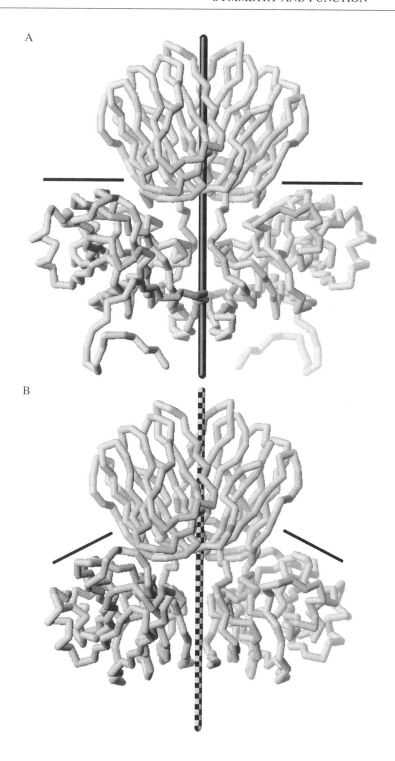

A

B

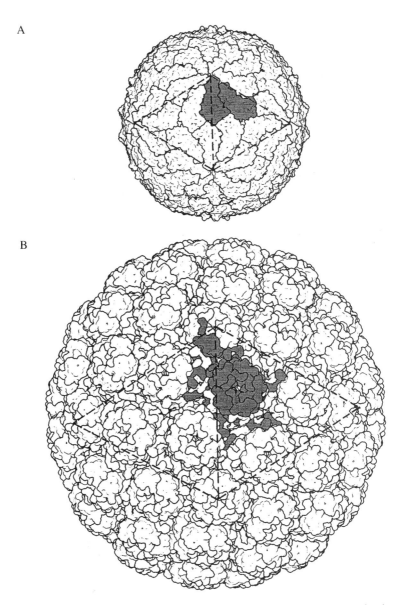

Figure 9 Broken quasisymmetry in viruses. A, bluetongue virus, which can be thought of as a $T = 1$ virus with two subunits in the asymmetric unit (*shaded*). These two subunits are packed back-to-back and adopt significantly different conformations. B, simian virus 40 can be thought of as a $T = 1$ virus, with six subunits in the asymmetric unit, shown shaded. One of the six forms a pentamer with neighbors at the icosahedral five-fold axis, and five form a pentamer on the icosahedral face. The pentamers are connected by flexible arms, seen surrounding the shaded pentamer.

Simian virus 40 (SV40) is an extreme case, straining the concept of quasisymmetry to its limits. The subunits form stable pentamers with extensive intersubunit contacts, but nearly all of the pentamer-pentamer contacts are mediated through swapping of C-terminal arms (62). The pentamers form a shell with apparent $T = 4$ quasisymmetry, but with a full pentamer at each vertex of the triangular lattice instead of an expected trimer. The flexibility of the C-terminal arms allows this unusual break of symmetry to occur, as shown in Figure 9b. In some cases, arms are swapped between two pentamers, around a true icosahedral two-fold axis or a quasisymmetrical two-fold axis. Interactions between pentamers sitting on the icosahedral five-fold axes and their neighbors, however, form a three-way swap between three pentamers.

Bacterial flagella provide another interesting example of quasisymmetry. Flagella are long superhelical filaments used to propel bacteria through their environment (93). Amazingly, these superhelical structures are often composed of a single type of protein subunit, termed flagellin. This requires that identical subunits adopt nonidentical environments, such that the subunits on the inner face of the superhelix are more crowded than those on the outer face. The current model of flagellar structure requires flagellin to adopt two states (10, 45). When flagellin self-assembles into the filament, it forms distinctive longitudinal columns, seen by electron micrograph reconstructions and X-ray diffraction (Figure 10). If an entire column switches conformation from a longer form to a shorter form, one side of the filament is compressed, forcing the entire filament to adopt a superhelical form. This model has been quite successful in predicting the various polymorphs observed under different experimental conditions. As different numbers of longitudinal columns switch from one conformation to the other, different straight or curly filaments are formed.

Pleomorphic Symmetry

Nature has also taken advantage of the idea of building several different structures from a single type of modular subunit. The term "pleomorphic" has been borrowed from chemistry, referring to compounds that crystallize in several different habits. In the present context, the term refers to subunits that assemble into different structures.

A popular example of pleomorphism with covalent bonds is the spectrum of different buckminsterfullerines, in which a single carbon atom is the subunit. By construction of lattices with six-fold and five-fold rings, a wide range of symmetrical closed spheres and tubes, as well as diverse of asymmetric structures, may be constructed. The key that makes this diversity of structure possible is the ability to form C-C linkages with a range of different C-C-C bond angles. If the covalent bonding chemistry were so specific that bond angles were rigid at $120°$, only hexagonal nets would be possible. But since the allowable range is wider, easily allowing six-fold and five-fold rings to form, a larger range of geometries is available to the final structures.

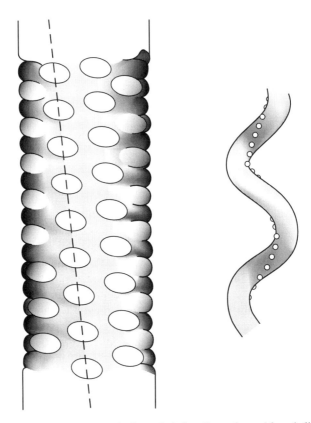

Figure 10   Model of flagellar superhelices. *Left*, flagella are formed from helical polymers of flagellin. Flagellin adopts two conformations, one of which has a shorter helical rise per subunit. *Right*, if an entire row of subunits, shown with the dotted line, shifts to the shorter conformation, it will distort the filament into a superhelix.

Several biological molecules show similar pleomorphism. Perhaps the most familiar example is clathrin (Figure 11). The clathrin subunit is a trimeric triskelion, with partially flexible arms. These triskelions then assemble, arm binding to arm, to form closed geodesic structures that mediate the invagination of coated pits. The structures show a wide range of geometry, from simple icosahedra to elongated ellipsoids, with five-fold and six-fold rings reminiscent of the smallest buckminsterfullerines (38).

Many viruses also show pleomorphic forms, particularly when the environmental conditions are changed during assembly. Cowpea chlorotic mottle virus is normally a $T = 3$ icosahedron, but changes in pH and ionic strength can cause the virion to reassemble into a variety of tubes, sheets, and multishelled particles (42). The HIV capsid may also be an example of pleomorphism. In a recent model based on electron microscopy of reconstructed cores, the cone-shaped HIV core

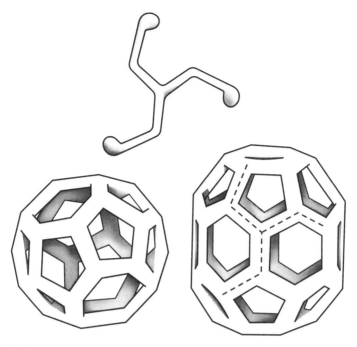

Figure 11 Clathrin pleomorphism. Clathrin coats are formed of three-armed triskelions (*top*). These arrange into a variety of geodesic structures. Smaller structures are rich in five-fold rings (*left*), and larger structures add sixfold rings (*right*). The proposed location of a triskelion is shown in *dotted lines* in the right structure.

is proposed to be constructed of two different structures: a hexagonal network, rolled to form a cone, and two fullerine-type hemispherical caps at each end (25).

Pseudosymmetry

Pseudosymmetry refers to oligomers composed of two or more types of similar chains, such that the entire complex resembles an homooligomer. Hemoglobin is a familiar example, composed of two α and two similar β subunits. The $\alpha_2\beta_2$ tetramer is strictly dimeric, but shows approximate D2 symmetry, as shown in Figure 12. Mammalian lactate dehydrogenase is another example, with oligomers formed with various mixtures of muscle and heart isoenzymes.

In the retroviral proteases, a symmetrical enzyme interacts with a pseudosymmetric substrate. These proteases are homodimers that form a long, two-fold–symmetric active site, with alternating hydrogen bond acceptors and hydrogen bond donors arrayed along its length. The substrate is a typical peptide with no internal symmetry. The peptide binds in extended form, interacting in a pseudosymmetrical manner with all of the hydrogen-bonding groups available from the protein (94). Bacterial L-lactate dehydrogenase is another example. The enzyme

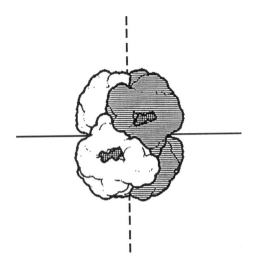

Figure 12 Hemoglobin pseudosymmetry. Hemoglobin is a heterotetramer of two α subunits, shown in *white*, and two β subunits, shown *shaded*. The heme groups are shown in *darker shading*. A perfect two-fold axis relates the two α and the two β subunits, shown as the horizontal line. Since the α and β subunits are similar in sequence and structure, they may be related by pseudosymmetry, forming pseudo-two-fold axes vertically, shown with a *dotted line*, and perpendicular to the plane of the paper through the center of the tetramer.

is a homotetramer with D2 symmetry, but only two molecules of the allosteric activator fructose-1,6-bisphosphate bind per oligomer. The binding site is formed by two subunits and is located exactly on one of the two-fold axes. The approximate dimeric symmetry of the substrate, with two phosphate groups extending in opposite directions from a compact sugar, facilitates binding to the two-fold symmetric site (41). Note that these interactions are also examples of symmetry mismatch, described below.

The human growth hormone receptor is an example of a pseudosymmetric association (22). The hormone itself is a small, monomeric protein. At the surface of a cell, it binds to two receptor molecules, forming a complex with approximate dimeric symmetry. The two receptor molecules bind to different faces of the hormone molecule, using similar binding surfaces on the receptor. One might expect that a dimeric hormone would be easier to develop evolutionarily. Perhaps the need for a small hormone, combined with the difficulty in creating a stable dimeric protein of small size, favors the evolution of a monomer.

Symmetry Mismatch

Large molecular complexes are often built of many different protein species. In some cases, such as the ribosome, the complex is built of many different proteins (and nucleic acids) associating in an asymmetric manner. In other cases, the entire complex adopts a given symmetry, with identical numbers of each protein chain. The picornavirus capsids, formed of 60 copies of four different chains, are an example. Occasionally, however, the different components of these large complexes may adopt different symmetries, which then associate, forming a symmetry mismatch at the site of interaction.

The α-keto acid dehydrogenase complexes, such as the pyruvate dehydrogenase complex linking glycolysis to the citric acid cycle, are good examples (80). They are composed of three different subunits, denoted E1, E2, and E3, which perform sequential steps in the oxidative decarboxylation reaction. The pyruvate dehydrogenase complex from *E. coli* is composed of a core of 24 E2 subunits arranged in octahedral symmetry, forming a cube-shaped structure. A hole is formed at each of the six faces of the cube, each with four-fold molecular symmetry. A dimer of E3 is thought to bind within each of these holes, forming a mismatch of two-fold symmetry within a four-fold symmetric environment.

Rotavirus is another example of a knob of lower symmetry fitting into a hole of higher symmetry (Figure 13). The viral capsid is composed of two concentric shells with typical $T = 13$ icosahedral quasisymmetry. Many small holes are formed between subunits, and the holes are in register between the two shells. Sixty dimeric hemagglutinin VP4 molecules bind within one class of these holes, extending from the capsid surface. The outer end of these molecules shows typical dimeric symmetry, but the inner end forms a globular structure with approximate hexagonal shape, fitting perfectly within the quasihexagonal holes (99).

Many examples of symmetry mismatch between monomeric proteins and oligomers with cyclic symmetry may be found. The pseudosymmetrical interactions of dimeric enzymes with monomeric substrates, described above, are examples. In those, the approximate dimeric nature of the substrate softens the mismatch. This is not so in ATP synthase, which has a three-fold symmetric complex composed of three α and three β subunits, pierced by a monomeric γ subunit. As described below, the interaction distorts the ring of α and β subunits, forcing each α-β pair into a different conformation and mediating the unusual rotary mechanism of action (1). Cholera toxin (100) and the heat-labile enterotoxin of *E. coli* (85) also each show a ring of subunits surrounding a monomeric subunit.

Symmetry mismatch has been evoked to explain several functional features of protein complexes. Hendrix proposed that a symmetry mismatch in bacteriophage could be the mechanism used for DNA injection (36). The tails of these phages show six-fold rotational symmetry, but they attach to the icosahedral heads at one unique vertex, through an axis of five-fold rotational symmetry. He proposed that this mismatch of symmetry might allow an ATP-driven motor to be formed at the interface, which, by turning, would forcibly eject DNA from the head. He further proposed that similar mismatches might be important in the flagellar motor. This is certainly the case in ATP synthase, in which the monomeric rotor is turned inside a three-fold symmetric ring (as described below), and the possibility of rotation in the mechanism of intracellular proteolysis has been proposed based on the seven-fold/six-fold symmetry mismatch of the components of the *E. coli* Clp chaperone-assisted protease (6).

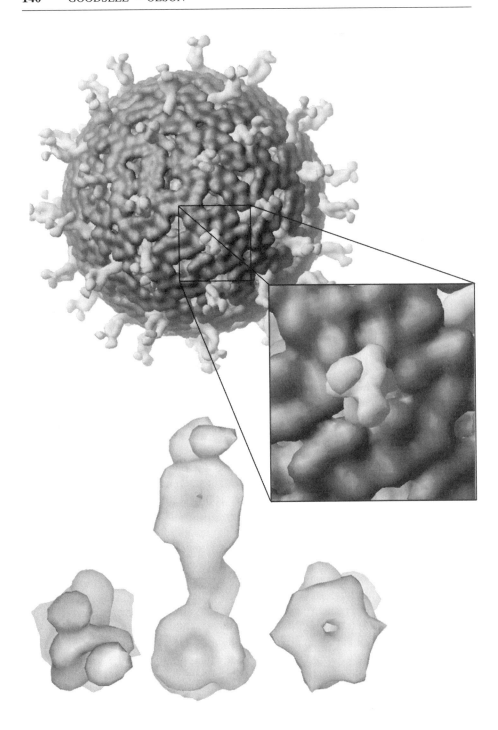

A "Vernier" mechanism that relies on symmetry mismatch has been proposed as the structural mechanism determining the shape of bacteriophage T4 heads (5, 77). The head of T4 is icosahedral, but it is extended in one direction by the addition of hexamers in an equatorial band around one five-fold axis. The amount of elongation is controlled by the interaction of an internal scaffolding with the shell during assembly (46). This scaffolding is later disassembled to form the mature phage. The Vernier method relies on the interaction of two concentric helical structures with different helical repeats. If formation of the caps that close each end of the oblate head are tied to a given alignment of the scaffolding core to the shell, then the length of the head could be determined by the repeat distance at which the two structures periodically come into phase. This mechanism is successful in explaining the aberrant head structures formed by mutant phage.

ASYMMETRY

Protein monomers are strongly asymmetric. As summarized by Chothia (13), the asymmetry of L-amino acids gives rise to a preferred handedness for α-helices and β-sheets. The packing of these units of secondary structure, which show a small number of preferred modes, then gives rise to asymmetric folded structures, including twisted β-sheets, curving β-ribbons, and tilted α-helical bundles. Cases with high internal symmetry, such as cylindrical α-β barrels, are relatively rare. Often, they are the result of gene duplications and might be thought of as a form of linked quaternary structure.

The asymmetry imposed by the limitation to L-amino acids does not appear to extend to the level of quaternary structure, as noted by Chothia (13). Instead, symmetry is the rule in protein association: Overall, oligomeric proteins adopt closed point group symmetry, and polymers adopt helical symmetry. Asymmetry is observed, however, at several levels. Local asymmetry, in which individual amino acids show different conformations when comparing different subunits in an assembly, is ubiquitous. Asymmetry is also a key element of allosteric interactions, in which individual subunits can adopt one of several alternate conformations. However, true global asymmetry, in which subunits with identical primary sequences adopt positions within a complex that are not related by symmetry, is rarely observed.

Figure 13   Symmetry mismatch in rotavirus. Rotavirus hemagglutinin VP4 is a dimer that binds to the viral capsid and extends into the surrounding environment. Many hemagglutinin spikes are shown in the reconstruction at top, and a detail of one is shown in the *inset*. As shown at *bottom*, the hemagglutinin shows typical dimeric symmetry at the outer end, with two separate lobes. At the inner end, however, the two chains form a hexagon-shaped globule, designed to fill the hexagonal holes left between subunits in the capsid. Cryoelectron microscope reconstruction data are courtesy of M Yeager at the Scripps Research Institute.

Local Asymmetry

Nearly every crystal structure of an homooligomeric protein will show local differences in sidechain conformation and occasional small differences in backbone conformation. These may be observed as actual differences in atomic coordinates, if more than one subunit is found in the asymmetric unit, or as disordered residues, if the subunits are related by crystallographic symmetry. Often, these can be attributed to lack of constraints on the sidechain. Sidechains or even entire loops that are exposed to solvent will show largely different conformations in different subunits. Alternatively, crystal packing may order sidechains and flexible loops in different conformations. These differences can provide valuable observations of the mobility of proteins and the deformability of surface residues and loops.

Location near a symmetry axis can force breaking of local symmetry in a way that is necessary for structural integrity. Often subunits will adopt different conformations when near symmetry elements to optimize interactions across the axis. This was noted at the two-fold interface of insulin: "The two-fold-axis is not exactly obeyed, probably as a consequence of the very congested packing of residues which is observed here" (2). The flaps of HIV-1 protease provide another example, as shown in Figure 14. The peptide between ILE-50 and GLY-51 interacts with its symmetry mate across the two-fold axis; in one subunit, the amine hydrogen faces across the axis; in the other, the peptide is rotated so that the carbonyl oxygen faces across the axis, allowing formation of a hydrogen bond.

Local asymmetry seems to play a functional role in half-of-sites reactivity, or negative cooperativity. In proteins that show half-of-sites reactivity, binding of ligand or effector to one subunit disfavors binding to the other subunit. Examples include D-glyceraldehyde-3-phosphate dehydrogenase, alcohol dehydrogenase,

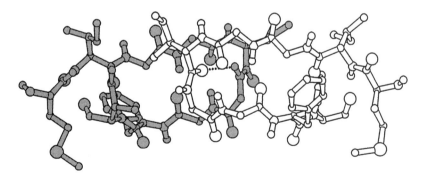

Figure 14 Local asymmetry in HIV-1 protease. Asymmetry of sidechains is often observed close to symmetry elements. The flaps of HIV-1 protease show asymmetry at a hydrogen bond (*dotted line*), that passes through the two-fold symmetry axis of dimeric protein, which runs top to bottom in the plane of the page, relating the flap in white to the shaded flap.

arginine kinase, tyrosyl-tRNA synthetase, and many others (83). The crystal structures of these enzymes show globally symmetric structures, with local asymmetry of loops, particularly around the active sites. The observation made by Moras et al seems to apply to the entire class: "The tetrameric molecule of glyceraldehyde-3-phosphate dehydrogenase has long been shown to have asymmetric properties which almost certainly reflect themselves in small but definite differences of conformation in the four polypeptide chains" (73).

Based on biochemical results that show half-of-sites reactivity, Degani & Degani propose that arginine kinase adopts a globally asymmetric structure (21). Crystal structures of this enzyme, however, show a symmetrical dimer. Crystal structure analyses have been reported for other proteins that show half-of-sites reactivity, including alcohol dehydrogenase, tyrosyl-tRNA synthetase, and D-glyceraldehyde-3-phosphate dehydrogenase. In all, the subunits are related by two-fold symmetry. The negative cooperativity appears to be effected through subtle motion sidechains, causing the two subunits to adopt different local structures at the active site when complexed, but still retaining an overall symmetrical structure when uncomplexed.

Reciprocating Mechanisms

Several examples of "reciprocating" mechanisms have been observed. In these, each subunit may adopt one or more states, but the state of one subunit is dependent on the states of the neighbors. For instance, envision a dimer in which each subunit may adopt two conformations, A and B. The dimer interaction will be such that if one subunit is in conformation A, the other must be in conformation B, and vice versa. Thus, at any given time, they do not adopt identical states, just like pistons on a crankshaft are all in different positions. However, if we take a time-averaged structure, the three A-B pairs are identical. Also, in analogy with the pistons and crankshaft, the reciprocating motion is processive; the conformation of one subunit will be optimized for catalysis, and the conformation of the other subunit will be optimized for binding to the next substrate.

ATP synthase is the best known example of this type of reciprocating engine. The reciprocating mechanism was proposed by Boyer (9), and the mechanism has been revealed at the atomic level (1). ATP synthase is composed of a $\alpha_3\beta_3$ ring of subunits, encircling a multisubunit membrane-bound axle. The reciprocating mechanism cycles between three conformations: an O site with very low affinity for ligands and no catalytic activity, an L site that binds ligands loosely and is inactive, and a T site that binds ligands tightly and performs the catalytic step. In the complex, one of the three $\alpha\beta$ heterodimers adopts each conformation at any given time, and physical turning of the axle converts one to the next.

The chaperonin GroEL acts, to a first approximation, through a two-state reciprocating mechanism (Figure 15). The asymmetric complex is composed of a 14-subunit GroEL, arranged as two rings of seven subunits bound back-to-back

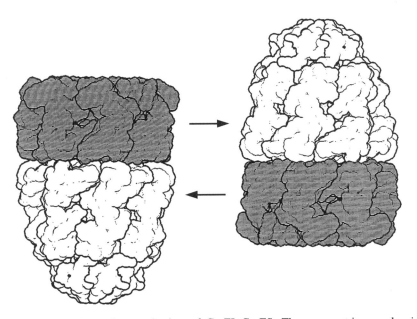

Figure 15 Reciprocating mechanism of GroEL:GroES. The asymmetric complex is formed of a 14-subunit GroEL and a conical GroES cap formed of seven subunits. To a first approximation, the complex cycles between two conformations. *Upper conformation*, the right half of GroEL is open, and the left half is capped by GroES, which induces a significant conformational change in the GroEL subunits that it contacts. *Lower conformation*, the roles have reversed. The left side has lost GroES and is open, allowing the folded protein to exit and new proteins to enter, and the right side is capped by GroES. The complex is always asymmetric for the two sides, but, looking at a time average, both sides cycle through identical conformations.

with approximate D7 symmetry, and GroES, which forms a C7-symmetric cap on one ring of the GroEL complex (97). GroEL undergoes large deformations upon binding of GroES, cycling between two conformations: a *cis* conformation, to which GroES is bound, which provides a closed space within which proteins fold, and the *trans* conformation, which is open to the surrounding solvent, releases and takes up polypeptides. One cycle allows about 15 seconds for the polypeptide to fold, and requires 7 ATP molecules. Communication between the two halves of the complex is mediated through a smooth tilt of subunits relative to the seven-fold axis, breaking the D7 symmetry of GroEL complex, but preserving the protein-protein interactions that bind one ring to the other.

Global Asymmetry

Homooligomers with asymmetrically arranged subunits are remarkably rare. One can easily imagine an oligomer with nonintegral rotation symmetry or screw symmetry that forms a complex of limited size, but without identical environments for

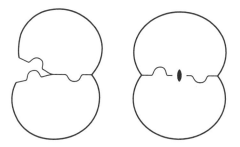

Figure 16 Evolutionary argument against asymmetry. *Right*, in a symmetrical complex as shown, a portion of the protein surface is optimized through evolution to form an interface. Both subunits have a "knob" and a complementary "hole" that match across a two-fold-symmetry axis, shown with the small football symbol. *Left*, in the asymmetric complex, the surface forming the interface must be simultaneously optimized for interface contact and for interaction with solvent: the upper subunit in the complex has its "knob" forming an interface contact and its "hole" exposed to solvent, and in the lower subunit, the roles are reversed. Similar diagrams can be envisioned for other cyclic and screw-related asymmetric complexes.

each subunit. One can envision a strong evolutionary force against such asymmetric dimers. Compare the two dimers in Figure 16. In the two-fold related dimer, the interaction surface is identical in the two subunits: evolution would proceed by optimizing the face to be complementary with its mate. In the asymmetric dimer, on the other hand, the interface surface must be simultaneously optimized to perform two roles. In one subunit, half of the "interface" will be in contact with the neighbor, and half will be exposed to solvent; in the other subunit, these roles are reversed. Thus, a large area must be evolutionarily optimized for interaction with the neighbor *and* with solvent, and only half of this surface actually makes contact in the dimer.

Such a complex has been proposed for hexokinase, based on screw-related subunits observed in crystal structures. However, the screw relationship is quite different in two different crystal habits, arguing against this as the unique dimerization mode. A similar screw relationship has been proposed for arginine kinase, based on biochemical data showing half-of-sites reactivity.

The BTV core (Figure 9a) is the first X-ray crystallographic example of this type of global asymmetry (31). In this structure, each position in a $T = 1$ icosahedron is filled with two subunits, bound back-to-back. The subunit is bean shaped and composed of three domains, and shows different conformations in the two different asymmetric positions. It has yet to be determined whether the back-to-back dimer is a stable intermediate in the process of assembly.

HIV-1 reverse transcriptase shows a severe example of asymmetry, as shown in Figure 17. The active complex is a dimer of a 66,000-Dalton subunit and a 51,000-Dalton subunit, the latter of which is a proteolyzed version of the first. The complex has a single polymerase active site, a single RNase H proofreading site,

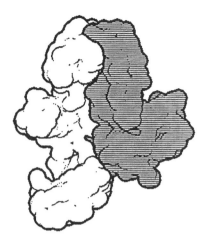

Figure 17 Asymmetry in human immunodeficiency virus-1 reverse transcriptase. The reverse transcriptase of HIV-1 is composed of two subunits, a 66,000-Dalton subunit (*white*) and a 51,000-Dalton subunit (*shaded*), which is a proteolyzed version of the larger. The two subunits adopt entirely different conformations in the complex.

and a single tRNA-binding site. Each subunit is composed of four similar subdomains, which pack together in entirely different orientation in the two subunits (52). Owing to the strictures of viral economy, here one sequence plays two very different structural roles.

EVOLUTION OF OLIGOMERIC PROTEINS

The remarkable solutions that cells have found to functional problems show that there are few limitations to what can be developed, given enough time. Just the same, there have been attempts to justify the observed forms of symmetry with underlying evolutionary arguments. Monod et al (72) presented one of the first ideas—that dimeric (isologous) interfaces are easier to create by mutation of existing monomers than are interfaces in complexes of higher symmetry (heterologous interfaces). They note that, on the surface of any monomer, pairs of complementary residues are prepositioned for formation of dimeric contacts owing to symmetry. For instance, a monomer with an arginine at one point on the surface and a glutamate some small distance away can immediately form two salt bridges with a second monomer, arginine on one to glutamate on the other, and glutamate on one to arginine on the other. The distance between the arginine and the glutamate on one subunit is necessarily identical with the distance between these two residues on the second subunit, providing the seed for a dimeric interface. This is not the case with higher symmetries. In complexes with higher cyclic symmetry, the distance and orientation of a putative "seeding" pair are not rigidly defined around the ring, so there exists the possibility of many nonproductive pairings.

In polymeric complexes, the existence of a prepositioned pair is not possible, because the two interacting surfaces are different, so evolution of a high-symmetry complex must begin with pairing of a single residue on each subunit. To give the same strength of binding for this nascent oligomer, the high-symmetry interfaces must have a fortuitous alignment of four residues on each subunit, two on one side of the interface and two on the other.

Evolution of a D2 tetramer may be favored over that of a C4 tetramer by this same argument. The D2 tetramer may be formed in two evolutionary steps, using an existing complementary pair to seed a dimer interface between two monomers, and then, after this dimer has been optimized by evolution, using a second complementary pair on the dimer to seed a tetramer interface. The creation of a C4 tetramer requires a concerted set of evolutionary steps, bringing the entire complex together at once. Hanson proposed that the requirement of evolution of an open dimer as a first step towards creation of a ring would be an improbable event and suggested that cyclic structures evolved sequentially by altering the relative orientation of the binding faces: "In this way, a D2 isologous ring could evolve successively into a D3 and then a D4 ring, or ring contraction could take place" (33). Looking to the many structures of oligomeric proteins, we see that this type of remodeling is probably not possible. It is difficult to postulate an evolutionary pathway that would change the angle between interfaces on a given subunit from 180° to 120°, either by repositioning an interface along the surface of a protein or by changing the angle by contracting the underlying protein fold.

Additional mutations favoring contact within interfaces are magnified in effect in oligomeric complexes. Monod et al write: "Because of the inherent cooperativity of their structure, symmetrical oligomers should constitute particularly sensitive targets for molecular evolution, allowing much stronger selective pressures to operate in the random pursuit of functionally adequate structures" (72). A single mutation will form two new hydrogen bonds in a dimer, and single mutations will simultaneously relieve two close steric contacts. The effect is further magnified in higher-order oligomers.

These evolutionary forces are easily overcome by a specific functional need. Two observations give insight into the strength of these intrinsic structural forces on evolution relative to the strength of functional need. Arguing for a strong evolutionary preference for dimer interfaces, dimers and tetramers with D2 "dimer-of-dimers" symmetry are the most prevalent symmetries for soluble enzymes, even for those not showing significant allosteric behavior. Arguing against a strong force, the processivity factors of DNA polymerase (Figure 5) use two different symmetries to fulfill the same need. In the *E. coli* β-subunit of polymerase III holoenzyme, two subunits assemble to form a ring with two interface patches. The eukaryotic processivity factor of DNA polymerase δ, on the other hand, adopts an identical ring-shape, but it is composed of three subunits. An identical functional need is fulfilled by a dimer and by a trimer. Obviously, the evolutionary forces seeding new interfaces are not strong enough to favor the dimer exclusively over the trimer or vice-versa.

Xu et al discuss three possible modes for evolution of dimeric proteins (96), based on a survey of modern dimeric proteins. The first is the traditional mechanism, in which a stable monomeric species develops a dimerization site, perhaps through the use of complementary pairs of residues as described above. We might expect this mechanism to account for most of the oligomeric species observed today, such as superoxide dismutase in Figure 2a. It is not hard to image superoxide dismutase as a primitive species, stable as a monomer. The second pathway is through domain swapping, as first proposed by Bennett et al (4). The interleukin shown in Figure 2b may have evolved in this manner, with a swap across the narrow linker at the center of the dumbbell-shaped molecule. The final mode for evolution of dimeric proteins is the most difficult of all—a one-step process, in which a dimeric species emerges fully formed. Xu et al propose several highly interlocked dimers, such as the gene V protein and the Trp aporepressor, as examples of this mechanism. Because of their extensive interdigitation, they are probably not stable as monomers, and the geometry of the backbone is not consistent with domain swapping.

Unexpected symmetries may reveal a "frozen accident" of evolution (95)—a symmetry formed in the past and then unable to evolve further without loss of function and a compromised organism. Hemoglobin provides a familiar example: One might expect that an α_4 tetramer would be more genetically compact than the observed $\alpha_2\beta_2$ heterotetramer. Presumably, early in the evolution of vertebrates, a gene duplication formed two copies of subunits for a tetrameric hemoglobin, and of the several competing forms—α_4, β_4, or $\alpha_2\beta_2$—the heterotetramer was selected.

THE AESTHETICS OF SYMMETRY

Looking at much of decorative and fine art, we find that symmetry has a strong aesthetic appeal for many cultures. Symmetrical patterns, arrangements, and objects adorn our rooms and define our architecture, and breaks from symmetry are incorporated deliberately and with artistic intent, because they will surprise and shock our expectations. When choosing vegetables or flowers, when looking at plants and animals, or when admiring the latest movie star, we favor the most symmetric, seeking out the most "perfect" individuals. This prediliction for symmetry may have its roots far back in our evolution, where symmetry was often a sign of a healthy mate or fresh food.

Nature also selects for symmetry, for reasons of economy and control. These symmetries occur at the molecular level, as described in this review, and extend to the cellular and organismal level, for much the same reasons. Because symmetrical complexes are functionally more successful and economical than asymmetric objects in many cases, our world is filled with five-pointed starfish, Y-shaped antibodies, spiral flowers, circular tree rings, geodesic diatoms, lenticular red blood cells, and perfectly icosahedral viruses. These symmetries were perfected through functional pressures on evolution; their appeal to our senses is merely a happy side effect.

Of course, there remain symmetries that likely exist simply through serendipitous combinations of physical forces—not selected for functional need, but appearing fully formed once the universe took its current shape. The crystalline beauty of minerals is one example, resulting from the minimization of inherent directional interactions of molecules. Similarly, the α-helix is another, with a structure defined not through evolutionary forces but through the intrinsic chemical geometry of the polypeptide chain. The rainbow is perhaps the most glorious example—a gift of Nature existing simply through combination of the surface tension and refractive index of water.

ACKNOWLEDGMENTS

This work was funded by grant DEFG03 96ER2272 from the U.S. Department of Energy. This is publication 12361-MB from the Scripps Research Institute.

Visit the Annual Reviews home page at www.AnnualReviews.org

LITERATURE CITED

1. Abrahams JP, Leslie AGW, Lutter R, Walker JE. 1994. Structure at 2.8 angstroms resolution of F1-ATPase from bovine heart mitochondria. *Nature* 370:621–28
2. Adams MJ, Blundell TL, Dodson EJ, Dodson GG, Vijayan M, et al. 1969. Structure of rhombohedral 2 zinc insulin crystals. *Nature* 224:491–95
3. Barford D, Johnson LN. 1989. The allosteric transition of glycogen phosphorylase. *Nature* 340:609–16
4. Bennett MJ, Schlunegger MP, Eisenberg D. 1995. 3D domain swapping: a mechanism for oligomer assembly. *Protein Sci.* 4:2455–68
5. Berger B, Shor PW. 1998. On the structure of the scaffolding core of bacteriophage T4 and its role in head length determination. *J. Struct. Biol.* 121:285–94
6. Beuron F, Maurizi MR, Belnap DM, Kocsis E, Booy FP, et al. 1998. At sixes and sevens: characterization of the symmetry mismatch of the ClpAP chaperone-assisted protease. *J. Struct. Biol.* 123:248–59
7. Blundell T, Dodson G, Hodgkin D, Mercola

D. 1972. Insulin: the structure in the crystal and its reflection in chemistry and biology. *Adv. Protein Chem.* 26:279–402
8. Blundell TL, Srinivasan N. 1996. Symmetry, stability, and dynamics of multidomain and multicomponent protein systems. *Proc. Natl. Acad. Sci. USA* 93:14243–48
9. Boyer PD. 1993. The binding site change mechanism for ATP synthase—some probabilities and possibilities. *Biochim. Biophys. Acta* 1140:215–50
10. Calladine CR. 1978. Change of waveform in bacterial flagella: the role of mechanics at the molecular level. *J. Mol. Biol.* 118:457–79
11. Caspar DLD. 1966. Design and assembly of organized biological structure. *Molecular Architecture in Cell Physiology, Symp. Soc. Gen. Physiol.,* pp. 191–207. New York: Prentice Hall
12. Caspar DLD, Klug A. 1962. Physical principles in the construction of regular viruses. *Cold Spring Harbor Symp. Quant. Biol.* 27: 1–24
13. Chothia C. 1991. Asymmetry in protein

structures. *CIBA Found. Symp.* 162:36–57

14. Chothia C, Janin J. 1975. Principles of protein-protein recognition. *Nature* 256: 705–8

15. Clegg JS. 1984. Properties and metabolism of the aqueous cytoplasm and its boundaries. *Am. J. Physiol.* 246:R133–51

16. Cornish-Bowden AJ, Koshland DE Jr. 1971. The quaternary structure of proteins composed of identical subunits. *J. Biol. Chem.* 246:3092–102

17. Crane HR. 1950. Principles and problems of biological growth. *Sci. Monthly* June:376–89

18. Crick FHC, Watson JD. 1956. Structure of small viruses. *Nature* 177:473–75

19. Crick FHC, Watson JD. 1957. Virus structure: general principles. *CIBA Found. Symp. "The Nature of Viruses",* pp. 5–13. Boston: Little, Brown

20. Crothers DM, Metzger H. 1972. The influence of polyvalency on the binding properties of antibodies. *Immunochemistry* 9:341–57

21. Degani Y, Degani C. 1980. Enzymes with asymmetrically arranged subunits. *Trends Biochem. Sci.* 5:337–41

22. DeVos AM, Ultsch M, Kossiakoff AA. 1992. Human growth hormone and extracellular domain of its receptor: crystal structure of the complex. *Science* 255:306–12

23. Evans PR. 1991. Structural aspects of allostery. *Curr. Opin. Struct. Biol.* 1:773–79

24. Fulton AB. 1982. How crowded is the cytoplasm? *Cell* 30:345–47

25. Ganser BK, Li S, Klishko VY, Finch JT, Sundquist WI. 1999. Assembly and analysis of conical models for the HIV-1 core. *Science* 283:80–83

26. Garcia-Bellido A. 1996. Symmetries throughout organic evolution. *Proc. Natl. Acad. Sci. USA* 93:14229–32

27. Goodsell DS. 1991. Inside a living cell. *Trends Biochem. Sci.* 16:203–6

28. Goodsell DS, Olson AJ. 1993. Soluble proteins: size, shape and function. *Trends Biochem. Sci.* 18:65–68

29. Gouax JE, Lipscomb WN. 1990. Crystal structures of phosphoacetamide ligated T and phosphoacetamide and malonate ligated R states of aspartate carbamoyltransferase at 2.8-Å resolution and neutral pH. *Biochemistry* 29:389–402

30. Greenbury CL, Moore DH, Nunn LAC. 1965. The reaction with red cells of 7S rabbit antibody, its sub-units and their recombinants. *Immunology* 8:420–31

31. Grimes JM, Burroughs JN, Gouet P, Diprose JM, Malby R, et al. 1998. The atomic structure of the bluetongue virus core. *Nature* 395:470–78

32. Groll M, Ditzel L, Lowe J, Stock D, Bochtler M, et al. 1997. Structure of the 20S proteasome from yeast at 2.4 Å resolution. *Nature* 386:463–71

33. Hanson KR. 1966. Symmetry of protein oligomers formed by isologous association. *J. Mol. Biol.* 22:405–9

34. Hargittai I, Hargittai M. 1995. *Symmetry through the Eyes of a Chemist.* New York: Plenum

35. Harrison SC, Olson AJ, Schutt CE, Winkler FK, Bricogne G. 1978. Tomato bushy stunt virus at 2.9 Angstroms resolution. *Nature* 276:368–73

36. Hendrix RW. 1978. Symmetry mismatch and DNA packaging in large bacteriophages. *Proc. Natl. Acad. Sci. USA* 75:4779–83

37. Herendeen DR, Kelly TJ. 1996. DNA polymerase III: running rings around the fork. *Cell* 84:5–8

38. Heuser J, Kirchhausen T. 1985. Deep-etch views of clathrin assemblies. *J. Ultrastruct. Res.* 92:1–27

39. Hewitt JA. 1977. On the influence of polyvalent ligands on membrane curvature. *J. Theor. Biol.* 64:455–72

40. Hoare MR, Pal P. 1975. Physical cluster mechanics: statistical thermodynamics and nucleation theory for monatomic systems. *Adv. Phys.* 24:645–78

41. Iwata S, Kamata K, Yoshida S, Minowa T, Ohta T. 1994. T and R states in the crystals of bacterial L-lactate dehydrogenase reveal

the mechanism for allosteric control. *Nature Struct. Biol.* 1:176–85

42. Johnson JE, Speir JA. 1997. Quasi-equivalent viruses: a paradigm for protein assemblies. *J. Mol. Biol.* 269:665–75

43. Jones S, Thornton JM. 1996. Principles of protein-protein interactions. *Proc. Natl. Acad. Sci. USA* 93:13–20

44. Juo ZS, Chiu TK, Leiberman PM, Baikalov I, Berk AJ, Dickerson RE. 1996. How proteins recognize the TATA box. *J. Mol. Biol.* 261:239–54

45. Kamiya R, Asakura S, Wakabayashi K, Namba K. 1979. Transition of bacterial flagella from helical to straight forms with different subunit arrangements. *J. Mol. Biol.* 131:725–42

46. Kellenberger E. 1990. Form determination of the heads of bacteriophages. *Eur. J. Biochem.* 190:233–48

47. Kelman Z, Finkelstein J, O'Donnell M. 1995. Why have six-fold symmetry? *Curr. Biol.* 5:1239–42

48. Klotz IM. 1967. Protein subunits: a table. *Science* 155:697–98

49. Klotz IM, Darnall DW, Langerman NR, eds. 1975. *Quaternary Structure of Proteins*, pp. 293–411. New York: Academic

50. Klotz IM, Langerman NR, Darnall DW. 1970. Quaternary structure of proteins. *Annu. Rev. Biochem.* 39:25–62

51. Klug A. 1968. Point groups and the design of aggregates. *Nobel Symp. "Symmetry and Function of Biological Systems at the Macromolecular Level" 11th, Stockholm*, pp. 425–36. Wiley & Sons, New York

52. Kohlstaedt LA, Wang J, Friedman JM, Rice PA, Steitz TA. 1992. Crystal structure at 3.5 Å resolution of HIV-1 reverse transcriptase complexed with an inhibitor. *Science* 256:1783–89

53. Kong X-P, Onrust R, O-Donnell M, Kuriyan J. 1992. Three-dimensional structure of the beta subunit of *E. coli* DNA polymerase III holoenzyme: a sliding DNA clamp. *Cell* 69:425–37

54. Koshland DE. 1976. The evolution of function in enzymes. *Fed. Proc.* 35:2104–11

55. Koshland DE, Nemethy G, Filmer D. 1966. Comparison of experimental binding data and theoretical models in proteins containing subunits. *Biochemistry* 5:365–85

56. Krishna TSR, Kong X-P, Gary S, Burgers PM, Kuriyan J. 1994. Crystal structure of the eukaryotic DNA processivity factor PCNA. *Cell* 79:1233–43

57. Kurland CG. 1992. Translational accuracy and the fitness of bacteria. *Annu. Rev. Genet.* 26:29–50

58. Labeit S, Kolmerer B. 1995. Titins: giant proteins in charge of muscle ultrastructure and elasticity. *Science* 270:293–96

59. Ladenstein R, Schneider M, Huber R, Bartunik H-D, Wilson K, et al. 1988. Heavy riboflavin synthase from *Bacillus subtilis*: crystal structure analysis of the icosahedral beta-60 capsid at 3.3 A resolution. *J. Mol. Biol.* 203:1045–70

60. Larsen TA, Olson AJ, Goodsell DS. 1998. Morphology of protein-protein interfaces. *Structure* 6:421–27

61. Lewis MS, Youle RJ. 1986. Ricin subunit association: thermodynamics and the role of the disulfide bond in toxicity. *J. Biol. Chem.* 261:11571–77

62. Liddington RC, Yan Y, Moulai J, Sahli R, Benjamin TJ, Harrison SC. 1991. Structure of simian virus 40 at 3.8-Angstrom resolution. *Nature* 354:278–84

63. Lipscomb WN. 1991. Structure and function of allosteric enzymes. *CHEMTRACTS-Biochem. Mol. Biol.* [Data Trace Chem. Publ.] 2:1–15

64. Lowe J, Stock D, Jap B, Zwickl P, Baumeister W, Huber R. 1995. Crystal structure of the 20S proteosome from the archaeon T. acidophilum at 3.4 Å resolution. *Science* 268:533–39

65. Lumry R, Rajender S. 1970. Enthalpy-entropy compensation phenomena in water solutions of proteins and small molecules: a ubiquitous property of water. *Biopolymers* 9:1125–227

66. Matsudaira P. 1991. Modular organization of actin crosslinking proteins. *Trends Biochem. Sci.* 16:87–92

67. Mattevi A, Rizzi M, Bolognesi M. 1996. New structures of allosteric proteins revealing remarkable conformational changes. *Curr. Opin. Struct. Biol.* 6:824–29

68. Mattevi A, Valentini G, Rizzi M, Speranza ML, Bolognesi M, Coda A. 1995. Crystal structure of *Escherichia coli* pyruvate kinase type I: molecular basis of the allosteric transition. *Structure* 3:729–41

69. Mitchison T, Kirschner M. 1984. Dynamic instability of microtubule growth. *Nature* 312:237–42

70. Mitchison TJ. 1988. Microtubule dynamics and kinetochore function in mitosis. *Annu. Rev. Cell Biol.* 4:527–49

71. Monod J. 1968. On symmetry and function in biological systems. *Nobel Symp. Symmetry Funct. Biol. Syst. Macromol. Lev., 11th, Stockholm,* pp. 15–27. New York: Wiley

72. Monod J, Wyman J, Changeux J-P. 1965. On the nature of allosteric transitions: a plausible model. *J. Mol. Biol.* 12:88–118

73. Moras D, Olsen KW, Sabesan MN, Buehner M, Ford GC, Rossmann MG. 1975. Studies of asymmetry in the three-dimensional structure of lobster D-glyceraldehyde-3-phosphate dehydrogenase. *J. Biol. Chem.* 250:9137–62

74. Olson AJ, Bricogne G, Harrison SC. 1983. Structure of tomato bushy stunt virus IV. The virus particle at 2.9 Å resolution. *J. Mol. Biol.* 171:61–93

75. Parker J. 1989. Errors and alternatives in reading the universal genetic code. *Microbiol. Rev.* 53:273–98

76. Pauling L. 1953. Protein interactions: aggregation of globular proteins. *Discov. Faraday Soc.* 13:170–76

77. Paulson JR, Laemmli UK. 1977. Morphogenetic core of the bacteriophage T4 head. Structure of the core in polyheads. *J. Mol. Biol.* 111:459–85

78. Pereira PJB, Bergner A, Macedo-Ribeiro S, Huber R, Matxchiner G, et al. 1998. Human beta-trypsin is a ring-like tetramer with active sites facing a central pore. *Nature* 392:306–11

79. Perutz MF. 1989. Mechanisms of cooperativity and allosteric regulation in proteins. *Q. Rev. Biophys.* 22:139–236

80. Reed LJ, Hackert ML. 1990. Structure-function relationships in dihydrolipoamide acyltransferases. *J. Biol. Chem.* 265:8971–74

81. Ricard J, Noat G. 1985. Kinetic cooperativity of monomeric mnemonical enzymes. *Eur. J. Biochem.* 152:557–64

82. Rossmann MG. 1984. Constraints on the assembly of spherical virus particles. *Virology* 134:1–11

83. Seydoux F, Malhotra OP, Bernhard SA. 1974. Half-site reactivity. *CRC Crit. Rev. Biochem.* 2:227–57

84. Sharp K, Fine R, Honig B. 1987. Computer simulations of the diffusion of a substrate to an active site of an enzyme. *Science* 236:1460–64

85. Sixma TK, Pronk SE, Kalk KH, Wartna ES, Zanten BAM, et al. 1991. Crystal structure of a cholera toxin-related heat-labile enterotoxin from *E. coli. Nature* 351:371–77

86. Srere PA. 1981. Protein crystals as a model for mitochondrial proteins. *Trends Biochem. Sci.* 6:4–7

87. Srere PA. 1984. Why are enzymes so big? *Trends Biochem. Sci.* 9:387–90

88. Stossel TP. 1989. From signal to pseudopod: How cells control cytoplasmic actin assembly. *J. Biol. Chem.* 264:18261–64

89. Strater N, Hakansson K, Schnappauf G, Braus G, Lipscomb WN. 1996. Crystal structure of the T state of allosteric yeast chorismate mutase and comparison with the R state. *Proc. Natl. Acad. Sci. USA* 93:3330–34

90. Svedberg T. 1929. Mass and size of protein molecules. *Nature* 123:871

91. Theil EC. 1987. Ferritin: structure, gene regulation, and cellular function in

animals, plants and microorganisms. *Annu. Rev. Biochem.* 56:289–315

92. vanHeel M, Orlova EV, Dube P, Tavares P. 1996. Intrinsic versus imposed curvature in cyclical oligomers: the portal protein of bacteriophage SPP1. *EMBO J.* 15:4785–88

93. Wilson DR. 1993. Bacterial flagellar filaments and their component flagellins. *Can. J. Microbiol.* 39:451–72

94. Wlodawer A, Erickson JW. 1993. Structure-based inhibitors of HIV-1 protease. *Annu. Rev. Biochem.* 62:543–85

95. Wolynes PG. 1996. Symmetry and the energy landscapes of biomolecules. *Proc. Natl. Acad. Sci. USA* 93:14249–55

96. Xu D, Tsai C-J, Nussinov R. 1998. Mechanism and evolution of protein dimerization. *Protein Sci.* 7:533–44

97. Xu Z, Horwich AL, Sigler PB. 1997. The crystal structure of the asymmetric GroEL-GroES-(ADP)7 chaperonin complex. *Nature* 388:741–50

98. Yang M, Chen X-p, Militello K, Hoffman R, Fernandez B, et al. 1997. Alanine-scanning mutagenesis of *Bacillus subtilis* trp RNA-binding attenuation protein (TRAP) reveals residues involved in tryptophan binding and RNA binding. *J. Mol. Biol.* 270:696–710

99. Yeager M, Berriman JA, Baker TS, Bellamy AR. 1994. Three-dimensional structure of the rotavirus haemagglutinin VP4 by cryo-electron microscopy and difference map analysis. *EMBO J.* 13:1011–18

100. Zhang R-G, Scott DL, Westbrook ML, Nance S, Spangler BD, et al. 1995. The three-dimensional crystal structure of cholera toxin. *J. Mol. Biol.* 251:563–73

101. Protein Data Bank accession codes for structures used in the figures. The PDB may be reached at http://www.rcsb.org/pdb. Figure 1: pepsin, 5pep; alcohol dehydrogenase, 2ohx; porin, 2por; neuraminidase, 1ivb; phosphofructokinase, 1pfk; aspartate carbamoyltransferase, 1at1; glycolate oxidase, 1gox; glutamine synthetase, 2gls; protocatechuate-3,4-dioxygenase, 3pcg; ferritin, 1hrs; satellite tobacco necrosis virus, 2stv. Figure 2 superoxide dismutase, 1xso; interleukin 10, 1ilk. Figure 4: fructose-1,6-bisphosphatase, 4fbp (T) and 5fbp (R); aspartate carbamoyltransferase, 4at1 (T) and 1at1 (R). Figure 5: β subunit of RNA pol III, 2pol; PCNA, 1axc. Figure 6: GroEL, 1der; proteasome, 1ryp. Figure 7: satellite tobacco necrosis virus, 2stv; tomato bushy stunt virus, 2tbv. Figure 8: bluetongue virus, 2btv; simian virus 40, 1sva. Figure 11: hemoglobin, 4hhb. Figure 13: HIV-1 protease, 7hvp. Figure 14: GroEL:GroES, 1aon. Figure 16: reverse transcriptase, 3hvt.

Annu. Rev. Biophys. Biomol. Struct. 2000. 29:155–81

ELECTROKINETICALLY CONTROLLED MICROFLUIDIC ANALYSIS SYSTEMS

Luc Bousse, Claudia Cohen, Theo Nikiforov, Andrea Chow, Anne R. Kopf-Sill, Robert Dubrow, and J. Wallace Parce

Caliper Technologies Corporation, 605 Fairchild Drive, Mountain View, California 94043; e-mail: luc.bousse@calipertech.com

Key Words   bioassays, integrated systems, microfabrication, lab-on-a-chip

■ **Abstract**   Electrokinetic forces are emerging as a powerful means to drive microfluidic systems with flow channel cross-sectional dimensions in the tens of micrometers and flow rates in the nanoliter per second range. These systems provide many advantages such as improved analysis speed, improved reproducibility, greatly reduced reagent consumption, and the ability to perform multiple operations in an integrated fashion. Planar microfabrication methods are used to make these analysis chips in materials such as glass or polymers. Many applications of this technology have been demonstrated, such as DNA separations, enzyme assays, immunoassays, and PCR amplification integrated with microfluidic assays. Further development of this technology is expected to yield higher levels of functionality of sample throughput on a single microfluidic analysis chip.

CONTENTS

1056-8700/00/0610-0155$14.00

155

INTRODUCTION

The concept of fabricating a miniaturized electrokinetic analysis device on an insulating planar substrate was first demonstrated by Harrison et al (36), Manz (58), and Manz et al (59) in 1991 and 1992. Since then, much work has been done on developing this concept, mostly by using electrokinetic driving forces. Most initial work concentrated on establishing the electrokinetic control of flow, using electroosmosis (25, 35, 75, 76), demonstrating separations of species such as amino acids (23, 35, 76), and fabricating devices (25). In 1994, Jacobson et al demonstrated methods to reproducibly inject confined sample plugs in the picoliter range (40, 42).

It quickly became apparent that these microfabricated systems could be used for a much wider range of applications than simple separations and that the real power of "on-chip" devices lies in the ability to design integrated devices. The first examples consisted of applying known concepts in separation science, such as pre- or postcolumn reactions, to microfabricated devices (28, 41, 43).

More recently, the concept of not just performing separations, but also integrating complete analysis systems in one device, has attracted most attention. Such systems are often called "Labs on a Chip." This implies that some of the greatest benefits of miniaturizing and integrating are in the reagent handling steps, not just separation and detection. In fact, several types of assays on a chip have been developed that do not involve any separation. The implied promise of microfluidic-analysis systems is the integration of reagent handling and of multiple operations such as dilution, mixing, incubation, separation, and detection (68). The automation involved is expected to improve the reproducibility of the results and eliminate the manual labor, time, and pipetting errors that occur in the intermediate stages of an analytical procedure.

This review examines the progress that has been made in the field of microfluidic-analysis systems, particularly in system integration. Because most of these systems are driven by electrokinetic driving forces, we limit our analysis to that particular mode of actuation. Advances in this field involve many aspects, such as device fabrication, device design and topology, assay chemistry, microfluidics, and detection methods. These elements are all connected; for instance, the sensitivity of detection dictates the required sample size in a separation, which in turn determines the geometry of the sample injection device. Thus, in the following sections we address these issues and also look at some examples of assays that have been carried out in microsystems, such as enzyme assays, immunoassays, polymerase chain reactions (PCR), and DNA separations.

MICROFLUIDICS

Channel Dimensions

The first design decision when making a microfluidic system is the cross-sectional dimensions of the flow channels. Channels with dimensions in the millimeter range are still low volume, that is, in the microliter range for each centimeter of length. But the biggest problem with such large channels is that diffusional mixing is very slow.

It is possible to deduce from basic principles that there exists an optimal fluidic size domain for microfluidics. In all fluidic technologies with channels <1 mm in width and height and velocities not greater than the centimeter-per-second range, the Reynolds numbers for flow will be so low that all flow will be laminar. That implies that mixing must occur by diffusion, unaided by turbulence. Diffusion at these length scales is a relatively slow process, and the time required for molecules to travel a distance x is given by $x^2/2D$, where D is the diffusion coefficient.

As an example, we can consider the case of channels $\sim$1 mm wide, in which two streams of different composition are brought together—side by side—at a junction. For the flow to be homogeneous, the molecules must diffuse about half the channel width. Assuming a D of 3 $\times$ 10^{-6} cm^2/s (typical for small molecules), that process will take 400 s. If the flow has a velocity of 1 cm/s, the channel must be 4 m long before the mix has homogenized. Such a long channel and long mixing time are not what we expect for a microfluidic system, and that problem is a serious obstacle to all devices with channels at a size scale in the millimeter range. However, the electrokinetic microsystems we discuss here typically use much smaller channels—70-μm wide, for instance. Then the mixing time under the same conditions is only 2 s. The velocity is usually $\sim$1 mm/s, so that the needed mixing length is only 2 mm.

On the other end of the dimension spectrum, a different physical issue constrains the ability to work in very low volumes, namely the problem of detecting very small numbers of molecules. A typical required detection sensitivity for many real-world biological assays is about 1 nM. In a volume of a 1 μm^3, the number of molecules present at that concentration is 0.6. In other words, about half the time there will be nothing to detect. In the other half, single-molecule detection sensitivity would be required. In general, $\geq$1000 molecules are needed before the statistical errors are negligible, and, at 1 nM, that means a volume of 12 μm^3.

We therefore conclude that the optimal size domain for microfluidic-channel cross sections is somewhere between 10 μm and 100 μm. Below that, detection is too difficult, and, above that, mixing is too slow or requires additional mixing devices.

Choice of Fluidic Driving Force

Given that the channel cross section will be $\sim$2 $\times$ 10^{-3} mm^2 and the flow velocity is typically a few millimeters or centimeters per second at most, it is clear that the flow rate in microfluidics at this scale will typically be in the range of 1 to 20 nanoliter-per-second range. This flow rate must be accurately controlled; for instance, when diluting an assay component, two flows must be controlled to within ~1%, which places the required accuracy in the picoliter-per-second range.

Several driving forces are available to generate these flows. One commonly used one is pressure, that is, pneumatic drive (1, 67) or a mechanical micropump. Although many types of micropumps exist (32, 78–80), none can provide accurate flow control in the nanoliters-per-second domain. Given these problems, many researchers have decided to use electroosmosis or electrophoresis as a driving force. This requires the use of electric fields in the range of several hundreds of volts per centimeter and thus of voltages up to a few kilovolts for channels that are 2–10 cm long. The implication is that on-chip electrophoresis systems must be made in an insulating substrate, to avoid electrical breakdown. With Caliper's multichannel high-voltage power supplies, flows can be directly controlled with accuracy >1% by using their current control capability (15). Another advantage is that electroosmotic flow is plug flow, and it will cause less dispersion than parabolic flow.

Use of High-Ionic-Strength Plugs for Sample Transport

Although electrokinetic fluid transport has the major advantage of allowing simultaneous control of the flow rate at many wells with picoliter-per-second accuracy, it has the potential disadvantage of unwanted separation of components during transport. Owing to the electrophoretic mobility of charged compounds, samples containing components with different charges will separate during transport. In many cases, such as screening large numbers of unknown compounds, this creates a problem. We have recently presented a solution to this problem, namely the use of sample plugs with high conductivity surrounded by low-conductivity buffers (20). This high-low salt plug transport prevents separation of the analyte mixtures under circumstances in which it is desired to keep all components together, independent of charge. Because the electric field in any region is inversely proportional to conductivity, the field will be lower in the high-conductivity regions and therefore the electrophoretic movement of compounds will also be lower.

To demonstrate this, we conducted experiments on glass microchips with two fluorescent dyes with different electrophoretic mobilities—rhodamine, which is neutral, and fluorescein, which is negatively charged. If the solution is of constant ionic strength, a plug of a mixture of fluorescein and rhodamine will separate during transport, as shown in Figure 1. To avoid this separation, we placed the same two dyes in a high-conductivity salt plug consisting of a 100-mM borate buffer at pH 8.9 (conductivity = 2.1 mS/cm). The low-conductivity buffer, 20 mM borate, also at pH 8.9 (conductivity = 0.54 mS/cm) was used as the low-conductivity driver solution. Using a microfluidic device with a cross intersection, we created a plug of fluorescein and rhodamine in high-conductivity buffer, surrounded by extra guard bands of the same high-conductivity buffer, which were in turn surrounded by the low-conductivity driver solution (see 20 for details). Figure 2

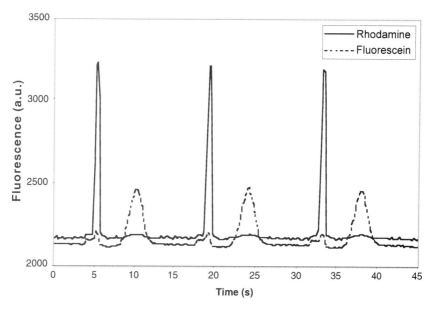

Figure 1 Separation of multiple plugs of fluorescein (*dashed line*) and rhodamine (*solid line*) as they travel down a channel.

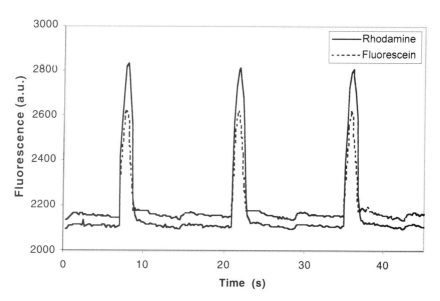

Figure 2 Same experiment as shown in Figure 1, but with confinement of the dye mixture in a high-conductivity plug. *dashed line*, fluorescein; *solid line*, rhodamine.

shows that, at the same observation point as in Figure 1, the two dye peaks stay together.

We conclude that high-low salt transport can successfully be used to keep components of different charges together. The use of solutions at different ionic strength and therefore different electroosmotic mobility does create a much more complex situation in the chip however. The electric fields are not in steady state anymore, because the low-field regions move with the plugs. In addition, pressure gradients are generated by the presence of plugs with different electroosmotic mobility, and therefore flow is driven by both pressure and electroosmosis and is not a pure plug flow anymore. Numerical modeling has proven to be useful in understanding and simulating the physics of flow in this domain (20).

DEVICE FABRICATION

Glass or Quartz Devices

In earlier reports of capillary electrophoresis on microfabricated glass chips, several types of glass were used, namely soda lime glass (23, 40, 42, 91), borosilicate glass (25, 75), and quartz (28, 44, 45). The fabrication method consists of photolithographically etching channels in the glass or quartz, using a hydrofluoric-acid–based solution, then thermally bonding another plate of the same glass to the first one. The etching step can be difficult for borosilicate glasses, which sometimes etch very poorly (25). The bonding step is very sensitive to the presence of any particulate between the plates. Quartz chips are more difficult to bond because they require much higher temperatures and still are more sensitive to particulates owing to their very high softening temperature.

Another step required in the process is drilling of holes for reagent access in either of the two glass plates before bonding, which can be done with a number of conventional machining methods.

Polymer Devices

A number of researchers have worked on making microfluidic devices from polymers instead of glass, to reduce the cost and effort involved. Ideally, devices could be fabricated by using mass-production methods such as injection molding. It is not yet clear, however, that this goal has been achieved.

There are two main directions in which the polymer chip work has been going, namely rigid transparent polymers such as acrylics and flexible polymers such as silicone rubber (polydimethylsiloxane). In rigid polymers, laser ablation was first used by Roberts et al (70) to create very precisely defined channel cross sections in a variety of polymers such as polycarbonate and polystyrene. The channels were sealed by laminating a thin film of poly(ethyleneterephtalate) with a polyethylene adhesive over the patterned polymer substrate, thereby creating channels with different materials on opposite sides. McCormick et al (61) used injection molding to pattern an acrylic polymer, and they also used an adhesive-tape lamination to seal the channels. This again creates a structure with different electroosmotic flows on opposite walls, but that may not be a problem as long as these devices are used only in DNA applications, where the electroosmotic flow is typically suppressed. Laser-ablated devices with integrated electrochemical detection were recently described by Rossier et al (71).

Another fabrication method in polymers that is becoming popular in microfluidics is embossing or imprinting (3, 60), first described in polymethylmethaceylate substrates by using a wire or an etched silicon chip (60).

All of the polymer fabrication processes above require a bonding step, in which a cover layer is bonded to close the channels. This is often a difficult process, because the same driving force that allows the bonding also tends to deform the channel shape. Using an adhesive tape avoids that problem, but at the cost of creating channels with different top and bottom surfaces. A fabrication method does exist that avoids the issue of bonding entirely; it uses a combination of depositions and a sacrificial layer etching to create a channel on top of a substrate (86). The polymer in this case is parylene-C.

The other type of polymer microfluidic circuit uses flexible silicone rubber (polydimethylsiloxane) replicates of masters that have been made by other means, often by silicon micromachining (21, 22). In this case bonding is a reversible, room-temperature process, because a small amount of pressure will create an adequate seal. Devices can also be peeled open, cleaned out, and reused. Duffy et al (21) have used oxidized silicone rubber devices, which form an irreversible seal at room temperature when pressed together.

Silicon Devices

Some of the earliest work done in this field used electrophoresis in channels fabricated in silicon substrates (51, 59, 66). This was a natural choice, because almost all advanced microfabrication technology was initially developed in silicon. However, the major problem that occurs on any conducting substrate is that high voltages cannot be used owing to breakdown problems (59). Thus, the use of silicon was quickly abandoned when it became clear that microchannels could just as easily be etched in glass or quartz.

Recently, however, work by Burns et al (7, 8) returns to the use of silicon substrates. Much of this work involves fluid control, metering, and heating of very small volumes of fluid. The electrical breakdown issue arises only in that it limits the fields used in electrophoresis to the 10-V/cm range, which results in separations much slower than those described above. This problem could be resolved in several ways, for instance by developing a better insulator layer or by scaling the devices to dimensions small enough that the needed voltages fall in the range that silicon can support. In any case, it leaves the question of what the possible advantages are to using silicon as a substrate material. The best justification is to also use the silicon for some other device, a detector for instance, as was done by Burns et al (7).

DETECTION METHODS

In the first extensive description of their work by Harrison et al (36), the microfluidic device included several platinum electrodes intended for electrochemical detection. However, they found that detection by fluorescence was much more powerful and convenient, and all of the data they reported used fluorescence detection. The vast majority of the work since then has followed the same path. Fluorescence detection scales well to microvolumes, because the excitation light is concentrated to a smaller area as the dimensions become smaller.

Detection by measuring optical absorbance does not scale as well and is very hard to do because the path length is so short in a microchip. The big advantage of UV-absorbance detection is that most organic compounds can then be detected without any labeling. A microfabricated device with longer path length for absorbance detection on a chip has been described by Liang et al (55).

Recently, there have been many reports describing detection methods other than fluorescence, usually with the hope of simplifying the detection system. Examples are electrochemical detection (71, 83, 90), luminescence (57), and Raman spectroscopy (82).

Another attractive detection concept is to interface the output of a microchip system with a mass spectrometer, typically by using electrospray ionization (26, 27, 29, 53, 69, 93). The potential advantages are that mass spectrometry is capable of generating very detailed information on a sample very quickly and the very small samples required are well matched to the flow rates of microchip systems.

Crabtree et al have recently described a variation on the theme of fluorescence detection that they call Shah Convolution Fourier Transform Detection (19), which attempts to improve detection limits by collecting light from each component as it passes behind a periodic array of slits. By collecting fluorescent emissions during the entire separation rather than only at a detection point, one can hope to improve the sensitivity of detection.

DNA SEPARATIONS

Scaling of Separation Efficiency

One area in which microfabrication has been shown to have clear benefits is rapid separations. Compared with conventional capillary electrophoresis, in which separation times are usually ≥ 10 min, microchip systems have proved to be capable of producing high-quality separations in seconds. This was first demonstrated by Jacobson et al (40), for the separation of fluorescent dyes with different charges. Since then, several authors have demonstrated the ability to separate DNA fragments rapidly, starting with Woolley & Mathies (91) and more recently Schmalzing et al (73) and Bousse et al (6). The most rapid separations have been reported recently by Jacobson et al (39), who demonstrated the ability to separate dyes in <1 ms, using very high electric fields.

The key to rapid separations is the ability to inject a very small sample plug, and microchip systems can do this very effectively by confining the plug at an intersection (42). This is achieved by controlling the voltage at all four terminals of a simple cross-topology and pinching the sample in the intersection. Thus, a very small plug can be injected, with dimensions approximately the same as the channel width. Electrophoretic separations are therefore a good example of the scaling laws involved when the system is miniaturized.

The following theoretical treatment is not limited to DNA separations; however, because most recent work on microchip separations has involved nucleic acids, we confine the examples to that case.

The ability of a channel to separate components of different mobilities is described by the number of theoretical plates. The main causes of sample broadening in electrophoretic systems are the width of the injected sample and diffusion. The detection area is usually narrow enough to be negligible, and thermal broadening does not occur because the very thin rectangular channels that are used have good heat transfer properties. It can then be shown (6) that the number of theoretical plates can be written as

$$N = \frac{L}{\left(\frac{2D}{\mu E} + \frac{w^2}{12L}\right)}, \qquad \text{1.}$$

where L is the column length, D the diffusion coefficient, μ the mobility, E the electric field, w_{inj} the injection length, and w_{det} the detection length, and $w = (w_{inj}^2 + w_{det}^2)^{1/2}$. This equation can be rearranged to show that, for small values of L, the number of theoretical plates increases as the square of column length:

$$N = 12\left(\frac{L}{w}\right)^2 \frac{1}{1 + L/L_0}, \qquad \text{2.}$$

in which a characteristic length appears, which is defined as

$$L_0 = \frac{\mu E w^2}{24D}. \qquad \text{3.}$$

The length L_0 is the distance down the separation channel at which diffusion and injection width contribute equally to the width of a sample plug. This defines a transition between two modes of separation:

1. $L \ll L_0$, and the number of theoretical plates is given by $N = 12(L/w)^2$. In this example, the separation is defined only by the injection width and does not depend on diffusion. Because the plate number increases as the square of column length, rapid increases in N are possible by using longer columns. In this region, microfabricated devices enable us to take maximal advantage of their ability to define a very small sample plug.

2. $L \gg L_0$, and the number of theoretical plates is $N = (\mu E L/2D)$, which is the usual expression seen in textbooks on capillary electrophoresis. In this region of operation, the plate number increases only linearly with time

owing to sample diffusion. The separation power of a device does not depend on the size of an injected sample, and therefore microsystems have no advantage when operating in this region.

The number of theoretical plates is not the only relevant figure of merit for separations. Another quantity we wish to optimize is the time needed to achieve a given degree of resolution between peaks. The resolution between peaks is proportional to $\sqrt{N}$, and thus we propose the following figure of merit:

$$\frac{\sqrt{N}}{t_m} = \mu E \frac{\sqrt{N}}{L} = 2\sqrt{3} \, \frac{\mu E}{w} \frac{1}{\sqrt{1 + L/L_0}}. \qquad 4.$$

This equation shows that the resolution per time unit is initially constant, but then decreases with increasing L when L is greater than L_0.

It can be concluded that L_0 is the optimal value of the column length in microfabricated separation systems. If L is much less than L_0, the system does not take full advantage of the fact that separation quality increases rapidly with L; either better separation can be obtained by increasing L or better detection limits by increasing w. If L is much greater than L_0, resolution per time unit declines, reflecting the fact that diffusion is now affecting the separations.

When $L = L_0$, the plate number is given by

$$N_0 = \frac{1}{96} \left(\frac{\mu E w}{D} \right)^2, \qquad 5.$$

and resolution per time unit is

$$\frac{\sqrt{N_0}}{t_m} = \sqrt{6} \, \frac{\mu E}{w}. \qquad 6.$$

These last two equations tell us that it is desirable to increase μE as much as possible and to decrease D. A small injection plug has mixed effects; it reduces the time before diffusion becomes dominant, but it improves the separation quality per unit time.

Assuming that a system has indeed been designed such that $L = L_0$, then the separation time is

$$t_0 = \frac{w^2}{24D}. \qquad 7.$$

This tells us how separation time scales with the dimensions of the channel, because w is proportional to the channel width at the intersection. Similar to silicon integrated circuits, simply scaling down the dimensions of the system increases device speed.

Double-Stranded DNA Sizing

The first DNA separations in a microchip were reported by Effenhauser et al (24). Their sample was a mixture of DNA oligomers with length from 10 to 15 bases, and the sieving matrix used was 10% polyacrylamide polymerized in the capillary. In these conditions, very high separation efficiencies were achieved in 38-mm separation lengths. Shortly thereafter, Woolley & Mathies demonstrated microchip separations of double-stranded DNA (dsDNA) (91). Subsequent authors have attempted to improve the speed of the separations (73) or have integrated restriction enzyme reactions with subsequent separations (46).

Based on the theory presented above, it can be deduced that, to increase the speed of dsDNA separations, it is necessary to reduce the injected sample plug. One way to accomplish this is to reduce the width of the channels so that the size of the sample plug will scale accordingly. We have performed separations of dsDNA in an acrylamide-based sieving matrix in channels 35 μm wide and 12 μm deep (6). These channels were half the width of those we used initially (48).

Typical conditions for the dsDNA separations, which we reported previously (6), are as follows: $D = 4 \times 10^{-8}$ cm^2/s, $E = 200$ V/cm, $\mu \approx 2 \times 10^{-4}$ cm^2/Vs, and $w = 0.005$ cm. This leads to $L_0 = 1$ cm, $N_0 = 2.6 \times 10^5$, and $t_0 = 26$ s. The devices we used have a separation length of 1.3 cm and are therefore close to the optimum. An example of a rapid separation in these conditions is shown in Figure 3. A 100-base-pair ladder is separated in <50 s, with excellent resolution. The number of theoretical plates is in the range of 1.7×10^5 to 2.0×10^5, and the number of plates per second is >5000. By increasing the electric field, even better

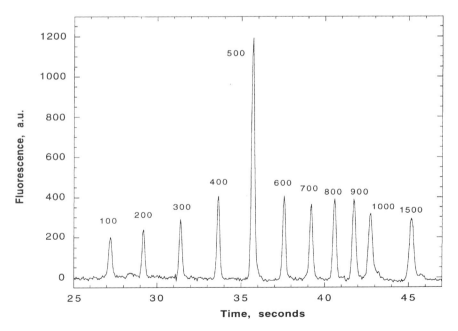

Figure 3 Separation of a Promega 100-bp DNA ladder. The field is 204 V/cm, and the separation distance is 13 mm.

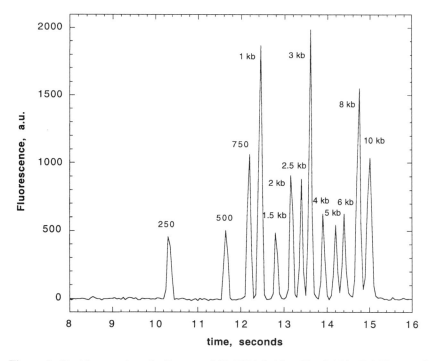

Figure 4   Rapid separation of a Promega 1-kb DNA ladder. The field is 534 V/cm, and the separation distance is 13 mm.

data are possible for larger dsDNA fragments. Figure 4 shows the separation of a 1-kb ladder in the same system, but with a field of 534 V/cm. All peaks are fully resolved in 15 s. The number of theoretical plates in this separation is even higher than in Figure 3, in the range of 2.0×10^5 to 2.2×10^5 for the larger peaks. As a result, the separation speed has increased to 16,000 plates/s.

These results also agree very well with the numbers expected based on the theory presented above, in particular N_0 and t_0. This also holds true for many results reported in the literature. For example, Burns et al (7) use a very low electric field, because their substrate is silicon, and a very thin injection plug, owing to stacking at the boundary of a cross-linked gel. Thus, L_0 will be short, and they indeed see separations in very short distances. Conversely, most work in single-base resolution for DNA sequencing has used larger injection plugs owing to detection constraints (56, 72, 92); as predicted by Equation 3, this leads to longer separation distances and slower separations.

Separations for DNA Sequencing

One particularly interesting application of microchip separations is the separation of single-stranded DNA fragments with single-base resolution for sequencing. The massive amount of sequencing that is being carried out for various genome projects, including the human genome, creates a strong demand for higher throughput. Woolley & Mathies (92) were the first to show that sequencing separations on a chip could reach reasonable read lengths while being much faster than with conventional capillaries. Since then, Schmalzing et al have modeled chip-sequencing separations (72), and Liu et al (56) have demonstrated read lengths of ≤ 600 bases in <20 min.

MICROVOLUME POLYMERASE CHAIN REACTION

For some years now, researchers have been working on using microfabricated devices of various types to perform PCR. The motivation for trying to accomplish this is usually twofold: first, faster cycling by using small chambers and integrated heaters and, second, integration of the PCR reaction with other operations on a microchip. As early as 1993, Northrup et al presented microfabricated chambers for PCR with integrated heaters (63) and continued to refine those devices (62, 64). The microfabricated PCR chambers reported by Cheng et al (10), Shoffner et al (77), and Wilding et al (88) did not include heaters, but they did carefully examine the factors that caused inhibition of PCR in chambers with a high surface-to-volume ratio (77).

Initially, all of the work done on PCR in these chambers used silicon devices with glass covers bonded to them, and detection required the removal of the sample and its analysis with gel electrophoresis. This procedure is, of course, cumbersome and slow, and it wastes the possible advantage gained from rapid cycling. A better detection method uses fluorogenic DNA probes (the TaqMan^{TM} method) that become fluorescent after they are cleaved by the 5′-to-3′ exonuclease activity of certain DNA polymerases (37, 54). This allows detection to be integrated with the PCR reaction. Several of these silicon/glass PCR devices have been used as miniaturized instruments by using integrated fluorescent TaqMan^{TM} detection (5, 38, 62), and recently a speed of 7 min or 17 s/cycle has been reached (4). Note that similarly fast PCR has been described in systems that do not use microfabrication technology but that rely instead on infrared heating (65) or resistive heating of a thin-film coating on the outside of a capillary (31).

All of these references use sample sizes in the 4- to 100-μl range, which is not small compared with conventional methods but has advantages in detecting certain pathogens at very low concentrations. These volumes are much greater than those of the channels of microfluidic devices, which are at the nanoliter level. They are about the same, however, as those of the wells used as inputs to those chips. It is therefore not surprising that some researchers have integrated PCR and subsequent detection by electrophoretic separation at the level of the wells of the electrophoretic microchips by transferring samples in some fashion between a PCR chamber and a well (11, 89). A simple variation of this approach is to use the well of a microchip itself as a PCR chamber, by thermally cycling the entire chip and then injecting a sample from the well for separation (84, 85).

Another type of integration is to combine the PCR chamber with a sample pretreatment device, for instance for selectively capturing and lysing cells from whole blood (87). The motivation in this case is to reduce the number of erythrocytes present in the sample, to avoid the inhibition caused by large amounts of hemoglobin.

None of the work cited so far has the capability to integrate with microfluidic operation at the nanoliter level. Yet that is the key integration step required if we want the PCR to be a preliminary step common to a number of genetic assays. Kalinina et al have demonstrated that PCR is possible at the 10-nl level, with a rapid cycle and a single starting copy number of the sequence to be amplified (47). This work was not done in a microchip, however, but in a sealed small capillary, and it could not be integrated with other assays.

A novel method for PCR amplification was recently demonstrated by Kopp et al (49), which does allow performance of very rapid cycles at the nanoliter scale in a microchip. It is a continuous-flow device in a glass chip with spatially fixed temperature zones. This method produced amplification at the fastest reported cycle times, namely 9 s/cycle, for samples that could be as small as a few nanoliters. One limitation was that the number of cycles is fixed at 20, which is not enough to amplify DNA from a small number of templates, and requires the use of samples with a copy number of 10^8. Detection was not integrated but was done with standard gel electrophoresis after the amplification.

Most recently, the work by Burns et al (7) showed a very promising on-chip integration of DNA amplification with a subsequent assay, using internal volumes in the hundreds of nanoliters. The assay consisted of electrophoretic separation in a cross-linked polyacrylamide gel. The differences from most of the other work discussed here are that they used a non-PCR isothermal amplification method [strand displacement amplification (81)] and that the structure was fabricated on a silicon substrate. That implies that the achievable electric fields are limited, because the substrate is conductive, and thus the maximum voltages are limited by the breakdown of the insulator. As a result, the separations were much slower than those obtained with microfabricated glass structures described above.

Although progress in on-chip PCR has been very rapid in the past few years, it has not yet achieved the goal of a rapid on-chip, nanoliter-level PCR process that can be integrated with a variety of equally rapid downstream assays. Examples of such integrated assays would initially be fast electrophoretic sizing, but should expand to include single-nucleotide polymorphism assays, or even DNA sequencing procedures.

ENZYME ASSAYS

The first work in the area of on-chip enzyme analysis was published by Hadd et al on beta-galactosidase (33). This was the first use of a chip for an integrated assay that did not involve separation. Before this work, the chip was primarily used as a miniature separation device. Here it was exploited as a sophisticated incubator and flow-through cell. The assay was integrated in the sense that the chip performed multiple functions typically required of the biochemist, namely, diluting substrate and buffer, mixing enzyme and substrate, incubating during conversion, and allowing for detection in a flow channel. In this fluorogenic assay, the simplest of chip designs can accommodate these functions. This first chip design included a single reagent dilution port. It was possible to control the on-chip reagent concentration via judicious selection of the proportion of flux from that reagent well and its accompanying buffer well. This was used to vary the substrate concentration and allowed for accurate Michaelis-Menten kinetic analyses.

The next step toward more sophisticated chip design was incorporating several sets of paired reagent wells such that multiple reagent dilution ports could be used to independently control the concentration of each component of the inhibition reaction (see Figure 5). The use of this chip, first presented by Cohen et al (18) allowed total on-chip control of all concentrations in an enzymatic reaction. Thus, an enzyme and its inhibitors can be characterized in an automated fashion. Both phosphatase and protease reactions were demonstrated. For the protease, resonance energy transfer quenching of the peptide substrate tagged with donor and acceptor moieties resulted in a nonfluorescent substrate. Cleavage of the peptide backbone during the protease reaction provided the fluorogenesis that could be monitored in the flow stream of the incubation channel.

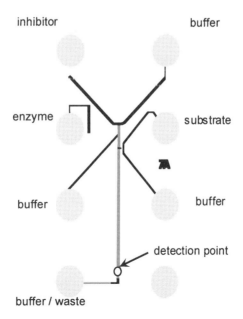

Figure 5   Diagram of a chip design used for fluorogenic-enzyme assays.

Figure 6 shows typical data obtained from a phosphatase reaction. The phosphatase served to convert 6,8-difluoro-4-methylumbellipheryl phosphate, a common fluorogenic substrate, to the coumarin product. The running buffer, 25 mM N-2-hydroxyethylpiperazine-N'-2-ethanesulfonic acid (HEPES), pH 7.9–10 mM dithiothreitol, contained a high concentration of a zwitterionic salt, 1 M NDSB-195, to reduce wall adsorption of the protein. The general strategy for using zwitterionic additives in capillary electrophoresis has been previously described by several authors (2, 9, 52). The continuous flow stream alternated between buffer (only), substrate (only), buffer (only), substrate and enzyme at four different substrate concentrations. The fluorescence response was continuously monitored in each of 16 steps written into the computer-controlled experiment. The substrate concentration was varied for each sequence of three controls followed by the enzyme reaction. This was accomplished by varying the ratio of currents used to pump the reagents, while maintaining a constant flux in the main reaction channel. The reproducible signal and ease of incorporating control experiments are typical for these experiments.

K_m determinations are often performed by incrementally changing the substrate concentration in the presence of a constant stream of enzyme. Figure 7 exemplifies the kind of data obtained on the microchip. The experiments can be conducted in the absence of inhibitor for the K_m determination and in the presence of inhibitor to evaluate K_i. Each trace represents a set of experiments performed in six-step cycles. The enzyme solution was pumped continuously, providing a final reaction channel concentration of 80-nM enzyme in 1 M NDSB-195–60 mM HEPES, pH 7.5, while the signal at various substrate concentrations was recorded. The first step of the cycle is an enzyme-only control. The entire experiment was repeated in the presence of two concentrations of the peptide inhibitor. The overlaid traces are three separate experiments and demonstrate the excellent reproducibility obtained in these flow systems.

A double-reciprocal plot in the absence of inhibitor gives K_m and V_{max} (see Figure 8). The rates are evaluated as a change in fluorescent-product signal over a fixed time. The fixed time is the incubation time. This is the time it takes for the product of the reaction to travel from the point of mixing of substrate and enzyme to the detector. This time was measured directly by using the product as a marker and selecting the detection distance downstream in the reaction channel that provided enough time for an appropriate amount of reaction conversion. Excellent agreement between on-chip and cuvette values was realized: K_m (microchip) was 60.5 μM $\pm$ 23%, and the cuvette value was 60 μM $\pm$ 25%. The K_i values also agree to within 1 SD for a triplicate measurement: K_i (microchip) was 151 μM $\pm$ 15%, and K_i (cuvette) was 167 μM. Moreover, it was possible to use the chip for 8 h of continuous analysis with no reagent replenishment. A continuous stream of enzyme was fed substrate or buffer or substrate and inhibitor in a repetitive fashion such that the conversion and inhibited conversion could be observed for an extended time. Less than 2.5 μl of reagent/h was consumed. Less than 20 μl of reagent was consumed for the entire 8-h study, in which 480 separate analyses

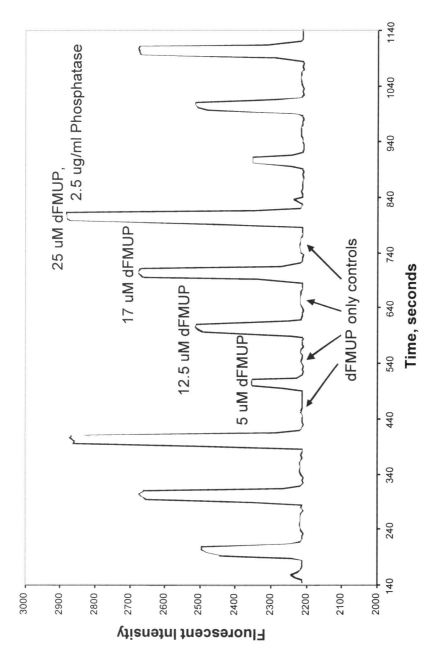

Figure 6   On-chip fluorogenic phosphatase assay, showing different substrate concentrations and controls with no enzyme. dFMUP, 6,8-difluoro-4-methylumbelliphryl phosphate.

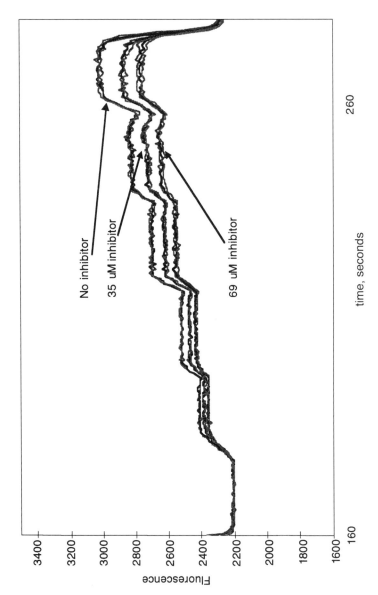

Figure 7 On-chip fluorogenic phosphatase assay, showing run-to-run reproducibility and the effect of different concentrations of a peptide inhibitor.

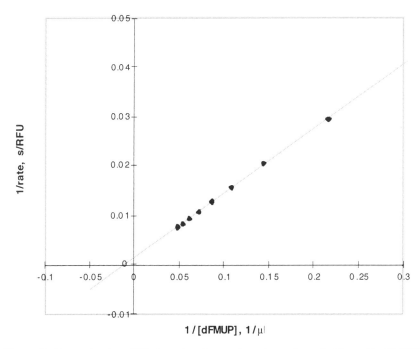

Figure 8 Determination of K_m by using data such as those shown in Figure 7. dFMUP, 6,8-difluoro-4-methylumbellipheryl phosphate.

were performed. The drift in the percent inhibition over that 8-h period was <5%.

Although these chemical mechanisms are ideal to directly detect fluorogenesis in a flow stream, fluorogenic substrates do not exist for many pharmaceutically interesting targets. One example is the kinases, which are enzymes that specifically add phosphate groups to serine, threonine, or tyrosine amino acid residues of certain peptides or proteins. Phosphorylation of another protein, which can be an enzyme itself, often acts to activate that protein and constitutes a very important signaling mechanism in biology. Many signal transduction pathways involve cascades of kinases activating each other. It is estimated that 2%–3% of all genes in eukaryotic cells encode for protein kinases (16). As a result, many of these kinases are valuable targets for drug discovery.

Monitoring kinase activity is a relatively involved measurement. Typically the transfer of the phosphate group from ATP, the cosubstrate of the reaction, to the peptide can be monitored with radiolabeled ATP or through the use of a fluorescently tagged peptide substrate. However the reaction product must be separated either from the unconverted radioactive ATP or from the fluorescently tagged, nonphosphorylated peptide. We have designed microchips that integrate all of these biochemical functions with the separation ability of miniature electrophoresis

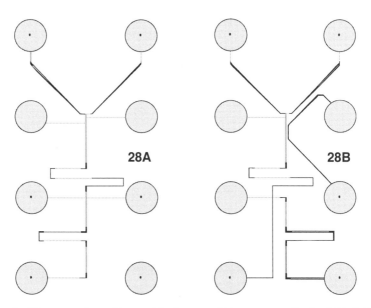

Figure 9   Diagrams of two chips used for integrated kinase assays. Design 28A (*left*) uses a gated injector such that samples are loaded into the separation channel with fields applied coaxially to the reaction and separation channels. Design 28B (*right*) uses a cross injector such that samples are loaded into the separation channel with fields applied perpendicularly to the reaction channel.

systems (Figure 9) (17). The upper portion of the chips feeds the serpentine incubation channel with reagents while the lower portion of the chips is fed by an injector. The distinction between designs 28A and 28B has implications for the amount of analyte injected. Aliquots of converted reagents are fed into the separation channel where they can be monitored in the flow stream. The electrophoretic separation is used to detect the relative amounts of fluorescently tagged substrate and product to determine the extent of conversion in the presence or absence of an inhibitor. The total of eight wells used in all of the designs dictates the number of on-chip diluters in each chip.

Figure 10 shows a sample of the separation data and analysis. Rhodamine-labeled kemptide, the substrate of the protein kinase A reaction, was titrated from the dilutor of chip 28A. Raw data are overlaid to show the progression in increasing signal and increasing conversion rate as more substrate is added to the reaction mixture. In the applied field used here (300 V/cm) for the separation, we observe three peaks elute in order of decreasing mass to charge: (*a*) cationic substrate, (*b*) a neutral marker (rhodamine-B), and (*c*) the phosphorylated product, which is an anion. The product peak area divided by the incubation time serves as a measure of the reaction rate. Inverse rate as a function of inverse substrate concentration is plotted, and the K_m of the reaction is evaluated. Error bars in Figure 10, *right*, represent ± 1 SD of the mean of three measurements.

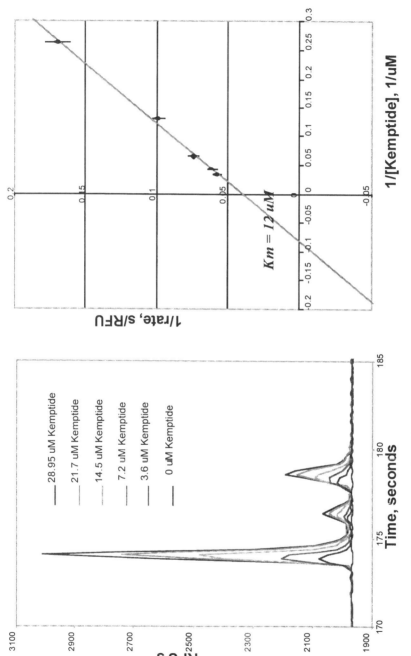

Figure 10 Data on kinase assays on a microchip. *Left*, Separation results at different substrate concentrations; *right*, corresponding K_m determinations.

This is an application in which chip technology really shines. Kinases are an exceedingly important pharmaceutical target in the area of drug discovery, yet assays for kinases have typically been cumbersome and labor intensive, most often involving complications caused by the handling and disposal of the radioactive reagents that are used. Microchip technology enables fast, flexible assay formats and consumes very little reagent. This is a noteworthy example of the benefits integrated microchip assays can offer in the realm of pharmaceutical research.

IMMUNOASSAYS

The first preliminary data for a competitive immunoassay performed on a microchip were presented by Harrison et al in 1995 (34). A mixture of labeled and unlabeled bovine serum albumin (BSA) was incubated off-chip with anti-BSA antibodies, and the result was separated on a microchip. A similar competitive immunoassay for cortisol was described by Koutny et al (50), and an assay for thyroxine by Schmalzing et al (74). Chiem & Harrison described an assay for theophylline (13).

In all of the examples cited above, the microchip technology was used only for the separation part of the immunoassay, and the incubation was carried out off-chip. Clearly, the reagent mixing and incubation then dominate the total assay time. For instance, Koutny et al (50) used 25–30 min of incubation, followed by loading and separation on a chip in a total of 25 s. The real benefits of an on-chip immunoassay can be obtained only if all steps, including the mixing and incubation, are done on-chip under full computer control. Such a complete on-chip immunoassay was first achieved by Chiem et al in 1997 (12) and further described in 1998 (14).

The main area of application of integrated on-chip immunoassays is clinical diagnostics (30), in which the goal is always to make the steps involved in an immunoassay invisible to the user.

CONCLUSIONS

It is clear that interest in electrokinetic microfluidic systems is rapidly increasing. The number of research groups active in this area has expanded considerably in the past year or two, in both industry and academia. Also, many researchers are striving to make new connections between microfluidics and other fields, as is evident for instance in the number of new detection schemes being proposed. We can thus expect considerable progress in this field in the coming years, including the first commercially available versions of this technology.

Despite this activity, it is also apparent that progress toward integrating many or all functions of an assay on a chip is difficult. The work on PCR assays on a chip illustrates this; the conditions needed for successful PCR amplification tend to be incompatible with other genetic-analysis methods. The enzyme assays described above are probably the most successful examples of assay integration, with reagent dilution, incubation, separation, and detection all under computer control on a single chip.

ACKNOWLEDGMENTS

This research was supported in part by an NIST ATP contract 70NANB8H4000, and by the DARPA ETO Composite CAD program, contract F30602-98-2-0151.

Visit the Annual Reviews home page at www.AnnualReviews.org

LITERATURE CITED

1. Anderson RC, Bogdan GJ, Barniv Z, Dawes TD, Winkler J, Roy K. 1997. Microfluidic biochemical analysis system. In *Transducers '97*, pp. 477–80. Chicago: Inst. Elect. Electronics Eng.

2. Arentoft AM, Frokiaer H, Michaelsen S, Sorensen H, Sorensen S. 1993. High-performance capillary electrophoresis for the determination of trypsin and chymotrypsin inhibitors and their association with trypsin, chymotrypsin and monoclonal antibodies. *J. Chromatogr. A* 652:189–98

3. Becker H, Dietz W, Dannberg P. 1998. Microfluidic manifolds by polymer hot embossing for μ-TAS applications. In *Micro Total Analysis Systems '98*, pp. 253–56. Banff, Alberta, Canada: Kluwer Academic

4. Belgrader P, Benett W, Hadley D, Richards J, Stratton P, et al. 1999. PCR detection of bacteria in seven minutes. *Science* 284:449–50

5. Belgrader P, Smith JK, Weedn VW, Northrup MA. 1998. Rapid PCR for identity testing using a battery-powered miniature thermal cycler. *J. Forensic Sci.* 43:315–19

6. Bousse L, Dubrow B, Ulfelder K. 1998. High-performance DNA separations in microchip electrophoresis systems. See Ref. 3, pp. 271–75

7. Burns MA, Johnson BN, Brahmasandra SN, Handique K, Webster JR, et al. 1998. An integrated nanoliter DNA analysis device. *Science* 282:484–87

8. Burns MA, Mastrangelo CH, Sammarco TS, Man FP, Webster JR, et al. 1996. Microfabricated structures for integrated DNA analysis. *Proc. Natl. Acad. Sci. USA* 93:5556–61

9. Bushey MM, Jorgenson JW. 1989. Capillary electrophoresis of proteins in buffers containing high concentrations of zwitterionic salts. *J. Chromatogr. A* 480:301–10

10. Cheng J, Shoffner MA, Hvichia GE, Kricka LJ, Wilding P. 1996. Chip PCR. II. Investigation of different PCR amplification systems in microfabricated silicon-glass chips. *Nucleic Acids Res.* 24:380–85

11. Cheng J, Waters LC, Fortina P, Hvichia G, Jacobson SC, et al. 1998. Degenerate oligonucleotide primed-polymerase chain reaction and capillary electrophoretic analysis of human DNA on microchip-based devices. *Anal. Biochem.* 257:101–6

12. Chiem N, Colyer C, Harrison DJ. 1997. Microfluidic systems for clinical diagnostics. See Ref. 1, pp. 183–86

13. Chiem N, Harrison DJ. 1997. Microchip-based capillary electrophoresis for immunoassays: analysis of monoclonal antibodies and theophylline. *Anal. Chem.* 69:373–78

14. Chiem NH, Harrison DJ. 1998. Microchip systems for immunoassay: an integrated immunoreactor with electrophoretic separation for serum theophylline determination. *Clin. Chem.* 44:591–98

15. Chow CYH, Parce JW. 1998. *US Patent No. 5800690*
16. Cobb MH, Boulton TG, Robbins DJ. 1991. Extracellular signal-regulated kinases: ERKs in progress. *Cell Regul.* 2:965–78
17. Cohen CB, Chin-Dixon E, Jeong S, Nikiforov TT. 1999. A microchip-based assay for protein kinase A. *Anal. Biochem.* 273:89–97
18. Cohen CB, Nikiforov TT, Parce JW. 1998. Microchip assays for enzyme analyses. *Pittsburgh Conf. Anal. Chem. Appl. Spectrosc.* 456 (Abstr.) New Orleans
19. Crabtree HJ, Kopp MU, Manz A. 1999. Shah convolution fourier transform detection. *Anal. Chem.* 71:2130–38
20. Deshpande M, Greiner K, Gilbert J, Bousse L, Chow A, Kopf-Sill AR. 1999. In *Transducers '99*. Sendai, Japan: Paper No. 2P1.1
21. Duffy DC, McDonald JC, Schueller OJA, Whitesides GM. 1998. Rapid prototyping of microfluidic systems in poly(dimethylsiloxane). *Anal. Chem.* 70:4974–84
22. Effenhauser CS, Bruin GJ, Paulus A, Ehrat M. 1997. Integrated capillary electrophoresis on flexible silicone microdevices: analysis of DNA restriction fragments and detection of single DNA molecules on microchips. *Anal. Chem.* 69:3451–57
23. Effenhauser CS, Manz A, Widmer HM. 1993. Glass chips for high-speed capillary electrophoresis separations with submicrometer plate heights. *Anal. Chem.* 65:2837–42
24. Effenhauser CS, Paulus A, Manz A, Widmer HM. 1994. High-speed separation of antisense oligonucleotides on a micromachined capillary electrophoresis device. *Anal. Chem.* 66:2949–53
25. Fan ZH, Harrison DJ. 1994. Micromachining of capillary electrophoresis injectors and separators on glass chips and evaluation of flow at capillary intersections. *Anal. Chem.* 66:177–84
26. Figeys D, Gygi SP, McKinnon G, Aebersold R. 1998. An integrated microfluidics-tandem mass spectrometry system for automated protein analysis. *Anal. Chem.* 70:3728–34
27. Figeys D, Ning Y, Aebersold R. 1997. A microfabricated device for rapid protein identification by microelectrospray ion trap mass spectrometry. *Anal. Chem.* 69:3153–60
28. Fluri K, Fitzpatrick G, Chiem N, Harrison DJ. 1996. Integrated capillary electrophoresis devices with an efficient post-column reactor in planar quartz and glass chips. *Anal. Chem.* 68:4285–90
29. Foret F, Kirby DP, Vouros P, Karger BL. 1996. Electrospray interface for capillary electrophoresis-mass spectrometry with fiber-optic UV detection close to the electrospray tip. *Electrophoresis* 17:1829–32
30. Freaney R, McShane A, Keaveny TV, McKenna M, Rabenstein K, et al. 1997. Novel instrumentation for real-time monitoring using miniaturized flow systems with integrated biosensors. *Ann. Clin. Biochem.* 34:291–302
31. Friedman NA, Meldrum DR. 1998. Capillary tube resistive thermal cycling. *Anal. Chem.* 70:2997–3002
32. Gravesen P, Branebjerg J, Jensen OS. 1993. Microfluidics—a review. *J. Micromech. Microeng.* 3:168–82
33. Hadd AG, Raymond DE, Halliwell JW, Jacobson SC, Ramsey JM. 1997. Microchip device for performing enzyme assays. *Anal. Chem.* 69:3407–12
34. Harrison DJ, Fluri K, Chiem N, Tang T, Fan Z. 1995. Micromachining chemical and biochemical analysis and reaction systems on glass substrates. In *Transducers '95*, pp. 752–55. Stockholm: Inst. Elect. Electronics Eng.
35. Harrison DJ, Fluri K, Seiler K, Fan Z, Effenhauser CS, Manz A. 1993. Micromachining a miniaturized capillary electrophoresis-based chemical analysis

system on a chip. *Science* 261:895–97

36. Harrison DJ, Manz A, Fan Z, Ludi H, Widmer HM. 1992. Capillary electrophoresis and sample injection systems integrated on a planar glass chip. *Anal. Chem.* 64:1926–32

37. Holland PM, Abramson RD, Watson R, Gelfand DH. 1991. Detection of specific polymerase chain reaction product by utilizing the 5′-3′ exonuclease activity of Thermus aquaticus DNA polymerase. *Proc. Natl. Acad. Sci. USA* 88:7276–80

38. Ibrahim MS, Lofts RS, Jahrling PB, Henchal EA, Weedn VW, et al. 1998. Real-time microchip PCR for detecting single-base differences in viral and human DNA. *Anal. Chem.* 70:2013–17

39. Jacobson SC, Culbertson CT, Daler JE, Ramsey JM. 1998. Microchip structures for submillisecond electrophoresis. *Anal. Chem.* 70:3476–80

40. Jacobson SC, Hergenröder R, Koutny LB, Ramsey JM. 1994. High-speed separations on a microchip. *Anal. Chem.* 66:1114–18

41. Jacobson SC, Hergenroder R, Koutny LB, Ramsey JM. 1994. Precolumn reactions with electrophoretic analysis integrated on a microchip. *Anal. Chem.* 66:4127–32

42. Jacobson SC, Hergenröder R, Koutny LB, Warmack RJ, Ramsey JM. 1994. Effects of injection schemes and column geometry on the performance of microchip electrophoresis devices. *Anal. Chem.* 66:1107–13

43. Jacobson SC, Koutny LB, Hergenroder R, Moore AW, Ramsey JM. 1994. Microchip capillary electrophoresis with an integrated postcolumn reactor. *Anal. Chem.* 66:3472–76

44. Jacobson SC, Moore AW, Ramsey JM. 1995. Fused quartz substrates for microchip electrophoresis. *Anal. Chem.* 67:2059–63

45. Jacobson SC, Ramsey JM. 1995. Microchip electrophoresis with sample stacking. *Electrophoresis* 16:481–86

46. Jacobson SC, Ramsey JM. 1996. Integrated device for DNA restriction fragment analysis. *Anal. Chem.* 68:720–23

47. Kalinina O, Lebedeva I, Brown J, Silver J. 1997. Nanoliter scale PCR with TaqMan detection. *Nucleic Acids Res.* 25:1999–2004

48. Kopf-Sill A, Nikiforov T, Bousse L, Nagle R, Parce JW. 1997. Complexity and performance of on-chip biochemical assays. In *Micro and Nanofabricated Electro-optical Mechanical Systems for Biomedical and Environmental Applications*, pp. 172–79. San Jose, CA: Int. Soc. Optical Eng.

49. Kopp MU, de Mello AJ, Manz A. 1998. Chemical amplification: continuous-flow PCR on a chip. *Science* 280:1046–48

50. Koutny LB, Schmalzing D, Taylor TA, Fuchs M. 1996. Microchip electrophoretic immunoassay for serum cortisol. *Anal. Chem.* 68:18–22

51. Kovacs GTA, Holland KC. 1989. *European Patent Application No. 0376611*

52. Krueger RJ, Hobbs TR, Mihal KA, Tehrani J, Zeece MG. 1991. Analysis of endoproteinase Arg C action on adrenocorticotrophic hormone by capillary electrophoresis and reversed-phase high-performance liquid chromatography. *J. Chromatogr. A* 543:451–61

53. Lazar IM, Ramsey RS, Sundberg S, Ramsey JM. 1999. Subattomole-sensitivity microchip nanoelectrospray source with time-of-flight mass spectroscopy detection. *Anal. Chem.* 71:3627–31

54. Lee LG, Connell CR, Bloch W. 1993. Allelic discrimination by nick-translation PCR with fluorogenic probes. *Nucleic Acids Res.* 21:3761–66

55. Liang Z, Chiem N, Ocvirk G, Tang T, Fluri K, Harrison DJ. 1996. Microfabrication of a planar absorbance and fluorescence cell for integrated capillary electrophoresis devices. *Anal. Chem.* 68:1040–46

56. Liu S, Shi Y, Ja WW, Mathies RA. 1999. Optimization of high-speed DNA sequencing on microfabricated capillary

electrophoresis channels. *Anal. Chem.* 71:566–73

57. Mangru SD, Harrison DJ. 1998. Chemiluminescence detection in integrated post-separation reactors for microchip-based capillary electrophoresis and affinity electrophoresis. *Electrophoresis* 19:2301–7

58. Manz A. 1991. Micromachining of monocrystalline silicon and glass for chemical analysis systems: a look into next century's technology or just a fashionable craze? *Trends Anal. Chem.* 10:144–49

59. Manz A, Harrison DJ, Verpoorte EMJ, Fettinger JC, Paulus A, et al. 1992. Planar chips technology for miniaturization and integration of separation techniques into monitoring systems: capillary electrophoresis on a chip. *J. Chromatogr. A* 593:253–58

60. Martynova L, Locascio LE, Gaitan M, Kramer GW, Christensen RG, MacCrehan WA. 1997. Fabrication of plastic microfluid channels by imprinting methods. *Anal. Chem.* 69:4783–89

61. McCormick RM, Nelson RJ, Alonso-Amigo MG, Benvegnu DJ, Hooper HH. 1997. Microchannel electrophoretic separations of DNA in injection-molded plastic substrates. *Anal. Chem.* 69:2626–30

62. Northrup MA, Bennett B, Hadley D, Landre P, Lehew S, et al. 1998. A miniature analytical instrument for nucleic acids based on micromachined silicon reaction chambers. *Anal. Chem.* 70:918–22

63. Northrup MA, Ching MT, White RM, Watson RT. 1993. DNA amplification with a microfabricated reaction chamber. In *Transducers '93*, pp. 924–26. Yokohama, Japan: Inst. Elect. Electron. Eng.

64. Northrup MA, Gonzalez C, Hadley D, Hills RF, Landre P, et al. 1995. A MEMS-based miniature DNA analysis system. See Ref. 34, pp. 764–67

65. Oda RP, Strausbauch MA, Huhmer AF, Borson N, Jurrens SR, et al. 1998. Infrared-mediated thermocycling for ultrafast polymerase chain reaction amplification of DNA. *Anal. Chem.* 70:4361–68

66. Pace SJ. 1990. Silicon semiconductor wafer for analyzing micronic biological samples. *US Patent No. 4908112*

67. Pan JY, VerLee D, Mehregany M. 1999. Latched valve manifolds for efficient control of pneumatically actuated valve arrays. See Ref. 1, pp. 817–20

68. Ramsey JM, Jacobson SC, Knapp MR. 1995. Microfabricated chemical measurement systems. *Nat. Med.* 1:1093–96

69. Ramsey RS, Ramsey JS. 1997. Generating electrospray from microchip devices using electroosmotic pumping. *Anal. Chem.* 69:1174–78

70. Roberts MA, Rossier JS, Bercier P, Girault H. 1997. UV laser machined polymer substrates for the development of microdiagnostic systems. *Anal. Chem.* 69:2035–42

71. Rossier JS, Schwarz A, Reymond F, Ferrigno R, Bianchi F, Girault HH. 1999. Microchannel networks for electrophoretic separations. *Electrophoresis* 20:727–31

72. Schmalzing D, Adourian A, Koutny L, Ziaugra L, Matsudaira P, Ehrlich D. 1998. DNA sequencing on microfabricated electrophoretic devices. *Anal. Chem.* 70:2303–10

73. Schmalzing D, Koutny L, Adourian A, Belgrader P, Matsudaira P, Ehrlich D. 1998. DNA typing in thirty seconds with a microfabricated device. *Proc. Natl. Acad. Sci. USA* 94:10273–78

74. Schmalzing D, Koutny LB, Taylor TA, Nashabeh W, Fuchs M. 1997. Immunoassay for thyroxine (T4) in serum using capillary electrophoresis and micromachined devices. *J. Chromatogr. Biomed. Sci. Appl.* 697:175–80

75. Seiler K, Fan ZH, Fluri K, Harrison DJ. 1994. Electroosmotic pumping and valveless control of fluid flow within a manifold of capillaries on a glass chip. *Anal. Chem.* 66:3485–91

76. Seiler K, Harrison DJ, Manz A. 1993.

Planar glass chips for capillary electrophoresis: repetitive sample injection, quantitation, and separation efficiency. *Anal. Chem.* 65:1481–88

77. Shoffner MA, Cheng J, Hvichia GE, Kricka LJ, Wilding P. 1996. Chip PCR. I. Surface passivation of microfabricated silicon-glass chips for PCR. *Nucleic Acids Res.* 24:375–79

78. Shoji S, Nakagawa S, Esashi M. 1990. Micropump and sample injector for integrated chemical analysis systems. *Sens. Actuators* A21–A23:189–92

79. van der Schoot BH, van den Berg A, Jeanneret S, de Rooij NF. 1991. A miniaturized chemical analysis system using two silicon micro pumps. In *Transducers '91*, pp. 789–91. San Francisco: Inst. Elect. Electronics Eng.

80. van Lintel HTG, van de Pol FCM, Bouwstra S. 1988. A piezoelectric micropump based on micromachining of silicon. *Sens. Actuators* 15:153–67

81. Walker GT, Little MC, Nadeau JG, Shank DD. 1992. Isothermal in vitro amplification of DNA by a restriction enzyme/DNA polymerase system. *Proc. Natl. Acad. Sci. USA* 89:392–96

82. Walker PA, Morris MD, Burns MA, Johnson BN. 1999. Isotachophoretic separations on a microchip. Normal raman spectroscopy detection. *Anal. Chem.* 70:3766–69

83. Wang J, Tian B, Sahlin E. 1999. Integrated electrophoresis chips/amperometric detection with sputtered gold working electrodes. *Anal. Chem.* 71:3901–4

84. Waters LC, Jacobson S, Kroutchinina N, Khandurina J, Foote RS, Ramsey JM. 1998. Microchip device for cell lysis, multiplex PCR amplification, and electrophoretic sizing. *Anal. Chem.* 70:158–62

85. Waters LC, Jacobson SC, Kroutchinina N, Khandurina J, Foote RS, Ramsey JM. 1998. Multiple sample PCR amplification and electrophoretic analysis on a microchip. *Anal. Chem.* 70:5172–76

86. Webster JR, Burns MA, Burke DT, Mastrangelo CH. 1998. An inexpensive plastic technology for microfabricated electrophoresis chips. See Ref. 3, pp. 249–52

87. Wilding P, Kricka LJ, Cheng J, Hvichia G, Shoffner MA, Fortina P. 1998. Integrated cell isolation and polymerase chain reaction analysis using silicon microfilter chambers. *Anal. Biochem.* 257:95–100

88. Wilding P, Shoffner MA, Kricka LJ. 1994. PCR in a silicon microstructure. *Clin. Chem.* 40:1815–18

89. Woolley AT, Hadley D, Landre P, deMello AJ, Mathies RA, Northrup MA. 1996. Functional integration of PCR amplification and capillary electrophoresis in a microfabricated DNA analysis device. *Anal. Chem.* 68:4081–86

90. Woolley AT, Lao K, Glazer AN, Mathies RA. 1998. Capillary electrophoresis chips with integrated electrochemical detection. *Anal. Chem.* 70:684–88

91. Woolley AT, Mathies RA. 1994. Ultrahigh-speed DNA fragment separations using microfabricated capillary array electrophoresis chips. *Proc. Natl. Acad. Sci. USA* 91:11348–52

92. Woolley AT, Mathies RA. 1995. Ultrahigh-speed DNA sequencing using capillary electrophoresis chips. *Anal. Chem.* 67:3676–80

93. Zhang B, Liu H, Karger BL, Foret F. 1999. Microfabricated devices for capillary electrophoresis-electrospray mass spectrometry. *Anal. Chem.* 71:3258–64

Annu. Rev. Biophys. Biomol. Struct. 1999. 3:183–212

DNA Recognition by Cys$_2$His$_2$ Zinc Finger Proteins

Scot A. Wolfe, Lena Nekludova, and Carl O. Pabo

Howard Hughes Medical Institute, Department of Biology, 68-580, Massachusetts Institute of Technology, Cambridge, Massachusetts 02139; e-mail: pabo@mit.edu

Key Words   recognition code, phage display, structure-based design, gene therapy, protein-DNA interactions

■ **Abstract**   Cys$_2$His$_2$ zinc fingers are one of the most common DNA-binding motifs found in eukaryotic transcription factors. These proteins typically contain several fingers that make tandem contacts along the DNA. Each finger has a conserved $\beta\beta\alpha$ structure, and amino acids on the surface of the α-helix contact bases in the major groove. This simple, modular structure of zinc finger proteins, and the wide variety of DNA sequences they can recognize, make them an attractive framework for attempts to design novel DNA-binding proteins. Several studies have selected fingers with new specificities, and there clearly are recurring patterns in the observed side chain–base interactions. However, the structural details of recognition are intricate enough that there are no general rules (a "recognition code") that would allow the design of an optimal protein for any desired target site. Construction of multifinger proteins is also complicated by interactions between neighboring fingers and the effect of the intervening linker. This review analyzes DNA recognition by Cys$_2$His$_2$ zinc fingers and summarizes progress in generating proteins with novel specificities from fingers selected by phage display.

CONTENTS

1056-8700/00/0610-0183$14.00   **183**

INTRODUCTION

There are a number of different families of "zinc finger" proteins that contain multiple cysteine and/or histidine residues and use zinc coordination to stabilize their folds (9, 10, 24, 70). Cys_2His_2 zinc finger proteins were the founding members of this superfamily and were first noted as repeating domains in the TFIIIA sequence (14, 38, 53, 85). Proteins that contain Cys_2His_2 zinc fingers are quite common in eukaryotic organisms, with this domain used not only for protein-DNA interactions but also for protein-RNA and protein-protein interactions (81, 111). The DNA-binding activity of these fingers has been the major focus of research (20). A number of studies have tried to determine the principles of zinc finger–DNA recognition (30–33, 61, 87, 88, 121) and to create zinc fingers that recognize novel DNA sites (18, 19, 50, 56, 58, 59, 104, 110, 124, 125). The selection of fingers with new specificities was inspired by the hope that their assembly into multifinger DNA-binding domains might provide useful new tools for diagnostics, biochemical research, and gene therapy. There has been exciting progress in understanding these proteins, but even this simple motif is remarkably complex. There still are significant challenges in understanding natural zinc finger proteins and in developing design methods that are versatile and reliable enough to find widespread application in biochemical research and gene therapy.

STRUCTURE OF THE ZINC FINGER DOMAIN

The Cys_2His_2 zinc finger unit was first identified in TFIIIA, which contains nine tandem repeats of this approximately 30 amino acid motif (14, 85). As additional zinc finger sequences became available, it was clear that these fingers share the consensus sequence $(F/Y)-X-C-X_{2-5}-C-X_3-(F/Y)-X_5-\psi-X_2-H-X_{3-5}-H$, where X represents any amino acid and ψ is a hydrophobic residue. These sequences fold in the presence of zinc (45) to form a compact $\beta\beta\alpha$ domain (78, 94, 95; Figure 1). Each finger binds a single zinc ion that is sandwiched between the two-stranded antiparallel β-sheet and the α-helix; the zinc is tetrahedrally coordinated between two cysteines at one end of the β-sheet and two histidines in the C-terminal portion of the α-helix. Detailed structural studies of zinc fingers show that the "α-helix" often contains sections of 3_{10} helix, particularly in the region between the histidines when the fingers have a HX_3H sequence pattern (35, 41, 55, 62, 78, 91, 92, 95, 96, 126).

   It is interesting to note that zinc fingers have a relatively small number of fully conserved residues. Most of the structural stability is provided by zinc coordination

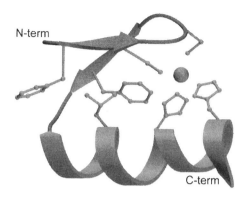

Figure 1   Diagram of the $\beta\beta\alpha$ motif from finger 2 of Zif268 (37, 95). The side chains of the conserved cysteines and histidines, which are involved in zinc coordination, and side chains of the three conserved hydrophobic residues are shown.

and by the conserved hydrophobic core that flanks the zinc binding site (84, 113). The hydrophobic residues are well conserved, but there are some examples where their spacing within the domain can change (85, 93): For example, finger 6 of human ZFY has a sequence of the form (Y-X-C-X$_2$-C-X-F-X$_7$-L-X$_2$-H-X$_4$-H) where the second conserved aromatic residue is two residues closer to the cysteine than in the standard consensus sequence. Studies have demonstrated that an aromatic residue at either position on this β-strand can pack into the core of the $\beta\beta\alpha$ motif and stabilize the fold (123).

The stability of the $\beta\beta\alpha$ architecture is largely derived from the intrastrand "crosslinking" that zinc coordination provides. Fingers are unfolded in the absence of zinc (45), and substituting a residue other than cysteine or histidine at one of the ligand positions usually results in a loss of function (25, 120). Conservative substitutions (interchanging cysteine and histidine) of the zinc-coordinating residues is tolerated at some positions (48, 74, 86), with the final histidine being the most amenable to change (48, 83). Because of the stability provided by zinc coordination, this structure provides an excellent scaffold for presenting diverse peptide sequences in a helical conformation.

BIOLOGICAL ROLES OF ZINC FINGER PROTEINS

Proteins containing Cys$_2$His$_2$ zinc fingers are quite common in the genomes of eukaryotes. Approximately 0.7% of the genes in *Saccharomyces cerevisiae* and *Caenorhabditis elegans* contain Cys$_2$His$_2$ zinc fingers (12, 22), and it is estimated that a similar fraction will be found in humans (54). Zinc fingers occur in animals, plants, and fungi, but the typical number of finger repeats and the length of the linker between neighboring fingers varies greatly between the kingdoms (12, 22, 119). Cys$_2$His$_2$ zinc fingers are absent from the genomes of *Escherichia coli* or *Methanococcus jannaschii* (22), but a potential zinc finger has been identified in *Synechococcus* PCC 7942 (11), suggesting that although this motif is uncommon in bacteria, it is not completely foreign to prokaryotes.

Cys$_2$His$_2$ zinc fingers that bind DNA have been studied in considerable detail. DNA recognition usually requires 2 to 4 tandemly arranged zinc fingers; when only one or two fingers are present, additional secondary structure elements are generally used to augment DNA recognition (13, 34, 40, 41, 90, 92). Zinc finger proteins can bind with sufficient specificity and affinity to function independently as the master regulator of a set of genes [TFIIIA (111) and NRSF/REST (109)], or like members of the SP1 family, they can work cooperatively with other DNA-binding proteins (75). Zinc fingers typically function in the context of a much larger protein, and certain other sequence motifs seem especially common in these proteins. The best characterized can be divided into four major classes: FAX (71), KRAB (8, 80), POZ (5), and FAR (69). These domains seem to have roles in transcriptional regulation or protein-protein interactions. It also has been shown that the zinc fingers themselves can be involved in protein-protein contacts, interacting directly with other transcription factors (49, 77, 82, 97).

A number of Cys$_2$His$_2$ zinc fingers have been identified that bind RNA, but aside from TFIIIA and p43, the biological significance of these interactions requires further study (2, 4, 15, 42, 43, 51, 72, 108, 111). Given the versatility and widespread distribution of this domain, it would not be surprising to find that many zinc fingers function as RNA-binding domains. The Wilms' tumor suppressor, WT1, is one good example. It was initially characterized only as a DNA-binding protein, but it now appears to function in gene regulation at the RNA level as well (15, 29, 39, 76).

DNA BINDING AND RECOGNITION

The crystal structure of Zif268 bound to DNA (95) has served as the prototype for understanding DNA recognition by this family of proteins (Figure 2). Zif268 contains three zinc fingers; the α-helical portion of each finger fits in the major groove of the DNA, and binding of successive fingers causes the protein to wrap around the DNA. Each finger has a similar docking arrangement and contacts an overlapping four base pair subsite (37, 95). However, the majority of base contacts occur in three base pair segments along one strand of the DNA (primary strand). Neighboring fingers are three base pairs apart: A helical motion that shifts the register of one finger by 3 base pairs superimposes neighboring fingers. The three fingers of Zif268 are oriented so that finger 1 is at the 3' end of the primary strand and finger 3 is at the 5' end. The DNA conformation is generally similar to that of B-form DNA, but the major groove is enough wider and deeper than normal that this seems to represent a distinctive DNA conformation (89). This

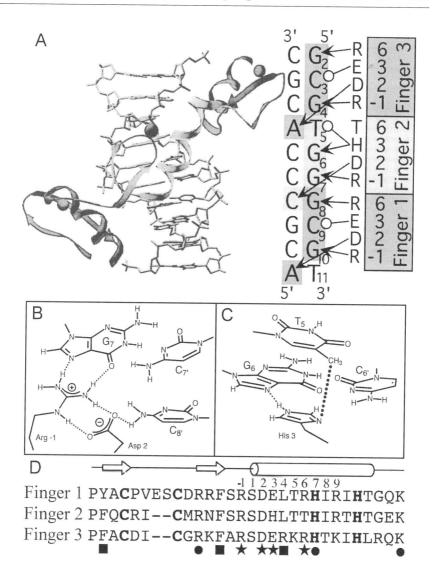

Figure 2 (*A*) Structure of the three fingers of Zif268 bound to DNA (37). Base contacts made from positions −1, 2, 3, and 6 of each α-helix are indicated schematically to the right of the structure. *Arrows* indicate contacts mediated by hydrogen bonds; *open circles* indicate hydrophobic interactions. For reference the base pairs are numbered (2 through 11) as in the original reference (95). (*B*) and (*C*) To give some idea of the structural details at the interface, this figure shows the base contacts made by finger 2 of Zif268. *Dashed lines* indicate hydrogen bonds and the **single** *dotted line* indicates a van der Waals contact of 3.4 Å. (*D*) The sequence of the three fingers of Zif268 is shown with the cysteines and histidines involved in zinc coordination indicated in *bold*. *Filled squares* below the sequence indicate the position of the conserved hydrophobic residues. *Filled circles* and *stars* indicate residue positions that are involved in phosphate and base contacts (respectively) in most of the fingers.

enlarged major groove is a common feature in the structures of most other zinc finger–DNA complexes and occurs in a number of other protein-DNA complexes (89).

Docking Arrangement and Base Recognition in Zif268

It may be useful to consider the structure of Zif268 in some detail because it provides a framework for the analysis and comparison of other zinc finger–DNA complexes, and because attempts to design novel zinc finger proteins have focused on fingers that have Zif-like docking arrangements. The base contacts in the Zif268 complex are made by amino acids in the N-terminal portion of the recognition helices. Each helix docks at a rather steep angle in the major groove, with the α-helical axis tipped at an angle of about 45° with respect to the double-helical axis (Figure 2). The amino acids at positions −1, 3, and 6 of the helix are well positioned to make contacts with bases in the primary DNA strand, whereas the amino acid at position 2 can make a contact to the complementary strand of the DNA. (In this numbering scheme, the −1 position is the residue immediately preceding the α-helix.) The base pair contacted by position 2 is just outside the "core" three base pair subsite, and this base also is typically recognized by position 6 of the neighboring N-terminal finger. (The Zif268 fingers recognize overlapping four base pair subsites, but neighboring fingers are only three base pairs apart.)

All three Zif268 fingers have identical residues at positions −1 and 2 (Arg and Asp), and these residues make coordinated DNA contacts (Figure 2B). The arginine at position −1 makes a pair of hydrogen bonds to the guanine at the 3′ position in the primary DNA strand of each binding site. This interaction is stabilized by the aspartate at position 2, which also makes two hydrogen bonds to the guanidinium group of arginine. The carboxylate group of the aspartate also forms a hydrogen bond with the exocyclic amine of adenine (or cytosine) on the complementary strand just outside of the primary three base pair subsite (although the geometry for these contacts does not always seem ideal; Figure 2A, B). The arginine and aspartate also form a number of water-mediated contacts with the bases and the phosphate backbone, but the contribution of these water contacts to DNA-binding specificity is unknown.

In the Zif268 structure, the remaining base contacts are mediated by residues at positions 3 and 6 of the α-helix. When glutamate is at position 3 (as in fingers 1 and 3) there appears to be a hydrophobic interaction between the Cγ and Cδ carbons of this residue and the C5-C6 edge of the neighboring cytosine (37). When histidine is at position 3 of the helix (as in finger 2; Figure 2C), it forms a hydrogen bond from Nε to the N7 (or O6) of guanine and simultaneously forms a van der Waals contact with the methyl group of the adjacent thymine. At position 6 of the helix (in fingers 1 and 3) there is an arginine that makes a pair of hydrogen bonds to guanine. Position 6 of finger 2 is a threonine, which does not make any direct contacts with the DNA.

Docking Arrangements and Base Contacts in Other Zinc Finger–DNA Complexes

Analysis of zinc finger–DNA interactions often focuses on fingers that have a DNA-docking arrangement very similar to that of Zif268, but it is important to recognize that a variety of docking arrangements are observed in zinc finger–DNA complexes. Comparing the known structures reveals that the vast majority of the base-specific contacts in the zinc finger–DNA complexes are made from positions −1, 2, 3, and 6 of the α-helix (presumably because these residues are the most prominently exposed on the surface of the helix), but variations in the docking arrangement of the fingers allows these residues to make alternative patterns of base contacts in different complexes. Analysis of known structures (92a) allows a provisional division of fingers into two sets (Figure 3): (a) Canonical fingers have the same pattern of base contacts as Zif268. This group of fingers includes Tramtrack finger 2 (TTK; 41), two Zif268 finger 1 variants (DSNR and QGSR; 35), TFIIIA finger 3 (91, 126), all three fingers from Berg's designed protein (1MEY; 62), and finger 3 of YY1 (55). (b) Nonstandard fingers have several different patterns of base contacts. They often use residues at positions 3 and 6 of the helix to recognize bases on the primary strand of the DNA in a manner similar to that of Zif268, but they deviate from the canonical recognition pattern in contacts made by residues at positions −1 and 2. There is also considerable variation in the length and spacing of the subsites for these zinc finger–DNA complexes. This set of nonstandard fingers includes TTK 1; TFIIIA fingers 1, 2, and 5; YY1 fingers 1, 2, and 4; GLI fingers 2, 4, and 5 (96); GAGA (92); and one Zif268 finger 1 variant (RADR; 35).

Analyzing zinc finger–DNA complexes by treating each three base pair subsite and each finger as a rigid body provides one way to assess differences in the docking arrangements of the various fingers. Zif268 was used as a reference, and docking arrangements were compared (in a pairwise fashion) by aligning the region of DNA duplex recognized by each finger and then calculating the translation and rotation necessary to overlay the α-carbons of the helices from the two different fingers. The results of this comparison are shown in Figure 4. Fingers with canonical docking patterns tend to cluster near the origin of this graph, whereas the majority of "nonstandard" fingers require much larger translations and rotations to be aligned with the fingers of Zif268. It also is interesting that proteins that contain three tandem fingers each making two or more base contacts (Zif268, QGSR, DSNR, 1MEY, YY1 fingers 2–4, TFIIIA fingers 1–3) tend to dock in a manner similar to Zif268. The canonical docking arrangement seems to allow a very favorable set of base contacts from three consecutive fingers and also appears to make the zinc finger complexes quite modular. Much of the past modeling, design, and selection of fingers has focused on such canonical docking arrangements, but it is important to recognize that a variety of different docking arrangements have been observed with zinc fingers, and for the recognition of some DNA sequences it is possible that a noncanonical docking arrangement may provide superior specificity.

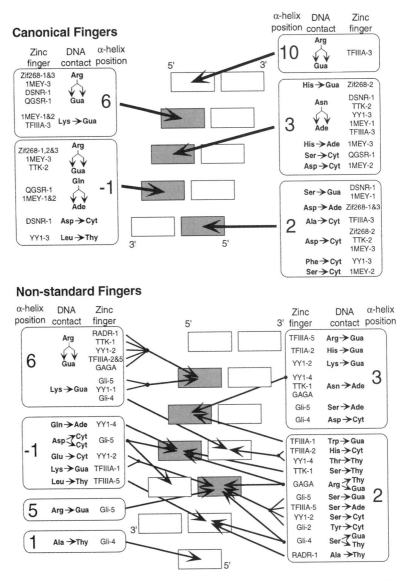

Figure 3 Summary of base contacts in various zinc finger–DNA complexes (35, 41, 55, 62, 91, 92, 95, 96, 126), showing how side chains at key positions along the α-helix contact bases in the respective subsites. Several complexes have a pattern of side chain–base interactions that are similar to those in Zif268 and thus are referred to as "canonical contacts." Other fingers (nonstandard) have somewhat different docking arrangements, showing a more diverse pattern of side chain–base interactions and sometimes contacting a larger subsite.

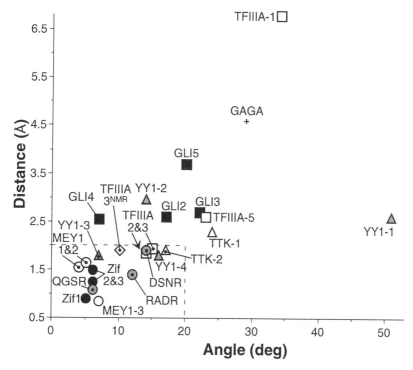

Figure 4 Comparison of the docking arrangement of individual zinc fingers in the major groove of DNA using Zif268 as a reference. Our comparison focuses on the position and orientation of the α-helix within the major groove, and complexes are compared in a pairwise manner by 1) aligning their DNA binding sites, and then 2) calculating the difference in docking arrangement between these two fingers. This difference is described by considering: (*a*) the distance between the center of mass for each α-helix and (*b*) the angle of rotation required to superimpose the first 8 C$_\alpha$ atoms of the helices. Each finger was compared successively with fingers 1, 2, and 3 of Zif268; the plot displays the average for the comparison of each finger with all three fingers of Zif268. In this figure, the "canonical" zinc fingers—which are most similar to Zif268—tend to cluster near the origin (within the 2.0 Å, 20° box). [Note: For finger 3 of TFIIIA both the NMR (*open diamond*; 126) and X-ray (*open squares*; 91) structures are indicated since they are rather different. Since these methods give good agreement about the orientation of fingers 1 and 2, only the parameters for the X-ray structure are plotted for these fingers.]

Phosphate Contacts

There are a number of phosphate contacts in the structures of zinc finger–DNA complexes, and these presumably are important in the energetics of zinc finger–DNA recognition, but their role in determining sequence specificity is not yet known. The majority of the phosphate contacts are made to the primary strand of the DNA, thereby securing the finger to the strand that also receives the majority of the base contacts. However, there are only three phosphate contacts that are conserved in the majority of the structures, and there is only a modest correlation between the presence (or absence) of a particular phosphate interaction and the docking arrangement (canonical or nonstandard) of the finger (117). The most conserved phosphate contact (observed ~80% of the time) is made by the histidine (through Nδ) at position 7 of the helix to the phosphate just to the 5′ side of the finger binding site. Because zinc is coordinated through Nε of the same residue, this interaction brings the core of the finger in close proximity to the DNA strand that is to be recognized. The fingers in which this contact is absent (TFIIIA finger 1, GLI fingers 3 and 5, TTK finger 1, and YY1 finger 4) tend to have large deviations from the canonical helix docking geometry (Figure 4), and all display nonstandard base recognition patterns (GLI finger 3 does not even interact with the DNA bases). However, we note that there are other nonstandard fingers that do make this phosphate contact, and thus its presence or absence does not provide any simple way of classifying fingers. The next most conserved phosphate contact (present in ~60% of the structures) involves the lysine or arginine at position 1 of the second β-strand (two residues beyond the second cysteine). A positively charged residue at this position of the β-strand also is strongly conserved among known zinc finger sequences (57). This phosphate contact also involves the primary strand of the DNA, and this basic residue contacts either the same phosphate contacted by histidine 7 or the phosphate just to the 3′ side of this position. In those structures where a direct contact is not observed, this lysine or arginine still is near the phosphate backbone, and it may contribute to binding. The third conserved phosphate contact is made from the linker region between fingers. As discussed below, when consecutive fingers contact the DNA the intervening linker tends to have the consensus sequence TGEKP, and the lysine (or arginine) at the fourth position of this linker usually makes a direct or water-mediated contact with a phosphate, typically one on the primary strand of the DNA (37).

Phosphate contacts are made by other positions in the zinc finger structure, but these contacts are poorly conserved among the various complexes. When tyrosine occupies either of the conserved aromatic positions, its hydroxyl group can make hydrogen bonds the phosphate backbone. Amino acids at positions -2, 1, and 5 of the α-helix also can make phosphate contacts, although contacts from positions 1 and 5 require long side chains when the fingers dock in a canonical arrangement. Amino acids at positions -1 and 2, which typically interact with the DNA bases, also can make direct or water-mediated contacts with the phosphate backbone. Even this list of phosphate contacts is not exhaustive: Because a large proportion of the $\beta\beta\alpha$ structure is so close to the DNA, and because a number of different docking arrangements are observed, phosphate contacts can be made from a number of positions on the zinc finger.

Linkers

The linker region that connects neighboring Cys_2His_2 zinc fingers is an important structural element that helps control the spacing of the fingers along the DNA site. The most common linker arrangement has five residues between the final histidine of one finger and the first conserved aromatic of the next finger. In the Transcription Factor Database (47), we find that roughly half of the fingers with this linker length match a consensus sequence of the form TGEKP. Among these linkers the consensus actually is so strong that the degenerate DNA sequence that encodes this linker has been used to identify new zinc finger proteins by hybridization or RT-PCR (1, 54). Mutagenesis studies of the TGEKP linkers in ADR1 (25, 120) and TFIIIA (17, 23, 107) have demonstrated that they are important for high-affinity DNA binding. Some point mutations result in 10–100-fold reductions in DNA-binding affinity when measured in vitro, and mutations in the TGEKP linker also can result in loss of function in vivo (28, 46).

NMR studies indicate that the TGEKP linker between fingers is flexible in the free protein, but becomes more rigid upon binding DNA (13, 44, 126). The TGEKP linker is actually well ordered and similarly organized in the structures of most zinc finger–DNA complexes. With one exception, the TGEKP linkers in the structures (Zif268 and its variants, YY1, 1MEY, GLI, and TFIIIA; 13 in all) overlay with a RMS deviation between 0.15 Å and 0.50 Å and have a very well conserved length falling between 13.9 Å and 14.5 Å. The lone exception is the linker between fingers 4 and 5 of GLI (SNEKP), which contains two changes from the consensus sequence and has a RMS deviation of >1 Å and a length of 11.8 Å. (These differences may be related to the HX$_4$H pattern that occurs in finger 4 immediately preceding the linker.) In the Zif268 structure, the TG(E/Q)KP linkers have crystallographic B-values (for side chain and backbone) that are similar to the fingers themselves; in the Tramtrack structure there is a nonconsensus linker, KRNVKV, which has very high B-value relative to the fingers, and presumably this reflects a higher degree of disorder and thermal motion.

Examining the conformation of the TGEKP linker in the various protein-DNA complexes allows us to assign a structural role to each of the residues. The linker caps the C terminus of the preceding finger's helix using an α_L motif (3). Threonine provides the C-cap, while glycine assumes a positive ϕ angle that also is needed to complete this cap. As discussed in the next paragraph, glutamate can play a distinctive role in stabilizing finger-finger contacts. The following positively charged residue (lysine or arginine) makes a direct or water-mediated contact to the phosphate backbone. Proline probably rigidifies the connection between the linker and the first β-strand of the subsequent finger, and the proline stacks on the first highly conserved aromatic residue of the next finger. This aromatic subsequently stacks on the main-chain atoms at the N terminus of the α-helix (at position -1), thereby helping to define their conformation.

The docking of adjacent fingers is further stabilized by a contact involving the side chain from position 9 of the preceding finger's helix (typically involving the sequence HXRXH) and the backbone carbonyl or side chain at position -2 of the subsequent finger. This contact appears to be correlated with the use of a canonical linker: When a TGEKP linker occurs between fingers in the Transcription Factor Database (47), there almost always (470 out of 475 examples) are three residues between the two histidines of the preceding finger, and in 80% of these cases there is an arginine or lysine at position 9. When an arginine occurs at the corresponding position in the known zinc finger–DNA complexes (in the context of a TGEKP linker), it invariably makes an interfinger contact to the backbone carbonyl at position −2. In some structures, the conformation of this arginine is stabilized by interactions with the glutamate from the linker. The highly conserved nature of the TGEKP linker and the interfinger contact from position 9 implies that interfinger organization is important in DNA recognition.

Biochemical Information about Zinc Finger–DNA Interactions

Cys_2His_2 zinc finger proteins often bind their DNA target sites with high affinity and specificity. In general, observed DNA affinities increase as the number of fingers increases from one to two to three. Proteins containing three fingers, such as Zif268 and SP1, bind their preferred sequences with dissociation constants typically between 10^{-8} M and 10^{-11} M (depending on the buffer conditions and assay methods) (7, 36, 50, 104, 113, 118, 124). These proteins also display good specificity for their binding sites (as determined by DNA site selections or by competition with nonspecific DNA) (113, 118, 124), and the arginine $\Rightarrow$ guanine contacts often provide highly specific interactions. Substituting alanine for arginine at either position −1 or 6 in finger 1 of Zif268 revealed that each arginine contributes about 3 kcal/mol of binding energy (36). Changing the aspartate at position 2 to alanine or the glutamate at position 3 to alanine results in much smaller changes to the affinity of the protein (the aspartate-to-alanine change is actually energetically favorable), but these acidic residues still do play a role in determining specificity.

It is not yet known how the stability of a zinc finger may affect the affinity and specificity of DNA binding, but a study by Shi & Berg (113) suggests that this may have an effect. They altered the sequence of the fingers of SP1 (except for those residues involved in DNA recognition) to match a consensus sequence that had been developed from a database of fingers (73) and that coordinates zinc with a higher affinity than does finger 3 of SP1 (73, 101). Since zinc coordination is coupled with folding, this suggests that the consensus backbone is more stable than finger 3 of SP1. Shi & Berg found that this new protein displayed improved affinity (sixfold) and specificity relative to SP1. Conversely, reduced affinity and specificity were observed if the sequence at most positions in a single finger was changed to alanine (retaining only the conserved and DNA-binding amino acids). This reduces the affinity of the finger for zinc and can result in some heterogeneity in its coordination (84).

CD studies have demonstrated that binding of Zif268 induces a conformational change in the DNA (37) that is consistent with induction of the enlarged-major-groove conformation observed in the structures of the zinc finger–DNA complexes (37, 89). [Analysis of the crystal structures shows that the enlarged major groove results from a combination of negative base pair displacement and unwinding of the DNA (89).] Biochemical studies of supercoiling levels also have shown that zinc finger binding unwinds the DNA by approximately 18° per finger (114). Unwinding may limit the number of fingers that contact neighboring subsites: With TGEKP linkers, binding energy tends to plateau after three fingers (103, 112), but further studies are needed to understand the basis of this effect.

SELECTING ZINC FINGERS THAT RECOGNIZE NOVEL DNA SITES

One of the most striking features observed in the Zif268 complex (95) involved the conserved pattern of base contacts in the tandemly linked fingers (using residues at positions −1, 2, 3, and 6 of the helix). Given that this family of proteins was known to recognize a variety of different sequences and that one might be able to "mix and match" fingers for new sites (88), these proteins provided an attractive framework for design efforts. Initial attempts to rationally alter the specificity of zinc finger proteins were based on sequence and structural comparisons of zinc fingers (30–33, 61, 87, 121). This approach met with some success. Selection by phage display (6, 116) provided another potential method for finding sequences (from a library of randomized fingers) that might recognize a desired target site. Because this method begins from an "unbiased" library (by fully randomizing key recognition positions), it can provide new information about DNA recognition by zinc fingers while revealing which amino acid sequences are best for a given site. Using the Zif268 framework and randomizing potential base-contacting residues, many of the initial studies succeeded in recovering fingers with novel specificities (18, 19, 58, 59, 104, 125). These results provided new information about the best finger sequences for recognizing a given DNA subsite, but these successes only involved purine-rich sites. Recent selection studies have focused on the recognition of a broader range of sequences and on generating functional proteins that recognize entirely novel sites.

Greisman & Pabo developed a sequential selection protocol that changes all three fingers of a protein, selecting one finger at a time while "walking" across the binding site in three stages (50; Figure 5): *Stage A*) In the first step, finger 1 is selected over the 3′ portion of the binding site while held in place by two Zif268 anchor fingers that recognize a DNA sequence fused to the target site. *Stage B*) In the second step, one anchor finger is discarded and an additional random finger 2 library is attached to the selected finger 1 clones. Finger 2 is then selected to bind to the central portion of the target site. *Stage C*) In the third step, the remaining anchor finger is discarded from the finger 1–finger 2 clones. A random finger 3 library is attached to these fingers and finger 3 is selected to recognize the 5′ portion of the target site. This process attempts to ensure the compatibility of neighboring fingers in DNA recognition by carrying a small pool of clones from one stage to the next (such that one finger can be reoptimized as the next is added), and

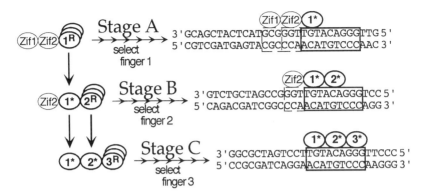

Figure 5 Overview of the sequential selection protocol (stages A, B, and C) that successively optimizes fingers 1, 2, and 3 to create a new zinc finger protein (50). The *left side* of the diagram indicates the constructs that are displayed in the phage libraries, and the *right side* shows fingers remaining after multiple rounds of selection and amplification (indicated with *small horizontal arrows*). *Zif1* and *Zif2* denote wild-type Zif268 fingers; the superscript *R* denotes a randomized finger library; and an *asterisk* denotes the set of selected sequences. The nine base pair recognition sequence that the fingers are selected against is *boxed*, as is the subsite for each Zif268 anchor finger. The set of fingers selected in one stage is incorporated into the phage libraries used in the next stage of selection, allowing a final optimization of previously selected fingers in their new context.

the process helps ensure that each finger is selected in the most relevant structural context. Using this method, proteins were selected for three biologically important control sites with very different G·C content. Subsequent studies have confirmed that these proteins have the desired DNA-binding specificity (124), demonstrating that the Zif268 framework can be adapted for recognition of many different DNA sequences (59).

Segal et al used a different strategy to address concerns about context dependence, choosing to focus on the development of a set of fingers that recognize each of the 16 possible 5'-GNNG-3' sequences (110). When sites of this form are combined to give any extended site of the form GNNGNNGNN, the overlap of neighboring subsites is always at a G·C base pair, and the residue at position 2 will readily be able to make the expected contacts with the flanking G·C base pair in the neighboring subsite. (Thus the four base pair subsites will always mesh with the three base pair repeat.) After the initial selection of these fingers by phage display, other variants were tested in an attempt to further improve the specificity of the fingers, and most of the resulting fingers display good discrimination against other sequences. Because of the large number of sites that were successful targeted, the sequences of these fingers provide further information about the preferred residues for DNA recognition at positions −1, 1, 2, and 3 (at least in the context of the arginine that is retained at position 6). There is also some evidence for cooperation between these residues in DNA recognition. Beerli et al have shown that fingers from this library can be assembled to target many G·C-rich sites (7).

Isalan et al took a rather different approach to deal with the subsite/subsite interface: Rather than fixing the identity of the base at this position, they randomized residues on both sides of the finger/finger interface that could contact this region (56). Most previous studies had been influenced by the use of Zif268 anchor fingers: Because these fingers contain aspartate at position 2 they tend to create a preference for G or T under position 6 of the preceding finger due to the partial overlap of recognition sites. Isalan et al prepared a library in which position 6 of finger 2 and positions −1, 1, 2, and 3 of finger 3 were randomized (again using a Zif268-based construct), and then used this library of selected proteins for all 16 possible dinucleotide sequences under position 6 of finger 2 and position −1 of finger 3. They recovered fingers that were specific for 15 of the 16 possible combinations, and specificity for the remaining junction sequence has been obtained by Greisman & Pabo (50, 124). Thus it appears that the specificity of zinc fingers is not inherently limited by structural requirements at the subsite/subsite interface (although more data still are needed on possible variations in affinity of these proteins). Because of the large number of sites used in this study, the resulting data also helped to clarify which amino acids at positions −1 and 6 define a given sequence specificity. Unfortunately the role of position 2 in sequence specificity is still poorly understood, and there is not yet any simple correspondence between amino acid type and observed sequence preference.

PREDICTING ZINC FINGER SPECIFICITY

As the body of data from zinc finger selections continues to grow, it becomes increasingly important to compile it in a manner that would facilitate the design of new zinc finger proteins. If relevant patterns could be recognized and such sequence motifs readily reused, the need for time-consuming phage display selection methods when creating new zinc finger proteins might be reduced. In principle, comparisons should be simplified by the fact that most selections have used a Zif268-like framework and have focused on variations of many of the same key residues.

The first attempts to predict zinc finger specificity focused on the idea of a recognition code that would correlate specific residues in the recognition helix with specific bases in the subsite (18, 30, 31). Past successes in altering finger specificity, and the analysis of natural zinc finger proteins, revealed some significant patterns in the observed side chain–base interactions. These patterns (which assume a canonical binding geometry for each finger) have been compiled into a "recognition code" that attempts to break down the contacts between the finger and DNA into a chart of 1:1 interactions between specific positions on the helix and specific base pairs in the finger-recognition site (Figure 6). Clearly, approximations are involved when analyzing the data in this way: Structural studies, mutagenesis, statistical analysis of sequences, and design studies all show that the amino acids at positions −1, 2, 3, and 6 do not play fully independent roles in DNA recognition (20, 30, 31). Nonetheless, the recognition code contains useful

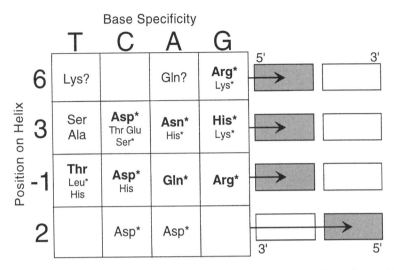

Figure 6 Pattern of side chain–base interactions that provide an approximate "recognition code" for zinc fingers that have a canonical binding mode. This chart describes contacts between residues at key positions in the α-helix ($-1, 2, 3,$ and 6) and bases at the corresponding positions in the canonical subsite (cf *upper panel* of Figure 3). *Boldface type* highlights amino acids that occur most frequently in phage display selections when a particular base specificity is desired, and an *asterisk* indicates contacts that have been observed in structural studies. Question marks (?) indicate that the specificity of the respective amino acid/base contact is uncertain. Positions for which base specificity is largely undefined are left blank. This way of representing the contacts ignores critical side chain–base interactions (such as the Asp(2) $\Rightarrow$ Arg(-1) interaction in Zif268) that are not taken into account in this chart.

information and there are cases in which it has strong predictive power (an arginine at position -1 usually does specify guanine). In the absence of other information, the recognition code provides a good place to start when attempting to predict or design the specificity of a new finger. Proteins containing three fingers have even been designed using the recognition code (26, 27), and they do bind their target sequence, although their specificity has not always been optimal.

Interpreting or evaluating the recognition code becomes more difficult in cases where several different amino acids might be used to recognize a particular base. Residues that appear in the same block of the code (Figure 6) are not always interchangeable, and their utility may depend on the context. For example, Segal et al found many situations in which a histidine at position 3 provides the best specificity for guanine, but in one instance lysine clearly gave better discrimination (110). The factors that determine such preferences are not yet known, and this complicates the use of a recognition code in design. The code may not fully account for factors such as: (a) side chain–side chain interactions, (b) sequence-dependent conformational flexibility of DNA, (c) the role of water in recognition,

(d) how particular contacts may subtly affect the docking arrangement, and (e) the effects of neighboring fingers and subsites on recognition.

A more conservative approach for the design of novel zinc finger proteins might employ a database that correlates an entire finger sequence with a given four base pair subsite (20). In principle, such a database would list fingers suitable for each of the 256 four base pair subsites, and such fingers might be combined to give new proteins for a desired nine-to-ten base pair site. This database might avoid some of the approximations inherent in a simple "recognition" code because side chain–side chain interactions, water-mediated contacts, and subtle changes in the docking arrangement could more readily be accounted for. There is some evidence that fingers displaying specificity for a given subsite in one context will also function similarly in other contexts. Thus many of the fingers that were obtained using the sequential selection protocol are similar in sequence to natural fingers that recognize very similar or identical four base pair subsites (50, 124). One excellent example of this conservation of finger specificity comes from finger 3 of a zinc finger protein (NRE), which was selected against the sequence 5'-AAGG-3' (50). The consensus sequence of the finger generated by phage display is identical at the base-recognition positions to finger 2 of Tramtrack, which happens to recognize the same DNA sequence. The modularity of fingers is also a fundamental assumption underlying the approach of Segal et al: Their project involved developing a "database" of fingers that will recognize each of the 16 possible 5'-GNNG-3' sequences.

Although some type of database may eventually prove more useful than a "code," there still are practical limits in implementing this strategy. Even if we simplify the problem by focusing on the core triplets (ignoring the contribution of the residue at position 2 for the moment) one should note that the most of the reported fingers with defined specificities recognize GNN triplets. (Most of the successful selections have involved sites of this form.) For the majority of the remaining 48 triplets, no finger with the desired specificity has been reported. It is not yet known to what extent this bias represents an intrinsic preference of fingers for GNN sequences or just the limits in the range of sites that have been tested. Assigning the specificity of an individual finger from a protein (so that it can be properly entered into the database) can also be complicated: Distinguishing the contribution of specific residues at the finger interface (separating the role of positions 6 and 2 from neighboring fingers) can be problematic since the determinants of specificity for position 2 are as yet poorly defined. Furthermore, the sequence specificity and affinity of fingers in the database may vary to a large degree, and it is important to recognize that not all fingers or triplets may make equal contributions to specificity.

Even the idea of a consistent finger/subsite correlation may have limits; there are some examples in which the same finger sequences seem to have context-dependent site preferences. For example, the selection (by Greisman & Pabo) of a zinc finger protein that would recognize the p53 site generated a finger containing the sequence QGTR (positions −1, 2, 3, and 6) that recognizes the triplet ACA (50, 124).

However, based on the recognition code, an arginine at position 6 would be expected to specify guanine rather than adenine. Indeed, in another context the QGTR finger does indeed recognize the triplet GCA (110). Both fingers were selected as the middle finger in a three finger protein, but the recognition helices on the neighboring fingers are much different. Presumably a difference in context, most likely the amino acid at position 2 of finger 3 or a somewhat different docking arrangement (which may be allowed by the Greisman & Pabo selections), is responsible for the divergent specificity of these fingers. Another interesting example of this phenomenon involves the recognition sequence RSDELVR (positions -1 through 6) engineered by Segal et al to bind to the triplet GTG while discriminating against GCG (110). This same recognition sequence occurs in WT1 in a different context (finger 4 instead of finger 2) and modestly prefers GCG over GTG (52). A very similar sequence (RSDELTR) also occurs in Zif268 (finger 1) and GLKF (finger 2), and these proteins also display a preference for GCG over GTG (115, 118, 124). More data will be needed to understand these effects, but these examples suggest that the context provided by neighboring fingers and subsites may affect the specificity of a finger. This may put inherent limits on the use of a database as a design tool. Thus a database may ultimately prove more useful than a 1:1 code, but it still may be necessary to try several different combinations or use some selection steps to optimize affinity.

The influence of context dependence on recognition (involving a finger's position within a protein and the sequence of any neighboring fingers) has been examined for two fingers that were created using the sequential selection protocol (124). During this protocol, finger 1 is initially selected to recognize its sequence as the C-terminal finger in a three finger construct, but it must function in the final construct as an N-terminal finger (Figure 5). For two of the proteins originally generated by this protocol, finger 1 was randomized and reselected (now as an N-terminal finger) to explore the possibility of context-dependent effects in the selection protocol. In both cases, the preferred residues at positions -1, 1, and 2 changed, implying that the best residues for DNA recognition can depend on the position of a finger in the protein or the effect of neighboring fingers. Although only a modest improvement in DNA affinity ($\sim$8-fold) was observed even in the more dramatic case, this type of improvement could be important for biomedical applications.

CREATING NOVEL TRANSCRIPTION FACTORS FROM ZINC FINGER PROTEINS

Cys_2His_2 zinc finger proteins can function as the DNA-binding domains of constructs designed to serve as biochemical or biomedical tools, and such proteins may eventually prove useful for gene therapy (98, 106, 127). Because of the wide variety of sequences that can be targeted with zinc fingers, they appear to be the most promising DNA-binding domains for this purpose. Attaching additional domains—for activation, repression, or enzymatic activity—should allow such proteins to carry out the desired function in a site-specific manner. However, several key issues must be addressed before this type of zinc finger chimera can be used for human gene therapy. These issues involve: (a) delivery, (b) adequate specificity in vivo for a desired target sequence, (c) ability to function effectively in vivo, and (d) evasion of immune system surveillance. It would also be useful if one could control the activity of the zinc finger construct via a bioavailable compound.

Preliminary studies involving issues of specificity and in vivo functioning seem quite promising. Thus it has been shown that Cys$_2$His$_2$ zinc finger proteins containing three designed or selected fingers can display sufficient affinity and specificity to function in vivo (7, 16, 21, 26, 64, 65, 79). Discrimination at the single-base pair level, in a transient transfection assay, can be achieved if the expression level of the protein is carefully controlled (16). However, it is not yet known whether three fingers will provide sufficient specificity for applications in gene therapy. (Statistically, one expects that there will be ∼10,000 identical nine base pair sites present in 3 billion base pairs of the human genome, and "side effects" caused by action at many different sites may be a significant problem.) In principle, the degree of discrimination within the genome can be improved by increasing the number of fingers (via covalent linkage or dimerization), using several three finger proteins simultaneously for synergistic activation, or by using fingers that dock in a nonstandard manner (such as finger 4 of GLI) to specify more base pairs per finger.

Increasing the number of covalently linked fingers would seem to be the obvious solution for improving specificity and targeting a particular site, but there appears to be a limit to the number of fingers that can be connected with TGEKP linkers and still bind DNA with a canonical docking arrangement. Proteins that contain three fingers (Zif268, its variants, and 1MEY) have a very regular arrangement on the DNA, but this does not seem to be the case for proteins with more than three fingers (YY1, GLI, TFIIIA), and even in these larger proteins there are, at most, three consecutive fingers that dock with the DNA in a canonical manner. Several groups have found that proteins with four or five fingers linked by the canonical TGEKP sequence display only very slight improvements in affinity relative to a three finger subset of the same construct (103, 112). Proteins containing six fingers that all are connected by TGEKP linkers display modest improvements in affinity (∼70-fold) over the three finger constructs, but this increased binding energy falls far short of the anticipated gains based on ideas about the chelate effect and simple effective concentration calculations (7, 68, 79). Even extending to a nine finger protein with the canonical linker appears to provide little improvement in affinity over just three fingers (60).

It appears that the affinity of such six finger proteins can be improved by including one longer linker at the center of the construct (65). Thus, by using either a LRQKDGERP or LRQKDGGGSERP linker between the two three finger proteins, a 6000–90,000-fold improvement in binding affinity (over either individual three finger protein) was achieved. These constructs are about 70-fold more specific than Zif268 when their discrimination against nonspecific DNA is compared (specificity ratio $\sim$1 in 10^7). These constructs should provide superior specificity to a three finger protein when targeting a site in the human genome, but they still may bind to many other sites (one would like specificity at the level of 1 in 3×10^9). Binding at even a small number of alternative sites may still be a problem for gene therapy.

Dimerization offers an interesting alternative to covalent linkage as a means for assembling more than three fingers at a target site. The cooperative association of two three-finger proteins on a DNA-binding site has several potential advantages over their covalent linkage: this may provide (a) a faster rate of equilibration with sites on genomic DNA (due to a lower inherent nonspecific affinity of each monomer), (b) a sharper transition as a function of protein concentration between the fully bound and unbound states, and (c) perhaps a greater degree of specificity (102). An artificial dimerization construct, which allows two different sets of zinc fingers to bind cooperatively to an asymmetric DNA site, was made by fusing the C-terminal coiled-coil domain of Gal4 to different sets of zinc fingers (100). N-terminal peptide sequences also have been selected that allow pairs of fingers to cooperatively bind DNA (122), and these might be used to allow recognition of extended sites. In short, it appears that dimerization may provide an interesting alternative to covalent linkage, but further data will be needed to see which methods are most useful in specific contexts.

Structure-based design (which begins by assembling known structural modules on a computer graphics system) has been used to create ZFHD1, a chimeric DNA-binding domain that shows promise for use in human gene therapy constructs. ZFHD1 was created by fusing fingers 1 and 2 of Zif268 to the Oct-1 homeodomain (99). The fusion protein specifically recognizes a composite binding site and displays good specificity in vitro and in vivo. ZFHD1 has been incorporated as the DNA-binding module in a prototype gene therapy system that allows drug-regulated expression of an added gene (containing upstream ZFHD1 binding sites). This drug-regulated expression system functions in human cells that have been introduced into mice (106) and has recently been used in an adeno-associated virus gene delivery system in monkeys (127). These exciting advances already suggest that zinc finger DNA-binding proteins may be useful in human gene therapy.

Chimeric proteins constructed using structure-based design also have been used as biochemical tools. Thus the ZFHD1 fusion protein has been used to study the role of the Oct-1 homeodomain in C1 complex assembly by herpes simplex virus (98). (ZFHD1 allows stable binding of the homeodomain in the absence of the POU-specific domain of Oct-1, and thus allows the roles of those domains to be clearly distinguished.) In other studies, zinc fingers have been linked to the cleavage domain of Fok I to create a restriction enzyme with sequence specificity that is defined by the zinc fingers (66, 67), and the fusion of zinc fingers to TBP has been used to create a chimera that could provide a novel method to regulate the expression of desired endogenous genes (63). Given that most eukaryotic transcription factors seem to be assembled from independently functioning domains, the use of zinc fingers in a structure-based design approach should provide a powerful method for the creation of new DNA-binding proteins with novel functions.

UNANSWERED QUESTIONS

Exciting progress has been made in the study of zinc finger proteins, but important questions remain. As noted in the introduction, relatively little is known about zinc finger–RNA interactions or about protein-protein interactions involving zinc fingers. More information is needed about how often zinc fingers adopt such roles. What is the structural basis for such contacts? What are the biological roles for these interactions? Do such zinc finger–zinc finger and zinc finger– RNA interactions tend to occur in larger polyfinger proteins that also have DNA-binding fingers? Are certain fingers specialized for such roles? Are there fingers with multiple alternative roles in different contexts? Are there other zinc fingers that have lost binding function over evolutionary history and now just play a more passive structure role?

Many of the studies of zinc finger–DNA interactions have focused on analyzing base contacts that are made by three finger Zif-like proteins. For these designs, perhaps the most important remaining question involves the potential limits of sequence specificity that can be achieved by varying residues in the recognition helix. To date, the majority of fingers created by selection or design recognize GNN triplets. While it is clear that zinc fingers can recognize a wide variety of different sequences, the limits are not yet known, and certain sites may be inherently more suitable than other sites. In particular, pyrimidine-rich sequences seem especially problematical, and it may not always be suitable to simply use the other binding orientation (thereby selecting for contacts along the purine-rich strand). Since zinc fingers seem to prefer a distinctive DNA conformation, sequence-dependent aspects of DNA structure could also affect the affinity and specificity of the zinc fingers that can be selected for a particular sequence. Although it is hard to interpret failures, there are good examples of thoughtful selection efforts that have failed to obtain desired finger specificities (110, 124). This may reflect the inherent difficulties with certain sequences or just indicate that other residues need to be randomized. More information is needed about the potential roles of the backbone residues, phosphate contacts, and the linker in defining the specificity of a finger. Thus experiments (113) with the consensus backbone demonstrate that other residues not directly involved in DNA recognition can have an impact on specificity and affinity. Changing other parts of the finger structure or using fingers (like GLI) with nonstandard recognition sites may improve the specificity for some of these "difficult sequences." It also will be interesting to see how readily one can create mixed proteins that have fingers with canonical and noncanonical docking arrangements. The issue of DNA recognition by polyfinger proteins also remains a challenging problem. What is the source of the energetic penalty that seems to limit the affinity when there are TGEKP linkers connecting more than three consecutive fingers? Perhaps zinc fingers connected by TGEKP linkers adopt a helical arrangement (when bound to DNA) that does not quite match the helical pitch of the DNA, and strain accumulates as more fingers are added. Using a longer linker between consecutive finger segments appears to alleviate some of this penalty, but these polyfinger proteins still do not bind as tightly as simple physical/chemical calculations would suggest.

Even for base contacts involving canonical docking arrangements, there is a considerable difference in the degree to which we understand the basis of DNA recognition from different positions in the helix, and there are questions about the utility of any simple "recognition code." Some of the greatest uncertainties involve the role of the residue at position 2, and the corresponding questions about interactions between neighboring fingers and subsites. There are many selection studies that have not obtained a consensus amino acid at position 2, and there may be cases in which the residue at this position plays only a peripheral role in DNA recognition. It is interesting that aspartate at position 2 is important in defining the finger specificity of Zif268 (36), but we note that serine, which does not appear to display a preference for any particular nucleotide, occurs most frequently at this position in natural proteins (57). There may be other cases in which the contribution of position 2 to finger specificity will be less direct, but still could be quite important. Thus a number of selections have found a preference for glycine at this position in certain DNA sequence contexts (50, 104, 110, 124). In the structure of QGSR (35), glycine at position 2 has α-helical ϕ/ψ values (-58 and -38; 105), implying that flexibility at this position is not important. Instead it appears that the absence of a β-carbon at position 2 is beneficial for binding at this site, allowing the main chain of the α-helix to approach the DNA more closely.

There also are important questions about the range of useful contacts that can be made from position 6 with a canonical docking arrangement, and it is still unclear how this position can be used to specify a base other than guanine (Figure 6). (A relatively small number of successful selections have a base other than G at the 5' position.) In part, understanding specificity at this position may also be complicated by the overlapping contacts that are made by residue 2 of the next (C-terminal) finger. However, there may also be geometric limitations imposed by the position and the orientation of the α-helix in the canonical docking arrangement. Thus the average distance (among the structures of canonical fingers) from the Cα of position 6 to the nearest heavy atom of the nucleotide that is contacted in the canonical docking arrangement is 8.8 ± 0.8 Å, a distance too large to be spanned by the majority of amino acids. This may limit the utility of position 6 in specifying bases other than guanine (which can readily be contacted with lysine or arginine). More structural data also are needed, since to date no contact between a residue at position 6 and a base other than guanine has been observed in a three-dimensional structure.

In general, DNA recognition by residues at positions -1 and 3 has been studied much more thoroughly than at the other positions, but even for these more carefully explored positions there are paradoxes that remained unexplained. For instance two selection studies have shown that serine at position 3 seems to prefer thymine as the central base (18, 19, 110), but in the QGSR Zif variant, the serine at position 3 specifies cytosine (EI Ramm, SA Wolfe, & CO Pabo, unpublished results). There also are important questions in cases where the "code" seems to suggest several side chains that might be used (this happens very frequently for position 3). Do these side chains represent relatively iso-energetic alternatives, or will the choice of residue depend on the structural context? Similar questions arise with respect to many other context-dependent effects. How often can fingers, which were designed or selected in one context, be "mixed and matched" to generate new specificities? Does the position of a finger within a protein affect the preferred residues for DNA recognition, or is context dependence purely a function of the neighboring finger and DNA sequences? Will a "database" approach, which tries to list fingers that are suitable for given three base pair or four base pair subsites, prove fundamentally more reliable than a "recognition code" (Figure 6) that tries to correlate specific residues in the recognition helix with particular bases in the site? Much remains to be learned, and the problems become even more challenging and interesting if we try to expand our analysis to include all the possibilities that become accessible via the addition of variant backbone structures, altered phosphate contacts, and nonstandard docking arrangements.

SUMMARY

Structural and biochemical studies have given us a wealth of information about zinc finger–DNA interactions. These fingers have a conserved sequence pattern that stabilizes the $\beta\beta\alpha$ fold, but they can present very different sequences on the surface of the α-helix and also can dock in the major groove with a variety of different orientations. Most design efforts have focused on fingers with a canonical (Zif-like) docking arrangement, and fingers with new specificities have been selected by phage display or designed using information about known interactions. These methods have allowed the construction of entire proteins with novel DNA-binding specificities, and phage display studies also have provided a considerable body of data about side chain–base interactions. Zinc fingers appear to provide a very powerful framework for the selection and design of new proteins, but phage display may still be required for finding the optimal contacts. The complexity of the protein-DNA interface suggests that no simple "recognition code" will ever provide a reliable, general method for designing proteins with optimal affinity for new sites. Developing a database of fingers that recognize particular subsites may be more useful, but much additional information is needed, and there still are important questions about the significance of context-dependent effects.

As answers to these and other unresolved questions are obtained, they will facilitate the ease with which zinc fingers are fused into site-specific transcription factors designed for a specific purpose, whether that is as part of a gene therapy construct or biochemical tool. As selection methods are improved, and as further biochemical and structural information is obtained, it seems quite possible that zinc finger proteins with almost any desired DNA specificity could be obtained, and this would have very exciting implications for biological research and gene therapy.

ACKNOWLEDGMENTS

We would like to thank B Wang, J Miller, and JK Joung for their comments on this manuscript. SAW was supported by the Howard Hughes Medical Institute and as a Special Fellow of the Leukemia Society of America; COP and LN were supported by the Howard Hughes Medical Institute.

Visit the Annual Reviews home page at www.AnnualReviews.org

LITERATURE CITED

1. Agata Y, Matsuda E, Shimizu A. 1998. Rapid and efficient cloning of cDNAs encoding Kruppel-like zinc finger proteins by degenerate PCR. *Gene* 213:55–64

2. Andreazzoli M, De Lucchini S, Costa M, Barsacchi G. 1993. RNA binding properties and evolutionary conservation of the *Xenopus* multifinger protein Xfin. *Nucleic Acids Res.* 21:4218–25

3. Aurora R, Rose GD. 1998. Helix capping. *Protein Sci.* 7:21–38

4. Bardeesy N, Pelletier J. 1998. Overlapping RNA and DNA binding domains of the wt1 tumor suppressor gene product. *Nucleic Acids Res.* 26:1784–92

5. Bardwell VJ, Treisman R. 1994. The POZ domain: a conserved protein-protein interaction motif. *Genes Dev.* 8:1664–77

6. Bass S, Greene R, Wells JA. 1990. Hormone phage: an enrichment method for variant proteins with altered binding properties. *Proteins* 8:309–14

7. Beerli RR, Segal DJ, Dreier B, Barbas CF 3rd. 1998. Toward controlling gene expression at will: specific regulation of the erbB-2/HER-2 promoter by using polydactyl zinc finger proteins constructed from modular

building blocks. *Proc. Natl. Acad. Sci. USA* 95:14628–33

8. Bellefroid EJ, Poncelet DA, Lecocq PJ, Revelant O, Martial JA. 1991. The evolutionarily conserved Kruppel-associated box domain defines a subfamily of eukaryotic multifingered proteins. *Proc. Natl. Acad. Sci. USA* 88:3608–12

9. Berg JM, Godwin HA. 1997. Lessons from zinc-binding peptides. *Annu. Rev. Biophys. Biomol. Struct.* 26:357–71

10. Berg JM, Shi Y. 1996. The galvanization of biology: a growing appreciation for the roles of zinc. *Science* 271:1081–85

11. Bird AJ, Turner-Cavet JS, Lakey JH, Robinson NJ. 1998. A carboxyl-terminal Cys2/His2-type zinc-finger motif in DNA primase influences DNA content in *Synechococcus* PCC 7942. *J. Biol. Chem.* 273:21246–52

12. Bohm S, Frishman D, Mewes HW. 1997. Variations of the C2H2 zinc finger motif in the yeast genome and classification of yeast zinc finger proteins. *Nucleic Acids Res.* 25:2464–69

13. Bowers PM, Schaufler LE, Klevit RE. 1999. A folding transition and novel zinc finger accessory domain in the transcription factor ADR1. *Nat. Struct. Biol.* 6:478–85

14. Brown RS, Sander C, Argos P. 1985. The primary structure of transcription factor TFIIIA has 12 consecutive repeats. *FEBS Lett.* 186:271–74

15. Caricasole A, Duarte A, Larsson SH, Hastie ND, Little M, et al. 1996. RNA binding by the Wilms tumor suppressor zinc finger proteins. *Proc. Natl. Acad. Sci. USA* 93:7562–66

16. Choo Y, Castellanos A, Garcia-Hernandez B, Sanchez-Garcia I, Klug A. 1997. Promoter-specific activation of gene expression directed by bacteriophage-selected zinc fingers. *J. Mol. Biol.* 273:525–32

17. Choo Y, Klug A. 1993. A role in DNA binding for the linker sequences of the first three zinc fingers of TFIIIA. *Nucleic Acids Res.* 21:3341–46

18. Choo Y, Klug A. 1994. Selection of DNA binding sites for zinc fingers using rationally randomized DNA reveals coded interactions. *Proc. Natl. Acad. Sci. USA* 91:11168–72

19. Choo Y, Klug A. 1994. Toward a code for the interactions of zinc fingers with DNA: selection of randomized fingers displayed on phage. *Proc. Natl. Acad. Sci. USA* 91:11163–67

20. Choo Y, Klug A. 1997. Physical basis of a protein-DNA recognition code. *Curr. Opin Struct. Biol.* 7:117–25

21. Choo Y, Sanchez-Garcia I, Klug A. 1994. In vivo repression by a site-specific DNA-binding protein designed against an oncogenic sequence. *Nature* 372:642–45

22. Clarke ND, Berg JM. 1998. Zinc fingers in *Caenorhabditis elegans*: finding families and probing pathways. *Science* 282:2018–22

23. Clemens KR, Zhang P, Liao X, McBryant SJ, Wright PE, Gottesfeld JM. 1994. Relative contributions of the zinc fingers of transcription factor IIIA to the energetics of DNA binding. *J. Mol. Biol.* 244:23–35

24. Coleman JE. 1992. Zinc proteins: enzymes, storage proteins, transcription factors, and replication proteins. *Annu. Rev. Biochem.* 61:897–946

25. Cook WJ, Mosley SP, Audino DC, Mullaney DL, Rovelli A, et al. 1994. Mutations in the zinc-finger region of the yeast regulatory protein ADR1 affect both DNA binding and transcriptional activation. *J. Biol. Chem.* 269:9374–79

26. Corbi N, Libri V, Fanciulli M, Passananti C. 1998. Binding properties of the artificial zinc fingers coding gene Sint1. *Biochem. Biophys. Res. Commun.* 253:686–92

27. Corbi N, Perez M, Maione R, Passananti C. 1997. Synthesis of a new zinc finger peptide; comparison of its 'code' deduced and 'CASTing' derived binding sites. *FEBS Lett.* 417:71–74

28. Crozatier M, Kongsuwan K, Ferrer P, Merriam JR, Lengyel JA, Vincent A. 1992. Single amino acid exchanges in separate domains of the *Drosophila* serendipity delta zinc finger protein cause embryonic and sex biased lethality. *Genetics* 131:905–16

29. Davies R, Moore A, Schedl A, Bratt E, Miyahawa K, et al. 1999. Multiple roles for the Wilms' tumor suppressor, WT1. *Cancer Res.* 59:S1747–50

30. Desjarlais JR, Berg JM. 1992. Redesigning the DNA-binding specificity of a zinc finger protein: a data base-guided approach. *Proteins* 12:101–4

31. Desjarlais JR, Berg JM. 1992. Toward rules relating zinc finger protein sequences and DNA binding site preferences. *Proc. Natl. Acad. Sci. USA* 89:7345–49

32. Desjarlais JR, Berg JM. 1993. Use of a zinc-finger consensus sequence framework and specificity rules to design specific DNA binding proteins. *Proc. Natl. Acad. Sci. USA* 90:2256–60

33. Desjarlais JR, Berg JM. 1994. Length-encoded multiplex binding site determination: application to zinc finger proteins. *Proc. Natl. Acad. Sci. USA* 91:11099–103

34. Dutnall RN, Neuhaus D, Rhodes D. 1996.

The solution structure of the first zinc finger domain of SWI5: a novel structural extension to a common fold. *Structure* 4:599–611

35. Elrod-Erickson M, Benson TE, Pabo CO. 1998. High-resolution structures of variant Zif268-DNA complexes: implications for understanding zinc finger-DNA recognition. *Structure* 6:451–64

36. Elrod-Erickson M, Pabo CO. 1999. Binding studies with mutants of Zif268. *J. Biol. Chem.* 274:19281–85

37. Elrod-Erickson M, Rould MA, Nekludova L, Pabo CO. 1996. Zif268 protein-DNA complex refined at 1.6 Å: a model system for understanding zinc finger-DNA interactions. *Structure* 4:1171–80

38. Engelke DR, Ng S-Y, Shastry BS, Roeder RG. 1980. Specific interaction of a purified transcription factor with an internal control region of 5S RNA genes. *Cell* 19:717–28

39. Englert C, Vidal M, Maheswaran S, Ge Y, Ezzell RM, et al. 1995. Truncated WT1 mutants alter the subnuclear localization of the wild-type protein. *Proc. Natl. Acad. Sci. USA* 92:11960–64

40. Fairall L, Harrison SD, Travers AA, Rhodes D. 1992. Sequence-specific DNA binding by a two zinc-finger peptide from the Drosophila melanogaster Tramtrack protein. *J. Mol. Biol.* 226:349–66

41. Fairall L, Schwabe JWR, Chapman L, Finch JT, Rhodes D. 1993. The crystal structure of a two zinc-finger peptide reveals an extension to the rules for zinc finger/DNA recognition. *Nature* 366:483–87

42. Finerty PJ JR, Bass BL. 1997. A *Xenopus* zinc finger protein that specifically binds dsRNA and RNA-DNA hybrids. *J. Mol. Biol.* 271:195–208

43. Finerty PJ Jr, Bass BL. 1999. Subsets of the zinc finger motifs in dsRBP-ZFa can bind double-stranded RNA. *Biochemistry* 38:4001–7

44. Foster MP, Wuttke DS, Radhakrishnan I, Case DA, Gottesfeld JM, Wright PE. 1997. Domain packing and dynamics in the DNA complex of the N-terminal zinc fingers of TFIIIA. *Nat. Struct. Biol.* 4:605–8

45. Frankel AD, Berg JM, Pabo CO. 1987. Metal-dependent folding of a single zinc finger from transcription factor IIIA. *Proc. Natl. Acad. Sci. USA* 84:4841–45

46. Gaul U, Redemann N, Jackle H. 1989. Single amino acid exchanges in the finger domain impair the function of the *Drosophila* gene Kruppel (Kr). *Proc. Natl. Acad. Sci. USA* 86:4599–603

47. Ghosh D. 1993. Status of the transcription factors database (TFD). *Nucleic Acids Res.* 21:3117–18

48. Green A, Sarkar B. 1998. Alteration of zif268 zinc-finger motifs gives rise to non-native zinc-co-ordination sites but preserves wild-type DNA recognition. *Biochem. J.* 333:85–90

49. Gregory RC, Taxman DJ, Seshasayee D, Kensinger MH, Bieker JJ, Wojchowski DM. 1996. Functional interaction of GATA1 with erythroid Kruppel-like factor and Sp1 at defined erythroid promoters. *Blood* 87:1793–801

50. Greisman HA, Pabo CO. 1997. Sequential optimization strategy yields high-affinity zinc finger proteins for diverse DNA target sites. *Science* 275:657–61

51. Grondin B, Bazinet M, Aubry M. 1996. The KRAB zinc finger gene ZNF74 encodes an RNA-binding protein tightly associated with the nuclear matrix. *J. Biol. Chem.* 271:15458–67

52. Hamilton TB, Borel F, Romaniuk PJ. 1998. Comparison of the DNA binding characteristics of the related zinc finger proteins WT1 and EGR1. *Biochemistry* 37:2051–58

53. Hanas JS, Hazuda DJ, Bogenhagen DF, Wu FY-H, Wu C-W. 1983. *Xenopus* transcription factor A requires zinc for binding to the 5 S RNA gene. *J. Biol. Chem.* 258:14120–25

54. Hoovers JMN, Mannens M, John R, Bliek J, van Heyningen V, et al. 1992. High-resolution localization of 69 potential human zinc finger protein genes: a number

are clustered. *Genomics* 12:254–63

55. Houbaviy HB, Usheva A, Shenk T, Burley SK. 1996. Cocrystal structure of YY1 bound to the adeno-associated virus P5 initiator. *Proc. Natl. Acad. Sci. USA* 93:13577–82

56. Isalan M, Klug A, Choo Y. 1998. Comprehensive DNA recognition through concerted interactions from adjacent zinc fingers. *Biochemistry* 37:12026–33

57. Jacobs GH. 1992. Determination of the base recognition positions of zinc fingers from sequence analysis. *EMBO J.* 11:4507–17

58. Jamieson AC, Kim SH, Wells JA. 1994. In vitro selection of zinc fingers with altered DNA-binding specificity. *Biochemistry* 33:5689–95

59. Jamieson AC, Wang H, Kim SH. 1996. A zinc finger directory for high-affinity DNA recognition. *Proc. Natl. Acad. Sci. USA* 93:12834–39

60. Kamiuchi T, Abe E, Imanishi M, Kaji T, Nagaoka M, Sugiura Y. 1998. Artificial nine zinc-finger peptide with 30 base pair binding sites. *Biochemistry* 37:13827–34

61. Kim CA, Berg JM. 1995. Serine at position 2 in the DNA recognition helix of a Cys$_2$-His$_2$ zinc finger peptide is not, in general, responsible for base recognition. *J. Mol. Biol.* 252:1–5

62. Kim CA, Berg JM. 1996. A 2.2 Å resolution crystal structure of a designed zinc finger protein bound to DNA. *Nat. Struct. Biol.* 3:940–45

63. Kim JS, Kim J, Cepek KL, Sharp PA, Pabo CO. 1997. Design of TATA box-binding protein/zinc finger fusions for targeted regulation of gene expression. *Proc. Natl. Acad. Sci. USA* 94:3616–20

64. Kim JS, Pabo CO. 1997. Transcriptional repression by zinc finger peptides. Exploring the potential for applications in gene therapy. *J. Biol. Chem.* 272:29795–800

65. Kim JS, Pabo CO. 1998. Getting a handhold on DNA: design of poly-zinc finger proteins with femtomolar dissociation constants. *Proc. Natl. Acad. Sci. USA* 95:2812–17

66. Kim YG, Cha J, Chandrasegaran S. 1996. Hybrid restriction enzymes: zinc finger fusions to Fok I cleavage domain. *Proc. Natl. Acad. Sci. USA* 93:1156–60

67. Kim YG, Shi Y, Berg JM, Chandrasegaran S. 1997. Site-specific cleavage of DNA-RNA hybrids by zinc finger/FokI cleavage domain fusions. *Gene* 203:43–49

68. Klemm JD, Pabo CO. 1996. Oct-1 POU domain-DNA interactions: cooperative binding of isolated subdomains and effects of covalent linkage. *Genes Dev.* 10:27–36

69. Klocke B, Koster M, Hille S, Bouwmeester T, Bohm S, et al. 1994. The FAR domain defines a new *Xenopus laevis* zinc finger protein subfamily with specific RNA homopolymer binding activity. *Biochim. Biophys. Acta* 1217:81–89

70. Klug A, Schwabe JW. 1995. Protein motifs 5. Zinc fingers. *FASEB J.* 9:597–604

71. Knochel W, Poting A, Koster M, el Baradi T, Nietfeld W, et al. 1989. Evolutionary conserved modules associated with zinc fingers in *Xenopus laevis. Proc. Natl. Acad. Sci. USA* 86:6097–100

72. Koster M, Kuhn U, Bouwmeester T, Nietfeld W, el-Baradi T, et al. 1991. Structure, expression and in vitro functional characterization of a novel RNA binding zinc finger protein from *Xenopus. EMBO J.* 10:3087–93

73. Krizek BA, Amann BT, Kilfoil VJ, Merkle DL, Berg JM. 1991. A consensus zinc finger peptide: design, high-affinity metal binding, a pH-dependent structure, and a His to Cys sequence variant. *J. Am. Chem. Soc.* 113:4518–23

74. Krizek BA, Merkle DL, Berg JM. 1993. Ligand variation and metal ion binding specificity in zinc finger peptides. *Inorg. Chem.* 32:937–40

75. Lania L, Majello B, De Luca P. 1997. Transcriptional regulation by the Sp family

proteins. *Int. J. Biochem. Cell Biol.* 29: 1313–23

76. Larsson SH, Charlieu JP, Miyagawa K, Engelkamp D, Rassoulzadegan M, et al. 1995. Subnuclear localization of WT1 in splicing or transcription factor domains is regulated by alternative splicing. *Cell* 81:391–401

77. Lee JS, Galvin KM, Shi Y. 1993. Evidence for physical interaction between the zinc-finger transcription factors YY1 and Sp1. *Proc. Natl. Acad. Sci. USA* 90:6145–49

78. Lee MS, Gippert GP, Soman KV, Case DA, Wright PE. 1989. Three-dimensional solution structure of a single zinc finger DNA-binding domain. *Science* 245:635–37

79. Liu Q, Segal DJ, Ghiara JB, Barbas CF 3rd. 1997. Design of polydactyl zinc-finger proteins for unique addressing within complex genomes. *Proc. Natl. Acad. Sci. USA* 94:5525–30

80. Losson R. 1997. KRAB zinc finger proteins and nuclear receptors: a possible cross-talk. *Biol. Chem.* 378:579–81

81. Mackay JP, Crossley M. 1998. Zinc fingers are sticking together. *Trends Biochem. Sci.* 23:1–4

82. Merika M, Orkin SH. 1995. Functional synergy and physical interactions of the erythroid transcription factor GATA-1 with the Kruppel family proteins Sp1 and EKLF. *Mol. Cell. Biol.* 15:2437–47

83. Merkle DL, Schmidt MH, Berg JM. 1991. Design and characterization of a ligand-binding metallopeptide. *J. Am. Chem. Soc.* 113:5450–51

84. Michael SF, Kilfoil VJ, Schmidt MH, Amann BT, Berg JM. 1992. Metal binding and folding properties of a minimalist Cys_2His_2 zinc finger peptide. *Proc. Natl. Acad. Sci. USA* 89:4796–800

85. Miller J, McLachlan AD, Klug A. 1985. Repetitive zinc-binding domains in the protein transcription factor IIIA from *Xenopus* oocytes. *EMBO J.* 4:1609–14

86. Miura T, Satoh T, Takeuchi H. 1998. Role of metal-ligand coordination in the folding pathway of zinc finger peptides. *Biochim. Biophys. Acta* 1384:171–79

87. Nardelli J, Gibson T, Charnay P. 1992. Zinc finger-DNA recognition: analysis of base specificity by site-directed mutagenesis. *Nucleic Acids Res.* 20:4137–44

88. Nardelli J, Gibson TJ, Vesque C, Charnay P. 1991. Base sequence discrimination by zinc-finger DNA-binding domains. *Nature* 349:175–78

89. Nekludova L, Pabo CO. 1994. Distinctive DNA conformation with enlarged major groove is found in Zn-finger-DNA and other protein-DNA complexes. *Proc. Natl. Acad. Sci. USA* 91:6948–52

90. Neuhaus D, Nakaseko Y, Schwabe JW, Klug A. 1992. Solution structures of two zinc-finger domains from SWI5 obtained using two-dimensional ^1H nuclear magnetic resonance spectroscopy. A zinc-finger structure with a third strand of beta-sheet. *J. Mol. Biol.* 228:637–51

91. Nolte RT, Conlin RM, Harrison SC, Brown RS. 1998. Differing roles for zinc fingers in DNA recognition: structure of a six-finger transcription factor IIIA complex. *Proc. Natl. Acad. Sci. USA* 95:2938–43

92. Omichinski JG, Pedone PV, Felsenfeld G, Gronenborn AM, Clore GM. 1997. The solution structure of a specific GAGA factor-DNA complex reveals a modular binding mode. *Nat. Struct. Biol.* 4:122–32

92a. Pabo CO, Nekludova L. 2000. Geometric analysis and comparisonj of protein-DNA interfaces: Why is there no simple code for recognition? Submitted

93. Page DC, Mosher R, Simpson EM, Fisher EM, Mardon G, et al. 1987. The sex-determining region of the human Y chromosome encodes a finger protein. *Cell* 51:1091–104

94. Parraga G, Horvath SJ, Eisen A, Taylor WE, Hood L, et al. 1988. Zinc-dependent structure of a single-finger domain of yeast ADR1. *Science* 241:1489–92

95. Pavletich NP, Pabo CO. 1991. Zinc finger-DNA recognition: crystal structure of a Zif268-DNA complex at 2.1 A. *Science* 252:809–17
96. Pavletich NP, Pabo CO. 1993. Crystal structure of a five-finger GLI-DNA complex: new perspectives on Zn fingers. *Science* 261:1701–7
97. Perkins ND, Agranoff AB, Pascal E, Nabel GJ. 1994. An interaction between the DNA-binding domains of RelA(p65) and Sp1 mediates human immunodeficiency virus gene activation. *Mol. Cell. Biol.* 14:6570–83
98. Pomerantz JL, Pabo CO, Sharp PA. 1995. Analysis of homeodomain function by structure-based design of a transcription factor. *Proc. Natl. Acad. Sci. USA* 92:9752–56
99. Pomerantz JL, Sharp PA, Pabo CO. 1995. Structure-based design of transcription factors. *Science* 267:93–96
100. Pomerantz JL, Wolfe SA, Pabo CO. 1998. Structure-based design of a dimeric zinc finger protein. *Biochemistry* 37:965–70
101. Posewitz MC, Wilcox DE. 1995. Properties of the Sp1 zinc finger 3 peptide: coordination chemistry, redox reactions, and metal binding competition with metallothionein. *Chem. Res. Toxicol.* 8:1020–28
102. Ptashne M. 1992. A *Genetic Switch*. Cambridge, MA: Blackwell Sci. Cell
103. Rebar EJ. 1997. *Selection studies of zinc finger–DNA recognition*. PhD thesis. MIT, Cambridge, MA
104. Rebar EJ, Pabo CO. 1994. Zinc finger phage: affinity selection of fingers with new DNA-binding specificities. *Science* 263:671–73
105. Richardson JS, Richardson DC. 1989. In *Principles and Patterns of Protein Conformation*, ed. GD Fasman, pp. 1–98. New York: Plenum
106. Rivera VM, Clackson T, Natesan S, Pollock R, Amara JF, et al. 1996. A humanized system for pharmacologic control of gene expression. *Nat. Med.* 2:1028–32
107. Ryan RF, Darby MK. 1998. The role of zinc finger linkers in p43 and TFIIIA binding to 5S rRNA and DNA. *Nucleic Acids Res.* 26:703–9
108. Sands MS, Bogenhagen DF. 1991. Two zinc finger proteins from *Xenopus laevis* bind the same region of 5S RNA but with different nuclease protection patterns. *Nucleic Acids Res.* 19:797–803
109. Schoenherr CJ, Anderson DJ. 1995. Silencing is golden: negative regulation in the control of neuronal gene transcription. *Curr. Opin. Neurobiol.* 5:566–71
110. Segal DJ, Dreier B, Beerli RR, Barbas CF 3rd. 1999. Toward controlling gene expression at will: selection and design of zinc finger domains recognizing each of the 5'-GNN-3' DNA target sequences. *Proc. Natl. Acad. Sci. USA* 96:2758–63
111. Shastry BS. 1996. Transcription factor IIIA (TFIIIA) in the second decade. *J. Cell. Sci.* 109:535–39
112. Shi Y. 1995. *Molecular mechanisms of zinc finger protein-nucleic acid interactions*. PhD thesis. John Hopkins Univ., Baltimore, MD
113. Shi Y, Berg JM. 1995. A direct comparison of the properties of natural and designed zinc-finger proteins. *Chem. Biol.* 2:83–89
114. Shi Y, Berg JM. 1996. DNA unwinding induced by zinc finger protein binding. *Biochemistry* 35:3845–48
115. Shields JM, Yang VW. 1998. Identification of the DNA sequence that interacts with the gut-enriched Krüppel-like factor. *Nucleic Acids Res.* 26:796–802
116. Smith GP. 1985. Filamentous fusion phage: novel expression vectors that display cloned antigens on the virion surface. *Science* 228:1315–17
117. Suzuki M, Gerstein M, Yagi N. 1994. Stereochemical basis of DNA recognition by Zn fingers. *Nucleic Acids Res.* 22:3397–405

118. Swirnoff AH, Milbrandt J. 1995. DNA-binding specificity of NGFI-A and related zinc finger transcription factors. *Mol. Cell. Biol.* 15:2275–87

119. Takatsuji H. 1998. Zinc-finger transcription factors in plants. *Cell. Mol. Life Sci.* 54:582–96

120. Thukral SK, Morrison ML, Young ET. 1991. Alanine scanning site-directed mutagenesis of the zinc fingers of transcription factor ADR1: residues that contact DNA and that transactivate. *Proc. Natl. Acad. Sci. USA* 88:9188–92

121. Thukral SK, Morrison ML, Young ET. 1992. Mutations in the zinc fingers of ADR1 that change the specificity of DNA binding and transactivation. *Mol. Cell. Biol.* 12:2784–92

122. Wang B, Pabo C. 1999. Dimerization of zinc fingers mediated by peptides evolved in vitro from random sequences. *Proc. Natl. Acad. Sci. USA* 96:9568–73

123. Weiss MA, Keutmann HT. 1990. Alternating zinc finger motifs in the male-associated protein ZFY: defining architectural rules by mutagenesis and design of an "aromatic swap" second-site revertant. *Biochemistry* 29:9808–13

124. Wolfe SA, Greisman HA, Ramm EI, Pabo CO. 1999. Analysis of zinc fingers optimized via phage display: evaluating the utility of a recognition code. *J. Mol. Biol.* 285:1917–34

125. Wu H, Yang WP, Barbas CF 3rd. 1995. Building zinc fingers by selection: toward a therapeutic application. *Proc. Natl. Acad. Sci. USA* 92:344–48

126. Wuttke DS, Foster MP, Case DA, Gottesfeld JM, Wright PE. 1997. Solution structure of the first three zinc fingers of TFIIIA bound to the cognate DNA sequence: determinants of affinity and sequence specificity. *J. Mol. Biol.* 273:183–206

127. Ye X, Rivera VM, Zoltick P, Cerasoli F Jr, Schnell MA, et al. 1999. Regulated delivery of therapeutic proteins after in vivo somatic cell gene transfer. *Science* 283:88–91

Annu. Rev. Biophys. Biomol. Struct. 2000. 29:213–38

Protein Folding Intermediates and Pathways Studied by Hydrogen Exchange

S. Walter Englander

*Johnson Research Foundation; Department of Biochemistry and Biophysics,
University of Pennsylvania School of Medicine, Philadelphia, Pennsylvania 19104;
e-mail: walter@HX2.Med.upenn.Edu*

Key Words protein folding, hydrogen exchange, intermediates, pathways, kinetic barriers

■ **Abstract**   In order to solve the immensely difficult protein-folding problem, it will be necessary to characterize the barriers that slow folding and the intermediate structures that promote it. Although protein-folding intermediates are not accessible to the usual structural studies, hydrogen exchange (HX) methods have been able to detect and characterize intermediates in both kinetic and equilibrium modes—as transient kinetic folding intermediates on a subsecond time scale, as labile equilibrium molten globule intermediates under destabilizing conditions, and as infinitesimally populated intermediates in the high free-energy folding landscape under native conditions. Available results consistently indicate that protein-folding landscapes are dominated by a small number of discrete, metastable, native-like partially unfolded forms (PUFs). The PUFs appear to be produced, one from another, by the unfolding and refolding of the protein's intrinsically cooperative secondary structural elements, which can spontaneously create stepwise unfolding and refolding pathways. Kinetic experiments identify three kinds of barrier processes: (*a*) an initial intrinsic search-nucleation collapse process that prepares the chain for intermediate formation by pinning it into a condensed coarsely native-like topology; (*b*) smaller search-dependent barriers that put the secondary structural units into place; and (*c*) optional error-dependent misfold-reorganization barriers that can cause slow folding, intermediate accumulation, and folding heterogeneity. These conclusions provide a coherent explanation for the grossly disparate folding behavior of different globular proteins in terms of distinct folding pathways.

CONTENTS

1056-8700/00/0610-0213$14.00

PERSPECTIVES AND OVERVIEW

The fundamental questions in protein folding concern the structure of folding intermediates, the nature of the barrier processes that accompany intermediate formation, and the implications for folding pathways. Convincing answers have not emerged. Part of the problem is that different proteins exhibit wildly disparate folding behavior. This has led to sharply opposed hypotheses, often based on fundamentally different conceptions of the protein-folding landscape.

Experimental data are often interpreted in terms of the classical pathway paradigm which holds that unfolded polypeptides move toward their native structures through one or more distinct pathways defined by discrete intermediate forms (36, 42, 80, 81, 92). Conventional free-energy diagrams, as in Figure 1A (see color insert), illustrate the system's important equilibrium and kinetic relationships. The wells portray the sequence and stability of intermediates and endstates, the barriers indicate their interconversion rates, and the reaction coordinate follows the important pathway events. One can choose to draw these diagrams in a multidimensional sense to indicate that the intermediates and the transition states retain considerable freedom, and one can include alternative folding routes, but that does not change the pathway paradigm.

A different paradigm is most often pictured in terms of a funnel-shaped reaction landscape (Figure 1B) to emphasize the multidimensionality of the folding reaction space of polypeptides (23, 40, 76, 97, 102, 135, 139). The vertical reaction-coordinate of the funnel is an increasingly negative scale of internal energy (enthalpy), often set proportional to the fraction of native contacts formed (Q). The XY dimension displays the conformational entropy of the polypeptide and its continuous decrease as folding proceeds. Since the determining free-energy parameter does not explicitly appear, the funnel representation itself is noncommittal with respect to intermediates and barriers. Detailed features have been suggested by experimental results with real proteins but especially by computer simulations of the folding of nonprotein models (22, 103, 126, 132) such as the lattice model shown. The central concept is that unfolded polymers diffuse energetically downhill toward their native state through an unlimited number, essentially a continuum, of intermediates and paths. Rates are determined by the slope of the landscape and its roughness, essentially a continuum of small barriers. The multiple nonnative wells within and at the bottom of the funnel acknowledge the fact of specific intermediate accumulation in many proteins, but these are viewed as misfolded off-pathway species formed by the accidental occupation of nonobligatory states that act to slow rather than promote folding.

These fundamentally different viewpoints lead to very different interpretations of any given observation. For example, some proteins fold in a fast (msecs) two-state manner with no apparent intermediates. This might mean that distinct intermediates do not exist (Figure 1B) or that the initial kinetic barrier in a discrete folding pathway is rate-limiting so that the pathway intermediates are not seen (Figure 1A, top). Other proteins fold more slowly (secs), in a three-state manner and do accumulate intermediates. This might mean that an optional off-pathway intermediate, accidentally trapped in a deep off-pathway well, causes the slow folding (Figure 1B). Alternatively, both slow folding and the accumulation of one of the obligatory pathway intermediates might be caused by an optionally encountered error-dependent barrier (Figure 1A, bottom). Many proteins fold heterogeneously, with different molecules exhibiting different behavior. This might reflect multiple parallel pathways as in Figure 1B or a single pathway in which different molecules happen to encounter different error-dependent barriers and thus populate different intermediates and fold at different rates (Figure 1A, top plus bottom).

Are intermediates and pathways continuous or discrete? Clearly, insightful structural studies of the intermediates are required. This is difficult. Kinetic intermediates are very short lived; most proteins that have been studied fold to their native state in less than one second. Possible intermediates are invisible when folding is two-state, and they cannot be isolated for structural studies even when they do accumulate in three-state folding. Most experimental methods used to observe such fast processes are able to provide only nonspecific information about unresolved aromatic side chains (fluorescence, absorbance) or some averaged property of the polypeptide main chain (circular dichroism, scattering, infrared). Such signals provide rate information and can imply the presence of folding intermediates, but they do not define structures and cannot distinguish the fundamentally different viewpoints just described.

In principle these limitations do not apply to the ingenious theoretical approaches that have been constructed to simulate the entire kinetic folding history of single molecules. However, computational limitations have so far restricted these studies mainly to simplified models (e.g. Figure 1B) that lack properties such as main chain and side chain stereochemistry, secondary structure and hydrogen bonding, tertiary structural topology, solvent interaction, and realistic potential functions. One does not know a priori whether any or all of these factors are crucial or irrelevant for modeling protein-folding behavior.

To resolve these primary issues and then to delve more deeply into folding processes, it is necessary to obtain clear information on the structure, stability, and interrelationships of the folding intermediates, whether continuous or discrete, that in fact carry real protein molecules from their unfolded state (U) to their native state (N). In this effort, methods based on hydrogen exchange (HX) have proven most useful. This article summarizes the pertinent HX developments, the results obtained, and their implications for the intermediates and the barriers in protein-folding pathways.

HYDROGEN EXCHANGE

How can hydrogen exchange data define the structure of nonnative molecules? HX results typically define the presence or absence of hydrogen bonding at a large number of identifiable residue amides in a protein. The pattern of H-bonding identifies secondary structure. One can then distinguish similarities to and differences from the known native structure. In addition, HX data can evaluate structural stability and flexibility at an amino acid–resolved level.

Some Principles

The basic facts of protein HX processes have been multiply recounted (30, 50, 55, 63, 143). Protons on polar side chains and on the main chain amides, distributed uniformly throughout all protein molecules, exchange naturally with solvent protons in a nonperturbing manner. Main chain NH protons are most informative. Their exchange rates depend on the protecting H-bonds that mark the regular elements of secondary structure and can evaluate protein structure, stability, and dynamics at very many probe points and at amino acid resolution.

Amide protons exchange with solvent by way of proton transfer reactions (45) that depend on a number of factors—pH, temperature, neighboring side chains, and the isotopes involved—all of which have been thoroughly calibrated (8, 33, 98). The exchange reaction requires direct contact between the catalyst ion and the amide group and so cannot occur when the group in question is involved in a protecting H-bond. For example, H-bonded groups in small molecules and at the aqueous surface of proteins exhibit slow exchange even though they are exposed to solvent. To permit exchange, the H-bond donor-acceptor pair must be separated, apparently by 5 Å or more (94), so that the proton can H-bond to and be carried away by solvent catalyst. Any given H-bond can be broken by the transient global unfolding reaction (stability), which severs all H-bonds (6, 9, 69, 77, 89, 121, 142), or by a local fluctuation that separates only the individual bond (flexibility) (94), or by subglobal unfolding reactions that break sets of neighboring H-bonds (7, 10, 53). We are especially interested in the latter because they must include the intermediates that come into play in protein-folding reactions.

In the usual kinetic limit, known as the EX2 condition (70), where structural reclosing is faster than the intrinsic unprotected exchange rate (k_{unp}), the HX rate measured for any given hydrogen (k_{ex}) provides the transient opening equilibrium constant ($K_{op} = k_{ex}/k_{unp}$). From this the free energy of the determining opening reaction can be obtained (70, 87) ($\Delta G_{op} = -RT \ln K_{op} = -RT \ln k_{ex}/k_{unp}$). Therefore the measurement of HX rates and their sensitivity to ambient parameters can provide site-resolved information on the presence or absence of H-bonded structure, its stability, dynamics, and other properties.

But how does one make the measurements necessary to study ephemeral folding intermediates?

HX Labeling

HX is a chemical rather than a spectroscopic method and therefore can be used in a labeling mode. One can perform experiments that selectively emplace hydrogen isotope label at positions that are functionally interesting, under conditions most suitable for the experimental purpose. The hydrogen isotope profile can then be held essentially frozen in place by the native protein structure and by ambient conditions that ensure slow exchange while the labeled protein is placed into conditions suitable for analysis of the H-label by NMR or mass spectrometry (52). The results provide information about the presence and stability of H-bonded structure at many identifiable points through the protein.

HX labeling methods were first applied to the folding problem in the laboratory of RL Baldwin in experiments that used tritium labeling and liquid scintillation counting analysis (20, 21, 79, 123). The advent of two-dimensional NMR provided access to the inherent amino acid resolution of HX measurements (136). Recent progress in mass spectrometry extends these capabilities and can make them applicable to larger proteins (96, 146), especially when the analytical resolution is enhanced by fragment separation methods (47, 49, 120).

The combination of HX labeling with NMR analysis has made it possible to measure the structure and stability of populated intermediates that exist for less than 1 sec in kinetic folding (reviewed in 12, 51, 81, 141). The same methods have been used to define the H-bonded secondary structural elements that are present in molten globule forms, often thought to represent equilibrium analogs of kinetic intermediates (109). Most recently a method known as native state HX has made it possible to study partially unfolded intermediates that exist at equilibrium as infinitesimally populated, conformationally excited forms in the high free-energy conformational space of proteins under native conditions (7, 10).

INTERMEDIATES BY KINETIC HX LABELING

pH Competition

The pH competition method was introduced by Schmid & Baldwin using radioactive tritium labeling in studies of ribonuclease A (RNase A) (123). The method measures the rate of folding-dependent H-bond formation by competing the known

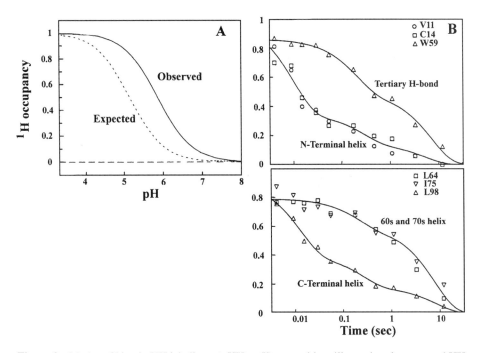

Figure 2 Modes of kinetic HX labeling. *A*. HX—pH competition, illustrating the expected HX labeling of a given amide NH site when no protection is present (*dashed line*) before native state formation and for a protection factor of 5 (*solid line*). *B*. HX pulse labeling data for cyt c (118) illustrating the selective early protection (H-bonding) of residues in the N- and C-terminal helices and folding heterogeneity.

rate of HX labeling against the to-be-determined rate of HX protection. Reviews are (78, 116).

In a typical pH competition experiment (Figure 2*A*), a denaturant-unfolded protein in H_2O is diluted into D_2O to initiate refolding in a stopped-flow apparatus that can mix solutions in ~1 msec. The pD of the diluent is varied. At low pD, HX is slow compared to folding and the protein folds before any of its amide NHs can exchange to ND. When the pD is increased, exchange is accelerated (catalyzed by OD^-) and competes more successfully with the folding rate. Amides then lose more of their H-label before the exchange period is terminated by hydrogen bond formation. The degree of H-label remaining at each amide is measured in the refolded native protein by NMR.

If the protein folds directly to the strongly protected native state in a two-state manner with folding rate constant k_f, each structurally protected amide will remain half labeled (H) when its intrinsic unprotected exchange rate (k_{unp}) equals the folding rate ($k_{ex} = k_{unp} = k_{ch} [OD^-] = k_f$). Here k_{ch} is the second-order exchange rate constant characteristic for each unprotected amide, and exchange is catalyzed by OD$^-$. The expected curve of label remaining for each amide as a function of the labeling pD (Figure 2*A*) can be drawn from its known unprotected HX rate and the known folding rate, obtained from other signals. If some structure that fully protects an amide proton forms faster, then the labeling curve for that residue will be right-shifted to higher pD, from which the rate for H-bond formation can be obtained. If a partially structured intermediate is formed, the amides that are protected and unprotected in the intermediate will exhibit different behavior, from which the identity of the intermediate might be inferred. If some degree of HX protection (P) exists during the labeling period, then $k_{ex} = k_{unp}/P$. This too will right-shift the labeling curve to higher pD, from which P can be calculated.

The pH competition analysis is limited to proteins with folding rate essentially unaffected by pH over the pH range studied. Also, it is not easy to disentangle the complex folding behaviors that often occur, such as partial protection and intermediate formation, or to discern heterogeneous folding in which different fractions of the population fold at different rates.

Gladwin & Evans (62) modified the competition method to focus selectively on structure that forms rapidly, within the dead time of stopped-flow mixing experiments (<1 msec) (62). The unfolded protein is diluted into folding conditions in D$_2$O at various pD as before, but labeling is terminated after a few msecs by mixing into lower pD rather than by the folding event itself. As before, protection that already exists during the labeling period is seen as a rightward shift of the labeling curve to higher pD (Figure 2*A*). Gladwin & Evans stress the need to carefully account for the HX protection that is due to the early stages of slower folding events, occurring after rather than within or before the labeling period. Also HX rates are impressively sensitive to steric blocking (8). These factors may spuriously mimic significant generalized protection.

Pulse Labeling

The Baldwin laboratory also pioneered a related experiment known as HX pulse labeling, which they used together with tritium labeling to study a late intermediate caused to accumulate in the folding of RNase A by a nonnative proline isomer (79). The experiment uses a brief pulse of HX labeling to test for the presence of H-bonding (HX protection) at particular times during the folding process. When used with H-D exchange, stopped-flow, and NMR analysis, the method can track H-bond formation at many amides throughout the protein and thus determine the structure of folding intermediates that form, accumulate, and disappear on a multi-millisecond time scale. This capability, initially demonstrated in RNase A (133) and cytochrome c (cyt c) (118), placed the study of folding intermediates on a firm structural basis and helped to transform the folding field into the vigorous effort that it has become. For reviews, see (12, 51, 141).

In the usual experimental design, a protein is initially unfolded at high denaturant in D$_2$O so that all of its amides are D-labeled. To start refolding, the solution is diluted into H$_2$O buffered at moderately low pH, e.g. pH 6 at 10°C, where the exchange of freely exposed amides is slow (k_{unp} ~ secs). After various refolding times, a second mix sharply raises the pH (pH 8.5 to 10) to initiate H-labeling (k_{unp} ~ msecs), for up to 50 msecs, and then the pulse is terminated by a third mix that drops the pH back to low values. During the labeling pulse, amides not yet protected by hydrogen bonding are quickly labeled, whereas strongly protected amides are not. Refolding proceeds to completion. The H-D profile imposed during the labeling pulse is held by the native structure and ambient slow exchange conditions while the protein is analyzed, either by NMR to obtain site resolution or by mass spectrometry which can determine whether the protection of different elements of structure occurs within the same molecule (96). The results provide a snapshot of the H-bonded structure that exists within the brief period of the labeling pulse.

An example using NMR analysis is shown in Figure 2B for cyt c folding (118). The data illustrate some amino acids that participate in an intermediate with only the N- and C-terminal helices folded. About half of the molecules form the N/C intermediate in ~20 msec. Other fractions of the population follow a different time course, reaching N either more rapidly (~20%), without accumulating the N/C intermediate, or more slowly. More complete data like this can determine the identity of intermediates and their rates of production. Also the HX rates of the protected amides (stability; flexibility) can be measured. An unforeseen result is the observation of folding heterogeneity. Chemically identical molecules under identical conditions fold at different rates and populate different intermediates, or none at all.

Ideally the pulse method labels or fails to label amides in a yes-no fashion, depending on whether they are protected at the time of the pulse or not. In reality, different unprotected amides have very different intrinsic HX rates (8). Thus at any given pulse strength, some amides with slow intrinsic rates may escape full labeling even though they are unprotected; others with fast intrinsic rates may become partly labeled even though they are already weakly protected in reforming structure. The protection factors of the different amides within an intermediate can be probed by using a series of pH values in the labeling pulse (46, 134), as in the pH competition experiment. A thorough analysis would involve a pH series at each of a series of folding times, but this has not been done.

Some questions arise. Does the measured protection reflect the reversible unfolding of the entire intermediate, or parts thereof (stability), or much more local fluctuations (flexibility)? Comparison of protection factors for neighboring amides may distinguish these options (94). Is exchange in the EX2 limit? The usual tests (pH dependence; comparison of measured rates with intrinsic chemical rates) (9) may be able to tell. Is the pulse time sufficiently long to allow H-bonds to open even once? The length of the pH pulse can serve as a useful variable (134). More generally, the problems that are intrinsic to kinetic experimentation remain. Only populated intermediates can be observed. Are observed intermediates merely a small fraction of a vast repertoire of possible folding intermediates? Are they obligatory or optional? On-pathway or off?

Summary Results

Kinetic HX labeling has been applied to a number of proteins with similar and noncontroversial results (25, 72, 75, 90, 91, 100, 113, 119). In the case of two-state folding, one sees all of the amides gain protection at the folding rate. In three-state folding, one generally sees behavior like that in Figure 2, showing the population of a discrete native-like intermediate. Some intermediates are clearly early with only a small fraction of the protein formed, as in Figure 2B. Others are closer to the entire native structure.

Significant folding heterogeneity is often observed. Folding heterogeneity has been interpreted variably in terms of multiple parallel pathways with different intermediates (113), or as a single folding pathway interrupted by alternative error-dependent barriers (Figure 1A, top plus bottom) (128). A decision in favor of two parallel pathways has often been further interpreted as support for the funnel model (Figure 1B), erroneously so since that model pictures an unlimited continuum of paths and intermediates and no distinct on-pathway forms.

Of major interest is the general observation from much HX labeling work that intermediates seen for various proteins always represent pieces of the native protein. An early concern was that these experiments would overinterpret apparently native-like structure because only amides that are protected in the native protein can be measured (34). The many native-like *patterns* of H-bonding that have now been seen for intermediates with various conformations and degrees of advancement lessen this concern although it is true that detailed nonnative interactions are unlikely to be detected.

MOLTEN GLOBULES: Intermediates by Equilibrium HX Labeling

A number of proteins when placed in mildly destabilizing conditions, especially low pH, assume an expanded but still somewhat structured form called a (or *the*) molten globule (59, 83, 108–110). Ptitsyn and his coworkers proposed that these forms represent a new thermodynamic state, structurally compact (globular), with some secondary structural content but lacking rigid tertiary packing (molten) (43), and that they represent equilibrium analogs of kinetic folding intermediates (93, 110) (see especially the work of Kuwajima and coworkers 82–84). This view appeared to be inconsistent with the conventional concept of proteins as monolithically cooperative two-state entities (although see Figure 4, see color insert) and was poorly received by protein chemists for many years. The thermodynamic status of molten globules hinges on whether they are connected to neighboring forms by a second-order continuum or separated by a first-order cooperative transition (107), analogous to the difference between continuous and distinct intermediates indicated in Figure 1.

We are more concerned here with the structural status of molten globules which, due to their dynamically disordered tertiary structure, cannot be specified by the usual X-ray and NMR methods except in the most well ordered examples (57, 115). Fortunately, the secondary structural elements that are present can be specified by HX labeling. Typically, the molten globule is placed into D_2O and allowed to exchange for increasing times. Amides in unstructured regions become rapidly deuterated, perhaps at the unprotected amide rate, while H-bonded amides exchange their proton label more slowly. Timed samples are returned to native conditions where the imposed H-D exchange profile is locked in and can be analyzed by NMR or mass spectrometry.

A turning point in molten globule studies came with the demonstration by HX labeling of native-like elements of secondary structure in the classical molten globule of α-lactalbumin (18), the namesake molten globule of cyt c (74), and the apomyoglobin pH 4 molten globule (68). The demonstration that molten globular structure lies between U and N modifies the long-entrenched concept that proteins are monolithically cooperative two-state entitites (see Figure 4, see color insert). Impressively, the very same partial structure found in the apomyoglobin molten globule was demonstrated in a kinetic folding intermediate by HX pulse labeling (75). A similar correspondence has been found for RNase H (38, 114). These results support the view that molten globules prepared at equilibrium represent analogs of kinetic folding intermediates (109), at least in some cases.

The powerful implications of the molten globule hypothesis led to an outpouring of new studies describing many partially folded proteins at equilibrium and also in kinetic experiments (3, 17, 28, 29, 38, 88, 96, 99, 112, 124, 125). These intermediates were invariably asserted to represent molten globules. Accordingly the concept of molten globule structure and thermodynamic character (65, 107) has evolved and become more synonymous with intermediates in general (37, 41, 109).

HX protection factors in molten globules are typically low, well under 1000. This presumably reflects their low structural rigidity which can be expected to facilitate local H-bond breaking fluctuations (94). Accordingly a pattern of protection factors may be seen that is different from the more rigid native protein (74, 125). Nevertheless, the easily discerned H-bonding pattern specifies the secondary structure that is present and implies supporting tertiary interactions. In all of these studies, one finds native-like secondary structural elements.

Whether all of these forms represent *true* molten globules, or whether *the* molten globule is something other than any generic partially folded intermediate is not at issue here. The large molten globule literature documents the same important conclusion that one can draw from the kinetic HX labeling literature discussed above. Distinct native-like structures are selected, form abundantly, and can be stably maintained. Further, in some cases these equilibrium intermediates have been shown to match the structure of kinetic intermediates observed independently by HX pulse labeling (75, 114).

INTERMEDIATES AT EQUILIBRIUM
IN THE FOLDING LANDSCAPE

In principle, protein molecules must continually cycle through all of the high free-energy states implied in Figures 1*A* and 1*B* and must populate each one as dictated by the Boltzmann distribution. Thus proteins unfold and refold even under fully native conditions. In favorable cases a native state HX method can characterize some of the intermediate forms.

The Staircase Hypothesis

The high free-energy states that populate the folding landscape include all of the partially folded intermediates utilized by protein molecules in folding from U to N and all of the partially unfolded intermediates, reaching from N to U, that determine HX reactions. In light of this commonality, Englander & Kallenbach suggested that progressively slower HX rates measured at equilibrium under native conditions might reflect an energetically uphill staircase of increasingly unfolded forms down which proteins might step in their folding sequence (50, 54). The staircase hypothesis was later discussed by Woodward and her coworkers (77, 140), especially the possibility that the slowest protons to exchange might show the first part of a protein to refold, based on newly available HX labeling results for pancreatic trypsin inhibitor (BPTI) (119), cyt c (118), and lysozyme (113).

In fact the results available for these and other proteins provide rather ambiguous support for these hypotheses (31, 32, 48). In cyt c, it is true that the slowest exchanging protons reflect the final global unfolding (9) and participate in the initial N/C helix intermediate found by HX pulse labeling (118). However, most of the residues in the C-terminal helix and all in the N-terminal helix exchange much faster. Similar ambiguities are seen in lysozyme (112, 113). In BPTI insufficient refolding data is available to judge (119).

Thus straightforward HX data although suggestive do not strongly support the staircase model of Englander & Kallenbach or the more limited last-out first-in model of Woodward and coworkers. The general problem is that HX in many proteins is dominated by local fluctuations that break only one H-bond (94). These forms cannot show us important folding intermediates, and they obscure the measurement of larger unfoldings that might.

Native State HX

A method known as native state HX (7, 10, 53) can ferret out the large unfoldings that might reveal the structure of folding intermediates. In this approach, one selectively promotes the large unfoldings so that they come to dominate the exchange of the many hydrogens that they expose. HX results can then identify the otherwise invisible partially unfolded forms (PUFs) and measure their stability.

The number and distribution of these forms can help to map the high free-energy reaction landscape between N and U. Do the intermediates describe an undifferentiated continuum, as in Figure 1*B*, or do a small number of native-like metastable intermediates occupy distinct free-energy wells that might shape a stepwise folding pathway, as in Figure 1*A*? A successful native state HX analysis should be able to document the true situation in either case.

An example in Figure 3 (see color insert) shows HX data for all of the amides in the 60s helix of cyt c and some in the right loop. HX was measured in increasing concentrations of denaturant to selectively promote the larger unfolding reactions. Data for the various amide hydrogens are plotted in terms of the free energy for the responsible opening reactions. These hydrogens exchange initially by way of different local fluctuations, shown by their insensitivity to denaturant and the very different ΔG_{op} values for neighboring NHs. The one exception is the Leu68 amide proton. It can exchange only by way of a large, denaturant sensitive, high free-energy unfolding. When this large unfolding is sufficiently promoted by increasing denaturant, all of the amide protons in the 60s helix merge into the same HX isotherm, i.e. they all become dominated by the same large unfolding. The measurable amides in the right loop do the same. This result reveals a state with the entire 60s helix and perhaps the green loop cooperatively unfolded but with other structure still intact (identified by the still protected residues, namely the N- and C-helices, shown as the blue unit in Figure 3*B*). Similar behavior is seen for the other secondary structural units in cyt c (10, 95), which merge into HX isotherms (indicated by the dashed lines in Figure 3*A*, color coded to match the protein segments that they represent in Figure 3*B*). These results show that the cyt c protein is made up of four cooperative units. In lattice model terminology, cyt c might be considered to correspond to four connected beads rather than 124 independently folding amino acids.

The native state HX experiment has been applied with analogous results to RNAse H (26) and apocyt b562 (60, 61), and in a more limited way to barstar (19) and a hyperthermophilic rubredoxin (66). One does not see intermediates distributed in a continuous manner on a downsloping (free) energy scale as in funnel models. Protein intermediates appear to be formed by the unfolding and refolding of entire secondary structural elements or sets thereof. The cooperative tertiary packing of secondary structural units greatly increases their stability but does not destroy their separate intrinsically cooperative nature. Approaches are being developed that may explain the determinants of the protein unfolding-refolding reactions (4, 67).

Clarke et al note the failure of the native state HX experiment to find intermediates—either continuous or discrete—in barnase and CI2 (31). The native state HX method does set certain requirements for any given protein in order to serve as a good model for these studies, as has been described (7, 48, 95). For example barnase may fail because it diverges from the EX2 limit at low denaturant (39). Clarke et al have also noted the inability of an equilibrium result all by itself to specify a kinetic sequence. Englander and coworkers list kinetic and equilibrium results that support the intermediates and pathways implied by the native state HX results (48, 56). Some are noted below.

SUMMARY: Discrete Intermediates

The information just summarized, obtained especially from HX experiments, in both equilibrium and kinetic modes, on many proteins, shows unquestionably that selected partially folded intermediates exist. In all cases the intermediates turn out to represent partial replicas of the native protein. Further, the intermediate forms are robust. The same intermediates are maintained over a broad range of destabilizing conditions including denaturants, temperature, and pressure. The intermediates utilize the built-in intrinsically cooperative secondary structural units of the protein. It appears that proteins naturally stabilize not only their unique native state but in addition a small number of discrete partially folded forms.

Why then do proteins most often melt in a highly cooperative two-state manner? Secondary structural elements packed in a globular protein cooperatively stabilize each other. When global stability is sufficiently reduced in melting studies, the loss of any unit causes the entire protein to unfold in what appears to be a highly cooperative two-state process. However, when stability is high, the individual elements can express their individually cooperative nature and unfold separately without destabilizing the entire molecule. The free-energy relationships that determine measurable unfolding patterns in conditions of low and high stability are illustrated in Figure 4 (see color insert).

At the first level, the various results just described help to map the equilibrium contours of the high free-energy reaction surface. In any given intermediate, distinct secondary structures are formed and others are unfolded. That is, the intermediates occupy discrete wells, albeit with some width, in the folding landscape. The immense collection of all other possible forms must also exist, as implied in Figure 1B, but apparently only at higher free-energy levels than the few selected metastable intermediates. In an equilibrium sense, these results are as expected from the classical view of the high free-energy folding landscape as suggested by the free-energy wells in Figure 1A, but not from the multiform continuum view in Figure 1B.

ON OR OFF PATHWAY

What is the role of the discrete intermediates in kinetic folding? Do these intermediates represent productive, even obligatory, on-pathway forms or are they off-pathway forms in deep local minima that inhibit rather than promote folding? Considerable evidence points to a productive pathway role.

In cyt c, the same N/C helix intermediate seen in the native state HX experiment (10) is found also as a kinetic folding intermediate by HX pulse labeling

(118). These separate measurements even find the same stability, ~3 kcal/mol (5). The N/C helix intermediate accumulates when the green segment (Figure 3*B*) is trapped, which is the next unit in line in the suggested folding sequence. Other results (144) indicate that the several PUFs are just the forms needed to construct a sequential unfolding pathway. These are, in order of increasing free energy, the entire red loop unfolded, the red plus yellow loops unfolded, those two plus the 60s helix and green loop unfolded, and finally all of these together with the blue helices to produce the globally unfolded state. If so, then the same sequence in the reverse direction must dominate refolding, as in the staircase model, since these experiments are done at equilibrium. These states are suggested in Figure 1A by I_1, I_2, I_3, and U.

In apomyoglobin, the same A/G/H helix intermediate seen in the equilibrium molten globule (68) is seen also as a kinetic folding intermediate (75). Jamin & Baldwin provide further evidence that defined apomyoglobin intermediates, with the native-like AGH and B helices formed, occur sequentially in a productive pathway (73). In RNase H, the same A/D helix intermediate is seen as a molten globule at low pH (38), as a high free energy intermediate under native conditions (26), and as a kinetic folding intermediate (114).

Bai has demonstrated the on-pathway nature of the kinetically blocked N/C helix intermediate of cyt c by showing that it reaches the native state faster than it could cycle back through the unfolded state (5). Laurents et al (85) have demonstrated the on-pathway nature of a kinetic RNase A intermediate by extending the length of the HX labeling pulse to show that the intermediate moves forward to the native state without going back through the unfolded state where the protected H-label would have been lost. In these advances, on-pathway is interpreted to mean that the trapped intermediate does not have to fully unfold in order to resume forward folding, although some degree of unfolding may well occur.

Intermediate accumulation in the slow three-state folding of a number of proteins does often depend on the trapping of some misfolded structure (see below) but apparently not in deep off-pathway wells. In cyt c the misfold-dependent slowing can be produced even at pH 4.9 where the histidine to heme misligation itself is unstable (pKa is 5.6) and contributes no stability to the intermediate populated (128). The same is true in BPTI, where two cysteine residues are prematurely buried in the reforming native structure so that a solvent-catalyzed disulfide bridge formation is blocked (137). A RNase T1 kinetic intermediate appears to show an analogous structural situation in which a mis-isomerized proline has steered some segments out of place where they become trapped, whereas other parts of the intermediate are impressively native-like, as shown by NMR (11). The nonnative proline isomer provides no obvious stabilization energy to the populated RNase T1 intermediate. The same is true of proline-dependent slowing and intermediate accumulation in general. In all of these cases, some distinct native-like intermediate is seen and it achieves major population. This is as expected for a discrete folding pathway but seems unlikely in a situation where many different off-pathway wells may be accidentally encountered.

These results argue that the discrete native-like metastable intermediates seen to populate the reaction surface act as kinetic intermediates in discrete stepwise folding pathways. It should be stressed that distinct folding pathways need not be rigorously sequential. For example, in the four helix bundle ($H_1H_2H_3H_4$) apo cyt b562 protein, a branched folding sequence suggested by native state HX can be written as U to H_2H_3 to $H_1H_2H_3$ or $H_2H_3H_4$ to $H_1H_2H_3H_4$ = N (60, 61). A similar conclusion is indicated for barstar (145).

These considerations are in line with the framework and hierarchic condensation models for protein folding which focus on a central role for native-like intermediates based on secondary structure formation (14, 15), although the present considerations do not bear on whether secondary or tertiary structure forms first.

THE KINETIC DETERMINANTS: Nucleation and Misfolding Barriers

The different folding paradigms considered in Figure 1 provide very different explanations for the disparate folding behavior shown by different proteins. In the continuum view (Figure 1*B*) fast two-state folding proceeds down a smooth landscape without specific intermediates, while slow three-state folding and heterogeneity are caused by the accidental trapping of non-obligatory intermediates in deep off-pathway wells. A classical pathway with discrete obligatory intermediates requires a different explanation. One alternative is that two-state folding occurs because the rate-limiting process is the first step in the pathway, whereas three-state folding and heterogeneity are caused by later, optional, error-dependent barriers.

Three-State Folding and Heterogeneity

Are proteins that fold in a two-state or a three-state manner different in some fundamental way? Apparently not. For example, cyt c can be induced to fold in either a fast two-state manner (msecs) or a much slower three-state manner ($\sim$sec), even though folding occurs under the same conditions in both cases (128). This special capability has made it possible to study the determining kinetic barriers and their structural bases.

When cyt c is unfolded, the weak Met80-S ligation to the heme iron dissociates and can be replaced by one of the two histidines in the green loop (Figure 3B) in a pH-dependent way with a pKa of 5.6. On dilution into folding conditions at pH 5, either two-state or three-state folding follows depending on the pH in the initial unfolding condition. At low unfolding pH, the histidines are protonated and do not bind the heme. On dilution into pH 5, cyt c folding is then fast and two-state. When the unfolding pH is above 5.6, a neutral histidine misligates to the heme iron, forcing the green loop segment in Figure 3 to the wrong side of the heme. The segment is trapped out of place by the early chain collapse when folding begins.

The N/C helix intermediate (blue in Figure 3) forms but then further folding is blocked. The newly inserted slow step ("misfold-reorganization") involves significant back unfolding, demonstrated by a reverse denaturant effect and by the fact that it requires about 300 msec while the histidine deligation by itself occurs in 15 msec. Evidently the slow step represents the time-consuming reorganization process necessary to free the trapped green segment so it can take its turn in the folding sequence (128).

The work on cyt c misfolding stimulated the influential 'New View' article of Baldwin (13) and a commentary by Creighton (35), which discussed the cyt c results in light of the view, based on theoretical studies, that discrete intermediates are actually misfolded off-pathway forms trapped in deep energy wells (Figure 1*B*). The cyt c study has therefore been widely cited as questioning the on-pathway nature of folding intermediates. In fact, Sosnick et al (128) considered that the misfolded form represents a normally occurring native-like on-pathway intermediate with, *in addition*, a mislocated and trapped segment.

An analogous situation has been seen for disulfide-reduced BPTI. A final step in BPTI refolding can be blocked by the native-like burial of two cysteines so that disulfide bridge formation cannot be catalyzed by added glutathione. As in cyt c, a kinetic barrier that involves some back unfolding necessary to allow disulfide formation slows folding and causes the intermediate to accumulate (137). As in cyt c, the intermediate is native-like but includes in addition an error, the premature burial of the unbridged cysteines.

A similar situation appears in RNase T1 where a nonnative proline isomer leads to slow folding (11). An intermediate accumulates in which part of the protein is strikingly native-like and could be characterized by NMR, while other segments are caught in a nonnative conformation. Apparently the well-known tendency of misisomerized prolines to produce slow three-state folding can also operate by inserting misfold-reorganization barriers.

In all of these cases, forward folding is blocked by some distinct structural misfolding error. Folding pauses. A native-like but corrupted error-containing intermediate accumulates. A time-consuming reorganization process is necessary to free the trapped groups so forward folding can resume. It does not seem to be the *population* of the misfolded intermediate state that *causes* the slow folding, for example in some deep well. Rather, slow folding and intermediate accumulation are both caused by the time-requiring error correction process, which can be viewed as an optionally inserted kinetic reorganization barrier (128), as in Figure 1*A*. The probabilistic nature of misfolding errors makes folding heterogeneous.

Protein folding can be described mathematically as a multidimensional process, as suggested by the funnel landscape diagram. In a multidimensional world, it is difficult to picture how on pathway barriers could block folding since proteins might simply bypass them in some higher dimension. Features that might slow folding would be limited to entropic search barriers and deep, necessarily optional wells. In reality, proteins operate in a three-dimensional world and kinetic folding barriers represent structural processes that should be considered in a 3-D structural sense. The cases just noted provide examples of structurally based barriers that cannot be simply circumnavigated. Similar considerations hold for the issue of obligatory intermediates. The previous discussion suggests that in this case the determining structural issues involve built-in intrinsically cooperative structural elements and the interactions that allow early intermediates to stabilize later ones.

Two-State Folding

Sosnick et al (127, 129) further exploited the two-state to three-state switch in cyt c to study the position along the reaction coordinate of the rate-limiting barrier in two-state folding. The rate-limiting two-state barrier was found to be identical to the initial barrier in three-state folding (compare Figures 1A top and bottom). They have the same thermodynamic parameters (ΔG^*, ΔH^*, ΔS^*) and the same structural surface burial parameters (complex GmCl dependence expressed as m^* in the chevron folding limb and an earlier rollover). In three-state folding, the initial barrier obviously precedes (or accompanies) the formation of the early N/C helix intermediate. Therefore the identical barrier in two-state folding must also occur before (or during) formation of the early N/C helix intermediate, i.e. at the initial step of the pathway.

Sosnick et al extensively characterized the initial barrier and concluded that it represents an energetically uphill search for interactions that produce a native-like chain topology and can nucleate chain collapse (56, 127, 129). There is general agreement for a nucleation barrier in protein folding (1, 58, 71, 101, 127, 129, 131) but different workers endow the barrier with different characteristics and place it at different positions in the folding sequence. The rate-limiting nucleation step in two-state folding is often assigned to be late in the folding process. This is because (a) a large fraction of the surface that is buried in the native protein becomes buried in the transition state and (b) nucleation is assumed to lead directly to the final product. Rather, the cyt c results place the intrinsic rate-limiting barrier at the very first step, before intermediate formation. What is nucleated is the initial collapse step, and this is accompanied by a large surface burial. It appears that multiple native-like interactions are necessary to overcome the loop closure entropy that resists chain collapse, and that chain collapse in turn is necessary to form a docking surface that can stabilize subsequent secondary structure formation (127). Thus a massive nucleated collapse occurs as the first committed step in folding. The need for an initial long-range search to find a correct set of native interactions is supported by the correlation of two-state folding rates in many proteins with the contact order, the averaged sequence distance of interacting residues (106).

The large-scale search necessary to implement the initial native-like chain collapse most often requires a msec time scale and can be obscured by an even earlier sub-millisecond burst phase chain contraction (117). Considerable evidence now suggests that the kinetic burst phase does not reflect the formation of an intermediate in the usual sense. Rather it represents a more random solvent-dependent polymer-like chain contraction on dilution from a good solvent (high denaturant) to a poor solvent (low denaturant) (2, 27, 56, 111, 127, 128, 130). In studied cases, the fast contraction produces signals (CD, fluorescence) identical to the U state characteristic for the same low denaturant (56, 111, 127, 130). The chain must then search for the native-like topology within the condensed phase prior to intermediate formation, leading to a kinetic slowing (rollover).

The nonspecific burst phase chain contraction is prominent at very low denaturant where hydrophobic interactions are strong and random interactions are probable. The slower nucleated collapse that produces the topologically native-like chain condensation can be seen in isolation at higher denaturant (on the chevron) where interactions are weaker and undirected burst phase interactions are suppressed. Lattice models simulate these two very different collapse modes when interactions are set to be either strong or weak, respectively (64).

If the very first on-pathway barrier is intrinsically large, the occurrence of two-state folding simply requires that the subsequent intrinsic barriers are smaller. In fact very fast on-pathway events have now been seen in a number of proteins and peptides (16, 24, 44, 105, 122, 138). It appears that ultrafast behavior can be explained in terms of events that occur after the initial nucleation barrier has been surpassed, since these experiments generally start with a certain amount of structure already in place (56).

CONCLUSIONS

The HX methods reviewed here have been able to provide fairly detailed structural information under the difficult conditions that are most pertinent to the folding problem. Many intermediate structures have now been characterized in kinetic folding experiments on a subsecond time scale, in labile molten globule forms under nonnative conditions, and in the high free-energy landscape under native conditions.

Results available show that distinct intermediates exist. They all turn out to represent partial replicas of the native protein. Clearly proteins are able to stabilize not only their lowest free-energy native state but also a small number of discrete partially folded native-like forms. These forms utilize as building blocks the intrinsically cooperative secondary structural elements of the protein and accordingly are robustly maintained over a wide range of conditions. The immense collection of all other possible forms must also exist, as implied in Figure 1B, but apparently only at higher free-energy levels than the few selected metastable intermediates (wells in Figure 1A). These conclusions relate to the equilibrium shape of the reaction landscape.

Additional evidence favors the view that these intermediates form distinct pathways in kinetic folding. It appears that globular proteins under folding conditions naturally condense into a native-like topology that acts to promote the formation of and to stabilize native-like secondary structural elements. The reversible folding and unfolding of these intermediates will naturally produce stepwise pathways that lead from U to N.

Kinetic folding experiments are consistent with discrete pathways that include three kinds of kinetic barriers, all of which can be seen to represent conformational searches for the specific intermediates. An initial conformational search culminates by finding a set of interactions that pins the chain into a coarsely native-like topology, nucleating chain collapse and preparing the way for subsequent propagation steps. Propagation depends on short range searches that add cooperative secondary structural units to pre-existing structure. When all goes well, the initial search then becomes the rate-limiting process, intermediates do not accumulate, and folding appears to be a two-state process. However, proteins tend to make errors and misfold. Error correction involves some reorganizational back unfolding and can be slow, inserting an effective barrier that can slow folding and cause the prior normally occurring but flawed intermediate to accumulate. The probabilistic nature of error formation leads naturally to folding heterogeneity. This view, illustrated in Figure 1A (top plus bottom), provides a straightforward explanation for the apparently contradictory folding behavior of different proteins.

Theoretical simulations of non-protein models project a different view, with an unlimited number of continuously distributed intermediates and pathways, and slow folding when specific intermediates are accidentally populated (Figure 1B). However, experimental results for real globular proteins discussed here demonstrate the existence of a small number of distinct native-like folding intermediates and their likely participation in distinct pathways. The probable reason for this discrepancy is that the models usually simulated are analogous to molecules with a single cooperative unit. They do not contain the separable independently cooperative secondary structural units that determine intermediate formation in the folding of real globular proteins. To investigate theoretically the kinds of intermediates and pathways that are utilized by typical globular proteins, it will be necessary to study more protein-like models with separable cooperative units (86, 104, 135).

If proteins utilize as folding units their few cooperative structural elements rather than their many separate amino acid residues, then the folding problem is immensely simplified. The astronomical number of possible folding intermediates considered by Levinthal becomes irrelevant. The previously enigmatic amino acid code for the folding pathway becomes the very same code that determines the final native structure. More broadly, this conclusion would have important implications for protein design, both in the laboratory and in biological evolution, and perhaps for the goal of predicting protein-folding pathways and their resulting native structures.

ACKNOWLEDGMENTS

Helpful discussions with Leland Mayne, Tobin Sosnick, Yawen Bai, Buzz Baldwin, and Ken Dill are gratefully acknowledged. This work was supported by the National Institutes of Health and the Mathers Charitable Trust.

LITERATURE CITED

1. Abkevich VI, Gutin AM, Shakhnovich EI. 1994. Specific nucleus as the transition state for protein folding: evidence from the lattice model. *Biochemistry* 33:10026–36

2. Agashe VR, Shastry MC, Udgaonkar JB. 1995. Initial hydrophobic collapse in the folding of barstar. *Nature* 377:754–57

3. Alexandrescu AT, Evans PA, Pitkeathly M, Baum J, Dobson CM. 1993. Structure and dynamics of the acid-denatured molten globule state of α-lactalbumin: A two-dimension NMR study. *Biochemistry* 32:1707–18

4. Bahar J, Wallqvist A, Covell DG, Jernigan RL. 1998. Correlation between native state hydrogen exchange and cooperative residue fluctuations from a simple model. *Biochemistry* 37:1067–75

5. Bai Y. 1999. Kinetic evidence for an on-pathway intermediate in the folding of cytochrome c. *Proc. Natl. Acad. Sci. USA* 96:477–80

6. Bai Y, Englander JJ, Mayne L, Milne JS, Englander SW. 1995. Thermodynamic parameters from hydrogen exchange measurements. *Methods Enzymol.* 259:344–56

7. Bai Y, Englander SW. 1996. Future directions in folding: the multi-state nature of protein structure. *Proteins: Struct. Funct. Genet.* 24:145–51

8. Bai Y, Milne JS, Mayne L, Englander SW. 1993. Primary structure effects on peptide group hydrogen exchange. *Proteins: Struct. Funct. Genet.* 17:75–86

9. Bai Y, Milne JS, Mayne L, Englander SW. 1994. Protein stability parameters measured by hydrogen exchange. *Proteins: Struct. Funct. Genet.* 20:4–14

10. Bai Y, Sosnick TR, Mayne L, Englander SW. 1995. Protein folding intermediates studied by native state hydrogen exchange. *Science* 269:192–97

11. Balbach J, Steegborn C, Schindler T, Schmid FX. 1999. A protein folding intermediate of ribonuclease T1 characterized at high resolution by 1D and 2D NMR spectroscopy. *J. Mol. Biol.* 285:829–42

12. Baldwin RL. 1993. Pulsed H/D-exchange studies of folding intermediates. *Curr. Opin. Struct. Biol.* 3:84–91

13. Baldwin RL. 1995. The nature of protein folding pathways: the classical versus the new view. *J. Biomol. NMR* 5:103–9

14. Baldwin RL, Rose GD. 1999. Is protein folding hierarchic? I. Local structure and peptide folding. *Trends Biochem. Sci.* 24:26–33

15. Baldwin RL, Rose GD. 1999. Is protein folding hierarchic? II. Folding intermediates and transition states. *Trends Biochem. Sci.* 24:77–83

16. Ballew RM, Sabelko J, Gruebele M. 1996. Direct observation of fast protein folding: the initial collapse of apomyoglobin. *Proc. Natl. Acad. Sci. USA* 93:5759–64

17. Barrick D, Baldwin RL. 1993. The molten globule intermediate of apomyoglobin and the process of protein folding. *Protein Sci.* 2:869–876

18. Baum J, Dobson CM, Evans PA, Hanley C. 1989. Characterization of a partly folded protein by NMR methods: studies on the molten globule state of guinea pig α-lactalbumin. *Biochemistry* 28:7–13

19. Bhuyan AK, Udgaonkar JB. 1998. Two structural subdomains of barstar detected by rapid mixing NMR measurement of amide hydrogen exchange. *Proteins: Struct. Funct. Genet.* 30:296–308

20. Brems DN, Baldwin RL. 1984. Amide proton exchange used to monitor the formation of a stable a-helix by residues 3-13 during folding of ribonuclease S. *J. Mol. Biol.* 180:1141–56

21. Brems DN, Baldwin RL. 1985. Protection

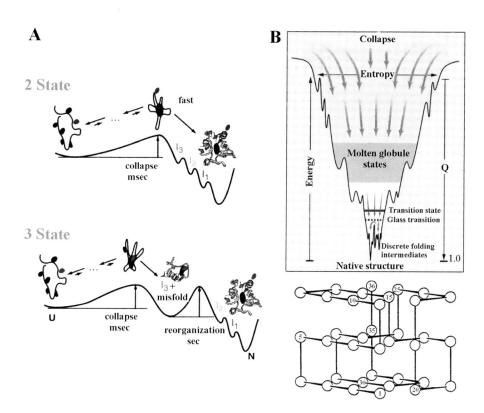

Figure 1 Alternative views of the folding reaction landscape. A. Conventional free-energy diagrams that represent two-state folding with an initial limiting barrier (*top*), three-state folding with the same initial barrier and a subsequently inserted misfold-reorganization barrier (bottom), and kinetic intermediates hidden or revealed by these barriers. Following Sosnick et al (127–129), the initial barrier is a search process that brings large hydrophobes (*black residues*) together to pin the chain into a native-like topology in the nucleated collapse. The segment carrying the *red residue* remains free in the nucleated collapse that leads to fast two-state folding. When it is internally trapped, it produces a kinetic reorganization barrier that causes slow folding, intermediate accumulation, and folding heterogeneity (127–129). B. A funnel-shaped reaction landscape, adapted from Wolynes et al (139), and a typical on-lattice model used to explore it, adapted from Abkevich et al (1). This landscape posits an unlimited number of intermediates and pathways. The accidental trapping and accumulation of defined intermediates causes slow folding and heterogeneity.

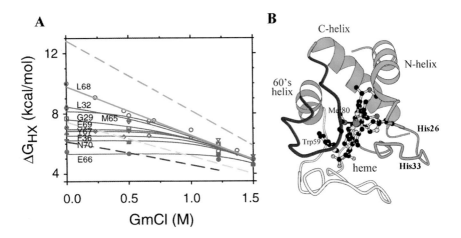

Figure 3 Native-state HX results for cyt c (10, 95). Data are shown for all of the slow amide hydrogens in the *green* cooperative element (60s helix plus the histidine-containing loop), which exchange through local fluctuations initially but become dominated by a recognizable larger unfolding when it is promoted by increasing GmCl. The *dashed lines*, color coded to match the cyt c diagram in panel B, indicate HX isotherms produced by sets of hydrogens that identify other cooperatively unfolding structural units. Conditions are pD 7, 30°C.

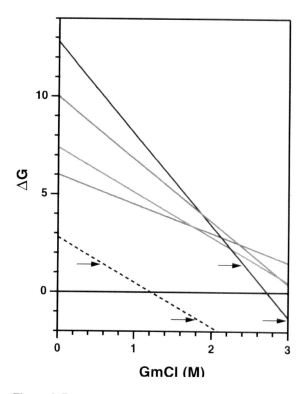

Figure 4 Free-energy cross over curve for the cooperative units in cyt c obtained from the native state HX results in Figure 3 (7). When stability is high, subglobal unfoldings can be seen separately by native state HX. When denaturant is increased, the larger global unfolding is most sharply promoted and, where it can be measured by the usual means (*arrows*), appears to be a two-state process. The *dashed curve* suggests a subglobal unfolding that crosses N earlier, which would produce a molten globule and would make the global unfolding transition appear to be less cooperative.

of amide protons in folding intermediates of ribonuclease A measured by pH-pulse exchange curves. *Biochemistry* 24:1689–93

22. Brooks CL 3rd. 1998. Simulations of protein folding and unfolding. *Curr. Opin. Struct. Biol.* 8:222–26

23. Bryngelson JD, Onuchic JN, Socci ND, Wolynes PG. 1995. Funnels, pathways, and the energy landscape of protein folding:a synthesis. *Proteins: Struct. Funct. Genet.* 21:167–95

24. Burton RE, Huang GS, Dougherty MA, Fullbright PW, Oas TG. 1996. Microsecond protein folding through a compact transition state. *J. Mol. Biol.* 263:311–22

25. Bycroft M, Matouschek A, Kellis JT Jr, Serrano L, Fersht AR. 1990. Detection and characterization of a folding intermediate in barnase by NMR. *Nature* 346:488–90

26. Chamberlain AK, Handel TM, Marqusee S. 1996. Detection of rare partially folded molecules in equilibrium with the native conformation of RNase H. *Nature Struct. Biol.* 3:782–87

27. Chan CK, Hu Y, Takahashi S, Rousseau DL, Eaton WA, et al. 1997. Submillisecond protein folding kinetics studied by ultrarapid mixing. *Proc. Natl. Acad. Sci. USA* 94:1779 84

28. Chung EW, Nettleton EJ, Morgan CJ, Gross M, Miranker A, et al. 1997. Hydrogen exchange properties of proteins in native and denatured states monitored by mass spectrometry and NMR. *Protein Sci.* 6:1316–24

29. Chyan CL, Wormald C, Dobson CM, Evans PA, Baum J. 1993. Structure and stability of the molten globule state of guinea pig α-lactalbumin: a hydrogen exchange study. *Biochemistry* 32:5681–91

30. Clarke J, Itzhaki LS. 1998. Hydrogen exchange and protein folding. *Curr. Opin. Struct. Biol.* 8:112–18

31. Clarke J, Itzhaki LS, Fersht AR. 1997. Hydrogen exchange at equilibrium: a short cut for analysing protein–folding pathways?

Trends Biochem. Sci. 22:284–87

32. Clarke J, Itzhaki LS, Fersht AR. 1998. A reply to Englander and Woodward. *Trends Biochem Sci.* 23:379–81

33. Connelly GP, Bai Y, Jeng M-F, Mayne L, Englander SW. 1993. Isotope effects in peptide group hydrogen exchange. *Proteins: Struct. Funct. Genet.* 17:87–92

34. Creighton TE. 1991. Characterizing intermediates in protein folding. *Current Biol.* 1:8–10

35. Creighton TE. 1994. The energetic ups and downs of protein folding. *Nature Struct. Biol.* 1:135–38

36. Creighton TE. 1995. Protein folding. An unfolding story. *Current Biol.* 5:353–56

37. Creighton TE. 1997. How important is the molten globule for correct protein folding? *Trends Biochem. Sci.* 22:6–10

38. Dabora JM, Pelton JG, Marqusee S. 1996. Structure of the acid state of *Escherichia coli* ribonuclease HI. *Biochemistry* 35:11951–58

39. Dalby PA, Clarke J, Johnson CM, Fersht AR. 1998. Folding intermediates of wild type and mutants of barnase. II. Correlation of changes in equilibrium amide exchange etc. *J. Mol. Biol.* 276:647–56

40. Dill KA, Chan HS. 1997. From Levinthal to pathways to funnels. *Nature Struct. Biol.* 4:10–19

41. Dill KA, Shortle D. 1991. Denatured states of proteins. *Annu. Rev. Biochem.* 60:795–825

42. Dobson CM. 1991. Characterization of folding intermediates. *Curr. Opin. Struct. Biol.* 1:22–27

43. Dolgikh DA, Gilmanshin RI, Brazhnikov EV, Bychkova VE, Semisotnov GV, et al. 1981. Alpha–lactalbumin:compact state with fluctuating tertiary structure? *FEBS Lett.* 136:311–315

44. Eaton WA, Munoz V, Thompson PA, Henry ER, Hofrichter J. 1998. Kinetics and dynamics of α–helices, β–hairpins, and fast-folding proteins. *Accts. Chem. Res.* 31:745–54

45. Eigen M. 1964. Proton transfer, acid-base catalysis, and enzymatic hydrolysis. *Angew. Chem. Intl. Ed. English* 3:1–19

46. Elöve GA, Roder H. 1990. Structure and stability of cytochrome c folding intermediates. In *Protein Refolding*, ed. G Georgiou, E De Bernadez-Clark, pp. 50–63. Washington, DC: Am. Chem. Soc.

47. Englander JJ, Rumbley JN, Englander SW. 1998. Intramolecular signal transduction: cross subunit effects in the hemoglobin T-state. *J. Mol. Biol.* 284:1707–16

48. Englander SW. 1998. Native state HX. *Trends Biochem. Sci.* 23:378

49. Englander SW, Calhoun DB, Englander JJ, Kallenbach NR, Liem RKH, et al. 1980. Individual breathing reactions measured in hemoglobin by hydrogen exchange methods. *Biophys. J.* 32:577–90

50. Englander SW, Kallenbach NR. 1984. Hydrogen exchange and structural dynamics of proteins and nucleic-acids. *Q. Rev. Biophys.* 16:521–655

51. Englander SW, Mayne L. 1992. Protein folding studied using hydrogen-exchange labeling and two-dimensional NMR. *Annu. Rev. Biophys. Biomol. Struct.* 21:243–65

52. Englander SW, Mayne L, McKinnie RE, Paterson Y, Englander JJ. 1991. Protein interaction, folding and energetics studied by hydrogen exchange labeling. In *Molecular Conformation and Biological Interactions*, ed. P Balaram, S Ramaseshan, pp. 245–68. Bangalore: Indian Acad. Sci.

53. Englander SW, Mayne LC, Bai Y, Sosnick TR. 1997. Hydrogen exchange:the modern legacy of Linderstrom-Lang. *Protein Sci.* 6:1101–9

54. Englander SW, Milne J. 1990. The protein folding problem studied by hydrogen exchange and 2D NMR. In *Protein Structure and Function*, ed. ZZH Karachi/New York:Twel

55. Englander SW, Sosnick TR, Englander JJ, Mayne L. 1996. Mechanisms and uses of hydrogen exchange. *Curr. Opin. Struc. Biol.* 6:18–23

56. Englander SW, Sosnick TR, Mayne LC, Shtilerman M, Qi PX, et al. 1998. Fast and slow folding in cytochrome c. *Accts. Chem. Res.* 31:737–44

57. Feng Y, Sligar SG, Wand AJ. 1994. Solution structure of apocytochrome b562. *Nature Struct. Biol.* 1:30–35

58. Fersht AR. 1997. Nucleation mechanisms in protein folding. *Curr. Opin. Struct. Biol.* 7:3–9

59. Fink AL. 1995. Compact intermediate states in protein folding. *Annu. Rev. Biophys. Biomol. Struct.* 24:495–522

60. Fuentes EJ, Wand AJ. 1998. Local dynamics and stability of apocytochrome b562 examined by hydrogen exchange. *Biochemistry* 37:3687–98

61. Fuentes EJ, Wand AJ. 1998. The local stability and dynamics of apocytochrome b562 examined by the dependence of hydrogen exchange on hydrostatic pressure. *Biochemistry* 37:3687–98

62. Gladwin ST, Evans PA. 1996. Structure of very early folding intermediates: new insights through a variant of hydrogen exchange labeling. *Folding Design* 1:407–17

63. Gregory RB, Rosenberg A. 1986. Protein conformational dynamics measured by hydrogen isotope exchange techniques. *Methods Enzymol.* 131:448–508

64. Gutin AM, Abkevich VI, Shakhnovich EI. 1995. Is burst hydrophobic collapse necessary for protein folding? *Biochemistry* 34:3066–76

65. Haynie DT, Freire E. 1993. Structural energetics of the molten globule state. *Proteins: Struct. Funct. Genet.* 16:115–40

66. Hiller R, Zhou ZH, Adams MWW, Englander SW. 1997. Stability and dynamics in a hyperthermophilic protein with melting temperature close to 200°C. *Proc. Natl. Acad. Sci. USA* 94:11329–32

67. Hilser VJ, Freire E. 1996. Structure based calculation of the equilibrium folding pathway of proteins. Correlation with hydrogen exchange protection factors. *J. Mol. Biol.* 262:756–72

68. Hughson FM, Wright PE, Baldwin RL. 1990. Structural characterization of a partly folded apomyoglobin intermediate. *Science* 249:1544–48

69. Huyghues-Despointes BMP, Scholtz JM, Pace CN. 1999. Protein conformational stabilities can be determined from hydrogen exchange rates. *Nature Struct. Biol.* 6:910–12

70. Hvidt A, Nielsen SO. 1966. Hydrogen exchange in proteins. *Adv. Protein Chem.* 21:287–386

71. Itzhaki LS, Otzen DE, Fersht AR. 1995. The structure of the transition state for folding of chymotrypsin inhibitor 2 analysed by protein engineering methods:evidence for a nucleation–condensation mechanism for protein folding. *J. Mol. Biol.* 254:260–88

72. Jacobs MD, Fox RO. 1994. Staphylococcal nuclease folding intermediate characterized by hydrogen exchange and NMR spectroscopy. *Proc. Natl. Acad. Sci. USA* 91:449–53

73. Jamin M, Baldwin RL. 1999. Two forms of the pH 4 folding intermediate of apomyoglobin. *J. Mol. Biol.* 276:491–504

74. Jeng M-F, Englander SW, Elöve GA, Wand AJ, Roder H. 1990. Structural description of acid-denatured cytochrome c by hydrogen exchange and 2D NMR. *Biochemistry* 29:10433–37

75. Jennings PA, Wright PE. 1993. Formation of a molten globule intermediate early in the kinetic folding pathway of apomyoglobin. *Science* 262:892–96

76. Karplus M, Sali A. 1995. Theoretical studies of protein folding and unfolding. *Curr. Opin. Struct. Biol.* 5:58–73

77. Kim KS, Fuchs JA, Woodward CK. 1993. Hydrogen exchange identifies native-state motional domains important in protein folding. *Biochemistry* 32:9600–8

78. Kim PS. 1986. Amide proton exchange as a probe of protein folding pathways. *Methods Enzymol.* 131:136–57

79. Kim PS, Baldwin RL. 1980. Structural

80. intermediates trapped during the folding of ribonuclease A by amide proton exchange. *Biochemistry* 19:6124–29

80. Kim PS, Baldwin RL. 1982. Specific intermediates in the folding reactions of small proteins and the mechanism of protein folding. *Annu. Rev. Biochem.* 51:459–89

81. Kim PS, Baldwin RL. 1990. Intermediates in the folding reactions of small proteins. *Annu. Rev. Biochem.* 59:631–60

82. Kita N, Kuwajima K, Nitta K, Sugai S. 1976. Equilibrium and kinetics of the unfolding of alpha–lactalbumin by guanidine hydrochloride (II). *Biochim. Biophys. Acta* 427:350–58

83. Kuwajima K. 1989. The molten globule state as a clue for understanding the folding and cooperativity of globular protein structure. *Proteins: Struct. Funct. Genet.* 6:87–103

84. Kuwajima K, Nitta K, Yoneyama M, Sugai S. 1976. Three-state denaturation of alpha-lactalbumin by guanidine hydrochloride. *J. Mol. Biol.* 106:359–73

85. Laurents DV, Bruix M, Jamin M, Baldwin RL. 1998. A pulse-chase-competition experiment to determine if a folding intermediate is on or off-pathway:application to ribonuclease A. *J. Mol. Biol.* 283:669–78

86. Lazaridis T, Karplus M. 1997. "New View" of protein folding reconciled with the old through multiple unfolding simulations. *Science* 278:1928–31

87. Linderstrøm-Lang KU. 1958. Deuterium exchange and protein structure. In *Symposium on Protein Structure*, ed. A. Neuberger. London: Methuen

88. Loh SN, Kay MS, Baldwin RL. 1995. Structure and stability of a second molten globule intermediate in the apomyoglobin folding pathway. *Proc. Natl. Acad. Sci. USA* 92:5446–50

89. Loh SN, Prehoda KE, Wang J, Markley JL. 1993. Hydrogen exchange in unligated and ligated staphylococcal nuclease. *Biochemistry* 32:11022–28

90. Lu J, Dahlquist FW. 1992. Detection and characterization of an early folding intermediate of T4 lysozyme using pulsed hydrogen exchange and two-dimensional NMR. *Biochemistry* 31:4749–56

91. Matouschek A, Serrano L, Meiering EM, Bycroft M, Fersht AR. 1992. The folding of an enzyme V. 1H/2H exchange-nuclear magnetic resonance studies on the folding pathway of barnase: complementarity to and agreement with protein engineering studies. *J. Mol. Biol.* 224:837–45

92. Matthews CR. 1991. The mechanism of protein folding. *Curr. Opin. Struct. Biol.* 1:28–35

93. Matthews CR. 1993. Pathways of protein folding. *Annu. Rev. Biochem.* 62:653–83

94. Milne JS, Mayne L, Roder H, Wand AJ, Englander SW. 1998. Determinants of protein hydrogen exchange studied in equine cytochrome c. *Protein Sci.* 7:739–45

95. Milne JS, Xu Y, Mayne LC, Englander SW. 1999. Experimental study of the protein folding landscape:unfolding reactions in cytochrome c. *J. Mol. Biol.* 290:811–22

96. Miranker A, Robinson CV, Radford AE, Dobson CM. 1996. Investigation of protein folding by mass spectrometry. *FASEB J.* 10:93–101

97. Mirny LA, Abkevich V, Shakhnovich EI. 1996. Universality and diversity of folding scenarios:a comprehensive analysis with the aid of a lattice model. *Folding Design* 1103–116

98. Molday RS, Englander SW, Kallen RG. 1972. Primary structure effects on peptide group hydrogen exchange. *Biochemistry* 11:150–58

99. Morozova LA, Haynie DT, Arico-Muendel C, Van Dael H, Dobson CM. 1995. Structural basis of the stability of a lysozyme molten globule. *Nature Struct. Biol.* 2:871–75

100. Mullins LS, Pace CN, Raushel FM. 1993. Investigation of ribonuclease T1 folding intermediates by hydrogen-deuterium amide exchange-two-dimensional NMR spectroscopy. *Biochemistry* 32:6152–56

101. Oliveberg M. 1998. Alternative explanations for multi-state kinetics in protein folding: transient aggregation and changing transition state ensembles. *Accts. Chem. Res.* 31:765–72

102. Onuchic JN, Wolynes PG, Luthey-Schulten Z, Socci ND. 1995. Toward an outline of the topography of a realistic protein-folding funnel. *Proc. Natl. Acad. Sci. USA* 92:3626–30

103. Pande VS, Grosberg A, Tanaka T, Rokhsar DS. 1998. Pathways for protein folding: is a new view needed? *Curr. Opin. Struct. Biol.* 8:68–79

104. Pande VS, Rokhsar DS. 1999. Folding pathway of a lattice model for proteins. *Proc. Natl. Acad. Sci.* 96:1273–78

105. Phillips CM, Mizutani Y, Hochstrasser RM. 1995. Ultrafast thermally induced unfolding of RNase A. *Proc. Natl. Acad. Sci. USA* 92:7292–96

106. Plaxco KW, Simons KT, Baker D. 1998. Contact order, transition state placement and the refolding rates of single domain proteins. *J. Mol. Biol.* 277:985–94

107. Privalov PL. 1996. Intermediate states in protein folding. *J. Mol. Biol.* 258:707–25

108. Ptitsyn OB. 1987. Protein folding: hypotheses and experiments. *J. Protein Chem.* 6:273–93

109. Ptitsyn OB. 1995. Molten globule and protein folding. *Adv. Protein Chem.* 47: 83–229

110. Ptitsyn OB. 1995. Structures of folding intermediates. *Curr. Opin. Struc. Biol.* 5:74–78

111. Qi PX, Sosnick TR, Englander SW. 1998. The burst phase in ribonuclease A folding: solvent dependence of the unfolded state. *Nat. Struct. Biol.* 5:882–84

112. Radford SE, Buck M, Topping KD, Dobson CM, Evans PA. 1992. Hydrogen exchange in native and denatured states

of hen egg-white lysozyme. *Proteins: Struct. Funct. Genet.* 14:237–48

113. Radford SE, Dobson CM, Evans PA. 1992. The folding of hen lysozyme involves partially structured intermediates and multiple pathways. *Nature* 358:302–7

114. Raschke TM, Marqusee S. 1997. The kinetic folding intermediate of ribonuclease H resembles the acid molten globule and partially unfolded molecules detected under native conditions. *Nature Struct. Biol.* 4:298–304

115. Redfield C, Smith RA, Dobson CM. 1994. Structural characterization of a highly-ordered 'molten globule' at low pH. *Nature Struct. Biol.* 1:23–29

116. Roder H. 1989. Structural characterization of protein folding intermediates by proton magnetic resonance and hydrogen exchange. *Methods Enzymol.* 176:447–73

117. Roder H, Colon W. 1997. Kinetic role of early intermediates in protein folding. *Curr. Opin. Struct. Biol.* 7:15–28

118. Roder H, Elöve GA, Englander SW. 1988. Structural characterization of folding intermediates in cytochrome c by H-exchange labeling and proton NMR. *Nature* 335:700–4

119. Roder H, Wuthrich K. 1986. Protein folding kinetics by combined use of rapid mixing techniques and NMR observation of individual amide protons. *Proteins: Struc. Funct. Genet.* 1:34–42

120. Rosa JJ, Richards FM. 1979. An experimental procedure for increasing the structural resolution of chemical hydrogen exchange measurements on proteins: application to ribonuclease S peptide. *J. Mol. Biol.* 133:399–416

121. Rosenberg A, Chakravarti K. 1968. Studies of hydrogen exchange in proteins. I. The exchange kinetics of bovine carbonic anhydrase. *J. Biol. Chem.* 243:5193–5201

122. Sabelko J, Ervin J, Gruebele M. 1999. Observation of strange kinetics in protein

folding [see comments]. *Proc. Natl. Acad. Sci. USA* 96:6031–36

123. Schmid FX, Baldwin RL. 1979. Detection of an early intermediate in the folding of ribonuclease A by protection of amide protons against exchange. *J. Mol. Biol.* 135:199–215

124. Schulman BA, Kim PS, Dobson CM, Redfield C. 1997. A residue-specific NMR view of the non-cooperative unfolding of a molten globule. *Nature Struct. Biol.* 4:630–34

125. Schulman BA, Redfield C, Peng ZY, Dobson CM, Kim PS. 1995. Different subdomains are most protected from hydrogen exchange in the molten globule and native states of human alpha-lactalbumin. *J. Mol. Biol.* 253:651–57

126. Shakhnovich EI. 1997. Theoretical studies of protein-folding thermodynamics and kinetics. *Curr. Opin. Struct. Biol.* 7:29–40

127. Sosnick TR, Mayne L, Englander SW. 1996. Molecular collapse: the rate-limiting step in two-state cytochrome c folding. *Proteins: Struct. Funct. Genet.* 24:413–26

128. Sosnick TR, Mayne L, Hiller R, Englander SW. 1994. The barriers in protein folding. *Nature Struct. Biol.* 1:149–56

129. Sosnick TR, Mayne LC, Hiller R, Englander SW. 1995. The barriers in protein folding. In *Peptide and Protein Folding Workshop*, ed. W. F. Degrado. Philadelphia: Int. Bus. Commun.

130. Sosnick TR, Shtilerman MD, Mayne L, Englander SW. 1997. Ultrafast signals in protein folding and the polypeptide contracted state. *Proc. Natl. Acad. Sci. USA* 94:8545–50

131. Thirumalai D, Guo Z. 1995. Nucleation mechanism for protein folding and theoretical predictions for hydrogen-exchange experiments. *Biopolymers* 35:137–40

132. Thirumalai D, Klimov DK. 1999. Deciphering the timescales and mechanisms of protein folding using minimal off-lattice

models. *Curr. Opin. Struct. Biol.* 9:197–207

133. Udgaonkar JB, Baldwin RL. 1988. NMR evidence for an early framework intermediate on the folding pathway of ribonuclease A. *Nature* 335:694–99

134. Udgaonkar JB, Baldwin RL. 1990. Early folding intermediate of ribonuclease A. *Proc. Natl. Acad. Sci. USA* 87:8197–8201

135. Veitshans T, Klimov D, Thirumalai D. 1997. Protein folding kinetics:timescales, pathways and energy landscapes in terms of sequence-dependent properties. *Folding Design* 2:1–22

136. Wagner G, Wüthrich K. 1982. Amide proton exchange and surface conformation of BPTI in solution:studies with 2D NMR. *J. Mol. Biol.* 160:343–61

137. Weissman JS, Kim PS. 1995. A kinetic explanation for the rearrangement pathway of BPTI folding. *Nature Struct. Biol.* 2:1123–30

138. Williams S, Causgrove TP, Gilmanshin R, Fang KS, Callender RH, et al. 1996. Fast events in protein folding:helix melting and formation in a small peptide. *Biochemistry* 35:691–97

139. Wolynes PG, Onuchic JN, Thirumalai D. 1995. Navigating the folding routes. *Science* 267:1619–20

140. Woodward C. 1993. Is the slow exchange core the protein folding core? *Trends Biochem. Sci.* 18:359–60

141. Woodward CK. 1994. Hydrogen exchange rates and protein folding. *Curr. Opin. Struc. Biol.* 4:112–16

142. Woodward CK, Hilton BD. 1979. Hydrogen exchange kinetics and internal motions in proteins and nucleic acids. *Annu. Rev. Biophys. Bioeng.* 8:99–127

143. Woodward CK, Simon I, Tuchsen E. 1982. Hydrogen exchange and the dynamic structure of proteins. *Mol. Cell. Biochem.* 48:135–60

144. Xu Y, Mayne L, Englander SW. 1998. Evidence for an unfolding and refolding pathway in cytochrome c. *Nature Struct. Biol.* 5:774–78

145. Zaidi FN, Nath U, Udgaonkar JB. 1997. Multiple intermediates and transition states during protein unfolding. *Nature Struct. Biol.* 4:1016–24

146. Zhang Z, Post CB, Smith DL. 1996. Amide hydrogen exchange determined by mass spectrometry:application to rabbit muscle aldolase. *Biochemistry* 35:779–91

Annu. Rev. Biophys. Biomol. Struct. 2000. 29:239–63

QUANTITATIVE CHEMICAL ANALYSIS
OF SINGLE CELLS*

D. M. Cannon, Jr., N. Winograd, and A. G. Ewing

Department of Chemistry, The Pennsylvania State University, University Park, Pennsylvania 16802; e-mail: dmc17@psu.edu, nxw@psu.edu, age@psu.edu

Key Words   electrochemistry, separation, mass spectrometry, fluorescence, imaging

■ **Abstract**   A fundamental perspective can be achieved by targeting single cells for analysis with the goal of deconvoluting complex biological functions. However, single-cell studies have their own difficulties, such as minute volumes and sample amounts. Quantitative chemical analysis of single cells has emerged as a powerful new area in recent years due to several technological advancements. The development of microelectrodes has allowed the measurement of redox-active species as a function of cellular dynamics. This miniaturization trend is also evident in the separation sciences with the application of small column separations to single cells. Desorption ionization methods with mass spectrometric detection have shown single-cell capability owing to numerous technological developments. Finally, fluorescence imaging has also progressed to the point where single-cell dynamics can be probed by native fluorescence utilizing either single or multiple photon excitation. The results of these studies are reviewed with an emphasis on the quantitation of single-cell dynamics.

CONTENTS

---

*Glossary of abbreviations – CE, capillary electrophoresis; DM, dichroic mirror; EOF, electroosmotic flow; ESI, electrospray ionization; FTICR, Fourier transform ion cyclotron resonance; i.d., inner diameter; LIF, laser-induced fluorescence; LLOD, lower limit of detection; MS, mass spectrometry; MALDI, matrix-assisted laser desorption/ionization; OTLC, open tubular liquid chromatography; ppb, part per billion; PMT, photo-multiplier tube; SIMS, secondary ion mass spectrometry; 3-D, three-dimensional; TOF, time-of-flight; zmol, zeptomole

1056-8700/00/0610-0239$14.00

PERSPECTIVES AND OVERVIEW

Qualitative and quantitative chemical analysis at the single-cell level has generated considerable interest in the biological and medical sciences and promises to further the understanding of cellular function within complicated cellular environments. Single cells are attractive models for in vivo processes. However, along with constraints of minute size and limited amount of material, single cells still present a vast complexity. Knowledge at the single-cell level will enhance the understanding of diverse cellular processes such as intracellular and intercellular communication (including transport, secretion, exocytosis, endocytosis, receptor-mediated signal transduction, and voltage-gated ion channels), cell differentiation, physiological effects of external stimuli (e.g., environment, drugs, toxins), disease states (e.g., cancer), and gene expression. Advances in these areas will require further development of analytical techniques capable of quantitatively monitoring minute chemical compositions associated with dynamic cellular events at the extracellular, whole-cell, and subcellular levels.

    The considerable interest in the chemical analysis of single cells has resulted in the development of numerous analytical methods. These include enzyme activity measurements (29), immunoassay (29), voltammetric electrodes (75), microscale ion selective electrodes (55), microgel electrophoresis (51), microcolumn liquid chromatography (23), capillary electrophoresis (25), mass spectrometry (53) (including secondary ion and matrix-assisted laser desorption), electron probe X-ray microanalysis (41), and various optical imaging modalities (5). Although these diverse bioanalytical methods provide a considerable amount of valuable information, most suffer from important limitations, including uncertainties in quantitation, inability to analyze small volumes, lack of sensitivity, inability to detect a variety of compounds simultaneously, and lack of sufficient temporal resolution to monitor chemical dynamics associated with cellular function. Combinations of analysis techniques have complemented the advantages associated with individual methods. Further advancements in bioanalytical chemistry will build on previous experiences to provide a better understanding of the complex chemistry and dynamics of single cells. This review presents a synopsis of the techniques that have pioneered this field as well as emerging technologies that hold promise for single-cell quantitative analysis.

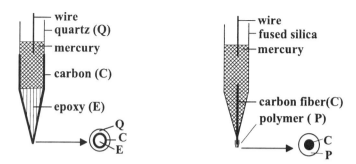

Figure 1 Schematics of two types of carbon microelectrodes. (Left) Carbon-ring electrode. (Right) Carbon disk-shaped electrode with polymer insulation.

ELECTROCHEMISTRY OF SINGLE CELLS

The development of microelectrodes has pushed electrochemical methods to the forefront in quantitative cellular analysis (75). The reduction in electroactive area for microelectrodes significantly reduces double-layer capacitance relative to conventional electrodes. This results in a microprobe with a rapid-response time [transient cellular functions have been measured on the μs time scale (24)], an increased signal-to-noise ratio (necessary for a limited single-cell environment), and reduced current production (reduced reactant production, potentially toxic to the biological matrix, and reduced interaction with cellular activity). Furthermore, voltammetric methods such as amperometry and fast-scan voltammetry are extremely sensitive, as low as zeptomole (zmol) levels (16), for many easily oxidized biochemicals. The ability of microelectrodes to monitor events at the cellular and subcellular levels in real time provides a powerful method for furthering the understanding of dynamically occurring cellular processes.

Single-cell investigations have primarily used ultra-small carbon microelectrodes. Carbon-ring microelectrodes (Figure 1) fabricated with 1- to 5-μm-tip diameters have been used for both the intracellular (40) and extracellular (38) monitoring of neurotransmitter reverse transport. More commonly used carbon-fiber microelectrodes (Figure 1) have been constructed in both the disk-shaped and cylindrical geometries with 5- to 35-μm-tip diameters (35). Carbon fibers have been electropolished to provide submicrometer conical tips (62). Unfortunately, electroactive tip diameters can be occluded by large glass structures, required for electrical insulation, thus restricting the placement in microenvironments needed for single-cell analysis. However, electropolymerized insulating layers as thin as 100 nm have resulted in total disk-shaped tip diameters as small as 400 nm (69). Further improvements in the fabrication of microelectrode structures promise the nanometer dimension required for investigation within subcellular compartments and nerve terminals.

Electrochemical quantitation is a result of integration of the transient current spikes to reveal the amount of charge (Q) transferred during a single event.

Assuming total oxidation at the electrode surface, Q (in coulombs) is directly related to the amount in the transient event via Faraday's law : Q = nFN, where n is the number of charge equivalents per mole (for catecholamines, n = 2 equivalents/mol), N is the number of moles oxidized, and F is Faraday's constant (96,485 coulombs/equivalent). Brief examples of applications to single-cell quantitative monitoring are discussed here, with a bias toward investigations of cellular communication and exocytosis.

Intracellular Voltammetry

Intracellular monitoring is essential for further knowledge of metabolism, function, and regulation of individual cells. Intracellular studies have included the use of ion-selective electrodes, with dimensions in the micrometer range (55). These studies monitor intracellular levels of such ions as H^+, Li^+, Ca^{2+}, and Mg^{2+}, whereas carbon and platinum microelectrodes have been used for direct detection of electroactive species within single nerve cells (40). Active transport of the neurotransmitter, dopamine, into the giant dopamine cell of *Planorbis corneus* has been investigated using intracellular carbon-ring microelectrodes with amperometric detection (17). For this protocol, the neuron is bathed in a 0.5-mM dopamine solution to induce dopamine transport into the cell. Current transients indicative of active transport are followed by metabolic clearance that occurs over a time span of minutes. Average peak concentrations of dopamine inside the giant dopamine cell due to active transport from the external solution are 44 ± 2 μM with a clearance rate of 0.29 μM/s. Quantitative kinetic monitoring of cellular transport mechanisms at the single-cell level will allow a more detailed understanding of such fields as pharmacology, toxicology, and pathology, to cite a few.

Intracellular quantitative oxygen monitoring is useful for investigating the synthesis, uptake, release, and metabolism of neurotransmitters. Increased oxygen consumption at the single-cell level is proposed to be vital to the necessary production of energy for cellular functions such as exocytosis. Once again, the giant dopamine neuron of *P. corneus* has been used as a model system for studying oxygen consumption during cellular function (40). A Nafion-coated platinized carbon-ring microelectrode is used to catalyze oxygen reduction. Average intracellular oxygen concentrations are 0.032 ± 0.004 mM, compared to average oxygen concentrations of 0.041 mM at 10 μm from the cell and 0.16 mM at 0.4 cm from the cell. Relative intracellular oxygen concentrations obtained for stimulated and control cells have given further evidence that immediate consumption of oxygen is required for dynamic cellular functions such as exocytosis.

Extracellular Voltammetry

Carbon-fiber microelectrodes have been extensively investigated for the monitoring of single, dynamically occurring exocytotic release events (26). This is accomplished by positioning an electrode directly on top of discrete regions of

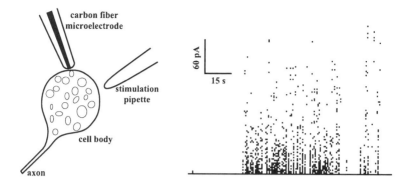

Figure 2   (Left) Experimental arrangement for direct voltammetric detection of stimulated release from the giant dopamine neuron of *Planorbis corneus*. (Right) An example of current transients measured with an amperometric (constant-voltage) microelectrode at an intact giant dopamine cell body. The horizontal bar below the trace indicates stimulation. (Reproduced with permission from Reference 15.)

the cell (Figure 2). A microinjector is filled with a compound and positioned close to the cell to initiate a given function. Microelectrode methods have quantitatively detected a variety of compounds released from single cells, including catecholamines, histamine, 5-hydroxytryptamine (serotonin), insulin, and certain other peptides.

Early single-cell electrochemical investigations have measured single exocytotic events at cultured bovine adrenal medullary chromaffin cells (44). The average catecholamine release amount ranges from 5 to 10 attomoles (amol)/event. Also, individual chromaffin cells have been used to continuously monitor, over repeated stimulations, the effects of autoreceptors on the amount of hormone released (79). For consecutive stimulations of the same cell, release following the second stimulation is approximately 32% of the total released in the first stimulation. An 80% decrease in the release amount for the third stimulation compared to that of the second stimulation further suggests an active regulatory mechanism on the release process. Quantitative monitoring of exocytosis strongly suggests that negative feedback pathways do exist and can be manipulated in adrenal cells.

Rat pheochromocytoma cells have also served as models for quantitative exocytosis investigations (16). The experimental method is similar to that described above for chromaffin cells with modifications providing a better lower limit of detection (LLOD) for catecholamine. Average catecholamine levels from single pheochromocytoma cells are 190 zmol/release event. Distributions of release events as a function of vesicle content show a relatively skewed, narrow profile indicating 85% of these events contain less than 333 zmol of catecholamine. As in the chromaffin cell studies, external stimuli effects on pheochromocytoma cells have been quantitatively compared to those of controls (70). For example, incubation in 10-mM amphetamine for 10 min before stimulation results in reduction of the average amount of catecholamine release to $48 \pm 5.4\%$ of those of controls. Quantal analysis studies generally assume a constant level of neurotransmitter is contained within vesicles. However, this study demonstrated that vesicle quantal size could be pharmacologically altered.

Quantitative investigations of single-cell release have also included invertebrate neuronal models, such as the leech *Hirudo medicinalis* and the pond snail *Planorbis corneus*. Studies on cultured neurons from the leech *H. medicinalis* have reported quantitative detection of serotonin from two proposed types of vesicles (8). Release of small clear vesicles (containing 8 zmol of serotonin) occurs more rapidly than the release of large dense core vesicles (containing 13 amol of serotonin) that are randomly distributed throughout the cell. Studies on an intact giant dopamine cell of *P. corneus* have reported the first dynamic chemical measurement of individual exocytotic events at an in vivo neuron having multiple synaptic connections to other cells (14). More importantly, the observation of calcium-dependent exocytosis from the cell body has been observed for the first time (15). Current transients with rise times from 2 to 5 ms and an average basewidth of 14 ± 0.8 ms are consistent with the expected timescale of exocytosis in these experiments (Figure 2). Quantitation of KCl-stimulated release shows a bimodal distribution for vesicular release amounts. The smaller distribution consists of only 9% of the total release events along with a considerably smaller average dopamine content (4%) compared to the dominant distribution. Electrochemistry allows the analysis of distributions of vesicular release from single cells and has recently been extended to concentration and vesicle radii distributions via modeling of the electrochemical information from individual events.

En route to the quantitation of exocytosis at a mammalian nerve terminal, superior cervical ganglion neurons developed from neonatal rats have been investigated using direct electrochemical methods (80). By monitoring release at varicosities along the axon, an average of 58 zmol is detected per event, similar to the amounts for the small clear vesicles in the leech studies. Extracellular voltammetry continues to be extensively used in investigations aimed toward a further chemical understanding of cellular function. It is hoped that further advances in electrochemical methods will approach the approximate 1000 molecules ($\sim$2 zmol) LLOD necessary for measuring single exocytotic events at mammalian nerve terminals.

MICROCOLUMN SEPARATIONS OF SINGLE CELLS

Separation methods offer several advantages in the areas of quantitation and multicomponent analysis of cellular samples. The emerging miniaturization trend has provided further advantages to single-cell separations, such as small-volume, decreased-time, and high-resolution capabilities (23). Microcolumn liquid chromatography, with either packed (19) or open tubular columns (36), is capable of multicomponent analysis of individual cells. Capillary electrophoresis (CE) within narrow-bore capillaries is capable of rapid, high-efficiency quantitative separations from extremely low volumes (25). Narrow-bore CE with laser-induced fluorecence (LIF) (30) or electrochemical detection (52) has been used for attomole quantitative chemical analysis of neurotransmitters and amino acids in individual cells and single-cell cytoplasm. These methods are discussed briefly in the next sections.

Microcolumn Liquid Chromatography

Microcolumn liquid chromatography utilizes a stationary phase in a small-volume microcolumn for a separation scheme (37). Typical open tubular liquid chromatography (OTLC) microcolumns have inner diameters (i.d.) of 2 to 50 μm and 1- to 3-m lengths. The small diameter of a microcolumn enhances the resolving power of that obtained with a packed-bed column, with theoretical predictions suggesting that the optimal resolving power is obtained for microcolumns with 2- to 5-μm i.d. Packed microcolumns, typically having 42- to 50-μm i.d. and lengths of approximately 50 cm, have also been used for single-cell investigations. Microcolumns have typically been packed with 5-μm-diameter spherical particles derivatized with a C18 hydrocarbon as stationary phase. The separation mechanism for packed microcolumns is similar to that of high-performance liquid chromatography (HPLC) or OTLC in that solutes differentially interact with a stationary phase, resulting in different elution times.

Capillary Electrophoresis

Capillary electrophoresis (CE) generally indicates an electrophoretic separation performed inside a solution-filled capillary. In the most basic form of CE, separation is due to the differential electrophoretic mobilities of ionic species in a potential field (Figure 3) There is no stationary support between the capillary walls (the flow origin). Moreover, since the bulk flow of solution is due to electroosmotic flow (EOF), a flat flow profile is achieved. Both phenomena lead to highly efficient separations. Capillary dimensions are typically 2- to 100-μm i.d. with lengths of 10 to 100 cm. Although alternative CE methods are sometimes used to

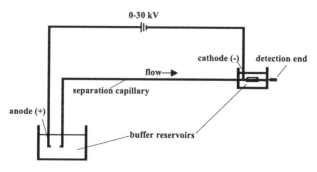

Figure 3   Schematic of capillary electrophoresis system with electrically conductive joint.

address limitations of the technique, most single-cell separations performed with CE are done in the basic zone electrophoresis mode.

There are several advantages to developing CE in narrow-bore capillaries. Solution heating from ion migration limits the potential fields that can be used in CE. When the inner bore of the capillary decreases, the surface area–to–volume ratio increases, thus providing enhanced dissipation of heating via the capillary wall. This reduces zone broadening due to convection and allows for larger potential fields to be used for separation. Separation times are then decreased while maintaining as many as 10^6 theoretical plates. Narrow-bore capillaries also require smaller volumes. In a 1-m-long capillary with 2- to 10-μm i.d., total volumes range from 13 to 300 nL with injection volumes being even smaller. The ultra-small volume flow rates in CE allow single-cell microenvironment sampling.

Sampling Techniques for Single-Cell Separations

The high efficiencies of microcolumn separations are conserved via sample introduction onto the column with both minimal sampling and band broadening. Thus, an integral trait of any injection technique is the ability to sample small volumes (<10 nL) efficiently and reproducibly. Sample preparation and injection methods have differed significantly between microcolumn liquid chromatography and CE separations due to the inherent nature of the techniques. An important aspect of injection for CE is electroosmotic flow, as this can be used to acquire cells within the entrance to the capillary (23).

In general, whole-cell chemical analysis for microcolumn liquid chromatography involves the isolation and transfer of a single cell via a micropipette to a 250- to 500-nL vial (36). An internal standard is added, followed by homogenization and centrifugation. A supernatant sample can then be transferred to a clean vial, where subsequent derivations necessary for detection are performed. The sample is then pressure-injected from a micropipette onto the microcolumn for separation. In CE, whole-cell sampling is used to directly draw a cell into the end of the capillary with EOF (39). Injection is aided by a microscope to position the capillary tip so it is in direct contact with the cell. This tip is chemically etched to a size comparable in diameter to that of the cell (Figure 4). An injection potential of 1–10 kV is used

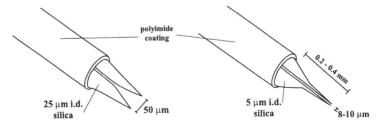

Figure 4 Schematic of CE injector at the end of (left) a 25-μm-i.d. capillary for whole-cell analysis and (right) a 5-mm-i.d. capillary for intracellular analysis.

to transport the cell into the capillary. Cells with diameters as large as 75 μm have been sampled in this manner, without rupturing, into electrophoresis capillaries with 25-μm i.d. After the cell is sufficiently inside the capillary, a plug of lysate is injected, followed by the voltage being turned off for a period of time to rupture the cell membrane inside the capillary. Injection of the whole cell directly onto the separation column provides a distinct advantage of total sampling that leads to better detection of low-level species.

The exceptionally low flow characteristics of microcolumn techniques allow for subcellular sampling. CE methods have used the end of the separation capillary directly to sample single-cell cytoplasm (58). Direct sample injection minimizes the need for sample preparation, reduces band-broadening effects due to large dead volumes, and eliminates laminar flow associated with microsyringe injection. The injection ends of the capillaries used for direct injection are constructed using chemical etching procedures similar to those used for whole-cell sampling (Figure 4), but with smaller tip diameters to penetrate the cell. Etching of 5-μm-i.d. capillaries has produced total tip diameters as small as 6 μm with injection volumes in the fL range. Further reduction of sample volume injection is expected by using smaller-i.d. capillaries, as they become available.

The chemical composition of the fluid around cells is naturally affected by cellular function. Extracellular sampling from single cells has been accomplished by placing a capillary with an etched tip close to the cell (15, 46). Electroosmotic injection is used to sample from around the cell at discrete times after a cellular event, permitting the dynamics of specific compounds to be monitored. Further improvements with respect to sampling schemes will include the adjustment of experimental paradigms to lead to smaller cellular regions and better temporal resolution.

Detection Schemes for Microcolumn Separations

Detection in microcolumn separations is critical in determining the success of single-cell analysis. Increased demands on selectivity and sensitivity in heterogeneous environments are apparent with extremely minute volumes. Due to high sensitivity, electrochemical and LIF methods have been the primary methods for detection following a single-cell separation. Recent developments, however, have demonstrated radiochemical (73) and mass spectrometric schemes (67) to be sensitive enough for single-cell investigations. Further developments in detection schemes will enable more selective and sensitive investigation of detectable and presently nondetectable compounds in smaller volumes.

Sensitive electrochemical schemes have been reported for both microcolumn and CE separations (52). Both these techniques have used a small carbon fiber electrode (5- to 10-μm diameter) placed inside the eluting end for detection. In CE experiments, the detection electrode must be isolated from the high potential field used for separation. Isolation was first accomplished with a porous glass tube epoxied around a small crack in the detection end of the capillary

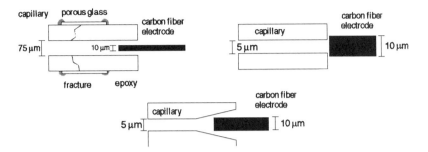

Figure 5   Electrochemical detection schemes for CE. (*Left*) Porous glass coupler, (*right*) end column, and (*lower middle*) optimized end-column electrochemical detection.

(Figure 5). More recent cell separations have used an end-column detection mode, where the detection electrode is positioned outside of the capillary end, directly against the bore (Figure 5). Further isolation of the detection electrode from the electrophoretic potential is not necessary because virtually all of the high potential is dropped across the highly resistive inner bore of the capillary versus the relatively conducting buffer solution in the reservoirs. Using a 10-μm-diameter carbon-fiber electrode for end-column detection from a 5-μm-i.d. capillary, the detection limit for catechol has been reported as low as 56 amol. Etching the inside wall of the detector end of the capillary has resulted in conical end-column detection (Figure 5). The considerably larger i.d. versus the rest of the capillary provides maintainable alignment of the electrode within the eluent stream. The LLOD for catechol can be as low as amol for 2-μm-i.d. capillaries and 10-μm-diameter electrodes. Notably, this allows routine use of 2-μm-i.d. capillaries, which is important for single-cell investigations involving ultra-low volume analysis.

Laser-induced fluorescence (LIF) detection for single-cell analysis has been used with both OTLC (56) and CE separation methods (48). In LIF studies, natively fluorescent or fluorescently derivatized compounds are detected by focusing a laser onto a detection window on the separation capillary. Schemes utilizing either precolumn or postcolumn derivatization have shown excellent performance in single-cell investigations. Furthermore, LIF detection schemes are being developed to include multiple-wavelength detection for the simultaneous detection of numerous analytes, enzymatic amplification for a decreased LLOD, and fluorescence imaging of capillary arrays or channels to allow either high-throughput or high-temporal-resolution separations.

Mass spectrometric detection is proving to be an extremely powerful detection method for microcolumn separations of single cells (67). The obvious advantage is the qualitative information of molecular weight and structure that is obtained. However, these methods are highly dependent on the mode of ionization for the analyte species. Electrospray ionization (ESI), continuous-flow fast-atom bombardment, pulsed sample introduction interface, and laser desorption/ionization methods, including continuous-flow, aerosol, and off-line or on-line matrix-assisted laser desorption ionization (MALDI), are examples of various ionization schemes for the coupling of CE to mass detection methods. Fourier transform ion cyclotron resonance (FTICR) has the ability to carry out MS/MS analysis to induce fragmentation and thereby facilitate compound identification. Sensitivity of FTICR-MS is now within reach for MS/MS analysis to determine partial sequence of proteins from a single cell (31). The ability of TOF mass spectrometry to collect an entire mass spectrum in less than 100 μs suggests that it is the most compatible with the time scale of the CE separation. Several groups have accomplished ESI coupling of TOFMS to microcolumn separations. However, detection limits are not yet sufficient for single-cell analysis. This could rapidly change with orthogonal-injection schemes and hybrid mass analyzers. Although sensitivities for quadrupoles are reported as low as the zeptomole level, to date, only FTICR has been used for CE mass-spectrometric detection in single-cell investigations.

A post-column radionucleotide detection system has been developed for CE analysis of single cells (73). Eluent from a CE experiment is deposited directly onto a peptide-binding membrane coated with a solid scintillator by using a translational stage. The stage is rastered in a pre-selected X-Y fashion to be correlated back to elution time. Radionucleotide labels such as ^{3}H, ^{35}S, or ^{32}P have allowed for selectivity within the detection scheme. The radionucleotide-labeled compounds emit β^- particles, causing photon emission from the solid scintillator coated on the collection membrane. Photon emission is detected (imaged) with a charge-coupled device. Radiochemical detection of 100 to 200 amol of [^{35}S]-cysteine-labeled peptides present in a single cell has been reported. ^{3}H- and ^{32}P-labeled analytes have LLODs that range from 8 fmol to 88 zmol, respectively.

Applications of Separations to Single Cells

Early applications of microcolumn separation techniques to single-cell analysis have used large invertebrate neurons for model systems. Studies with the land snail *Helix aspersa* have shown the coexistence of two classical neurotransmitters, namely, dopamine and serotonin (36). The detection of similar amounts of dopamine and serotonin within the same neuron has led to the conclusion that two classical neurotransmitters can function in one nerve cell. Both OTLC and CE methods have also been used to separate amino acids in individual neurons of *H. aspersa* (56). Seventeen amino acids at femtomole levels in a single cell have been characterized, with alanine and glutamine being the most abundant.

Single-cell CE separations of intracellular samples were first demonstrated in the giant dopamine neuron of *P. corneus* (58). These studies targeted dopamine intracellular stores that were speculated to be largely contained within vesicles. In one experiment, ethanol treatment of the dopamine neuron induced the lysing of internalized vesicles (17). Approximately 14 fmol of dopamine was detected from a single neuron after ethanol treatment, providing an estimate of internal dopamine concentration in the range of 46 to 140 μM. Improvements in this method have allowed for the determination of cytoplasmic dopamine levels of 2.2 $\pm$ 0.52 μM in untreated neurons, suggesting that up to 97% of internal dopamine is compartmentalized within vesicles. This same system has been used to separate cytoplasmic samples of the large serotonin cell of *P. corneus* (57). With apparent injection volumes ranging from 73 to 134 pL, serotonin levels in the cytoplasm of an individual serotonin cell have been reported to be 3.1 ± 0.57 μM. There are numerous examples of compounds or single-cell models that have been studied using microcolumn techniques. Direct whole-cell sampling and direct extracellular detection of secreted compounds from the giant dopamine neuron of *P. corneus* have led to new, interesting theories such as a two-compartment model of neurotransmitter storage (39) and calcium-dependent dopamine release from the cell body (15). Amino acids, proteins, and neuropeptides are all critical compounds being analyzed for further understanding of dynamic cellular function. Additionally, several research groups have used erythrocytes (red blood cells) as a model system for numerous applications (31, 32, 51). Separation of the α and β chains of hemoglobin has been shown, and due to the improved sensitivity available with FTICR-MS, studies of single cells have been demonstrated (31). Analyses of white blood cells have also been conducted with CE separation methods (4). CE analysis of single lymphocytes from human cerebrospinal fluid led to the discovery that catecholamines are present in these cells at an average level of 2.3 ± 1.7 amol (Figure 6). This then led to the discovery that dopamine synthesis and uptake occur in lymphocytes. Combined with the discovery of dopamine inhibition of lymphocyte differentiation and proliferation, these studies have indicated that dopamine may be a critical component in suppressing the immune activation of lymphocytes in the nervous system, thereby providing a mechanism for the immune privilege of the brain.

From the vast diversity of research being conducted at the single-cell level, it is apparent that microcolumn separations provide a powerful approach to unraveling biochemical mechanisms occurring in these microenvironments. Further improvements in sampling, separation, and specifically, detection methodologies

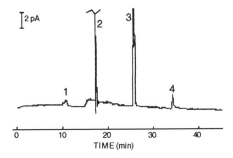

Figure 6   A capillary electropherogram of a single human lymphocyte. Detection was with an amperometric microelectrode. Electrophoretic mobilities correspond to standard mobilities of dopamine (peak 1), neutral species (peak 2), uric acid (peak 3), and dihydroxyphenylacetic acid (peak 4). (Reproduced with permission from Reference 4.)

are needed to realize the potential that microcolumn separations can have concerning single-cell compositional dynamics.

MASS SPECTROMETRY OF SINGLE CELLS

Mass spectrometry has evolved over the last several decades to a point where it is possible to detect a wide variety of ionizable species of biological interest ranging from elemental to large molecular weight molecules. The development of numerous ionization methods has allowed for characterization of a variety of biological matrices. These ionization schemes have also been coupled to a wide variety of mass spectrometric detection techniques to provide the necessary characteristics for bioanalytical analysis. Excellent reviews are already in the literature covering general as well as biological aspects of the various combinations of ionization and detection schemes (3, 20, 53). Here, we focus on quantitative schemes of induced-desorption techniques that are being applied to the study of single-cell analyses.

Secondary Ion Mass Spectrometry

Secondary ion mass spectrometry (SIMS) involves bombardment of a sample surface with an incident ion beam resulting in desorption of surface species (Figure 7). These species range from electrons to atoms and molecules that are either in the neutral or ionized state. The sputtered ions are electrostatically focused into a mass analyzer for mass-to-charge separation and detection of surface species. Lateral resolution is less than 1 μm for the ion microscope mode and about 50 nm for the focused ion microprobe technique. Applications of these ion microscopy techniques to the quantitation of single cells have been diverse (Figure 7, see color insert).

Two classifications are generally considered for SIMS investigations. Dynamic SIMS utilizes a high-flux primary ion beam ($>1 \times 10^{13}$ primary ions/cm^2) to probe tens of monolayers beneath the solid surface (60). This beam produces significant damage and limits the amount of molecular information. However, for elemental quantification, dynamic SIMS is considered the most sensitive general solid-state technique with a 1-ppb LLOD (68). Dynamic SIMS has been used to probe the spatial distribution of atomic and small molecular fragment ions, including isotope differences, at or near biological surfaces. Depth profiling is achieved with a resolution of a few nanometers. With increased mass-analyzer sensitivity associated with the development of the TOF mass analyzer, a surface-sensitive analysis is possible in the static SIMS regime ($<10^{13}$ primary ions/cm^2) (3, 7). For this regime the beam probes less than 1% of the first monolayer, ensuring the molecules in the top layer will be relatively undisturbed. When beam damage artifacts are eliminated, the quantity and quality of molecular information are maximized.

Since the mid-1980s, the primary motivation for the development of quantitative SIMS measurements has come from the semiconductor community (68). More recently, a number of quantification schemes used for dynamic SIMS studies of solid-state materials have been adapted to investigate softer biological materials (74). Comparison schemes are useful to evaluate control samples versus treated samples through relative intensity analysis. Further comparison to standards from other techniques results in semiquantitative to quantitative data with accuracy values of $\pm 100\%$ to as low as $\pm 5\%$, respectively. These broad ranges of quantitative capability must be compared to the advantages of SIMS analysis, such as high elemental and isotope sensitivity, that allow measurements of elemental stable isotope and labeled isotope dynamics. Imaging capabilities have provided localized quantification in structures as small as subcellular organelles with lower concentration sensitivities than attainable for electron probe X-ray microanalysis (43), suggesting the possibility for the routine application of SIMS to quantitative biochemical analysis at the single-cell level.

Direct imaging of analyte species within living cells is fundamentally not feasible with SIMS because this method is performed in an ultra-high vacuum environment (64). Thus, SIMS analysis of single cells has required the development of sample preparation protocols based on proven electron microscopy methods. Preparation techniques must preserve the local analyte distribution within the cell (1). Preservation is highly dependent on volume preservation of the sample as well as the analyte location and chemistry within the cell. Biological systems are analyzed by either fixation, freeze-drying, or fast-freezing methods to avoid sublimation of water and cellular components when inside a vacuum environment. Analysis of nondiffusable or bound species can be accomplished with traditional fixation techniques such as resin embedment or cryo-fixation/substitution methods. Quantitative analysis of diffusable ions has proven more difficult because of differential shrinkage of subcellular areas or the washing out of appreciable amounts. The time required for freeze-drying is longer than many cellular events; therefore the study of dynamic cellular events is restricted. Conversely, fast freezing provides ultra-fast (millisecond) times to completely freeze the entire sample to preserve chemical spatial integrity and to reduce ice-crystal damage to below the resolution capabilities of the method. Freeze-substitution following fast freezing has been the recent choice for electron and ion microscopy studies.

To directly quantitate SIMS intensities, numerous critical parameters such as sputter yield and ionization probability must be known (21, 68). Sputter yield is influenced by such parameters as the mass, energy, and angle of incidence of the primary ion probe, the masses of sampled atoms, crystal type and orientation, topography (native and induced), sample temperature, and chemical interactions with the sputtered surface. Ionization probability depends on the electronic state of the material [matrix effects (6)] and the adsorption of residual gas molecules. Complications to quantification in dynamic SIMS depth analysis include preferential sputtering, induced topography, segregation of trace elements between the bulk and altered top layers, beam-induced mixing and diffusion, and electrical effects such as surface charging. The uncertainty in these contributing factors has restricted the application of direct quantification through a basic equation and has led to the systematic development of alternative schemes. Calibration standards, internal standards, relative sensitivity factors, and isotope ratio measurements are all proven methods for quantitating SIMS intensities. However, relative sensitivity factors and isotope ratio measurements have stood out in the application of dynamic SIMS to quantitative single-cell analysis. Due to the vast scope of applications, only brief examples of each respective quantitative scheme are presented here.

Relative sensitivity methods allow for calibration of the analyte intensity with respect to a reference ion intensity via traditional bulk analysis techniques. For single-cell analysis, standards are produced from homogenates of cultured cells to generate a factor for a given analyte versus a reference ion. For a cellular matrix, carbon is used as a reference element with the assumption that relative carbon-content differences as a function of cellular location are negligible. Using this approach, absolute quantification of local concentrations via SIMS analysis of various elements has been shown at the single-cell and subcellular levels (Figure 7, see color insert) (2, 47). These studies have been extended past physiological proof-of-concept to investigate many diverse areas of biological interest, such as cancer therapy (66).

Quantitative schemes using isotope ratios have also shown vast utility for biochemical quantitation due to the unique ability of SIMS to analyze all elements and the respective isotopes. SIMS microscopy has been used to study the subcellular distributions of various species labeled with stable isotope tracers (12). Relative quantitation has been accomplished by evaluating the $^{14}C/^{12}C$, $^{15}N/^{14}N$, or $^{2}D/^{1}H$ ratios from various localized regimes. SIMS sensitivities for ^{14}C have been reported to be at least a thousand times more sensitive than those from autoradiography techniques. Quantitative isotope studies have been developed to investigate human chromosomes after simulated mitosis as an evaluation scheme for the mutagenic properties of various compounds (45).

The recently developed multi-isotope mass spectrometer has evolved from earlier designs of high-resolution parallel detection of secondary ions (65). Parallel detection minimizes matrix effects and optimizes the relative quantitative capabilities of stable isotope analysis with dynamic SIMS techniques. The ability to sufficiently separate $^{12}C^{15}N^-$ from $^{13}C^{14}N^-$ enables the use of ^{15}N as a general probe of proteins and nucleotides (42). If an organism is fed a ^{15}N-leucine–spiked diet, relative protein turnover rates can be presented as a function of biological location. By selecting regions of interest, researchers have determined nitrogen turnover percentage in hair cells and surrounding tectorial membrane tissue at approximately 92% and 26%, respectively. This study, along with protein turnover studies in samples such as mouse kidney tissue, has shown that micro-dissection along with air-dried or sample fixation techniques is sufficient for the analysis of relatively immobile proteins.

To ideally preserve the native chemical state of single cells for vacuum analysis, cells should be frozen quickly and analyzed in the frozen-hydrated state (13). Until recently, SIMS analyses of frozen-hydrated single cells have been traditionally done in the dynamic mode for the subcellular localization of diffusable ions such as K^+, Na^+, and Ca^{2+} (12). Freeze-fractured, frozen-hydrated paramecia

(18), red blood cells (59), and liposomes (10) have been used to demonstrate the special considerations of fracturing criteria that are required for molecule-specific static SIMS imaging of frozen-hydrated cells. Optimization of freeze-fracture methodology specific to SIMS molecular imaging of native chemical species (glycerophospholipids and cholesterol) within model membranes has recently been reported. The fast-freezing times that are used in the cell-sized liposome studies provide a relatively artifact-free method of capturing membrane dynamics at discrete times during an event (11). This represents a unique approach in our development of membrane bioanalytical chemistry for the single cell. Furthermore, possible quantitative schemes, such as have been reported for the molecular SIMS tissue analysis of cationic liposomes (54), should be systematically developed for static SIMS quantitative imaging of single cells.

Quantitative mapping at the single-cell and subcellular levels using SIMS methods is quite feasible for a number of biologically interesting elements or compounds. Dynamic SIMS, by demonstrating localized quantitative capabilities for numerous elements and stable isotopes, has been accepted for investigation of real biological issues at the single-cell level. Static SIMS has made significant biological contributions, such as diagnosis of disease states from whole blood. However, this has not yet been accomplished at the single-cell level. Along with the further development of quantitative analysis schemes, advances in sample preparation methods promise to provide quantitative molecular analysis of frozen-hydrated single cells and their dynamics in numerous biological investigations.

Laser Desorption/Ionization

Mass spectrometric techniques using laser desorption/ionization rely on energy transfer from an incident laser beam to induce desorption and ionization of condensed-phase molecules for analysis (20). The better known hybrid of MALDI overcomes the limitation of high fragmentation by use of an added matrix, presumably to absorb some of the laser energy, thus providing a softer ionization process (34). Although the mechanism of the matrix involvement is not completely understood, ionization is generally accepted to occur in the condensed phase or very close to the surface after desorption. Several criteria have been set for the relative success of a matrix, including a high extinction coefficient for the laser wavelengths used, solubility similar to the analyte, and vacuum stability. The application of several different matrices has allowed MALDI to analyze large, nonvolatile molecules of greater than 500,000 Daltons without extensive fragmentation.

Quantitative determination with MALDI, in general, has several key limitations (33). Sample preparation, matrix crystallization and incorporation, and substrate characteristics have all been reported to affect the reproducibility of the MALDI signal. Several methods have evolved to compensate for limitations and constraints. Internal standard analysis is a relatively simple method for minimizing variances due to sample preparation and data acquisition, but is not directly applicable to the investigation of native compositions at the single-cell level. Calibration standards have also shown promise for the use of MALDI as a quantitative probe of single-cell chemistry within flowing streams. Additionally, relative comparisons of cell-to-cell variations have been utilized for biological investigations of single cells cultured on substrates. Two examples are presented here to demonstrate the quantitative capabilities of MALDI analysis at the single-cell level. These capabilities are likely to lead to further developments and applications of this powerful but relatively new bioanalytical technique.

Matrix-assisted laser vaporization/ionization (a synonym for MALDI of a liquid), coupled to TOF MS, has been used to directly quantitate histamine and serotonin within individual rat peritoneal mast cells in a flowing stream of a cell flow-cytometer (27). Using appropriate flow rates for a suspension with a matrix ($CuCl_2$, 0.1 mM) added, hundreds of mast cells can be analyzed over a 5-min span. Within the vacuum interface, a focused laser-beam pulse probed the flowing stream at 80 Hz, thus analyzing individual cells over either one or two spectral cycles. Molecular adducts or high-mass fragments of histamine and serotonin have been observed in spectra from single mast cells. Wide variations in amounts have been observed as a function of cell-to-cell variance. Average histamine and serotonin levels are 0.75 ± 0.33 fmol and 0.11 ± 0.06 fmol, respectively. This example of coupling laser-induced ionization to flowing streams shows the promise of high-throughput quantitative determination of various compounds from single cells by using mass spectrometric methods.

The semiquantitative analysis of neuropeptides from single neurons of *Aplysia californica* has recently been reported using MALDI-TOF (28). In this study, numerous neurons have been placed on a substrate with the matrix. Employing MALDI imaging techniques, peptides have been localized to single neurons allowing comparison of single-cell profiles using spectral normalization. Differential peptide distributions have been reported for specific neuronal types along with low-frequency variations of specific peptides for an individual *Aplysia*. The semiquantitative analysis of peptides from individual cells isolated on a substrate demonstrates the utility of MALDI in the field of biochemistry. Further understanding of the mechanism of matrix assistance along with technological developments such as smaller-diameter beam sizes, will undoubtedly extend the biological applications of MALDI mass spectrometry to quantitative single-cell analysis.

FLUORESCENCE IMAGING

Fluorescence imaging has long been a powerful analytical technique for investigating biological systems. Furthermore, recent developments have shown the possibility of quantitative imaging, with lateral and depth resolution, of various natively fluorescent compounds in live, single cells during dynamic cellular events (77, 78). A complete discussion of the various approaches for the application of quantitative fluorescence imaging to single cells is beyond the scope of this review. The intent of this section is to briefly outline the progression toward the quantitative monitoring of cellular events at the single-cell level and to give an example of a promising technique that has been increasingly optimized for this task, namely multiphoton excitation imaging (22).

Quantitation of components within single cells via fluorescence microscopy is not as straightforward as solution fluorescence in cuvettes. Fluorescent dyes have been extensively developed for high sensitivity and selectivity within bioanalytical investigations at the single-cell level. However, analyte derivatization schemes have commonly introduced uncertainty in quantitation, such as a lack of complete specificity for the analyte, incomplete derivatization of analyte, introduction of background, photobleaching, and induced cellular changes. Despite these uncertainties, fluorescence investigations at the single-cell level continue to be further developed by technological advancements for relative quantitation of single-cell dynamics.

One example of advancement is the development of lasers suitable for native fluorescence detection of biomolecules (61). Single-photon UV-laser excitation of natively fluorescent serotonin has been used to monitor uptake and secretion dynamics from single astrocytes (72). This has been done to investigate the recently proposed role of glial cells in neuronal communication. These studies have been extended to include native fluorescence detection for the investigation of neurotransmitter release dynamics from single bovine adrenal cells, leech Retzius cells, and mast cells (78). These studies demonstrate the difficulty in even relative quantitation owing to factors such as background fluorescence and analysis-induced damage, such as degranulation.

Gene transcription techniques are another example of how technological developments from another field have been extended into the fluorescence quantitation of single-cell dynamics (82). Through gene transcription, a reporter enzyme can be used to quantitatively monitor the relative gene expression in single cells with a 5-fM in vitro LLOD. The relative amount of reporter enzyme is determined by the magnitude of gene expression. The reporter enzyme that is produced reacts with a cell-permeable fluorescence resonance energy transfer compound to induce quantitative fluorescence changes. This promises genetic applications as diverse as following genetically tagged transfected cells, separation of specifically expressing phenotypes, identification of receptor ligands, and high-throughput screening of drug candidates (81).

Developments in analytical methodology have shown the most dramatic impact on the potential of fluorescence for the quantitative monitoring of single-cell dynamics. One obstacle to obtaining accurate single-cell quantitation using fluorescence is the uncertainty in the probed volume. However, two analytical techniques, confocal (61) and multiphoton excitation imaging, have been emerging in the field of bioanalytical imaging due to intrinsic three-dimensional (3-D) imaging capabilities. Confocal microscopy has been extensively used for numerous single-cell applications. Apparent limitations of UV-induced cell damage along with high aberrations and low transmissions of deep UV optics have been overcome with the development of two-photon and three-photon excitation schemes. Nevertheless,

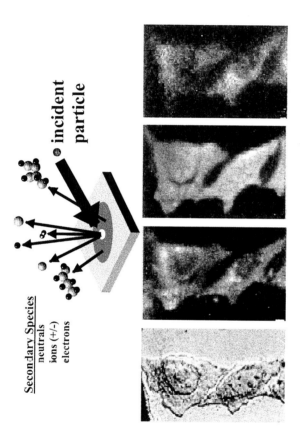

Figure 7 (*Top*) Simplified representation of the sputtering process involved in SIMS analysis. (*Bottom*) Dynamic SIMS images of boronated-drug treated human cervix epitheloid carcinoma cells. From left to right: optical image, ^{40}Ca image, ^{39}K image, and ^{11}B image. Cell nuclei are nominally 10 μm in diameter. These images show the effectiveness of drug localization around the cell nucleus at levels higher than proposed to be needed for cancer treatment. (Reproduced with permission from Reference 47.)

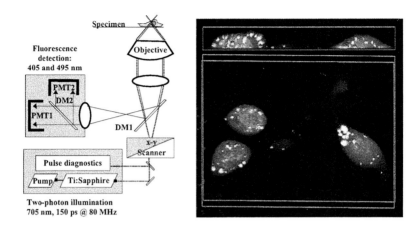

Figure 8 (*Left*) Multiphoton microscope with multiple possible detection schemes. The fluorescence signal is guided by dichroic mirrors (DM) to the photon multiplier tube (*PMT*) for the given detection scheme. (Adapted with permission from Reference 9.) (*Right*) Multiphoton excitation imaging of serotonin-loaded rat basophilic leukemia cells. Front view (*inset top*) and top view (*inset bottom*) reconstructed with 20 optical slices. Bright regions correspond to high serotonin levels. Images are approximately 80-µm wide. (Reproduced with permission from Reference 49.)

confocal microscopy continues to be an important tool in single-cell analysis by addressing limitations with the development of such schemes as 4Pi-confocal microscopy (63).

Multiphoton Excitation Imaging

Multiphoton excitation fluorescence microscopy is a relatively nondestructive optical technique capable of analysis at the single-cell level, providing depth information of 500 μm into a biological matrix with a resolution of less than a micrometer (76). Multiphoton excitation processes have been realized through the invention of high-power infrared lasers. Invented in 1989 by Winfried Denk and Watt Webb, multiphoton excitation fluorescence microscopy (Figure 8, see color insert) has shown numerous advantages over other similar conventional imaging techniques such as confocal microscopy. Multiphoton excitation microscopy studies have included investigations of in vivo skin fluorescence (50), the development of embryos extremely sensitive to light analysis (71), calcium waves in fish keratocytes (9), and the localization of neurotransmitters within single cells (49).

Multiphoton excitation occurs via a two- or three-photon absorption occurring as a single quantum event. This enables the use of longer wavelengths of light than those of harmful ultraviolet excitation and allows deeper penetration into tissue before scattering becomes dominant. Emission wavelengths of much shorter wavelengths than excitation reduce the need for emission filtering and thus increase fluorescence intensity. Multiphoton excitation requires the use of high-intensity mode-locked infrared lasers capable of delivering a high-energy packet of photons on an extremely small temporal level. Excitation via two photons shows a quadratic dependence of the light intensity versus the probability of absorption, resulting in a localized 3-D focal point of analysis. This nonlinear absorption process allows the use of a large area detector to collect scattered fluorescence from the sample, affording higher sensitivities than confocal microscopy. The confined region of multiphoton excitation also minimizes tissue damage due to decreased photobleaching of various compounds. Multiphoton excitation provides a unique chance to image at various levels within tissue by knowing that those levels have not been damaged. Image processing techniques of several two-dimensional scans allows the creation of 3-D fluorescence maps, thereby allowing for a volume perspective of the chemical distributions and dynamics during cellular events.

Natively UV-fluorescent tryptophan and serotonin distributions have been investigated by infrared multiphoton excitation microscopy in live single cells (Figure 8). Initial studies have included the quantitative analysis of static vesicles of serotonin-loaded cells (49). An average concentration of approximately 50 mM of serotonin for individual vesicles has been calculated through calibration standards. Furthermore, the 3-D imaging capabilities have been used to calculate the average volume of individual vesicles and to quantitate the average serotonin/vesicle at 5×10^8 molecules. The time dependence of cell loading shows a localization of vesicles at the base of the cells with increased incubation times. Unloaded cell investigations using HPLC techniques report an average of 1.5 fmol/cell. By using multiphoton excitation imaging on numerous single cells, average endogenous levels determined by HPLC have been determined to be from only 1% of the unloaded cell population. These cells contain vesicles of similar dimensions and serotonin amounts to those found in loaded cells. The use of multiphoton excitation imaging in this study compared to HPLC demonstrates the need for single-cell analysis because of the heterogeneity of cell populations.

These studies have been further developed to include the monitoring of chemical dynamics during cellular events (77). To avoid disturbing cellular function, low-illumination schemes have been employed. Although not as sensitive and having decreased lateral resolution, this technique is capable of monitoring changes in the concentration of natively fluorescent serotonin at a secretion plane located directly above the cell. Subsequent high-resolution images have validated the structural interpretation of the release kinetic data. Multiphoton excitation imaging has been used to determine that 73% of vesicles experience slow leakage after the initial release of the majority of their contents. These studies show the ability to provide a unique perspective that is not obtainable by traditional methods.

SUMMARY AND FUTURE DIRECTIONS

A fundamental perspective can be achieved by targeting single cells with the goal of deconvoluting complex biological functions. However, single-cell studies have their own difficulties, such as minute volumes and sample amounts. Quantitative chemical analysis of single cells has emerged in recent years due to numerous technological advancements. The development of microelectrodes has allowed the cellular and subcellular measurement of redox-active species during dynamic cellular events. This miniaturization trend has also been observed in the separation sciences with the application of small column separations to single cells. Numerous injection schemes and detection schemes have allowed a diverse set of components to be measured from single cells. Desorption ionization methods with mass spectrometric detection have shown single-cell capability owing to a number of technological developments. These have mainly been in the areas of FTICR, TOF-SIMS imaging, and methods involving MALDI-MS. Finally, fluorescence imaging can now be used to probe single-cell dynamics by native fluorescence processes utilizing either single- or multiple-photon excitation. Multiphoton excitation has come to the forefront of three-dimensional detection of chemical dynamics.

Future directions likely will be dictated by the increased development of technology applicable to single-cell analysis. A better understanding at the single-cell level will further our knowledge in all related biological sciences. Investigations of transient cellular events have the potential to unravel these processes at the chemical level but pose the greatest challenges. Single-cell investigations should be extended to include the responses of surrounding single cells in a biological environment to gain a further understanding of the substantial impact that a single cell can have on biological processes.

For further reading on general aspects of capillary electrophoresis, *The Handbook of Capillary Electrophoresis*, ed. JP Landers, 1997, Baca Raton, FL: CRC. 2nd ed. For reading on general aspects of multiphoton excitation imagins: "Multiphoton excitation of molecular fluorophores and nonlinear laser microscopy," in *Top. Fluoresc. Spectrosc.* 5:471–540.

ACKNOWLEDGMENTS

This work was funded in part by grants from the National Institutes of Health. In addition, we gratefully acknowledge our coworkers, past and present, for the studies cited in this review.

Visit the Annual Reviews home page at www.AnnualReviews.org

LITERATURE CITED

1. Ausserer WA, Chandra S, Morrison GH. 1998. Morphological and elemental integrity of freeze-fractured, freeze-dried cultured cells during ion microscopic analysis. *J. Microsc.* 154:39–57

2. Ausserer WA, Ling YC, Chandra S, Morrison GH. 1989. Quantitative imaging of boron, calcium, magnesium, potassium, and sodium distributions in cultured cells with ion microscopy. *Anal. Chem.* 61:2690–95

3. Benninghoven A. 1977. Secondary ion mass spectrometry—new analytical technique for biologically important molecules. *Org. Mass Spectrom.* 12:595–97

4. Bergquist J, Tarkowski A, Ekman R, Ewing AG. 1994. Discovery of endogenous catecholamines in lymphocytes and evidence for catecholamine regulation of lymphocyte function via an autocrine loop. *Proc. Natl. Acad. Sci. USA* 91:12912–16

5. Betzig E, Trautman JK, Harris TD, Weiner JS, Kostelak RL. 1991. Breaking the diffraction barrier: optical microscopy on a nanometric scale. *Science* 251:1468–70

6. Brenna JT, Morrison GH. 1986. Ionization probability variations due to matrix in ion microscopic analysis of plastic-embedded and ashed biological specimens. *Anal. Chem.* 58:1675–80

7. Briggs D, Brown A, Vickerman JC. 1989. *Handbook of Static Secondary Ion Mass Spectrometry*, p. 164. Chichester, UK: Wiley

8. Bruns D, Jahn R. 1995. Real-time measurement of transmitter release from single synaptic vesicles. *Nature* 377:62–65

9. Brust-Mascher I, Webb WW. 1998. Calcium waves induced by large voltage pulses in fish keratocytes. *Biophys. J.* 75:1669–78

10. Cannon DM Jr, Pacholski ML, Ewing AG, Winograd N. 1998. Molecular imaging of frozen-hydrated model membrane systems. In *The 11th Int. Conf. Secondary Ion Mass Spectrometry (SIMS XI)*, ed. G Gillen, R Lareau, J Bennett, F Stevie, pp. 489–92. Orlando, FL: Wiley & Sons

11. Cannon DM Jr, Pacholski ML, Winograd N, Ewing AG. 2000. Molecule specific imaging of frozen-hydrated, freeze-fractured model membrane systems using mass spectrometry. *J. Am. Chem. Soc.* 122:603–10

12. Chandra S, Morrison GH. 1996. A novel approach for imaging the influx of Ca^{2+}, Na^+, and K^+ in the same cell at subcellular resolution. Ion microscopy imaging of stable tracer isotopes. *Ann. NY Acad. Sci.* 15:295–98

13. Chandra S, Morrison GH. 1992. Sample preparation of animal tissues and cell cultures for secondary ion mass spectrometry (SIMS) microscopy. *Biol. Cell* 74:31–42

14. Chen GY, Ewing AG. 1995. Multiple classes of catecholamine vesicles observed during exocytosis from the *Planorbis* cell body. *Brain Res.* 701:167–74

15. Chen GY, Gavin PF, Luo GA, Ewing AG. 1995. Observation and quantitation of exocytosis from the cell body of a fully developed neuron in *Planorbis corneus. J. Neurosci.* 15:7747–55

16. Chen TK, Luo GO, Ewing AG. 1994. Amperometric monitoring of stimulated catecholamine release from rat pheochromocytoma (PC12) cells at the zeptomole level. *Anal. Chem.* 66:3031–35

17. Chien JB, Wallingford RA, Ewing AG. 1990. Estimation of free dopamine in the cytoplasm of the giant dopamine cell of *Planorbis corneus* by voltammetry and capillary electrophoresis. *J. Neurochem.* 54:633–38

18. Colliver TL, Brummel CL, Pacholski ML, Swanek FD, Ewing AG, Winograd N. 1997. Atomic and molecular imaging at the single-cell level with TOF-SIMS. *Anal. Chem.* 69:2225–31

19. Cooper BR, Jankowski JA, Leszczyszyn DJ, Wightman RM, Jorgenson JW. 1992. Quantitative determination of catecholamines in individual bovine adrenomedullary cells by reversed-phase microcolumn liquid chromatography with electrochemical detection. *Anal. Chem.* 64:691–94

20. Cotter RJ. 1987. Laser mass spectrometry: an overview of techniques, instruments and applications. *Anal. Chem. Acta* 195:45–59

21. Deng RC, Williams P. 1989. Factors affecting precision and accuracy in quantitative analysis by secondary ion mass spectrometry. *Anal. Chem.* 61:1946–48

22. Denk W, Strickler JH, Webb WW. 1990. Two-photon laser scanning fluorescence microscopy. *Science* 248:73–76

23. Ewing AG. 1993. Microcolumn separations of single cell components. *J. Neurosci. Methods* 48:215–24

24. Ewing AG, Strein TG, Lau YY. 1992. Analytical chemistry in microenvironments: single nerve cells. *Acc. Chem. Res.* 125:440–47

25. Ewing AG, Wallingford RA, Olefirowicz TM. 1989. Capillary electrophoresis. *Anal. Chem.* 61:A292–303

26. Finnegan JM, Pihel K, Cahill PS, Huang L, Zerby SE, et al. 1996. Vesicular quantal size measured by amperometry at chromaffin, mast, pheochromocytoma and pancreatic beta-cells. *J. Neurochem.* 66:1914–23

27. Fung EN, Yeung ES. 1998. Direct analysis of single rat peritoneal mast cells with laser vaporization/ionization mass spectrometry. *Anal. Chem.* 70:3206–12

28. Garden RW, Shippy SA, Li L, Moroz TP, Sweedler JV. 1998. Proteolytic processing of the *Aplysia* egg-laying hormone prohormone. *Proc. Natl. Acad. Sci. USA* 95:3972–77

29. Giacobini E. 1987. Neurochemical analysis of single neurons—a mini-review dedicated to Oliver H. Lowry. *J. Neurosci. Res.* 18:632–37

30. Hernandez L, Escalona J, Joshi N, Guzman NA. 1991. Laser-induced fluorescence and fluorescence microscopy for capillary electrophoresis zone detection. *J. Chromatogr.* 559:183–96

31. Hofstadler SA, Severs JC, Smith RD, Swanek FD, Ewing AG. 1996. High performance Fourier transform ion cyclotron resonance mass spectrometric detection for capillary electrophoresis. *J. High Resolut. Chromatogr.* 19:617–21

32. Hogan BL, Yeung ES. 1993. Single-cell analysis at the level of a single human eurythrocyte. *Trends Anal. Chem.* 12:4–9

33. Jesperson S, Niessen WMA, Tjaden UR, van der Greef JJ. 1995. Quantitative bioanalysis by matrix assisted laser desorption ionization mass spectrometry. *Mass Spectrom.* 30:357–64

34. Karas M, Bahr U, Giessmann U. 1991. Matrix assisted laser desorption ionization mass spectrometry. *Mass Spectrom. Rev.* 10:335–57

35. Kelly RS, Wightman RM. 1986. Bevelled carbon-fiber ultramicroelectrodes. *Anal. Chem. Acta* 187:79–87

36. Kennedy RT, Jorgenson JW. 1989. Quantitative analysis of individual neurons by open tubular liquid chromatography with voltammetric detection. *Anal. Chem.* 61:436–41

37. Kennedy RT, Oates MD, Cooper BR, Nickerson B, Jorgenson JW. 1989. Microcolumn separations and the analysis of single cells. *Science* 246:57–63

38. Kim YT, Scarnulis DM, Ewing AG. 1986. Carbon ring electrodes with 1 micrometer tip diameter. *Anal. Chem.* 58:1782–86

39. Kristensen HK, Lau YY, Ewing AG. 1994. Capillary electrophoresis of single cells: observation of two compartments of neurotransmitter vesicles. *J. Neurosci. Methods* 51:183–88

40. Lau YY, Abe T, Ewing AG. 1992. Voltammetric measurement of oxygen in single neurons using platinized carbon ring electrodes. *Anal. Chem.* 64:1702–5

41. Lechene C. 1980. Electron probe microanalysis of biological soft tissues: principle and technique. *Fed. Proc.* 39:2871–80

42. Lechene CP. 1999. *Quantitative imaging of stable-isotope tracers.* Presented at Biomed. Imaging Symp., Natl. Inst. Health, Bethesda, MD

43. Lee JJ, Linton RW, Hunter JL, Shelbourne JD, Burchette JL, et al. 1989. Correlative ion and electron microscopy for immunocytochemistry. In *Microbeam Analysis,* ed. PE Russel, pp. 45–49. San Francisco: San Francisco Press

44. Leszczyszyn DJ, Jankowski JA, Viveros OH, Dilberto EJ, Near JA, Wightman RM. 1991. Secretion of catecholamines from individual adrenal medullary chromaffin cells. *J. Neurochem.* 56:1855–63

45. Levi-Setti R, Chabala JM, Gavrilov K, Espinosa R, Le Beau MM. 1997. Imaging of BrdU-labeled human metaphase chromosomes with a high resolution scanning ion microprobe. *Microsc. Res. Tech.* 36:301–12

46. Lillard SJ, McCloskey MA, Yeung ES. 1996. Monitoring exocytosis and release from individual mast cells by capillary electrophoresis with laser-induced native fluorescence detection. *Anal. Chem.* 68:2897–904

47. Lorey DR II, Chandra S, Smith DR, Morrison GH. 1994. Quantitative localization of boron in single cells at subcellular resolution with ion microscopy for boron neutron capture therapy of brain cancer. In *The 10th Int. Conf. Secondary Ion Mass Spectrometry (SIMS X),* ed. A Benninghoven, B Hagenhoff, HW Werner, pp. 823–26. Chichester, UK: Wiley

48. MacTaylor CE, Ewing AG. 1997. Critical review of recent developments in fluorescence detection for capillary electrophoresis. *Electrophoresis* 18:2279–90

49. Maiti SJ, Shear JB, Williams RM, Zipfel WR, Webb WW. 1997. Measuring serotonin distribution in live cells with three-photon excitation. *Science* 275:530–32

50. Masters BR, So PTC, Gratton E. 1997. Multiphoton excitation fluorescence microscopy and spectroscopy of in vivo human skin. *Biophys. J.* 72:2405–12

51. Matioli GT, Niewisch HB. 1965. Electrophoresis of hemoglobin in single eurythrocytes. *Science* 150:1824–26

52. Mesaros JM, Ewing AG, Gavin PF. 1994. Electrochemical detection in microcolumn separations. *Anal. Chem.* 66:A527–36

53. Muddiman DC, Gusev AI, Hercules DM. 1995. Application of secondary ion and matrix-assisted laser desorption-ionization time-of-flight mass spectrometry for the quantitative analysis of biological molecules. *Mass Spectrom. Rev.* 14:383–429

54. Muddiman DC, Nicola AJ, Proctor A,

Hercules DM. 1996. Important aspects concerning the quantification of biomolecules by time-of-flight secondary ion mass spectrometry. *Appl. Spectrosc.* 50:161–66

55. Nicholson C, Rice ME. 1988. Use of ion-selective microelectrodes and voltammetric microsensors to study brain cell microenvironment. In *Neuromethods: Neuronal Microenvironment,* ed. AA Boulton, GB Baker, W Walz, pp. 247–361. Totowa, NJ: Humana

56. Oates MD, Cooper BR, Jorgenson JW. 1990. Quantitative amino acid analysis of individual snail neurons by open tubular liquid chromatography. *Anal. Chem.* 62:1573–77

57. Olefirowicz TM, Ewing AG. 1990. Capillary electrophoresis in 2 and 5 μm i.d. capillaries: application to cytoplasmic analysis. *Anal. Chem.* 62:1872–76

58. Olefirowicz TM, Ewing AG. 1990. Dopamine concentration in the cytoplasmic compartment of single neurons determined by capillary electrophoresis. *J. Neurosci. Methods* 34:11–15

59. Pacholski ML, Cannon DM Jr, Ewing AG, Winograd N. 1999. Imaging of exposed headgroups and tailgroups of phospholipid membranes by mass spectrometry. *J. Am. Chem. Soc.* 121:4716–17

60. Patkin AJ, Morrison GH. 1982. Secondary ion mass spectrometric image depth profiling for three-dimensional elemental analysis. *Anal. Chem.* 54:2–5

61. Pawley JB, ed. 1995. *Handbook of Biological Confocal Microscopy.* New York: Plenum. 632 pp. 2nd ed.

62. Pendley BD, Abruna HD. 1990. Construction of submicrometer voltammetric electrodes. *Anal. Chem.* 62:782–84

63. Schrader M, Bahlmann K, Giese G, Hell SW. 1998. 4Pi-confocal imaging in fixed biological specimens. *Biophys. J.* 75:1659–68

64. Severs NJ, Shotton DM, eds. 1995. *Rapid Freezing, Freeze Fracture and Deep Etching.* New York: Wiley-Liss. 372 pp.

65. Slodzian G, Daigne B, Girard F, Boust F, Hillion F. 1992. Scanning secondary ion analytical microscopy with parallel detection. *Biol. Cell* 74:43–50

66. Smith DR, Chandra S, Coderre JA, Morrison GH. 1996. Ion microscopy imaging of ^{10}B from p-boronophenylalanine in a brain tumor model. *Cancer Res.* 56:4302–6

67. Smith RD, Wahl JH, Goodlett DR, Hofstadler SA. 1993. Capillary electrophoresis/mass spectrometry. *Anal. Chem.* 65:A574–84

68. Stingeder G. 1994. Optimization of secondary ion mass spectrometry for quantitative trace analysis. *Anal. Chem. Acta* 297:231–51

69. Strein TG, Ewing AG. 1992. Characterization of submicron-sized carbon electrodes insulated with a phenol-allylphenol copolymer. *Anal. Chem.* 64:1368–73

70. Sulzer D, Chen TK, Lau YY, Kristensen H, Rayprot S, Ewing AG. 1995. Amphetamine redistributes dopamine from synaptic vesicles to the cytosol and promotes reverse transport. *J. Neurosci.* 15:4102–8

71. Summers RG, Piston DW, Harris KM, Morrill JB. 1996. The orientation of first cleavage in the sea urchin embryo, *Lytechinus variegatus,* does not specify the axes of bilateral symmetry. *Dev. Biol.* 175:177–83

72. Tan W, Haydon PG, Yeung ES. 1997. Imaging neurotransmitter uptake and depletion in astrocytes. *Appl. Spectrosc.* 51:1139–43

73. Tracht S, Toma V, Sweedler JV. 1994. Post-column radionucleotide detection of low-energy β emitters in capillary electrophoresis. *Anal. Chem.* 66:2382–89

74. Valaskovic GA, Morrison GH. 1992. Quantitative imaging ion microscopy: a short review. *Scanning Microsc.* 6:305–18

75. Wightman RM. 1981. Microvoltammetric electrodes. *Anal. Chem.* 53:A1125–34

76. Williams RM, Piston DW, Webb WW. 1994. Two-photon molecular excitation provides intrinsic 3-dimensional resolution

for laser-based microscopy and micropho-
tochemistry. *FASEB J.* 8:804–13

77. Williams RM, Shear JB, Zipfel WR, Maiti S, Webb WW. 1999. Mucosal mast cell secretion processes imaged using three-photon microscopy of 5-hydroxytryptamine autofluorescence. *Biophys. J.* 76:1835–46

78. Yeung ES. 1999. Following single cell dynamics with native fluorescence microscopy. *Anal. Chem.* 71:A522–29

79. Zhou R, Luo G, Ewing AG. 1994. Direct observation of the effect of autoreceptors on stimulated release of catecholamine from adrenal cells. *J. Neurosci.* 14:2402–7

80. Zhou Z, Misler S. 1995. Amperometric detection of stimulus-induced quantal release of catecholamines from cultured superior cervical ganglion neurons. *Proc. Natl. Acad. Sci. USA* 92:6938–42

81. Zlokarnik G. 1999. Fluorescent molecular sensor for drug discovery. *Anal. Chem.* 71:A322–28

82. Zlokarnik G, Negulescu PA, Knapp TE, Mere L, Burres N, et al. 1998. Quantitation of transcription and clonal selection of single living cells with β-lactamase as reporter. *Science* 279:84–88

Annu. Rev. Biophys. Biomol. Struct. 2000. 29:265–89

THE STRUCTURAL BIOLOGY OF MOLECULAR RECOGNITION BY VANCOMYCIN

Patrick J. Loll* and Paul H. Axelsen*†

Departments of Pharmacology and Medicine†, Infectious Disease Section, The Johnson Foundation for Molecular Biophysics, University of Pennsylvania School of Medicine, Philadelphia, Pennsylvania 19104-6084;
e-mail: loll@pharm.med.upenn.edu, axe@pharm.med.upenn.edu*

Key Words   glycopeptide antibiotics, molecular dynamics simulation, entropy-enthalpy compensation, cooperativity, allosterism

■ **Abstract**   Vancomycin is the archetype among naturally occurring compounds known as glycopeptide antibiotics. Because it is a vital therapeutic agent used worldwide for the treatment of infections with gram-positive bacteria, emerging bacterial resistance to vancomycin is a major public health threat. Recent investigations into the mechanisms of action of glycopeptide antibiotics are driven by a need to understand their detailed mechanism of action so that new agents can be developed to overcome resistance. These investigations have revealed that glycopeptide antibiotics exhibit a rich array of complex cooperative phenomena when they bind target ligands, making them valuable model systems for the study of molecular recognition.

CONTENTS

1. INTRODUCTION

This review focuses on biophysical aspects of molecular recognition by vancomycin and related glycopeptide antibiotics. Comprehensive presentations of structure-activity relationships in this class of antibiotics are available elsewhere (1, 2).

1.1 Classification

There have been over a hundred different glycopeptide antibiotics identified in the fermentation broth of various bacteria. Virtually all have a *heptapeptide* core of *seven amino acid* residues with the side chains of residues 2 and 4, 4 and 6, and 5 and 7 covalently joined, and sugar substituents at various positions. In a classification scheme based on the type of residues at positions 1 and 3, vancomycin and eremomycin are assigned to group I with other compounds bearing aliphatic residues at these positions (Figure 1). Group II compounds such as avoparcin have individual aromatic residues at positions 1 and 3, whereas group III compounds such as ristocetin and teicoplanin have aromatic residues at positions 1 and 3 that are covalently joined (Figure 2). There are some compounds that do not fit in this scheme, and teicoplanin-like compounds with a lipophilic chain attached to a sugar residue are often considered a separate group.

Vancomycin is a genuine archetype among the glycopeptide antibiotics, being the first to be discovered, in 1956, and the only one to see widespread acceptance as a human therapeutic agent. Ristocetin is used as a diagnostic reagent for von Willibrand's disease. The teicoplanins have some pharmacokinetic advantages over vancomycin, but they have seen only limited clinical use, primarily in Europe. Avoparcin is used as an animal feed additive in Europe.

1.2 Mechanism of Action

Vancomycin binds to polypeptide intermediates terminating in -D-Ala-D-Ala and inhibits the biosynthesis of peptidoglycan. One of these intermediates is undecaprenyl-(muramyl-glucosaminyl)-pentapeptide or lipid II. By binding to the C terminus of this intermediate, vancomycin blocks the action of transglycosylases that transfer the (muramyl-glucosaminyl)-pentapeptide to a polyglycan chain. The other targeted intermediate is the same pentapeptide segment after it has been attached to polyglycan. Vancomycin binding to the C terminus of the pentapeptide at this stage blocks the action of transpeptidases that join the side chain of the third residue in the pentapeptide (either L-Lys or L-Dap $=$ *meso*-diaminopimelate) to the fourth residue (D-Ala) in an adjacent pentapeptide. When not inhibited, this reaction creates a cross-linked meshwork of polyglycan and polypeptide chains, and the C-terminal fifth residue of the pentapeptide (D-Ala) is lost.

Vancomycin thus inhibits two of the same reactions inhibited by β-lactam antibiotics (transglycosylation and transpeptidation). One might surmise that if vancomycin and the enzymes inhibited by penicillin both target polypeptide segments

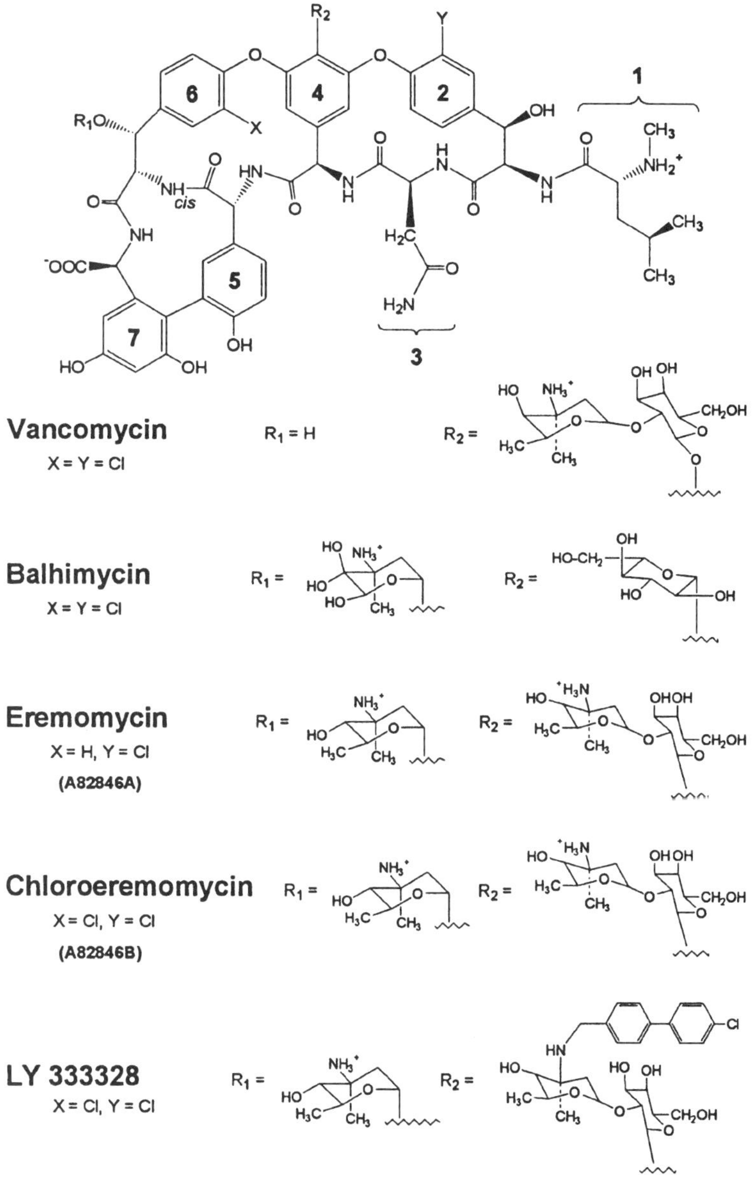

Figure 1   Group I antibiotics.

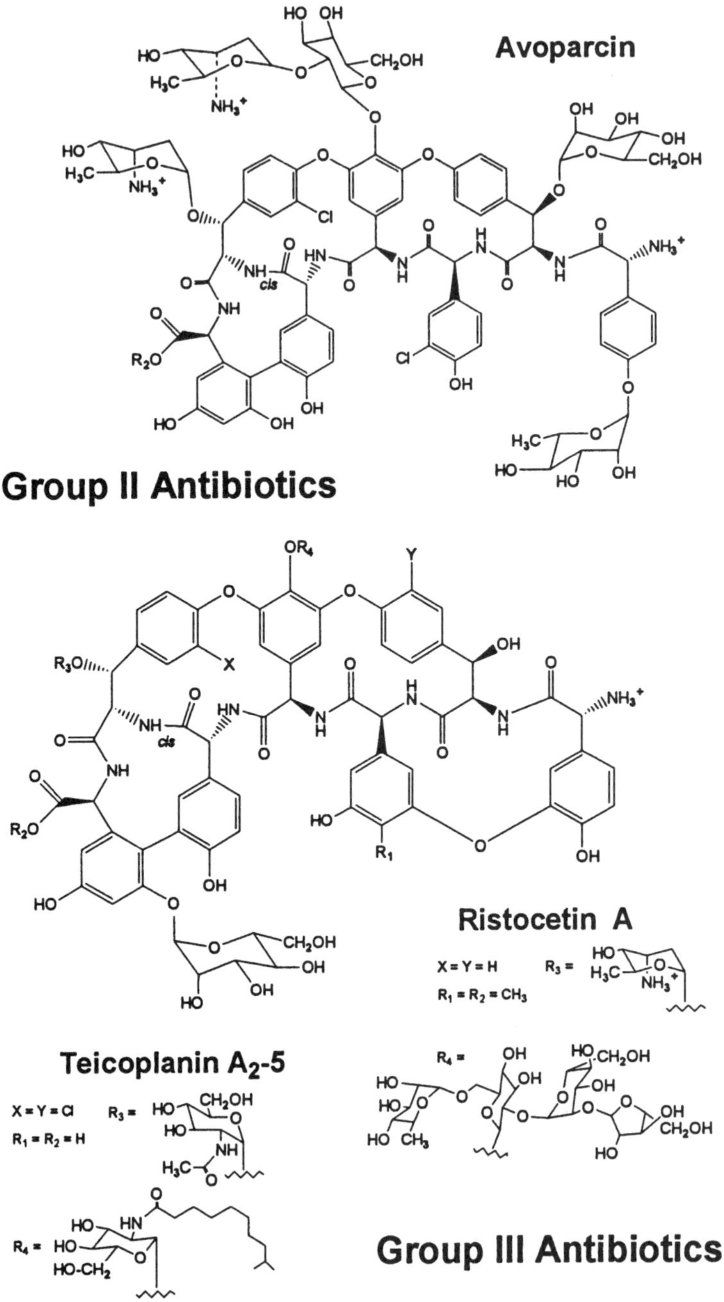

Figure 2 Group II and III antibiotics.

terminating in D-Ala-D-Ala, then there is likely to be some chemical similarity between D-Ala-D-Ala and penicillin (3). Indeed this is the case, and penicillin even binds to vancomycin with modest affinity (4).

1.3 Resistance

Glycopeptide antibiotics are ineffective against gram-negative bacteria because their outer lipid membrane prevents access of the drug to the cell wall (5). *Staphylococci* and *Streptococci* are generally susceptible, but isolated cases of intermediate resistance have been recently reported (6–8).

Resistance to vancomycin among *Enterococci* has become a major international health problem. The most common forms involve peptidoglycan synthesis via intermediates that terminate in -D-Ala-D-lactate (9). Vancomycin is ineffective on these species because it has a low affinity for this terminus. Nevertheless, biosynthetic enzymes can proceed, losing the terminal D-lactate in the course of cross-linking reactions (just as the terminal D-Ala is normally lost) to yield peptidoglycan that is cross-linked in the same way as in vancomycin-susceptible bacteria. A less common form of resistance involves intermediates terminating in -D-Ala-D-Ser (10).

2. CHEMICAL STRUCTURE

Information about the chemical structure of vancomycin was fragmentary until a structure for the degradation product of vancomycin, crystalline degradation product-1 or CDP-1, was determined in 1978 (Figure 3) (11). Although CDP-1 does not bind target ligands and has no antimicrobial activity, it was assumed that the structure of vancomycin would be identical to that of CDP-1 except for the presence of a primary amide instead of an isoaspartic acid residue at residue 3.

NMR studies of vancomycin, however, determined that the chlorine of residue 2 was found only on the back (convex) side of the molecule, whereas in CDP-1 both aryl chloride rings are oriented with the chlorine atoms toward the concave aspect of the molecule (the "front" side that binds ligand) (12). Other investigators showed that vancomycin had an asparagine residue at position 3, not isoasparagine as in CDP-1 (13, 14). The macrocycle of CDP-1 is, therefore, larger by one atom. This permits rotation of the aryl chloride ring of residue 2, and both the "chlorine-front" and "chlorine-back" isomers are present in solution. However, only the isomer with the chlorine in the "front" of the molecule is seen in the crystal structure of CDP-1. NMR studies determined a correct structure for ristocetin (15) prior to these revisions of the vancomycin structure, and for teicoplanin somewhat later (Figure 2) (16).

Vancomycin base has the formula $C_{66}H_{75}Cl_2N_9O_{24}$, a formula weight of 1449, and a formal charge of $+1$ at neutral pH. For pharmaceutical purposes, it is supplied as the HCl salt and is freely soluble in water. The polypeptide portion consists of an

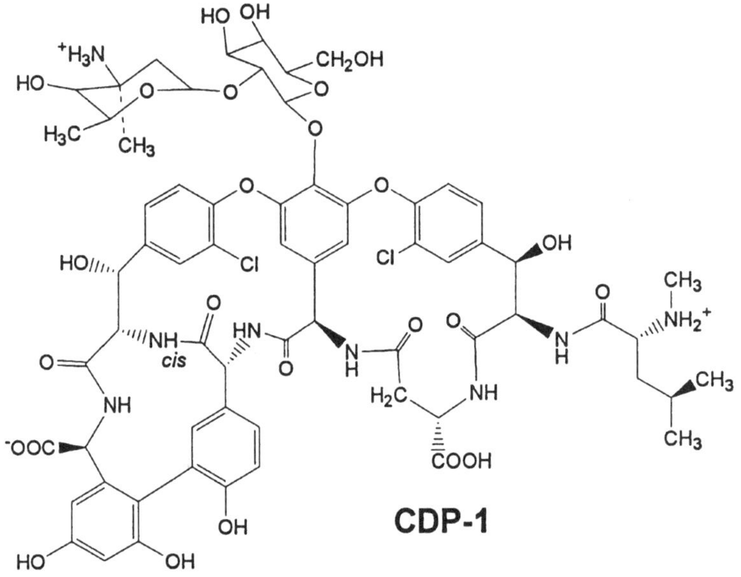

Figure 3   CDP-I.

N-methyl leucine at position 1; substituted phenylglycines at positions 2, 4, 5, 6, and 7; and an asparagine at position 3 with stereochemical configurations of R, R, S, R, R, S, and S. An L-vancosaminyl-α(1 → 2)-D-glucopyranosyl disaccharide is linked via a β-glysosidic bond to the side chain of residue 4.

The peptide bond between residues 5 and 6 is in the *cis* configuration. Although it is less stable by 8 kJ/mole (17), all known glycopeptide antibiotics have this configuration except in unusual circumstances (18).

The aromatic rings of residues 2 and 6 are prohibited from rotating by other atoms in their cycles (chiefly the side chain of residue 4). Thus, when bearing substitutions, these rings give rise to stable and distinct rotational isomers, i.e. atropisomers. In vancomycin and other glycopeptide antibiotics that have one chlorine atom on one or both rings, the chlorine on ring 2 is on the edge facing away from the ligand binding site, whereas on ring 6 it is on the edge facing toward the ligand binding site.

3.   LIGAND RECOGNITION

3.1   Chemical Studies

Nearly all known ligands have a free carboxyl terminus. Among polypeptide ligands, the tripeptide Ac₂-L-Lys-D-Ala-D-Ala exhibits the highest known affinity at 35 kJ/mole, even slightly exceeding the affinity of a natural target, undecaprenyl-N-acetylmuramyl-L-Ala-D-Glu-L-Dap-D-Ala-D-Ala at 33 kJ/mole. The two

C-terminal positions exhibit a modest tolerance for amino acids other than D-ala, although residues with shorter side chains than that of L-Lys, as well as L-Ala, L-Tyr, Gly, and even myristate, are well tolerated in place of L-Lys (19).

3.2 Early NMR Studies

The group of DH Williams at Cambridge has conducted the majority of studies in this area over the past 20 years. The interesting chronology of these investigations is described in a series of reviews (20–23).

In one of the first applications of the nuclear Overhauser effect (nOe) to determine intermolecular distances, NMR studies provided 9 nOe-derived distances between ristocetin and Ac-D-Ala-D-Ala that established the bound position of the dipeptide as lying antiparallel to the antibiotic backbone in the concave aspect of the molecular surface (Figure 4) (24).

Many subsequent NMR studies of Ac_2-L-Lys-D-Ala-D-Ala confirmed this model of the binding mode and pointed to a direct interaction between the charged N-methyl-leucine residue and the ligand carboxylate that was not initially suggested by the CDP-I crystal structure (25). This residue appears to fold in, helping to form a carboxylate binding pocket in vancomycin (26) and ristocetin (27), providing the pocket with hydrophobic shielding. Shielding is energetically advantageous because it lowers the dielectric in the vicinity of key electrostatic interactions and potentiates the energy of these interactions (28). Shielding also isolates these interactions from direct competition with hydrogen bonds to water. An analogous and energetically significant role has been proposed for hydrophobic side chains on residue 3 based on computational simulations (29).

The carboxylate binding pocket appears to be somewhat unstable in the absence of ligand. Residue 1 undergoes rapid rotation under some conditions, and the amide bond between residues 2 and 3 in vancomycin can rotate 180°. These motions grossly distort the carboxylate binding pocket (Figure 5) (30). A role for this rotation of this peptide bond in desolvating the active site is proposed in Section 3.5.1. The dynamic nature of the carboxylate binding pocket was also illustrated by an NMR study of a pentapeptide ligand binding to chloroeremomycin in which 683 distance constraints were established (31). Among the structures best satisfying these constraints were a significant number in which the carboxylate either formed an alternative array of hydrogen bonds, interacted with the asparagine side chain, or situated outside the binding site interacting with the sugar residues.

The Lys side chain appeared to lie close to an anomeric sugar proton on residue 6 in ristocetin and to the β-proton of residue 6 in vancomycin (32). In contrast, studies of avoparcin (33), the ristocetin pseudo-aglycone (34), and chloroeremomycin (35) characterized the side chain as flexible, but with a tendency to locate near the ring of residue 7. No preferred orientation was apparent in an A-40,926 derivative (36), but studies of a pentapeptide ligand binding to chloroeremomycin (31) and aridicin (37) localized the Lys side chain quite close to the ring of residue 7.

Depsipeptide ligands apparently bind to chloroeremomycin in the same manner as an ordinary peptide (38). Likewise, peptides mimicking vanC-resistant bacterial

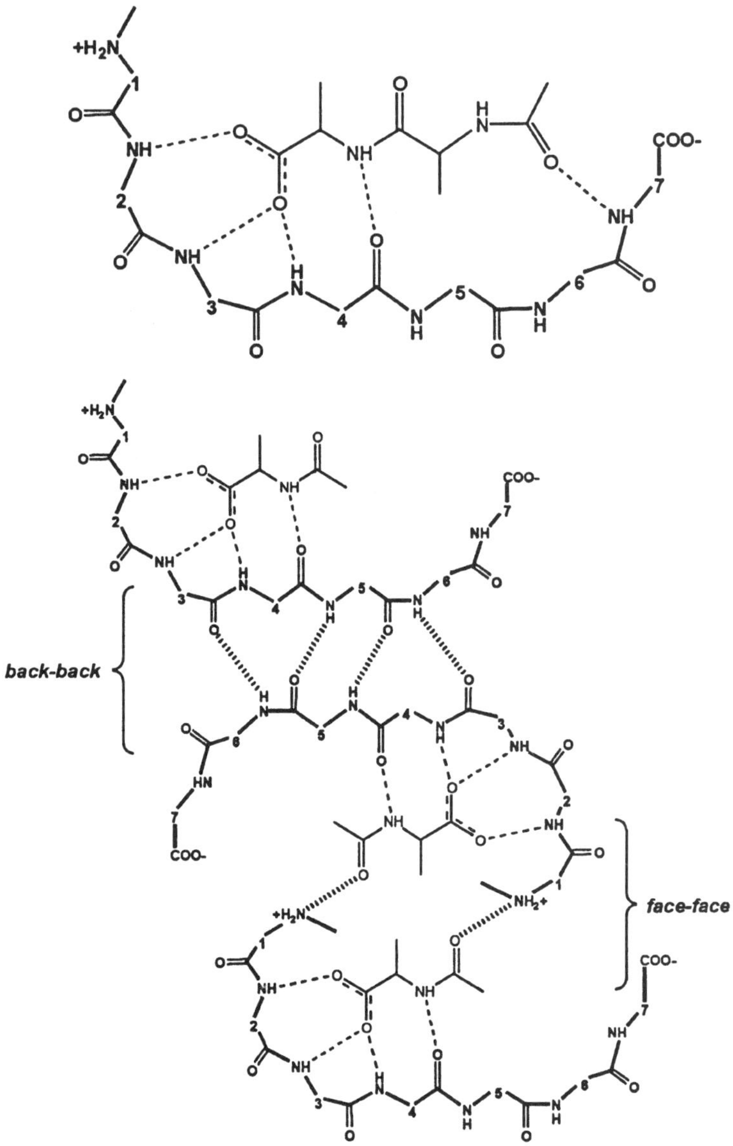

Figure 4 Schematic intermolecular relationships. (*Top*) The antiparallel orientation of Ac-D-Ala-D-Ala relative to the heptapeptide backbone of a glycopeptide antibiotic, and its intermolecular hydrogen bond configuration. (*Bottom*) The dimeric relationships seen in crystals of the vancomycin:Ac-D-Ala complex. The back-to-back interface is stabilized by four hydrogen bonds (shown) as well as numerous hydrophobic contacts. The face-to-face interface is stabilized by hydrophobic contacts, in part mediated by the ligand, as well as hydrogen bonds involving the ligand. In models of this dimer, tetrapeptide ligands can be fitted into this structure, making numerous hydrophobic contacts and additional hydrogen bonds across the interface.

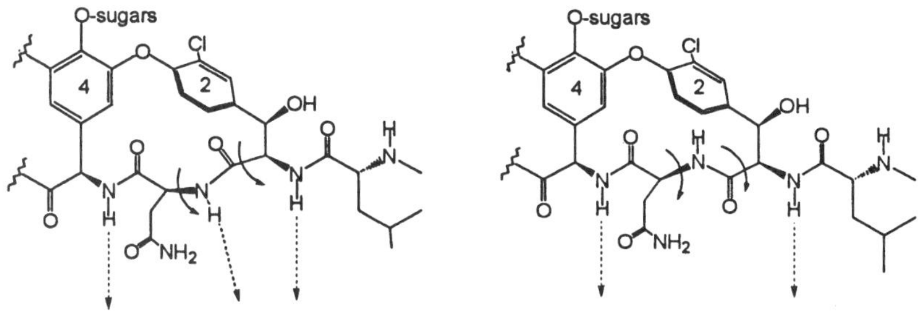

Figure 5   Rotation of the peptide bond between residues 2 and 3 in the heptapeptide backbone. (*Left*) The peptide bond contributes an intermolecular hydrogen bond when a ligand is bound in the active site (confirmed crystallographically). (*Right*) 180° rotation removes a potential hydrogen bond partner from the ligand binding site and distorts its shape. A role for this motion in desolvation of the binding site is proposed (see Section 3.5.1).

peptidoglycan synthesis intermediates terminating in -L-Lys-D-Ala-D-Ser bind to vancomycin, chloroeremomycin, and teicoplanin in the same manner, albeit with lower affinity (39).

3.3   Computational Studies

The most common role for computer simulations in the study of molecular recognition by glycopeptide antibiotics is in the determination and interpretation of distance constraints derived from NMR studies, i.e. restrained molecular dynamics (31, 34, 40, 41). Their twofold purpose is to determine the best set of solutions for a given set of distance constraints and to illustrate the dynamic freedom of molecules within these constraints to assume alternative conformations. Simulations performed for these purposes do not require solvent in the simulated system to be valid, nor are the results especially sensitive to the particular parameter set applied to the system.

Unrestrained simulations, in contrast, require careful design and execution to be suitable for drawing conclusions about molecular systems. Important design considerations include the nature and quantity of solvent, the shape and properties of the solvent boundaries, the choice of parameters, the strategy for conditioning and equilibrating the system prior to data collection, the method of statistical analysis applied to the data, and experimental validation of the system. For example, in a study that compared the binding of vancomycin aglycon to Ac-D-Ala-D-Ala and Ac-D-Ala-Gly, the simulations were validated by their ability to reproduce nOe data and to predict a correct value for the difference in free energy of binding (41).

From these simulation studies, five important conclusions were drawn about the recognition of dipeptides by vancomycin. 1. There is a significant amount of internal motion in the bound complexes (Figure 6). Conformational changes in the antibiotic, the ligand, and in the intermolecular interface belie the impression

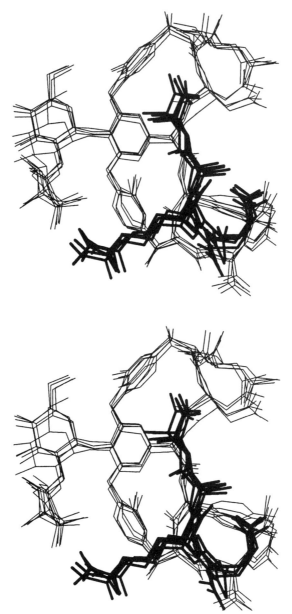

Figure 6 Cross-eye stereo view of Ac-D-Glu-L-Dap-D-Ala-D-Ala (*bold lines*) in a molecular dynamics simulation. Not shown are a second ligand and antibiotic molecule in a face-to-face dimeric relationship, nearly 2000 water molecules, and 2 sodium ions filling a 40 Å periodic box. Five structures at 5-ps intervals from an 800-ps simulation are superimposed to illustrate the amount of residual motion seen in a stable complex.

that these complexes are rigid entities. Furthermore, vibrational analyses of their dynamics suggest that differences in configurational entropy between the complexes are more than sufficient to account for differences in their binding affinity (PH Axelsen, unpublished data). 2. Although both ligands make the same hydrogen bonds with the antibiotic, the absence of an α-methyl group in Ac-D-Ala-Gly causes a change in the geometry of a hydrogen bond that may significantly decrease its contribution to binding affinity (see Section 3.4.4). 3. The overall size of the vancomycin: Ac-D-Ala-Gly complex is smaller and more compact. Although this might imply greater packing efficiency, and perhaps stronger intermolecular VdW interactions, these advantages are negated by a combination of reduced residual motions and less buried hydrophobic surface area in the Ac-D-Ala-Gly complex. 4. Interactions between the α-methyl group of the C-terminal residue and the aromatic ring of residue 4 have a significant attractive electrostatic component. This is possible because the dipole strength of a C-H bond is not zero, the aromatic ring faces have a well recognized ability to serve as hydrogen bond acceptors, and the dielectric susceptibility of space in the vicinity of this interaction is relatively low. 5. The difference in affinity between the Ac-D-Ala-D-Ala and Ac-D-Ala-Gly complexes ($\sim$2.5 kJ/mole) can be accounted for several times over (i.e. the component energies are not additive). Average measurements of various energy terms do not yield a true indication of their overall contribution to complex stability because they are often correlated in time (see Section 3.5.1).

3.4 Crystallographic Studies

3.4.1 The Crystallographic Challenge   Glycopeptide antibiotics are challenging compounds for crystallographic studies because they crystallize into units cells of intermediate size that are difficult to approach with either large molecule or small molecule phasing methods. Determination of the first crystal structures had to await four significant technical advances: (*a*) the availability of intense synchrotron radiation, (*b*) the development of cryo-crystallographic methods that minimized sample damage produced by high-intensity synchrotron radiation, (*c*) expanded access to high-speed computers, and (*d*) the development of new ab initio phasing methods.

The first structure solved with the aid of these advances was that of ureido-balhimycin (42). This work made use of the Patterson vector superposition method (43). It was followed by determination of the structure of A-40926 aglycone using an iterative real space–reciprocal space recycling procedure that combined tangent expansion in reciprocal space with optimization of peaks in an electron density map of real space (42, 44, 45). Finally, three different crystal structures for vancomycin were determined (46–48) using novel real space–reciprocal space recycling techniques. The recent structure of balhimycin, however, was solved by molecular replacement (49).

3.4.2 Back-to-Back Dimers   The structure of ureido-balhimycin provided the first detailed information about the structure of a glycopeptide antibiotic dimer (42). Balhimycin is a relative of vancomycin, differing only in the location and nature of the carbohydrate moieties (Figure 1). Ureido-balhimycin is produced from the parent compound via treatment with potassium isocyanate; its ability to bind ligands and its antimicrobial properties are not known. As expected, the structure shows that the chlorine atoms in residues 2 and 4 lie on opposite sides of the molecule and that residue 3 is asparagine, not isoasparagine. It also demonstrated that back-to-back dimers were stabilized by 4 hydrogen bonds between antiparallel polypeptide backbones, in good agreement with the model derived about the same time from NMR measurements (Figure 4) (50).

The crystal structure of vancomycin was determined simultaneously and independently in two different laboratories, using similar crystallographic approaches (46, 47). Like ureido-balhimycin, vancomycin forms back-to-back dimers with 4 hydrogen bonds between two antiparallel polypeptide backbones exhibiting twofold symmetry. The disaccharide groups do not obey this twofold symmetry, however, yielding an overall structure for the dimer that is asymmetric. As anticipated (51), the disaccharides interact over a large hydrophobic surface. The concave surfaces forming the substrate binding pockets are opposite the dimer interface. Therefore, dimer formation does not interfere with access to the binding pockets, and the structure is consistent with the hypothesis that the drug binds to bacterial cell walls as a dimer. Because the disaccharides overhang the binding pockets and are asymmetric, the two binding pockets of the dimer are nonequivalent.

The vancomycin crystals for these studies were grown in the presence of acetate ions, and acetate is a weak ligand for vancomycin (52). Consequently, there is a single, well-defined acetate ion bound in the binding site of one monomer in each vancomycin dimer. This provided a fortuitous glimpse of ligand recognition by a glycopeptide antibiotic. The acetate ion binds with its carboxylate group forming hydrogen bonds with amide protons of residues 2, 3, and 4 of the antibiotic and its methyl group packing against the aromatic ring of residue 4.

Only one of the two binding pockets in the vancomycin dimer is occupied by an acetate ion; the other is partially occluded by a crystal lattice contact. In the monomer that binds acetate, no interactions are seen between the asparagine side chain (Asn_3) and the ligand. Instead, Asn_3 has swung out of the way to allow ligand access to the binding pocket. However, in the monomer that binds no ligand, Asn_3 partially occupies the binding site and forms hydrogen bonds to the amide protons of residues 3 and 4. Hence, Asn_3 appears to serve as a surrogate ligand, occupying the binding pocket in the absence of ligand. This may provide some thermodynamic benefit and promote ligand binding by preventing solvation of the binding site in the absence of ligand. If the Asn_3 side chain were not present to carry out this function, the binding site could possibly bind one or more water molecules that compete with ligand.

The role of Asn_3 as an intermolecular "flap" controlling access to the binding pocket was originally suggested in the description of ureido-balhimycin (42); it finds further support in the crystal structure of balhimycin in its native form (49). In native balhimycin, both binding sites of the dimer are occupied and both Asn_3 side chains are swung back away from the ligands. An acetate in one binding site, and one carboxylate of a citrate molecule in the other, both bind in the same manner observed for the acetate in the vancomycin structure, forming three strong hydrogen bonds to the amide protons of residues 2, 3, and 4.

3.4.3 Face-to-Face Dimers   The crystal structure of the complex of vancomycin with the cell-wall mimetic N-acetyl-D-alanine revealed a previously unrecognized ligand-mediated dimerization mode for vancomycin (47). In this structure, vancomycin forms back-to-back dimers, as previously observed, but in addition, each dimer also interacts with another dimer in a face-to-face relationship (Figure 4). Thus, the crystal contains infinite chains of vancomycin monomers with alternating back-to-back and face-to-face contacts. The bound ligand comprises a substantial fraction of the face-to-face contact surface, suggesting that this dimer interface can form only in the presence of ligand. Modeling studies indicate that larger ligands, such as the L-Ala-D-Glu-L-Lys-D-Ala-D-Ala pentapeptide found in bacterial cell walls, would fit comfortably into this face-to-face dimer structure, forming a plausible and extensive interaction surface between the two vancomycin monomers. The ability of vancomycin to form both back-to-back and face-to-face dimers in the presence of ligand suggests that the drug might be capable of forming higher-order assemblies on a bacterial surface, with attendant increases in affinity. To this point, NMR studies have neither confirmed nor denied the presence of face-to-face interactions in solution-phase complexes.

The face-to-face interaction is significant to the design of new antibiotics with activity against resistant bacterial strains. For example, covalent dimers of vancomycin have been produced by joining two monomers with a linker segment attached to the vancosamine sugar (53). Some of these dimers are active against vancomycin-resistant organisms, and this activity is strongly dependent on the length of the linker segment used. The optimal linker length appears to be about 14 Å, which corresponds well to the distance between linkage sites in the face-to-face dimer in the crystal structure (13.6 Å). This suggests that the enhanced antimicrobial activity of these covalently linked dimers may be due to the formation of face-to-face complexes (see Section 4.2).

3.4.4 Low-Affinity Ligands   Crystal structures of vancomycin complexed to *N*-acetyl-glycine, D-lactate, and acetyl-D-lactate (2-acetoxy-D-propanoate) have recently become available (PJ Loll, J Kaplan, BS Selinsky, and PH Axelsen (102)). These are of interest because they indicate that the relatively high affinity ligand Ac-D-Ala induces a structural change in vancomycin that is not observed with more weakly bound ligands. This change is not seen with *N*-acetyl-glycine, reflecting the importance of interactions between the α-methyl group of Ac-D-Ala and the aromatic ring of residue 4 (see Section 3.3). The results also suggest that simultaneous interactions between N-terminal acetyl groups and both monomers in a face-to-face dimer (48) are critical to high-affinity binding. This can explain the unexpected finding that the free amino acids Gly and D-Ala bind more weakly than the corresponding N-acetyl forms (52).

3.5   Cooperative Phenomena

3.5.1 Weak Interactions   Short polypeptide segments generally do not associate together in solution as antiparallel β sheets because enthalpy gains from hydrogen bond formation do not compensate for the translational, rotational, and configurational entropy losses that would ensue. There must be additional design features inherent in glycopeptide antibiotics that stabilize their association with short polypeptides. In his studies of these features, DH Williams makes two preliminary assumptions about complex formation (54). First, that the steric complementarity of antibiotic and ligand is near optimal in a complex. Second, that both molecules assume low energy conformations in both free and bound states.

With these assumptions, the free energy of association is separated into four terms: (a) loss of translational and rotational entropy, (b) loss of configurational entropy, (c) sequestration of hydrophobic surface from water, and (d) favorable polar interactions. With various estimates and simplifying assumptions (51, 55–57), an estimate of 1–7 kJ/mole is made for the contribution of a single hydrogen bond to the free energy of binding, and of 3.5–5.5 kJ/mole for the cost of restricting the rotation of a bond.

Among the key insights to emerge from these analyses is that residual motions in the complex make a large and favorable contribution to the entropy of interaction (58, 59). Such motions are graphically apparent in molecular dynamics simulations of the complexes (see Section 3.3 and Figure 6) (41). Conversely, it is recognized that complex formation is also dependent on pre-existing rigidity in the antibiotic backbone (55). If this were not the case, rigidification of the backbone upon ligand binding would entail a large entropic cost, and failure to rigidify the backbone would preclude stable complex formation. As aptly stated for another system, "flexibility is the enemy" (60).

These analyses have not yet considered the implications of binding site desolvation. Ligands must compete with 55 M water for hydrogen bond partners in the ligand binding site. It is interesting to speculate on a role for the aforementioned rotation of the peptide bond between residues 2 and 3 in desolvating the binding site prior to ligand binding (see Section 3.2 and Figure 5) (30). This rotation will strip hydrogen-bonded water off the amide proton as it passes under the ring of residue 2 and will distort relationships between residue 2 and the rest of the molecule. One can imagine that this rotation gives rise to a breathing motion that may help unbind and expel water from the binding site prior to ligand binding. Kinetic studies indicate that on-rates for ligand binding are too slow to be diffusion controlled by 2 orders of magnitude, suggesting that complex formation does indeed involve a relatively slow conformational rearrangement or desolvation step (61).

Of necessity, these analyses must assume that contributions to the free energy of association are both separable and additive. However, interactions between hydrophobic portions of residue 1 and electrostatic interactions have been shown to be cooperative—and therefore nonadditive—in studies of vancomycin and ristocetin (62, 63), eremomycin and teicoplanin (64), N-terminal derivatives of vancomycin (65), and various other glycopeptide antibiotics (66). The origins of cooperativity among weak interactions have been attributed to an inherent curvature in enthalpy-entropy compensation plots. Curvature arises because there is a limit to the adverse entropy of bimolecular association, but not to the enthalpy of interaction (67–69). Consequently, increases in binding entropy only partially compensate for increases in binding enthalpy, and two weak interactions can contribute more to overall binding than the sum of their individual interactions.

Computational studies provide a microscopic perspective of this phenomenon by showing how cooperativity arises when different energy terms are correlated in time. In such cases, the enthalpic components of each free energy term may be easy to define and easily separable, whereas the entropic components typically are not easily defined or separated. If a given free energy term is truly "weak" and is only one among many terms of similar magnitude, then its loss will have a minor effect on the structure and configurational entropy of the complex. Thus, when each free energy term is evaluated individually, the same entropic component opposes each of the two different enthalpic components and it is, effectively, counted twice. When the energy terms are evaluated together, the entropic component is counted only once, and the energy terms will appear to be cooperative. This problem of nonorthogonal free energy contributions is well known in computational studies of ligand association wherein the magnitude of a free energy contribution depends on the path chosen to reach an intermediate state (70). With careful interpretation, however, such analyses are not without value (41, 71).

3.5.2 Dimerization   As described above in section 3.4.2, many glycopeptide antibiotics form dimers (27, 72–75). In general, dimerization is enthalpically driven, aided by an array of hydrogen bonds between polypeptide chains, VdW interactions involving the chlorine atoms, and σ-π interactions between aromatic rings (76). Glycopeptide dimers are also stabilized by hydrophobic contacts between the sugar residues (46, 47), as anticipated (51). Removal of both sugar residues yields aglycovancomycin. This derivative is predominantly dimeric at concentrations of 10–50 μM, implying a dimerization constant of at least 10^5 M^{-1} (i.e. at least that of chloroeremomycin) (41). Monomer formation can be induced by ligand binding or by lowering the temperature from 20°C to 4°C. Thus, dimer formation by aglycovancomycin is anticooperative with ligand binding and is endothermic, suggesting a different basis for its formation than dimers of native vancomycin.

Because the sugars in a glycopeptide dimer are oriented asymmetrically, the two halves of the dimer may exhibit different ligand affinities for reasons unrelated to cooperative effects. Asymmetry of binding in the two different halves of a dimer is evident in ristocetin but not in eremomycin (77, 78). In ristocetin, differences between the halves can be reduced to the point where dimerization and ligand binding are cooperative by enzymatically removing rhamnose from the tetrasaccharide (79). Binding asymmetry can also be demonstrated for acetate in eremomycin and chloroeremomycin (80). It isn't clear in these studies, however, which monomer has which affinity.

It has been proposed that the physiological role of dimerization in enhancing antibiotic affinity for cell wall targets involves the chelate effect (27, 76). The chelate effect is a cooperative phenomenon: The binding of an antibiotic dimer to one target ligand in the cell wall enhances the binding of a second target ligand to the other half of the dimer because there is an increased effective concentration of binding sites in the vicinity of other ligands (i.e. by a reduction in dimensionality for the second binding reaction). Establishing the relationship between ligand affinity and antimicrobial activity in terms of dimerization, however, has not been straightforward. Eremomycin and vancomycin are similar in structure, but eremomycin has a much higher dimerization constant. Eremomycin is also a much more potent antimicrobial, but dimerization does not explain its greater effectiveness because the eremomycin dimer still binds soluble ligands with less affinity than does vancomycin monomer (73).

A clearer relationship between ligand affinity and antimicrobial activity emerges if an ability to form dimers is considered in binding studies with surface-bound ligands. Enhanced binding of various antibiotics, correlating with their tendency to dimerize, has been demonstrated using detergent micelles (81), lipid vesicles (82, 83), bacterial cells (84, 85), and self-assembled molecular monolayers (86). In each case, surface affinities better correlate with antimicrobial potency than do solution-phase affinities.

Experimental data suggest that the lipophilic chain of teicoplanin enhances the binding of antibiotics to target ligand by anchoring in a lipid membrane and increasing the local concentration of antibiotic on the membrane surface (81, 84). It has been proposed that dimerization and membrane anchoring are both operating in biphenylchloroeremomycin to enhance its activity against vancomycin-resistant bacteria, although the apparent affinity for depsipeptide targets was not high enough in this compound to be therapeutically useful (87). One should note, however, that the assay for membrane anchoring employed in these studies only demonstrates nonspecific association between the antibiotic and the surface. The actual insertion of biphenyl derivatives into membranes in a manner brought to mind by the term anchor has not yet demonstrated, and an alternative explanation for their enhanced antimicrobial activity has been offered (see Section 4.1) (88). It should also be noted that membrane anchoring will enhance activity by the mechanism being suggested only if the target ligands themselves are adjacent to or are bound to a membrane. Thus in the present case, if membrane anchoring enhances antimicrobial activity, it isn't clear whether this enhancement is due to more effective binding to target ligands, a redirection of binding to a more critical target ligand (e.g. lipid II), or both.

An examination of pentapeptide target models suggests that they can form dimeric antiparallel β sheets. Although polypeptide segments tend either to not form stable β structures or to aggregate in solution (89), the high local concentration of pentapeptide segments tethered to a surface will tend to favor the formation of β structure, and steric interactions between side chains in the mixture of D- and L-isomers will preclude aggregation beyond dimer formation. It is possible, therefore, that the natural target of cell wall enzymes and glycopeptide antibiotics is itself a dimer.

3.5.3 Allosterism   Dimerization and ligand binding are cooperative processes for nearly all glycopeptide antibiotics except ristocetin (67). The physicochemical consequences of dimerization most likely to influence ligand binding are (*a*) restricted dynamics, (*b*) polarization of peptide dipoles, and (*c*) coulombic attraction between the charged groups across the dimer interface (73, 74). In lieu of being able to conduct direct investigations into these mechanisms, the origins of cooperativity were explored in a set of glycopeptide antibiotics with techniques that monitored the strength of the dimer and the monomer-ligand interfaces (90). When dimerization was weak in the absence of ligand, binding of a ligand caused dimerization constants to increase and dimer interfaces to tighten. When dimerization was strong in the absence of a ligand, dimerization constants also increased, but it was primarily the ligand binding interface that tightened.

These results may be understood by considering that hydrogen bonds at the dimer interface are somewhat shielded from the close approach of solvent. Thus, the transition state for dissociation resembles a gas phase separation with a large activation barrier to dissociation of the dimer and an energy well for the dimeric state that is much deeper than suggested by the equilibrium constant for dimerization (91). This will primarily affect the kinetics of dissociation, not its overall energy change, but it will also affect entropy/enthalpy compensation in the system. A tighter complex with a deeper energy well implies less residual entropy, and less of a capacity for changes in entropy to compensate for changes in enthalpy. Hence, with antibiotics that dimerize strongly in the absence of ligands, the enthalpy of ligand binding can be more efficiently transduced across the dimer interface to another ligand.

These results suggest that increases in the energy of dimerization upon binding a ligand need not require changes at the dimer interface, but can arise almost entirely from changes occurring at the monomer-ligand interface. Cooper has proposed that allosterism may be mediated by large-scale vibrational modes without conformational change (92). This possibility in vancomycin is supported by simulation studies that suggest the binding of even a small ligand may alter the dynamics of a dimer interface without altering its time-average structure (93).

These phenomena arise from subtle design features in these molecules. They can be expected to manifest themselves only if by optimizing molecular geometry for the dimer interface interaction, one also simultaneously optimizes the geometry of the ligand interface. This will not be the case for all ligands, as seen by the ability of rigid, non-natural ligands to distort the dimer interface and bind anticooperatively to ristocetin (more anticooperative than the natural ligand) (94). Indeed, it may be a rare ligand that meets the structural and dynamic requirements for cooperative binding, and it could represent a general mechanism used elsewhere in nature to enhance the specificity of receptor binding (67) or the ability of a receptor to tranduce signals over long distances (92).

4.   RATIONAL MODIFICATION

4.1   Semisynthetic Derivatives

Scientists at Eli Lilly in Indiana and the Lepetit Research Center in Gerenzano, Italy, have performed extensive studies of structure-activity relationships based on semisynthetic modification of naturally occurring glycopeptide antibiotics. The dozens of individual papers published by these groups are probably best approached through a recent comprehensive review (95). Of particular note is a procedure described to rebuild the carboxylate binding pocket of teicoplanins. Remarkably, residues at positions 1 and 3 can be selectively removed and replaced with residues bearing alternative side chains. One of the compounds produced by this strategy, MDL 63,166, was devoid of sugar residues but exhibited significant anti-vanA activity as well as better activity than fully glycosylated vancomycin or teicoplanin against several vancomycin-sensitive strains. In light of results of computational free energy simulations (29), the improved activity of MDL 63,166 may be due to lengthening the side chain of residue 3 and decreasing its hydrophobicity.

Another important compound resulted from investigations into *N*-alkyl derivatives. The major product when chloroeremomycin is subjected to reductive alkylation is an *N*-alkyl derivative of the disaccharide amino function. Although chlorophenyl and biphenyl derivatives have enhanced activity, the greatest enhancement of activity against both vancomycin-sensitive and vancomycin-resistant organisms is found with a chlorobiphenyl derivative (96). This compound, dubbed LY333328, is now in clinical trials.

It should be recalled that the enhanced activity of the biphenyl derivative had been attributed in part to anchoring of the compound in a lipid membrane in a manner analogous to teicoplanin (87). However, in a remarkable line of investigation, it has been shown that a chlorobiphenyl derivative of vancomycin inhibits the synthesis of both mature and immature peptidoglycan, whereas vancomycin inhibited the synthesis of only mature peptidoglycan (88). The chlorobiphenyl derivative thus inhibits an earlier stage in cell wall biosynthesis, and appears to interact directly with immature peptiodglycan, lipid II, and proteins involved in transglycosylation. Even more remarkable is the observation that this activity does not require binding to D-Ala-D-Ala target ligands, and that some early stage-inhibition is preserved even after removing all but the chlorobiphenyl disaccharide and a portion of residue 4. A variant of chlorobiphenyl vancomycin with a methyl group removed from position 6 of vancosamine was found to exhibit the greatest potency.

4.2   Covalent Dimers

The naturally occurring tendency for some glycopeptide antibiotics to form dimers with desirable characteristics has led several investigators to explore the properties of covalently linked dimers. Griffin, for example, linked two vancomycin monomers tail-to-tail with various linking segments and found several of them to have little or no better activity against *Staphylococci* and vancomycin-susceptible *Enterococci*, but to have a surprising level of activity against vancomycin-resistant *Enterococci* (97). This type of linkage seems unlikely to facilitate the formation of individual back-to-back dimers but may operate through the chelate effect discussed above, or through the formation of dimers-of-dimers.

Whitesides has examined the binding properties of dimeric ligands to tail-to-tail vancomycin dimers using a capillary electrophoresis method to measure binding affinities (98). Compared to monomeric Ac$_2$-L-Lys-D-Ala-D-Ala binding to monomeric vancomycin with a binding energy of 33 kJ/mole, dimeric ligand binding to dimeric vancomycin has a binding affinity of 50 kJ/mole, for an increase of 17 kJ/mole (99). This corresponds to an effective concentration of 20 mM for the second binding event. More recently, the binding of these vancomycin dimers to self-assembled molecular monolayers displaying Ac$_2$-L-Lys-D-Ala-D-Ala was characterized with surface plasmon resonance, and similar conclusions were reached (100). These experiments showed that surface display of a ligand was thermodynamically similar—if not equivalent—to a covalent solution-phase dimeric ligand. Venturing beyond dimers, the binding of trimeric ligands to trimeric vancomycin has also been described (101). In this case, the binding affinity was almost threefold that of the monomer, at 94 kJ/mole, making its affinity higher than that of avidin-biotin.

Researchers at Eli Lilly have prepared top-to-top dimers by attaching a bifunctional linking segment to pairs of antibiotic molecules via their amino sugars (53). In this case, it was expected that short linking segments would encourage the formation of back-to-back dimers, and that this would be advantageous if antibiotic monomers are used in which ligand binding and dimerization are highly cooperative. Unexpectedly, it was found that the antimicrobial activity of these compounds depended in a complex way on the length of the linking segment. Short linkers were effective against *S. aureus* but not vancomycin-resistant *Enterococci*. Longer linkers, however, progressively gained activity against vancomycin-resistant *Enterococci* and lost activity against *S. aureus*. There appeared to be intermediate lengths where high activity was seen for both species. Interestingly, this length corresponds to the distance between the amino sugar linkage sites in the crystal structure of the face-to-face vancomycin dimer (48). This suggests the possibility that top-to-top dimers act in a face-to-face configuration, at least against *Enterococci*.

5. CONCLUSIONS

Molecular recognition by glycopeptide antibiotics involves an abundance of complex cooperative phenomena. NMR, X-ray crystallography, computational analysis, and new semi-synthetic derivatives have provided us with some intimate details about the molecular mechanisms that give rise to these phenomena. We should expect additional study to reveal new levels of complexity, and new insights into fundamental processes that also operate in larger ligand receptors.

Visit the Annual Reviews home page at www.AnnualReviews.org

LITERATURE CITED

1. Nagarajan R. 1993. Structure-activity relationships of vancomycin glycopeptide antibiotics. *J. Antibiot.* 46:1181–95
2. Nagarajan R. 1994. *Glycopeptide Antibiotics.* New York: Marcel Dekker
3. Tipper DJ, Strominger JL. 1965. Mechanism of action of penicillins: a proposal based on their structural similarity to acyl-D-alanyl-D-alanine. *Proc. Natl. Acad. Sci. USA* 54:1133–41
4. Popieniek PH, Pratt RF. 1987. A fluorescent ligand for binding studies with glycopeptide antibiotics of the vancomycin class. *Anal. Biochem.* 165:108–13
5. Shlaes DM, Shlaes JH, Davies J, Williamson R. 1989. Escherichia coli susceptible to glycopeptide antibiotics. *Antimicrob. Agents Chemother.* 33:192–97
6. Sieradzki K, Roberts RB, Haber SW, Tomasz A. 1999. The development of vancomycin resistance in a patient with methicillin-resistant Staphylococcus aureus infection. *N. Engl. J. Med.* 340:517–23
7. Smith TL, Pearson ML, Wilcox KR, Cruz C, Lancaster MV, et al. 1999. Emergence of vancomycin resistance in Staphylococcus aureus. *N. Engl. J. Med.* 340:493–501
8. Novak R, Henriques B, Charpentier E, Normark S, Tuomanen E. 1999. Emergence of vancomycin tolerance in Streptococcus pneumoniae. *Nature* 399:590–93
9. Reynolds PE. 1998. Control of peptidoglycan synthesis in vancomycin-resistant entero-

rococci: D,D-peptidases and D,D-carboxypeptidases. *Cell. Mol. Life Sci.* 54:325–31
10. Billot-Klein D, Gutmann L, Sable S, Guittet E, van Heijenoort J. 1994. Modification of peptidoglycan precursors is a common feature of the low-level vancomycin-resistant vanB-type Enterococcus D366 and of the naturally glycopeptide-resistant species Lactobacillus casei, Pediococcus pentosaceus, Leuconostoc mesenteroides, and Enterococcus gallinarum. *J. Bacteriol.* 176: 2398–405
11. Sheldrick GM, Jones PG, Kennard O, Williams DH, Smith GA. 1978. Structure of vancomycin and its complex with acetyl-D-alanyl-D-alanine. *Nature* 271:223–25
12. Williamson MP, Williams DH. 1981. Structure revision of the antibiotic vancomycin. The use of nuclear overhauser effect difference spectroscopy. *J. Am. Chem. Soc.* 103:6580–85
13. Harris CM, Harris TM. 1982. Structure of the glycopeptide antibiotic vancomycin. Evidence for an asparagine residue in the peptide. *J. Am. Chem. Soc.* 104:4293–95
14. Harris CM, Kopecka H, Harris TM. 1983. Vancomycin: structure and transformation to CDP-1. *J. Am. Chem. Soc.* 105:6915–22
15. Kalman JR, Williams DH. 1980. An NMR study of the structure of the antibiotic ristocetin A. The negative nuclear overhauser effect in structure elucidation. *J. Am. Chem. Soc.* 102:897–905

16. Barna JC, Williams DH, Stone DJM, Leung T-WC, Doddrell DM. 1984. Structure elucidation of the teicoplanin antibiotics. *J. Am. Chem. Soc.* 106:4895–902

17. Schulz GE, Schirmer RH. 1979. *Principles of Protein Structure*. New York: Springer

18. Skelton NJ, Williams DH, Rance MJ, Ruddock JC. 1991. Structure elucidation of a novel antibiotic of the vancomycin group. The influence of ion-dipole interactions on peptide backbone conformation. *J. Am. Chem. Soc.* 113:3757–65

19. Perkins HR. 1969. Specificity of combination between mucopeptide precursors and vancomycin or ristocetin. *Biochem. J.* 111:195–205

20. Williams DH. 1984. Structural studies on some antibiotics of the vancomycin group, and on the antibiotic-receptor complexes, by ^{1}H NMR. *Acc. Chem. Res.* 17:364–69

21. Williams DH, Waltho JP. 1988. Molecular basis of the activity of antibiotics of the vancomycin group. *Biochem. Pharmacol.* 37:133–41

22. Williams DH. 1996. The glycopeptide story—how to kill the deadly 'superbugs.' *Nat. Prod. Rep.* 13:469–77

23. Williams DH, Bardsley B. 1999. The vancomycin group of antibiotics and the fight against resistant bacteria. *Angew. Chem. Int. Ed.* 38:1173–93

24. Kalman JR, Williams DH. 1980. An NMR study of the interaction between the antibiotic ristocetin A and a cell wall peptide analogue. Negative nuclear overhauser effects in the investigation of drug binding sites. *J. Am. Chem. Soc.* 102:906–12

25. Convert O, Bongini A, Feeney J. 1980. A ^{1}H nuclear magnetic resonance study of the interactions of vancomycin with N-Acetyl-D-alanyl-D-alanine and related peptides. *J. Chem. Soc. Perkin Trans. 2*, pp. 1262–70

26. Waltho JP, Cavanagh J, Williams DH. 1988. Aspects of molecular recognition: use of a truncated driven pseudo-NOESY experiment to elucidate the environment of intermolecular electrostatic interactions in vancomycin. *J. Chem. Soc. Chem. Commun.*, pp. 707–9

27. Waltho JP, Williams DH. 1989. Aspects of molecular recognition: solvent exclusion and dimerization of the antibiotic ristocetin when bound to a model bacterial cell-wall precursor. *J. Am. Chem. Soc.* 111:2475–80

28. Waltho JP, Williams DH. 1991. The natural design of vancomycin family antibiotics to bind their target peptides. *Ciba Found. Symp.* 158:73–91

29. Axelsen PH, Li D. 1998. A rational strategy for enhancing the affinity of vancomycin towards depsipeptide ligands. *Bioorg. Med. Chem.* 6:877–81

30. Waltho JP, Williams DH, Stone DJM, Skelton NJ. 1988. Intramolecular determinants of conformation and mobility within the antibiotic vancomycin. *J. Am. Chem. Soc.* 110:5638–43

31. Prowse WG, Kline AD, Skelton MA, Loncharich RJ. 1995. Conformation of A828468B, a glycopeptide antibiotic, complexed with its cell wall fragment: an asymmetric homodimer determined using NMR spectroscopy. *Biochemistry* 34:9632–44

32. Williams DH, Williamson MP, Butcher DW, Hammond SJ. 1983. Detailed binding sites of the antibiotics vancomycin and ristocetin A: determination of intermolecular distances in antibiotic/substrate complexes by use of the time-dependent NOE. *J. Am. Chem. Soc.* 105:1332–39

33. Fesik SW, Armitage IM, Ellestad GA, McGahren WJ. 1984. Nuclear magnetic resonance studies on the interaction of avoparcin with model receptors of bacterial cell walls. *Mol. Pharmacol.* 25:281–86

34. Fesik SW, O'Donnell TJ, Gampe RT Jr, Olejniczak ET. 1986. Determining the structure of a glycopeptide-Ac2-Lys-D-Ala-D-Ala complex using NMR parameters and molecular modeling. *J. Am. Chem. Soc.* 108:3165–70

35. Linsdell H, Toiron C, Bruix M, Rivas G, Menendez M. 1996. Dimerization of

A82846B, vancomycin and ristocetin: influence on antibiotic complexation with cell wall model peptides. *J. Antibiot.* 49:181–93

36. Kurz M, Guba W, Andreini BP. 1996. 3D structure of the complex of MDL 63,246 with the cell wall model peptide Ac$_2$-Lys-D-Ala-D-Ala. *J. Am. Chem. Soc.* 118:5874–80

37. Mueller L, Heald SL, Hempel JC, Jeffs PW. 1989. Determination of the conformation of molecular complexes of the aridicin aglycon with Ac$_2$-L-Lys-D-Ala-D-Ala and Ac-L-Ala-γ-D-Gln-L-Lys(Ac)-D-Ala-D-Ala: an application of nuclear magnetic resonance spectroscopy and distance geometry in modeling of peptides. *J. Am. Chem. Soc.* 111:496–505

38. Dancer RJ, Try AC, Sharman GJ, Williams DH. 1996. Binding of a vancomycin group antibiotic to a cell wall analogue from vancomycin-resistant bacteria. *Chem. Commun.*, pp. 1445–46

39. van Wageningen AA, Staroske T, Williams DH. 1998. Binding of D-serine-terminating cell-wall analogues to glycopeptide antibiotics. *Chem. Commun.*, pp. 1171–72

40. Molinari H, Pastore A, Lian L, Hawkes GE, Sales K. 1990. Structure of vancomycin and a vancomycin/D-Ala-D-Ala complex in solution. *Biochemistry* 29:2271–77

41. Li DH, Sreenivasan U, Juranic N, Macura S, Puga FJI, et al. 1997. Simulated dipeptide recognition by vancomycin. *J. Mol. Recogn.* 10:73–87

42. Sheldrick GM, Paulus E, Vertesy L, Hahn F. 1995. Structure of ureido-balhimycin. *Acta Crystallogr.* B51:89–98

43. Sheldrick GM, Dauter Z, Wilson KS, Hope H, Sieker LC. 1993. The application of direct methods and Patterson interpretation to high-resolution native protein data. *Acta Crystallogr.* D 49:18–23

44. Schafer M, Pohl E, SchmidtBase K, Sheldrick GM, Hermann R, et al. 1996. The molecular and crystal structure of the glycopeptide A-40926 aglycone. *Helv. Chim. Acta* 79:1916–24

45. Sheldrick GM, Gould RO. 1995. Structure solution by interactive peaklist optimization and tangent expansion in space group P1. *Acta Crystallogr.* B 51:423–31

46. Schafer M, Schneider TR, Sheldrick GM. 1996. Crystal structure of vancomycin. *Structure* 4:1509–15

47. Loll PJ, Bevivino AE, Korty BD, Axelsen PH. 1997. Simultaneous recognition of a carboxylate-containing ligand and an intramolecular surrogate ligand in the crystal structure of an asymmetric vancomycin dimer. *J. Am. Chem. Soc.* 119:1516–22

48. Loll PJ, Miller R, Weeks CM, Axelsen PH. 1998. A ligand-mediated dimerization mode for vancomycin. *Chem. Biol.* 5:293–98

49. Schafer M, Sheldrick GM, Schneider TR, Vertesy L. 1998. Structure of balhimycin and its complex with solvent molecules. *Acta Crystallogr.* D 54:175–83

50. Eberstadt M, Guba W, Kessler H, Kogler H, Mierke DF. 1995. Conformation and dynamics of dimeric ureido-balhimycin. *Biopolymers* 36:429–37

51. Williams DH, Searle MS, Mackay JP, Gerhard U, Maplestone RA. 1993. Toward an estimation of binding constants in aqueous solution: studies of associations of vancomycin group antibiotics. *Proc. Natl. Acad. Sci. USA* 90:1172–78

52. Pearce CM, Gerhard U, Williams DH. 1995. Ligands which bind weakly to vancomycin: studies by ^{13}C NMR spectroscopy. *J. Chem. Soc. Perkin Trans. 2*, pp. 2:159–63

53. Stack DR, Letourneau DL, Mullen DL, Butler TF, Allen NE, et al. 1998. Covalent glycopeptide dimers: synthesis, physical characterization, and antibacterial activity. *37th Intersci. Conf. Antimicrob. Agents Chemother.* 37:146

54. Williams DH. 1991. The molecular basis of biological order. *Aldrichim. Acta* 24:71–80

55. Williams DH, Cox JPL, Doig AJ, Gardner M, Gerhard U, et al. 1991. Toward the semiquantitative estimation of binding constants. Guides for peptide-peptide binding in aqueous solution. *J. Am. Chem. Soc.* 113:7020–30

56. Searle MS, Williams DH, Gerhard U. 1992. Partitioning of free energy contributions in the estimation of binding constants: residual motions and consequences for amide-amide hydrogen bond strengths. *J. Am. Chem. Soc.* 114:10697–704

57. Gerhard U, Searle MS, Williams DH. 1993. The free energy change of restricting a bond rotation in the binding of peptide analogues to vancomycin group antibiotics. *Bioorg. Med. Chem. Lett.* 3:803–8

58. Searle MS, Williams DH. 1992. The cost of conformational order: entropy changes in molecular associations. *J. Am. Chem. Soc.* 114:10690–97

59. Williams DH, Westwell MS. 1996. Weak interactions and lessons from crystallization. *Chem. Biol.* 3:695–701

60. Breslow R. 1979. Biomimetic chemistry in oriented systems. *Isr. J. Chem.* 18:187–91

61. Popieniek PH, Pratt RF. 1991. Kinetics and mechanism of binding of specific peptides to vancomycin and other glycopeptide antibiotics. *J. Am. Chem. Soc.* 113:2264–70

62. Williamson MP, Williams DH. 1984. Hydrophobic interactions affect hydrogen bond strengths in complexes between peptides and vancomycin or ristocetin. *Eur. J. Biochem.* 138:345–48

63. Groves P, Searle MS, Westwell MS, Williams DH. 1994. Expression of electrostatic binding cooperativity in the recognition of cell-wall peptide analogues by vancomycin group antibiotics. *J. Chem. Soc. Chem. Commun.*, pp. 1519–20

64. Sharman GJ, Searle MS, Benhamu B, Groves P, Williams DH. 1995. Burial of hydrocarbon causes cooperative enhancement of electrostatic binding. *Angew. Chem. Int. Ed.* 34:1483–85

65. Cristofaro MF, Beauregard DA, Yan HS, Osborn NJ, Williams DH. 1995. Cooperativity between nonpolar and ionic forces in the binding of bacterial-cell wall analogs by vancomycin in aqueous solution. *J. Antibiot.* 48:805–10

66. Searle MS, Sharman GJ, Groves P, Benhamu B, Beauregard DA, et al. 1996. Enthalpic (electrostatic) contribution to the chelate effect: a correlation between ligand binding constant and a specific hydrogen bond strength in complexes of glycopeptide antibiotics with cell wall analogues. *J. Chem. Soc. Perkin Trans. 1*, pp. 2781–86

67. Williams DH, Searle MS, Westwell MS, Mackay JP, Groves P, Beauregard DA. 1994. The role of weak interactions, dimerization, and cooperativity in antibiotic action and biological signaling. *Chemtracsts Org. Chem.* 7:133–55

68. Searle MS, Westwell MS, Williams DH. 1995. Application of a generalized enthalpy-entropy relationship to binding cooperativity and weak associations in solution. *J. Chem. Soc. Perkin Trans. 2*, pp. 141–51

69. Westwell MS, Searle MS, Klein J, Williams DH. 1996. Successful predictions of the residual motion of weakly associated species as a function of the bonding between them. *J. Phys. Chem.* 100:16000–1

70. Smith PE, van Gunsteren WF. 1994. When are free-energy components meaningful? *J. Phys. Chem.* 98:13735–40

71. Boresch S, Archontis G, Karplus M. 1994. Free energy simulations: the meaning of the individual contributions from a component analysis. *Proteins: Struct. Funct. Genet.* 20:25–33

72. Groves P, Searle MS, Mackay JP, Williams DH. 1994. The structure of an asymmetric dimer relevant to the mode of action of the glycopeptide antibiotics. *Structure* 2:747–53

73. Mackay JP, Gerhard U, Beauregard DA, Westwell MS, Searle MS, Williams DH. 1994. Glycopeptide antibiotic-activity and

the possible role of dimerization–a model for biological signaling. *J. Am. Chem. Soc.* 116:4581–90

74. Mackay JP, Gerhard U, Beauregard DA, Maplestone RA, Williams DH. 1994. Dissection of the contributions toward dimerization of glycopeptide antibiotics. *J. Am. Chem. Soc.* 116:4573–80

75. Groves P, Searle MS, Waltho JP, Williams DH. 1995. Asymmetry in the structure of glycopeptide antibiotic dimers: NMR studies of the ristocetin a complex with a bacterial cell wall analog. *J. Am. Chem. Soc.* 117:7958–64

76. Gerhard U, Mackay JP, Maplestone RA, Williams DH. 1993. The role of the sugar and chlorine substituents in the dimerization of vancomycin antibiotics. *J. Am. Chem. Soc.* 115:232–37

77. Batta G, Cristofaro MF, Sharman GJ, Williams DH. 1996. Demonstration of the difference in binding affinity between the two binding sites of the ristocetin A asymmetric dimer. *Chem. Commun.*, pp. 101–3

78. Cho YR, Maguire AJ, Try AC, Westwell MS, Groves P, Williams DH. 1996. Cooperativity and anti-cooperativity between ligand binding and the dimerization of ristocetin A: asymmetry of a homodimer complex and implications for signal transduction. *Chem. Biol.* 3:207–15

79. Bardsley B, Williams DH. 1998. Cooperativity between ligand binding and dimerisation in a derivative of ristocetin A. *J. Chem. Soc. Perkin Trans. 2*, pp. 1925–29

80. Bardsley B, Williams DH. 1997. Measurement of the different affinities of the two halves of glycopeptide dimers for acetate. *Chem. Commun.*, pp. 1049–50

81. Westwell MS, Bardsley B, Dancer RJ, Try AC, Williams DH. 1996. Cooperativity in ligand binding expressed at a model cell membrane by the vancomycin group antibiotics. *Chem. Commun.*, pp. 589–90

82. Entress RM, Dancer RJ, O'Brien DP, Try AC, Cooper MA, Williams DH. 1998. 19F NMR in the measurement of binding affini-

ties of chloroeremomycin to model bacterial cell-wall surfaces that mimic VanA and VanB resistance. *Chem. Biol.* 5:329–37

83. O'Brien DP, Entress RH, Cooper MA, O'Brien SW, Hopkinson A, Williams DH. 1999. High affinity surface binding of a strongly dimerizing vancomycin-group antibiotic to a model of resistant bacteria. *J. Am. Chem. Soc.* 121:5259–65

84. Beauregard DA, Williams DH, Gwynn MN, Knowles DJC. 1995. Dimerization and membrane anchors in extracelluar targetting of vancomycin group antibiotics. *Antimicrob. Agents. Chemother.* 39:781–85

85. Beauregard DA, Maguire AJ, Williams DH, Reynolds PE. 1997. Semiquantitation of cooperativity in binding of vancomycin group antibiotics to vancomycin susceptible and resistant organisms. *Antimicrob. Agents Chemother.* 41:2418–23

86. Cooper MA, Williams DH, Cho YR. 1997. Surface plasmon resonance analysis of glycopeptide antibiotic activity at a model membrane surface. *Chem. Commun.*, pp. 1625–26

87. Sharman GJ, Try AC, Dancer RJ, Cho YR, Staroske T, et al. 1997. The roles of dimerization and membrane anchoring in activity of glycopeptide antibiotics against vancomycin-resistant bacteria. *J. Am. Chem. Soc.* 119:12041–47

88. Ge M, Chen Z, Onishi HR, Kohler J, Silver LL, et al. 1999. Vancomycin derivatives that inhibit peptidoglycan biosynthesis without binding D-Ala-D-Ala. *Science* 284:507–11

89. Nesloney CL, Kelly JW. 1996. Progress towards understanding beta-sheet structure. *Bioorg. Med. Chem.* 4:739–66

90. Williams DH, Maguire AJ, Tsuzuki W, Westwell MS. 1998. An analysis of the origins of a cooperative binding energy of dimerization. *Science* 280:711–14

91. Williams DH, Searle MS, Westwell MS, Gerhard U, Holroyd SE. 1993. Towards a semi-quantitative description of a

biomolecular association involving weak interactions in aqueous solution. *Philos. Trans. R. Soc. London Ser. A.* 345:11–21

92. Cooper A, Dryden DTF. 1984. Allostery without conformational change: a plausible model. *Eur. Biophys. J.* 11:103–9

93. Axelsen PH, Loll PJ. 1998. Allosteric regulation of ligand recognition in the vancomycin dimer. *Biophys. J.* 74:A281

94. Groves P, Searle MS, Chicarelli-Robinson I, Williams DH. 1994. Recognition of the cell-wall binding-site of the vancomycin group antibiotics by unnatural structural motifs: ^{1}H-NMR Studies of the effects of ligand binding on antibiotic dimerization. *J. Chem. Soc. Perkin Trans.1,* pp. 6:659–65

95. Malabarba A, Nicas TI, Thompson RC. 1997. Structural modifications of glycopeptide antibiotics. *Med. Res. Rev.* 17:69–137

96. Cooper RD, Snyder NJ, Zweifel MJ, Staszak MA, Wilkie SC, et al. 1996. Reductive alkylation of glycopeptide antibiotics: synthesis and antibacterial activity. *J. Antibiot.* 49:575–81

97. Sundram UN, Griffin JH. 1996. Novel vancomycin dimers with activity against vancomycin-resistant enterococci. *J. Am. Chem. Soc.* 118:13107–8

98. Rao JH, Colton IJ, Whitesides GM. 1997. Using capillary electrophoresis to study the electrostatic interactions involved in the association of D-Ala-D-Ala with vancomycin. *J. Am. Chem. Soc.* 119:9336–40

99. Rao JH, Whitesides GM. 1997. Tight binding of a dimeric derivative of vancomycin with dimeric L-Lys-D-Ala-D-Ala. *J. Am. Chem. Soc.* 119:10286–90

100. Rao JH, Yan L, Xu B, Whitesides GM. 1999. Using surface plasmon resonance to study the binding of vancomycin and its dimer to self-assembled monolayers presenting D-Ala-D-Ala. *J. Am. Chem. Soc.* 121:2629–30

101. Rao JH, Lahiri J, Isaacs L, Weis RM, Whitesides GM. 1998. A trivalent system from vancomycin.D-ala- D-Ala with higher affinity than avidin-biotin. *Science* 280:708–11

102. Loll PJ, Kaplan J, Selinsky BS, Axelsen PH. 1999. Vancomycin Binding to Low Affinity Ligands: Delineating a Minimum Set of Interactions Necessary for High Affinity Binding. *J. Med. Chem.* 42:4714–4719

Annu. Rev. Biophys. Biomol. Struct. 2000. 29:291–325

Comparative Protein Structure Modeling of Genes and Genomes

Marc A. Martí-Renom, Ashley C. Stuart, András Fiser,
Roberto Sánchez, Francisco Melo, and Andrej Šali
*Laboratories of Molecular Biophysics, Pels Family Center for Biochemistry and
Structural Biology, Rockefeller University, 1230 York Ave, New York, NY 10021;
e-mail: sali@rockefeller.edu*

Key Words protein structure prediction, fold assignment, alignment, homology modeling, model evaluation, fully automated modeling, structural genomics

■ **Abstract** Comparative modeling predicts the three-dimensional structure of a given protein sequence (target) based primarily on its alignment to one or more proteins of known structure (templates). The prediction process consists of fold assignment, target–template alignment, model building, and model evaluation. The number of protein sequences that can be modeled and the accuracy of the predictions are increasing steadily because of the growth in the number of known protein structures and because of the improvements in the modeling software. Further advances are necessary in recognizing weak sequence–structure similarities, aligning sequences with structures, modeling of rigid body shifts, distortions, loops and side chains, as well as detecting errors in a model. Despite these problems, it is currently possible to model with useful accuracy significant parts of approximately one third of all known protein sequences. The use of individual comparative models in biology is already rewarding and increasingly widespread. A major new challenge for comparative modeling is the integration of it with the torrents of data from genome sequencing projects as well as from functional and structural genomics. In particular, there is a need to develop an automated, rapid, robust, sensitive, and accurate comparative modeling pipeline applicable to whole genomes. Such large-scale modeling is likely to encourage new kinds of applications for the many resulting models, based on their large number and completeness at the level of the family, organism, or functional network.

CONTENTS

1056-8700/00/0610-0291$14.00

INTRODUCTION

The aim of comparative or homology protein structure modeling is to build a three-dimensional (3D) model for a protein of unknown structure (the target) on the basis of sequence similarity to proteins of known structure (the templates) (10, 17, 80, 145, 155). Two conditions must be met to build a useful model. First, the similarity between the target sequence and the template structure must be detectable. Second, a substantially correct alignment between the target sequence and the template structures must be calculated. Comparative modeling is possible because small changes in the protein sequence usually result in small changes in its 3D structure (34). Although considerable progress has been made in ab initio protein structure prediction (92), comparative protein structure modeling remains the most accurate prediction method. The overall accuracy of comparative models spans a wide range, from low resolution models with only a correct fold to more accurate models comparable to medium resolution structures determined by crystallography or nuclear magnetic resonance (NMR) spectroscopy (155). Even low resolution models can be useful in biology because some aspects of function can sometimes be predicted only from the coarse structural features of a model.

The 3D structures of proteins in a family are more conserved than their sequences (101). Therefore, if similarity between two proteins is detectable at the sequence level, structural similarity can usually be assumed. Moreover, even proteins that have nondetectable sequence similarity can have similar structures. It has been estimated that approximately one third of all sequences are recognizably related to at least one known protein structure (54, 77, 81, 144, 157). Because the number of known protein sequences is approximately 500,000 (9), comparative modeling could in principle be applied to more than 150,000 proteins. This number can be compared to approximately 10,000 protein structures determined by experiment (1, 211). The usefulness of comparative modeling is steadily increasing because the number of unique structural folds that proteins adopt is limited (204) and because the number of experimentally determined new structures is increasing exponentially (70). It is possible that in less than 10 years at least one example of most structural folds will be known, making comparative modeling applicable to most protein sequences (70, 155).

All current comparative modeling methods consist of four sequential steps (Figure 1) (155): fold assignment and template selection, template–target alignment, model building, and model evaluation. If the model is not satisfactory, template selection, alignment, and model building can be repeated until a satisfactory

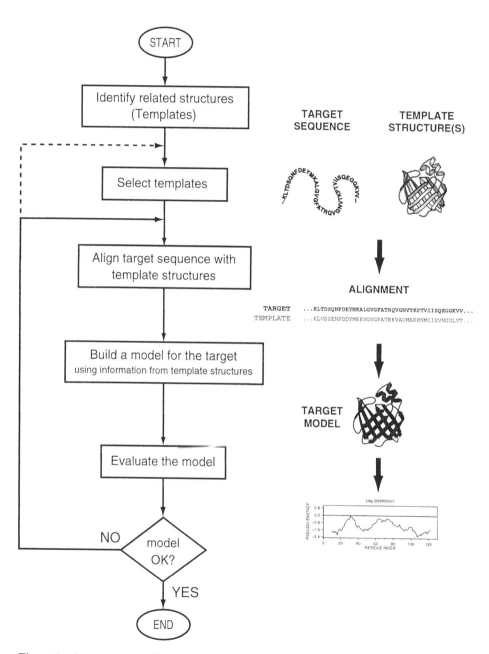

Figure 1   Steps in comparative protein structure modeling. See text for description.

model is obtained. For each of the steps in the modeling process, there are many different methods, programs, and World Wide Web servers (Table 1).

We begin this review by describing the techniques used for all the steps in comparative modeling. We continue by discussing the errors in model structures and methods for detecting these errors, and we conclude by outlining the applications of comparative modeling to individual proteins and to whole genomes. The review focuses on using the methods and tools for comparative modeling, rather than on the physical principles on which the methods are based. The bibliography is not exhaustive, but an attempt was made to quote the latest papers or reviews in the relevant fields.

STEPS IN COMPARATIVE MODELING

Fold Assignment and Template Selection

The starting point in comparative modeling is to identify all protein structures related to the target sequence, and then to select those that will be used as templates. This step is facilitated by numerous protein sequence and structure databases, and database scanning software available on the World Wide Web (4, 11, 70, 163) (Table 1). Templates can be found using the target sequence as a query for searching structure databases such as the Protein Data Bank (1, 211), SCOP (76), DALI (71), and CATH (124). Depending on a genome, the probability of finding a related protein of known structure for a sequence randomly picked from a genome ranges from 20% to 50% (54, 77, 81, 144, 157).

There are three main classes of protein comparison methods that are useful in fold identification. The first class includes the methods that compare the target sequence with each of the database sequences independently, using pairwise sequence–sequence comparison (7). The performance of these methods in searching for related protein sequences (128) and structures (22) has been evaluated exhaustively. Frequently used programs in this class include FASTA (129) and BLAST (5).

The second set of methods relies on multiple sequence comparisons to improve the sensitivity of the search (6, 63, 67, 94, 144). A widely used program in this class is PSI-BLAST (6), which iteratively expands the set of homologs of the target sequence. For a given sequence, an initial set of homologs from a sequence database is collected, a weighted multiple alignment is made from the query sequence and its homologs, a position-specific scoring matrix is constructed from the alignment, and the matrix is used to search the database for new homologs. These steps are repeated until no new homologs are found. In comparison to BLAST, PSI-BLAST finds homologs of known structure for approximately twice as many sequences (125, 176). A related approach (144) also begins by finding all sequences clearly related to the target sequence to obtain the target sequence profile. In addition, similar profiles are constructed for all known protein structures. The potential templates are then found by comparing the target sequence profile with each of the sequence profiles for known structures. Another variation uses multiple sequence

TABLE 1 Programs and World Wide Web servers useful in comparative modeling

Name	Type[a]	World Wide Web address[b]	Reference[c]
Databases			
CATH	S	www.biochem.ucl.ac.uk/bsm/cath/	124
GenBank	S	www.ncbi.nlm.nih.gov/GenBank	15
GeneCensus	S	bioinfo.mbb.yale.edu/genome	58
MODBASE	S	guitar.rockefeller.edu/modbase/	159
PDB	S	www.rcsb.org/pdb/	16
PRESAGE	S	presage.stanford.edu	21
SCOP	S	scop.mrc-lmb.cam.ac.uk/scop/	76
SWISSPROT+TrEMBL	S	www.ebi.ac.uk/swissprot	9
Template search			
123D	S	www.lmmb.ncifcrf.gov/~nicka/123D.html	2
BLAST	S	www.ncbi.nlm.nih.gov/BLAST/	5
DALI	S	www2.ebi.ac.uk/dali/	71
FastA	S	www2.ebi.ac.uk/fasta3	127
MATCHMAKER	P	bioinformatics.burnham-inst.org	59
PHD, TOPITS	S	www.embl-heidelberg.de/predictprotein/ predictprotein.html	139
PROFIT	P	www.came.sbg.ac.at	57
THREADER	P	globin.bio.warwick.ac.uk/~jones/threader.html	82
UCLA-DOE FRSVR	S	www.doe-mbi.ucla.edu/people/frsvr/frsvr.html	53
Sequence alignment			
BCM SERVER	S	dot.imgen.bcm.tmc.edu:9331/	170
BLAST	S	www.ncbi.nlm.nih.gov/BLAST	6
BLOCK MAKER	S	blocks.fhcrc.org/blocks/blockmkr/ make_blocks.html	68
CLUSTAL	S	www2.ebi.ac.uk/clustalw/	78
FASTA3	S	www2.ebi.ac.uk/fasta3/	127
MULTALIN	S	pbil.ibcp.fr/	41
Modeling			
COMPOSER	P	www-cryst.bioc.cam.ac.uk	179
CONGEN	P	www.congenomics.com/congen/congen.html	29
CPH models	S	www.cbs.dtu.dk/services/CPHmodels/	206
DRAGON	P	www.nimr.mrc.ac.uk/~mathbio/a-aszodi/ dragon.html	8
ICM	P	www.molsoft.com	(a)
InsightII	P	www.msi.com	(b)
MODELLER	P	guitar.rockefeller.edu/modeller/modeller.html	148
LOOK	P	www.mag.com	102
QUANTA	P	www.msi.com	(b)
SYBYL	P	www.tripos.com	(c)
SCWRL	P	www.cmpharm.ucsf.edu/~bower/scrwl/ scrwl.html	19
SWISS-MOD	S	www.expasy.ch/swissmod	131
WHAT IF	P	www.sander.embl-heidelberg.de/whatif/	194

(continued)

TABLE 1   (*Continued*)

Name	Type[a]	World Wide Web address[b]	Reference[c]
Model evaluation			
ANOLEA	S	www.fundp.ac.be/pub/ANOLEA.html	113
AQUA	P	www-nmr.chem.ruu.nl/users/rull/aqua.html	98
BIOTECH[d]	S	biotech.embl-ebi.ac.uk:8400/	73, 96
ERRAT	S	www.doe-mbi.ucla.edu/errat_server.html	40
PROCHECK	P	www.biochem.ucl.ac.uk/~roman/procheck/ procheck.html	96
ProCeryon[e]	P	www.proceryon.com/	(d)
ProsaII[e]	P	www.came.sbg.ac.at	169
PROVE	S	www.ucmb.ulb.ac.be/UCMB/PROVE	134
SQUID	P	www.yorvic.york.ac.uk/~oldfield/squid	121
VERIFY3D	S	www.doe-mbi.ucla.edu/verify3d.html	105
WHATCHECK	P	www.sander.embl-heidelberg.de/whatcheck/	73

[a]S, server; P, program.

[b]Some of the sites are mirrored on additional computers.

[c](a) MolSoft Inc., San Diego. (b) Molecular Simulations Inc., San Diego. (c) Tripos Inc., St Louis. (d) ProCeryon Biosciences Inc. New York.

[d]The BIOTECH server uses PROCHECK and WHATCHECK for structure evaluation.

[e]ProCyon is a new software package that includes PeeP, PROFIT and PROSUP, a structure comparison program.

alignments combined with structural information predicted from the sequence of the target (54). The multiple sequence methods for fold identification are especially useful for finding significant structural relationships when the sequence identify between the target and the template drops below 25%. This class of methods appears to be one of the most sensitive fully-automated approaches for detecting remote sequence–structure relationships (6, 77, 203, 213).

The third class of methods are the so-called threading or 3D template matching methods (20, 59, 82), reviewed in (83, 103, 173, 185). These methods rely on pairwise comparison of a protein sequence and a protein of known structure. Whether or not a given target sequence adopts any one of the many known 3D folds is predicted by an optimization of the alignment with respect to a structure-dependent scoring function, independently for each sequence–structure pair. That is, the target sequence is threaded through a library of 3D folds. These methods are especially useful when there are no sequences clearly related to the modeling target, and thus the search cannot benefit from the increased sensitivity of the sequence profile methods.

A useful fold assignment approach is to accept an uncertain assignment provided by any of the methods, build a full-atom comparative model of the target sequence based on this match, and make the final decision about whether or not the match is real by evaluating the resulting comparative model (64, 115, 156).

Once a list of all related protein structures has been obtained, it is necessary to select those templates that are appropriate for the given modeling problem.

Usually, a higher overall sequence similarity between the target and the template sequence yields a better template. In any case, several other factors should be taken into account when selecting the templates:

- The family of proteins, which includes the target and the templates, can frequently be organized in subfamilies. The construction of a multiple alignment and a phylogenetic tree (46) can help in selecting the template from the subfamily that is closest to the target sequence.

- The template "environment" should be compared to the required environment for the model. The term environment is used in a broad sense and includes all factors that determine protein structure except its sequence (e.g., solvent, pH, ligands, and quaternary interactions).

- The quality of the experimental template structure is another important factor in template selection. The resolution and the R-factor of a crystallographic structure and the number of restraints per residue for an NMR structure are indicative of its accuracy.

The priority of the criteria for template selection depends on the purpose of the comparative model. For instance, if a protein–ligand model is to be constructed, the choice of the template that contains a similar ligand is probably more important than the resolution of the template. On the other hand, if the model is to be used to analyze the geometry of the active site of an enzyme, it is preferable to use a high resolution template. It is not necessary to select only one template. In fact, the use of several templates approximately equidistant from the target sequence generally increases the model accuracy (156, 174).

Target–Template Alignment

Most fold assignment methods produce an alignment between the target sequence and template structures. However, this is often not the optimal target–template alignment for comparative modeling. Searching methods are usually tuned for detection of remote relationships, not for optimal alignments. Therefore, once templates have been selected, a specialized method should be used to align the target sequence with the template structures (14, 23, 70, 171, 180). For closely related protein sequences with identity over 40%, the alignment is almost always correct. Regions of low local sequence similarity become common when the overall sequence identity is under 40% (160). The alignment becomes difficult in the "twilight zone" of less than 30% sequence identity (140). As the sequence similarity decreases, alignments contain an increasingly large number of gaps and alignment errors, regardless of whether they are prepared automatically or manually. For example, only 20% of the residues are likely to be correctly aligned when two proteins share 30% sequence identity (79). Maximal effort to obtain the most accurate alignment possible is needed because no current comparative modeling method can recover from an incorrect alignment. There is a great variety of protein sequence alignment methods, many of which are based on dynamic programming techniques (120, 172). A frequently used program for multiple sequence alignment is CLUSTAL (78), which is also available as a World Wide Web server (Table 1).

In the more difficult alignment cases, it is frequently beneficial to rely on multiple structure and sequence information (12, 181). First, the alignment of the potential templates is prepared by superposing their structures. Next, the sequences that are clearly related to the templates and are easily aligned with them are added to the alignment. The same is done for the target sequence. Finally, the two profiles are aligned with each other, taking structural information into account as much as possible (78, 93, 152). In principle, most sequence alignment and structure comparison methods can be used for these tasks (11, 70, 104, 171). The information from structures helps to avoid gaps in secondary structure elements, in buried regions, or between two residues that are far in space. It is generally necessary to check and edit the alignment by inspecting the template structures visually, especially if the target–template sequence identity is low. Secondary structure predictions for the target sequence and its profile are also frequently useful in obtaining a more accurate alignment (3, 141). Because evaluation of a model is more reliable than an evaluation of an alignment, a good way to proceed in the difficult cases is to generate 3D models for all alternative alignments, evaluate the corresponding models, and pick the best model according to the 3D model evaluation rather than the alignment score (64, 115, 156).

Model Building

Once an initial target–template alignment has been built, a variety of methods can be used to construct a 3D model for the target protein. The original and still widely used method is modeling by rigid-body assembly (17, 27, 61). Another family of methods, modeling by segment matching, relies on the approximate positions of conserved atoms in the templates (38, 85, 102, 187). The third group of methods, modeling by satisfaction of spatial restraints, uses either distance geometry or optimization techniques to satisfy spatial restraints obtained from the alignment (8, 24, 66, 148, 175). Accuracies of the various model building methods are relatively similar when used optimally. Other factors such as template selection and alignment accuracy usually have a larger impact on the model accuracy, especially for models based on less than 40% sequence identity to the templates. However, it is important that a modeling method allows a degree of flexibility and automation, making it easier and faster to obtain better models. For example, a method should permit an easy recalculation of a model when a change is made in the alignment; it should be straightforward to calculate models based on several templates; and the method should provide the tools to incorporate prior knowledge about the target (e.g., experimental data or predicted features such as secondary structure). There are many reviews of comparative model building methods (10, 17, 80, 145, 155). Several programs and World Wide Web servers for comparative modeling are listed in Table 1.

Modeling by Assembly of Rigid Bodies   This method assembles a model from a small number of rigid bodies obtained from aligned protein structures. The approach is based on the natural dissection of the protein folds into conserved core regions, variable loops, and side chains. For example, the following semiautomated procedure is implemented in the computer program COMPOSER (179). First, the template structures are selected and superposed. Second, the frame-work is calculated by averaging the coordinates of the C_α atoms of structurally conserved regions in the template structures. Third, the main chain atoms of each core region in the target model are generated by superposing the core segment from the template with the highest sequence similarity to the target on the framework. Fourth, the loops are generated by scanning a database of all known protein structures to identify the structurally variable regions that fit the anchor core regions and have a compatible sequence. Fifth, the side chains are modeled based on their intrinsic conformational preferences and on the conformation of the equivalent side chains in the template structures. And finally, the stereochemistry of the model is improved either by a restrained energy minimization or a molecular dynamics refinement. The accuracy of a model can be somewhat increased if more than one template structure is used to construct the framework and if the templates are averaged into the framework using weights corresponding to their sequence similarities to the target sequence (174). For example, differences between the model and X-ray structures may be slightly smaller than the differences between the X-ray structure of the modeled protein and the best template used to build the model. Future improvements in modeling by rigid body assembly may include the incorporation of rigid body shifts, such as the relative shifts in the packing of α-helices.

Modeling by Segment Matching or Coordinate Reconstruction   The basis of modeling by coordinate reconstruction is the finding that most hexapeptide segments of protein structure can be clustered into approximately 100 structural classes (187). Thus, comparative models can be constructed by using a subset of atomic positions from template structures as "guiding" positions, and by identifying and assembling short, all-atom segments that fit these guiding positions. Usually the C_α atoms of the segments, which are conserved in the alignment between the template structure and the target sequence, are taken as the guiding positions. The all-atom segments that fit the guiding positions can be obtained either by scanning all the known protein structures, including those that are not related to the sequence being modeled (38, 69), or by a conformational search restrained by an energy function (13, 190). For example, a general method for modeling by segment matching is guided by the positions of some atoms (usually C_α atoms) to find the matching segments in a representative database of all known protein structures (102). This method can construct both main chain and side chain atoms and can also model insertions and deletions. It is implemented in the program SEGMOD (Table 1). Some side chain modeling methods (195) and loop construction methods based on finding suitable fragments in the database of known structures (85) can be seen as segment matching or coordinate reconstruction methods.

Modeling by Satisfaction of Spatial Restraints   The methods in this class generate many constraints or restraints on the structure of the target sequence, using its alignment to related protein structures as a guide. The restraints are generally obtained by assuming that the corresponding distances and angles between aligned residues in the template and the target structures are similar. These homology-derived restraints are usually supplemented by stereochemical restraints on bond lengths, bond angles, dihedral angles, and nonbonded atom–atom contacts obtained from a molecular mechanics force field. The model is then derived by minimizing the violations of all the restraints. This can be achieved either by distance geometry or real–space optimization. A distance geometry approach constructs all-atom models from lower and upper bounds on distances and dihedral angles (66). A real–space optimization method, such as that implemented in the computer program MODELLER (148), starts by building the model using the distance and dihedral angle restraints on the target sequence derived from its alignment with template 3D structures. Then, the spatial restraints and the CHARMM22 force field terms, which enforce proper stereochemistry (106), are combined into an objective function. Finally, the model is generated by optimizing the objective function in Cartesian space. Because modeling by satisfaction of spatial restraints can use many different types of information about the target sequence, it is perhaps the most promising of all comparative modeling techniques. One of the strengths of modeling by satisfaction of spatial restraints is that constraints or restraints derived from a number of different sources can easily be added to the homology-derived restraints. For example, restraints might be obtained from NMR experiments, cross-linking experiments, fluorescence spectroscopy, image reconstruction in electron microscopy, site-directed mutagenesis, etc. In this way, a comparative model, especially in the difficult cases, could be improved by making it consistent with available experimental data.

Loop Modeling

In a given fold family, structural variability is a result of substitutions, insertions, and deletions of residues between members of the family. Such changes frequently correspond to exposed loop regions that connect elements of secondary structure in the protein fold. Thus, loops often determine the functional specificity of a given protein framework. They contribute to active and binding sites. Examples include binding of metal ions by metal-binding proteins, small protein toxins by their receptors, antigens by immunoglobulins, nucleotides by a variety of proteins, protein substrates by serine proteases, and DNA by DNA-binding proteins. Consequently, the accuracy of loop modeling is a major factor determining the usefulness of comparative models in studying interactions between the protein and its ligands. This includes the use of models for recognizing ligand binding sites (47, 84) and for ligand docking computations (87). Unfortunately, no generally reliable method is available for constructing loops longer than 5 residues (108), although recently some progress has been made and occasionally longer loops can be modeled correctly (122, 135, 142, 153, 191). An exhaustive set of references for loop modeling papers can be found in (55).

Loop modeling can be seen as a mini–protein folding problem. The correct conformation of a given segment of a polypeptide chain has to be calculated mainly from the sequence of the segment itself. However, loops are generally too short to provide sufficient information about their local fold. Segments of up to 9 residues sometimes have entirely unrelated conformations in different proteins (114). Thus, the conformation of a given segment is also influenced by the core stem regions that span the loop and by the structure of the rest of a protein that cradles the loop.

Many loop modeling procedures have been described. Similarly to the prediction of whole protein structures, there are ab initio methods (30, 50, 119), database search techniques (35, 60, 85), and procedures that combine these two basic approaches (107, 191).

The ab initio loop prediction is based on a conformational search or enumeration of conformations in a given environment, guided by a scoring or energy function. There are many such methods, exploiting different protein representations, energy function terms, and optimization or enumeration algorithms. The search algorithms include sampling of main chain dihedral angles biased by their distributions in known protein structures (119), minimum perturbation random tweak method (165), systematic conformational search (26, 29), global energy minimization by mapping a trajectory of local minima (43), importance-sampling by local minimization of randomly generated conformations (95), local energy minimization (110), molecular dynamics simulations (28, 55), genetic algorithms (111, 136), biased probability Monte Carlo search (45, 183), Monte Carlo with simulated annealing (33, 39, 192), Monte Carlo and molecular dynamics (135), extended-scaled-collective-variable Monte Carlo (88), scaling relaxation and multiple copy sampling (138, 205), searching through discrete conformations by dynamic programming (51, 188), random sampling of conformations relying on dimers from known protein structures (177), self-consistent field optimization (91), and an enumeration based on the graph theory (153). A variety of representations have been used, such as unified atoms, all nonhydrogen atoms, nonhydrogen and "polar" hydrogen atoms, all atoms, as well as implicit and explicit solvent models. The optimized degrees of freedom include Cartesian coordinates and internal coordinates, such as dihedral angles, optimized in continuous or discrete spaces. Loop prediction by optimization is in principle applicable to simultaneous modeling of several loops and loops interacting with ligands, which is not straightforward for the database search approaches.

The database approach to loop prediction consists of finding a segment of main chain that fits the two stem regions of a loop (36, 60, 85, 122, 142, 166, 178, 198). The stems are defined as the main chain atoms that precede and follow the loop but are not part of it. They span the loop and are part of the core of the fold. The search is performed through a database of many known protein structures, not only homologs of the modeled protein. Usually, many different alternative segments that fit the stem residues are obtained and possibly sorted according to geometric criteria or sequence similarity between the template and target loop sequences. The selected segments are then superposed and annealed on the stem regions. These initial crude models are often refined by optimization of some energy function. The database search approach to loop modeling is accurate and efficient when a specific set of loops is created to address the modeling of that class of loops, such as β-hairpins (167) and the hypervariable regions in immunoglobulins (36). For immunoglobulins, an analysis of the hypervariable regions in known immunoglobulin structures resulted in rules with high prediction accuracy for other members of the family. These rules are possible because of the relatively small number of conformations for each loop and because of the dependence of loop conformation on loop length and certain key residues. There are attempts to classify loop conformations into more general categories, thus extending the impressive performance of the key residues approach to more cases (122, 142, 198). However, the database methods are limited by the exponential increase in the number of geometrically possible conformations as a function of loop length. Consequently, only segments of 7 residues or less have most of their conceivable conformations present in the database of known protein structures (48).

The problem of database completeness has recently been ameliorated by restrained energy minimization of the candidate loops obtained from a database search (191). Both the internal conformation and the global orientation relative to the rest of the protein have been optimized. It was concluded that the candidate segments from a database were suitable starting points for modeling loops up to 9 residues long, but extensive optimization was required for loops longer than 4 residues.

Sidechain Modeling

As with loops, side chain conformations are predicted from similar structures and from steric or energetic considerations (145, 193). Disulphide bridges can be treated as a special case in side-chain modeling. They are modeled using structural information from proteins in general (86) and from equivalent disulfide bridges in related structures (150).

Vásquez reviewed and commented on various approaches to side-chain modeling (193). The importance of two effects on sidechain conformation was emphasized: The first effect was the coupling between the main chain and side chains, and the second effect was the continuous nature of the distributions of side-chain dihedral angles; for example, 5–30% of side chains in crystal structures are significantly different from their rotamer conformations (162) and 6% of the χ_1 or χ_2 values are not within $\pm 40°$ of any rotamer conformation (19). Both effects appear to be important when correlating packing energies and stability (100). The correct energetics may be obtained for the incorrect reasons; i.e., the side chains may adopt distorted conformations to compensate for the rigidity of the backbone.

Correspondingly, the backbone shifts may hinder the use of these methods when the template structures are related at less than 50% sequence identity (37). Some attempts to include backbone flexibility in side-chain modeling have been described (65, 75, 91) but are not yet generally applicable.

Significant correlations were found between side-chain dihedral angle probabilities and backbone Φ, Ψ values (19). These correlations go beyond the dependence of side chain conformation on the secondary structure (112). For example, the preferred rotamers can vary within the same secondary structure, even when Φ, Ψ dihedral angles change by as little as 20° (19). Because these changes are smaller than the differences between closely related homologs, the prediction of the side-chain conformations generally cannot be uncoupled from the backbone prediction. This partly explains why the conformation of equivalent side chains in homologous structures is useful in side-chain modeling (148).

Chung & Subbiah gave an elegant structural explanation for the rapid decrease in the conservation of sidechain packing as the sequence identity falls below 30% (37). Although the fold is maintained, the pattern of side-chain interactions is generally lost in this range of sequence similarity (143). Two sets of computations were done for two sample protein sequences: The side-chain conformation was predicted by maximizing packing on the fixed native backbone and on a fixed backbone with approximately 2 Å RMSD from the native backbone; the 2 Å RMSD generally corresponds to the differences between the conserved cores of two proteins related at 25–30% sequence identity. The side-chain predictions on the two backbones turned out to be unrelated. Thus, inasmuch as packing reflects the true laws determining side-chain conformation, a backbone with less than 30% sequence identity to the sequence being modeled is not sufficient to produce the correct packing of the buried side chains.

The solvation term is important for the modeling of exposed sidechains (42, 133, 161, 196), many of which are expected to be highly flexible without a single dominant conformation. It was also demonstrated that treating hydrogen bonds explicitly could significantly improve side-chain predictions (44, 49). Calculations that do not account for the solvent, either implicitly or explicitly, may introduce errors in the hydrogen-bonding patterns even in the core regions of a protein (133).

A recent survey analyzed the accuracy of three different side-chain prediction methods (75). These methods were tested by predicting side-chain conformations on near-native protein backbones with <4 Å RMSD to the native structures. The three methods include the packing of backbone-dependent rotamers (19), the self-consistent mean-field approach to positioning rotamers based on their van der Waals interactions (89), and the segment-matching method of Levitt (102). The accuracies of the methods were surprisingly similar. All were able to correctly predict approximately 50% of χ_1 angles and 35% of both χ_1 and χ_2 angles. In typical comparative modeling applications where the backbone is closer to the native structures (<2 Å RMSD), these numbers increase by approximately 20% (151).

ERRORS IN COMPARATIVE MODELS

As the similarity between the target and the templates decreases, the errors in the model increase. Errors in comparative models can be divided into five categories (151, 156) (Figure 2):

- Errors in side-chain packing. As the sequences diverge, the packing of side chains in the protein core changes. Sometimes even the conformation of identical side chains is not conserved, a pitfall for many comparative modeling methods. Side-chain errors are critical if they occur in regions that are involved in protein function, such as active sites and ligand-binding sites.

- Distortions and shifts in correctly aligned regions. As a consequence of sequence divergence, the main chain conformation changes, even if the overall fold remains the same. Therefore, it is possible that in some correctly aligned segments of a model, the template is locally different (<3 Å) from the target, resulting in errors in that region. The structural differences are sometimes not due to differences in sequence but are a consequence of artifacts in structure determination or structure determination in different environments (e.g., packing of subunits in a crystal). The simultaneous use of several templates can minimize this kind of error (156, 174).

- Errors in regions without a template. Segments of the target sequence that have no equivalent region in the template structure (i.e., insertions or loops) are the most difficult regions to model. If the insertion is relatively short, less than 9 residues long, some methods can correctly predict the conformation of the backbone (191). Conditions for successful prediction are the correct alignment and an accurately modeled environment surrounding the insertion.

- Errors due to misalignments. The largest source of errors in comparative modeling are misalignments, especially when the target–template sequence identity decreases below 30%. However, alignment errors can be minimized in two ways. First, it is usually possible to use a large number of sequences to construct a multiple alignment, even if most of these sequences do not have known structures. Multiple alignments are generally more reliable than pairwise alignments (12, 181). The second way of improving the alignment is to iteratively modify those regions in the alignment that correspond to predicted errors in the model (156).

- Incorrect templates. This is a potential problem when distantly related proteins are used as templates (i.e., less than 25% sequence identity). Distinguishing between a model based on an incorrect template and a model based on an incorrect alignment with a correct template is difficult. In both cases, the evaluation methods will predict an unreliable model. The

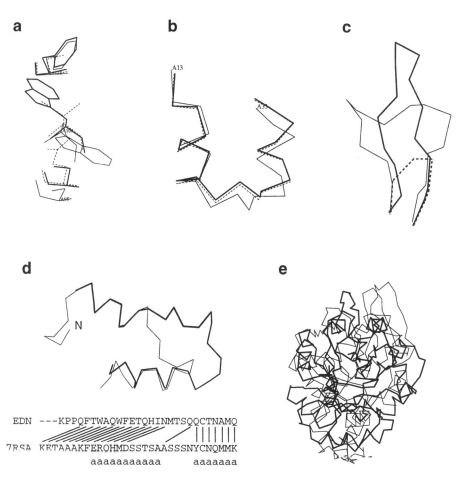

Figure 2 Typical errors in comparative modeling (151, 156). (*a*). Errors in side chain packing. The Trp 109 residue in the crystal structure of mouse cellular retinoic acid binding protein I (thin line) is compared with its model (thick line), and with the template mouse adipocyte lipid-binding protein (broken line). (*b*) Distortions and shifts in correctly aligned regions. A region in the crystal structure of mouse cellular retinoic acid binding protein I is compared with its model and with the template fatty acid binding protein using the same representation as in panel a. (*c*) Errors in regions without a template. The C_α trace of the 112–117 loop is shown for the X-ray structure of human eosinophil neurotoxin (thin line), its model (thick line), and the template ribonuclease A structure (residues 111–117; broken line). (*d*) Errors due to misalignments. The N-terminal region in the crystal structure of human eosinophil neurotoxin (thin line) is compared with its model (thick line). The corresponding region of the alignment with the template ribonuclease A is shown. The black lines show correct equivalences, that is residues whose C_α atoms are within 5 Å of each other in the optimal least-squares superposition of the two X-ray structures. The "a" characters in the bottom line indicate helical residues. (*e*) Errors due to an incorrect template. The X-ray structure of α-trichosanthin (thin line) is compared with its model (thick line) which was calculated using indole-3-glycerophosphate synthase as the template.

conservation of the key functional or structural residues in the target sequence increases the confidence in a given fold assignment.

Comparative modeling has been criticized for its inability to provide a final model closer to the target-experimental structure than the template used to generate the model (108). This is only the case when there are errors in the template–target alignment used for modeling. When the evaluation of the template–target similarity is based on the template–target alignment used for modeling the model is generally closer to the target structure than is any of the templates (156).

An informative way to test protein structure modeling methods as well as the modelers using them is provided by the biannual meetings on Critical Assessment of Techniques for Protein Structure Prediction (CASP) (92, 118). The last meeting was held in December of 1998 and is summarized in the special issue of *Proteins* Suppl. 3, 1999 (212). Protein modelers are challenged to model sequences with unknown 3D structure and to submit their models to the organizers before the meeting. At the same time, the 3D structures of the prediction targets are being determined by X-ray crystallography or NMR methods. They only become available after the models are calculated and submitted. Thus, a bona fide evaluation of protein structure modeling methods is possible. An important extension of the CASP meetings is a completely automated and online evaluation of protein structure modeling servers on the World Wide Web. The idea has so far been implemented in the threading category only (52). It is likely to be extended to other kinds of structural prediction.

EVALUATION OF MODELS

The quality of the predicted model determines the information that can be extracted from it. Thus, estimating the accuracy of 3D protein models is essential for interpreting them. The model can be evaluated as a whole as well as in individual regions. There are many model evaluation programs and servers (97, 197) (Table 1).

The first step in model evaluation is to assess if the model has the correct fold (157). A model will have the correct fold if the correct template is picked and if that template is aligned at least approximately correctly with the target sequence. The fold of a model can be assessed by a high sequence similarity with the closest template, an energy based Z-score (157, 169), or by conservation of the key functional or structural residues in the target sequence.

Once the fold of a model is assessed, a more detailed evaluation of the overall model accuracy can be obtained based on the similarity between the target and template sequences (Figure 3) (157). Sequence identity above 30% is a relatively good predictor of the expected accuracy. The reasons are the well-known relationship between structural and sequence similarities of two proteins (34), the 'geometrical' nature of modeling that forces the model to be as close to the template as possible

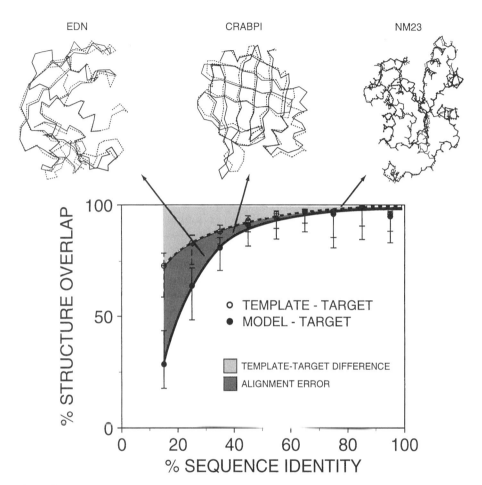

Figure 3 Average model accuracy as a function of the template–target sequence similarity. At the top, sample models (solid line) at three typical accuracy levels are compared with corresponding actual structures (dotted line). The models were calculated with MODELLER in a completely automated fashion before the experimental structures were available (151). When multiple sequence and structure information is used, and the alignments are edited by hand, the models can be significantly more accurate than shown here (156). At the bottom, the models of known protein structures used to determine the dependence of the overall model accuracy as a function of template–target sequence identity were calculated entirely automatically, based on single templates (157). Percentage structure overlap is defined as the fraction of equivalent residues. Two residues are equivalent when their C_α atoms are within 3.5 Å of each other upon rigid-body, least-squares superposition of the two structures.

(148), and the inability of any current modeling procedure to recover from an incorrect alignment (156). The dispersion of the model–target structural overlap increases with the decrease in sequence identity. If the target–template sequence identity falls below 30%, the sequence identity becomes unreliable as a measure of expected accuracy of a single model. Models that deviate significantly from the average accuracy are frequent. It is in such cases that model evaluation methods are particularly useful.

In addition to the target–template sequence similarity, the environment can strongly influence the accuracy of a model. For instance, some calcium-binding proteins undergo large conformational changes when bound to calcium. If a calcium-free template is used to model the calcium-bound state of the target, it is likely that the model will be incorrect irrespective of the target–template similarity or accuracy of the template structure (126). This also applies to the experimental determination of protein structure; a structure must be determined in the functionally meaningful environment.

A basic requirement for a model is to have good stereochemistry. Some useful programs for evaluating stereochemistry are PROCHECK (96), PROCHECK-NMR (98), AQUA (98), SQUID (121), and WHATCHECK (72). The features of a model that are checked by these programs include bond lengths, bond angles, peptide bond and side-chain ring planarities, chirality, main-chain and side-chain torsion angles, and clashes between nonbonded pairs of atoms.

Distributions of many spatial features have been compiled from high resolution protein structures, and large deviations from the most likely values have been interpreted as strong indicators of errors in the model. Such features include packing (62), formation of a hydrophobic core (31), residue and atomic solvent accessibilities (90), spatial distribution of charged groups (32), distribution of atom–atom distances (40), atomic volumes (134), and main-chain hydrogen bonding (96).

There are also methods for testing 3D models that implicitly take into account many of the criteria listed above. These methods are based on 3D profiles and statistical potentials of mean force (105, 168). Programs implementing this approach include VERIFY3D (105), PROSAII (169), HARMONY (184), and ANOLEA (113). The programs evaluate the environment of each residue in a model with respect to the expected environment as found in the high-resolution X-ray structures. There is a concern about the theoretical validity of the energy profiles for detecting regional errors in models. It is likely that the contributions of the individual residues to the overall free energy of folding vary widely, even when normalized by the number of atoms or interactions made. If this is correct, the correlation between the prediction errors and energy peaks is greatly weakened, resulting in the loss of predictive power of the energy profile. Despite these concerns, error profiles have been useful in some applications (115).

Recently, a physics-based approach to deriving energy functions has been tested for use in protein structure evaluation. Lazaridis & Karplus (99) used an effective energy function that combined the CHARMM (25) vacuum potential with a Gaussian model for the solvation free energy. The results showed that the native state was always more stable than grossly misfolded conformations. Moreover, the authors concluded that molecular mechanics energy functions, complemented by a simple model for the solvation free energy, can perform as well as statistical functions in discriminating correct and misfolded models.

APPLICATIONS OF COMPARATIVE MODELING

Comparative modeling is an increasingly efficient way to obtain useful information about the proteins of interest. For example, comparative models can be helpful in designing mutants to test hypotheses about a protein's function (18, 200), identifying active and binding sites (164), identifying, designing and improving ligands for a given binding site (137), modeling substrate specificity (201), predicting antigenic epitopes (149), simulating protein–protein docking (189), inferring function from a calculated electrostatic potential around the protein (109), facilitating molecular replacement in X-ray structure determination (74), refining models based on NMR constraints (116), testing and improving a sequence–structure alignment (199), confirming a remote structural relationship (64, 115), and rationalizing known experimental observations. For an exhaustive review of comparative modeling applications see (80).

Fortunately, a 3D model does not have to be absolutely perfect to be helpful in biology, as demonstrated by the applications listed above. However, the type of question that can be addressed with a particular model does depend on its accuracy (Figure 4). Three levels of model accuracy and some of the corresponding applications are as follows.

- At the low end of the spectrum, there are models based on less than 30% sequence identity and have sometimes less than 50% of their C_α atoms within 3.5 Å of their correct positions. Such models still have the correct fold, which is frequently sufficient to predict approximate biochemical function. More specifically, only nine out of 80 fold families known in 1994 contained proteins (domains) that were not in the same functional class, although 32% of all protein structures belonged to one of the nine superfolds (123). Models in this low range of accuracy combined with model evaluation can be used to confirm or reject a match between remotely related proteins (156, 157).

- In the middle of the accuracy spectrum are the models based on approximately 30–50% sequence identity, corresponding to 85% of the C_α atoms modeled within 3.5 Å of their correct positions. Fortunately, the active and binding sites are frequently more conserved than the rest of the fold and are thus modeled more accurately (157). In general, medium

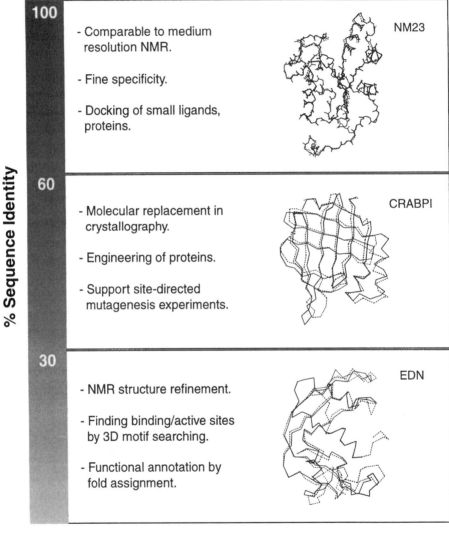

Figure 4   Applications of comparative modeling. The potential uses of a comparative model depend on its accuracy. This in turn depends significantly on the sequence identity between the target and the template structure on which the model was based. Sample models from Figure 3 are shown on the right.

resolution models frequently allow refinement of the functional prediction based on sequence alone because ligand binding is most directly determined by the structure of the binding site rather than by its sequence. It is frequently possible to correctly predict important features of the target protein that do not occur in the template structure. For example, the location of a binding site can be predicted from clusters of charged residues (109), and the size of a ligand can be predicted from the volume of the binding site cleft (201). Medium-resolution models can also be used to construct site-directed mutants with altered or destroyed binding capacity, which in turn could test hypotheses about sequence–structure–function relationships. Other problems that can be addressed with medium resolution comparative models include designing proteins that have compact structures without long tails, loops, and exposed hydrophobic residues for better crystallization; or designing proteins with added disulfide bonds for extra stability.

- The high end of the accuracy spectrum corresponds to models based on more than 50% sequence identity. The average accuracy of these models approaches that of low resolution X-ray structures (3 Å resolution) or medium resolution NMR structures (10 distance restraints per residue) (156). The alignments on which these models are based generally contain almost no errors. In addition to the already listed applications, high quality models can be used for docking of small ligands (137) or whole proteins onto a given protein (186, 189).

COMPARATIVE MODELING IN STRUCTURAL GENOMICS

The aim of structural genomics is to determine or accurately predict the 3D structure of all the proteins encoded in the genomes (117, 147, 182, 202, 207–209). This aim will be achieved by a focused, large-scale determination of protein structures by X-ray crystallography and NMR spectroscopy, combined efficiently with accurate protein structure modeling techniques. The structural genomics project will deliver improved methods and a process for high-throughput protein structure determination. The process involves (*a*) selection of the target proteins or domains, (*b*) cloning, expression, and purification of the targets, (*c*) crystallization and structure determination by X-ray crystallography or by NMR spectroscopy, and (*d*) archiving and annotation of the new structures. Given the current state of comparative modeling, a target sequence should have at least 30% sequence identity to a structural template. This corresponds to one experimentally determined structure per sequence family, rather than fold family. Because there are approximately five times more sequence families than fold families (70), it is likely that structural genomics will have to determine the structure of approximately 10,000 protein domains. Experimental structure determination of approximately 10,000 properly chosen proteins should result in useful 3D models for domains in hundreds of thousands of other protein sequences.

For comparative modeling to contribute to structural genomics, automation of all the steps in the modeling process is essential. There are at least five good reasons for automation. First, modeling of hundreds of thousands of protein sequences is obviously feasible only when it is completely automated. Second, automation makes it efficient for both the experts and non-experts to use comparative models, allowing them to spend more time designing experiments. Third, it is important that the best possible models are easily accessible to the non-experts. The results of the CASP meetings have shown that human expertise is usually a critical component of modeling success (92). However, modeling experts will not be on hand for every template selection or alignment question, just as structural biologists cannot solve every protein structure of biological interest. Fourth, automation encourages development of better methods. And finally, automated modeling removes any human bias, thus making the models more objective. Model evaluation by computational means is an essential component of large-scale modeling.

The automation of large-scale comparative modeling involves assembling a software pipeline that consists of modules for fold assignment, template selection, target–template alignment, model generation, and model evaluation. Computer programs for these individual operations already exist, and it may seem trivial to combine them. Yet, manual intervention is prevalent in setting many modeling parameters, especially during template selection and alignment. This enables an expert to implement various sources of information that can be difficult to exploit in an automated fashion. Thus, the primary challenge in large-scale comparative modeling is to build an automated, rapid, robust, sensitive, and accurate comparative modeling pipeline applicable to whole genomes; such a pipeline should perform at least as well as a human expert on individual proteins.

Two examples of large-scale comparative modeling for complete genomes have been described (132, 157). The sequences encoded in the *E. coli* genome have been used to build models for 10–15% of the proteins using the SWISS-MODEL web server (130, 132). Peitsch et al have also recently modeled many proteins in the SWISS-PROT database and made the models available on their web site (Table 1). The second large-scale modeling pipeline, MODPIPE, produced models for five procaryotic and eukaryotic genomes (157, 159). This calculation resulted in models for substantial segments of 17.2%, 18.1%, 19.2%, 20.4%, and 15.7% of all proteins in the genomes of *Saccharomyces cerevisiae* (6218 proteins in the genome); *Escherichia coli* (4290 proteins), *Mycoplasma genitalium* (468 proteins), *Caenorhabditis elegans* (7299 proteins, incomplete), and *Methanococcus janaschii* (1735 proteins), respectively. An important element in this study was the evaluation of the model's reliability. This is important because most of the related protein pairs share less than 30% sequence identity, resulting in significant errors in many models. The models were assigned to a reliable or unreliable class by a procedure (157) that depends on the statistical potential function from PROSAII (169). This allowed the identification of those models that were likely to be based on correct templates and approximately correct alignments. As a result, 236 yeast proteins lacking any prior structural information were assigned to a fold family; 40 of these proteins had no prior functional annotations. A more precise evaluation was used to calibrate the relationship between model accuracy and the percentage of sequence identity on which the model was based (157). Almost half of the 1071 reliably modeled proteins in the yeast genome share more than approximately 35% sequence identity with their templates. All the alignments, models, and model evaluations are available in the MODBASE database of comparative protein structure models (159, 210). Most recently, the MODPIPE pipeline software has been improved by using PSI-BLAST (6) for fold assignment, multiple templates and sequences for target–template alignment, and a complex statistical potential of mean force for model evaluation. This resulted in models for approximately 17,000 proteins, covering substantial segments of 18–45% of the proteins in 12 complete genomes (210).

Large-scale comparative modeling will extend opportunities to tackle a myriad of problems by providing many protein models for many genomes. A large database of experimental structures leveraged by comparative models will arouse questions about protein evolution, such as the physical origins of protein structure stability and protein activity, regulatory differences among similar enzymes, and the specificity and plasticity of ligand binding sites. Structural genomics will also aid in the process of drug design. A collection of experimentally determined complexes of proteins with their ligands, aligned with comparative models for the rest of the family members, will permit a facile comparison of ligand binding requirements and also reveal permitted substitutions in and around important residues. Structural genomics will provide an obvious resource for many questions and, hopefully, will provoke new ones

A specific example of a new opportunity for tackling existing problems by virtue of providing many protein models from many genomes is the selection of a target protein for drug development. A protein that is likely to have high ligand specificity is a good choice; specificity is important because specific drugs are less likely to be toxic. Large-scale modeling facilitates imposing the specificity filter in target selection by enabling a structural comparison of the ligand binding sites of many proteins, from human or other organisms. Such comparisons may make it possible to rationally select a target whose binding site is structurally most different from the binding sites of all the other proteins that may potentially react with the same drug. For example, when a human pathogenic organism needs to be inhibited, it may be possible to select a pathogen target that is structurally most different from all the human homologs. Alternatively, when a human metabolic pathway needs to be regulated, the target identification could focus on the particular protein in the pathway that has the binding site most dissimilar from its human homologs.

CONCLUSION

Over the past few years, there has been a gradual increase in both the accuracy of comparative models and the fraction of protein sequences that can be modeled with useful accuracy. The magnitude of errors in fold assignment, alignment, and the modeling of sidechains, loops, distortions, and rigid body shifts has decreased measurably. This is a consequence of both better techniques and a larger number of known protein sequences and structures. Nevertheless, all the errors remain significant and demand future methodological improvements. In addition, there is a great need for more accurate detection of errors in a given protein structure model. Error detection is useful both for refinement and interpretation of the models.

It is now possible to predict by comparative modeling significant segments of approximately one third of all known protein sequences. One half of these models are in the least accurate class, based on less than 30% sequence identity to known protein structures. The remaining 35 and 15% of the models are in the medium (<50% sequence identity) and high (>50% identity) accuracy classes. The fraction of protein sequences that can be modeled by comparative modeling is currently increasing by approximately 4% per year (158). It has been estimated that globular protein domains cluster in only a few thousand fold families, approximately 900 of which have already been structurally defined (70, 76). Assuming the current growth rate in the number of known protein structures, the structure of at least one member of most of the globular folds will be determined in less than 10 years (70). According to this argument, comparative modeling will be applicable to most of the globular protein domains soon after the expected completion of the human genome project. However, there are some classes of proteins, such as membrane proteins, that will not be amenable to modeling without improvements in structure determination and modeling techniques. To maximize the number of proteins that can be modeled reliably, a concerted effort toward structure determination of new folds by X-ray crystallography and nuclear magnetic resonance spectroscopy is in order, as envisioned by structural genomics (117, 147, 182, 202, 207–209). The full potential of the genome sequencing projects will only be realized once all protein functions are assigned and understood. This will be facilitated by integrating genomic sequence information with databases arising from functional and structural genomics. Comparative modeling will play an important bridging role in these efforts.

ACKNOWLEDGMENTS

We are grateful to Dr. Azat Badretdinov and Mr. Eric Feyfant for many discussions about comparative protein structure modeling. MAM-R and AF are Burroughs Wellcome Fellows. RS is a Howard Hughes Medical Institute predoctoral fellow. FM is a Norman and Rosita Winston Biomedical Research Foundation Fellow. AŠ is a Sinsheimer Scholar and an Alfred P. Sloan Research Fellow. The investigations have also been aided by grants from NIH (GM 54762) and NSF (BIR-9601845). This review is based on (55, 56, 145, 146, 154, 156, 158).

Visit the Annual Reviews home page at www.AnnualReviews.org

LITERATURE CITED

1. Abola EE, Bernstein FC, Bryant SH, Koetzle TF, Weng J. 1987. Protein data bank. In *Crystallographic Databases—Information, Content, Software Systems, Scientific Applications*, ed. FH Allen, G Bergerhoff, R Sievers, pp. 107–132. Bonn/Cambridge/Chester. Data Commission Int. Union of Crystallography.

2. Alexandrov NN, Nussinov R, Zimmer RM. 1995. Fast protein fold recognition via sequence to structure alignment and contact capacity potentials. In *Pacific Symposium on Biocomputing '96*, ed. L Hunter, TE Klein, pp. 53–72, Singapore: World Sci. Pub.

3. Aloy P, Mas JM, Martí-Renom MA, Querol E, Avilés FX, Oliva B. 2000. Human a2 pro-carboxypeptidase model: secondary structure prediction as a powerful tool for homology modelling improvement. *J. Computer-Aided Molec. Design.* 14:83–92

4. Altschul SF, Boguski MS, Gish W, Wootton JC. 1994. Issues in searching molecular sequence databases. *Nat. Genet.* 6:119–29

5. Altschul SF, Gish W, Miller W, Myers EW, Lipman DJ. 1990. Basic local alignment search tool. *J. Mol. Biol.* 215:403–10

6. Altschul SF, Madden TL, Schaffer AA, Zhang J Zhang, Miller W, Lipman DJ. 1997. Gapped BLAST and PSI-BLAST: a new generation of protein database search programs. *Nucleic Acids Res.* 25:3389–402

7. Apostolico A, Giancarlo R. 1998. Sequence alignment in molecular biology. *J. Comput. Biol.* 5:173–96

8. Aszódi A, Taylor WR. 1996. Homology modelling by distance geometry. *Folding Design* 1:325–34

9. Bairoch A, Apweiler R. 1999. The SWISS-PROT protein sequence data bank and its supplement TrEMBL in 1999. *Nucleic Acids Res.* 27:49–54

10. Bajorath J, Stenkamp R, Aruffo A. 1994. Knowledge-based model building of proteins: Concepts and examples. *Protein Sci.* 2:1798–810

11. Barton GJ. 1998. Protein sequence alignment and database scanning. In *Protein Structure Prediction: A Practical Approach*, ed. MJE Sternberg. Oxford, UK: Oxford Univ. Press

12. Barton GJ, Sternberg MJE. 1987. A strategy for the rapid multiple alignment of protein sequences; confidence levels from tertiary structure comparisons. *J. Mol. Biol.* 198:327–37

13. Bassolino-Klimas D, Bruccoleri RE. 1992. Application of a directed conformational search for generating 3-D coordinates for protein structures from α-carbon coordinates. *Proteins* 14:465–74

14. Baxevanis AD. 1998. Practical aspects of multiple sequence alignment. *Methods Biochem. Anal.* 39:172–88

15. Benson DA, Karsch-Mizrachi I, Lipman DJ, Ostell J, Rapp BA, Wheeler DL. 2000. GenBank. *Nucleic Acid Res.* 28:15–18

16. Bernstein FC, Koetzle TF, Williams GJB, Meyer EF, Brice MD, Rodgers JR, Kennard O, Shimanouchi T, Tasumi M. 1977. The protein data bank: a computer-based archival file for macromolecular structures. *J. Mol. Biol.* 112:535–42

17. Blundell TL, Sibanda BL, Sternberg MJE, Thornton JM. 1987. Knowledge-based prediction of protein structures and the design of novel molecules. *Nature* 326:347–52

18. Boissel JP, Lee WR, Presnell SR, Cohen FE, Bunn HF. 1993. Erythropoietin

structure-function relationships. Mutant proteins that test a model of tertiary structure. *J. Biol. Chem.* 268:15983–93

19. Bower MJ, Cohen FE, Dunbrack RL Jr. 1997. Prediction of protein side-chain rotamers from a backbone-dependent rotamer library: a new homology modeling tool. *J. Mol. Biol.* 267:1268–82

20. Bowie JU, Lüthy R, Eisenberg D. 1991. A method to identify protein sequences that fold into a known three-dimensional structure. *Science* 253:164–70

21. Brenner SE, Barken D, Levitt M. 1999. The PRESAGE database for structural genomics. *Nucleic Acids Res.* 27:251–53

22. Brenner SE, Chothia C, Hubbard TJ. 1998. Assessing sequence comparison methods with reliable structurally identified distant evolutionary relationships. *Proc. Natl. Acad. Sci. USA* 95:6073–78

23. Briffeuil P, Baudoux G, Lambert C, Bolle X De, Vinals C, Feytmans E, Depiereux E. 1998. Comparative analysis of seven multiple protein sequence alignment servers: clues to enhance reliability of predictions. *Bioinformatics* 14:357–66

24. Brocklehurst SM, Perham RN. 1993. Prediction of the three-dimensional structures of the biotinylated domain from yeast pyruvate carboxylase and of the lipolyated H-protein from the pea leaf glycine cleavage system: a new automated methods for the prediction of protein tertiary structure. *Protein Sci.* 2:626–39

25. Brooks BR, Bruccoleri RE, Olafson BD, States DJ, Swaminathan S, Karplus M. 1983. CHARMM: a program for macromolecular energy minimization and dynamics calculations. *J. Comp. Chem.* 4: 187–217

26. Brower RC, Vasmatzis G, Silverman M, DeLisi C. 1993. Exhaustive conformational search and simulated annealing for models of lattice peptides. *Biopolymers* 33:329–34

27. Browne WJ, North ACT, Phillips DC, Brew K, Vanaman TC, Hill RC. 1969. A possible three-dimensional structure of bovine α-lactalbumin based on that of hen's egg-white lysozyme. *J. Mol. Biol.* 42:65–86

28. Bruccoleri BR, Karplus M. 1990. Conformational sampling using high temperature molecular dynamics. *Biopolymers* 29:1847–62

29. Bruccoleri RE. 1993. Application of systematic conformational search to protein modeling. *Molec. Simulat.* 10:151–74

30. Bruccoleri RE, Karplus M. 1987. Prediction of the folding of short polypeptide segments by uniform conformational sampling. *Biopolymers* 26:137–68

31. Bryant SH, Amzel LM. 1987. Correctly folded proteins make twice as many hydrophobic contacts. *Int. J. Peptide Protein Res.* 29:46–52

32. Bryant SH, Lawrence CE. 1991. The frequency of ion-pair substructures in proteins is quantitatively related to electrostatic potential: a statistical model for nonbonded interactions. *Proteins* 9:108–19

33. Carlacci L, Englander SW. 1996. Loop problem in proteins: developments on the Monte Carlo simulated annealing approach. *Comp. Chem.* 17:1002–12

34. Chothia C, Lesk AM. 1986. The relation between the divergence of sequence and structure in proteins. *EMBO J.* 5:823–26

35. Chothia C, Lesk AM. 1987. Canonical structures for the hypervariable regions of immunoglobulins. *J. Mol. Biol.* 196:901–17

36. Chothia C, Lesk AM, Tramontano A, Levitt M, Smith-Gill SJ, Air G, Sheriff S, Padlan EA, Davies D, Tulip WR, Colman PM, Spinelli S, Alzari PM, Poljak RJ. 1989. Conformation of immunoglobulin hypervariable regions. *Nature* 342:877–83

37. Chung SY, Subbiah S. 1996. A structural explanation for the twilight zone of protein sequence homology. *Structure* 4:1123–27

38. Claessens M, Cutsem EV, Lasters I, Wodak S. 1989. Modelling the polypeptide back-

bone with 'spare parts' from known protein structures. *Protein Eng.* 4:335–45

39. Collura V, Higo J, Garnier J. 1993. Modeling of protein loops by simulated annealing. *Protein Sci.* 2:1502–10

40. Colovos C, Yeates TO. 1993. Verification of protein structures: patterns of non-bonded atomic interactions. *Protein Sci.* 2:1511–19

41. Corpet F. 1988. Multiple sequence alignment with hierarchical clustering. *Nucleic Acids Res.* 16:10881–90

42. Cregut D, Liautard J-P, Chiche L. 1994. Homology modeling of annexin I: implicit solvation improves side-chain prediction and combination of evaluation criteria allows recognition of different types of conformational error. *Protein Eng.* 7:1333–44

43. Dudek MJ, Ramnarayan K, Ponder JW. 1998. Protein structure prediction using a combination of sequence homology and global energy minimization: II. Energy functions. *J. Comp. Chem.* 19:548–73

44. Dunbrack RL, Karplus M. 1993. Prediction of protein side-chain conformations from a backbone conformation dependent rotamer library. *J. Mol. Biol.* 230:543–71

45. Evans JS, Mathiowetz AM, Chan SI, Goddard WA III. 1995. De novo prediction of polypeptide conformations using dihedral probability grid Monte Carlo methodology. *Protein Sci.* 4:1203–16

46. Felsenstein J. 1985. Confidence limits on phylogenies: an approach using the bootstrap. *Evolution* 39:783–91

47. Fetrow JS, Godzik A, Skolnick J. 1998. Functional analysis of the *Escherichia coli* genome using the sequence-to-structure-to-function paradigm: identification of proteins exhibiting the glutaredoxin/thioredoxin disulfide oxidoreductase activity. *J. Mol. Biol.* 282:703–11

48. Fidelis K, Stern PS, Bacon D, Moult J. 1994. Comparison of systematic search and database methods for constructing segments of protein structure. *Protein Eng.* 7:953–60

49. Filippis V De, Sander C, Vriend G. 1994. Predicting local structural changes that result from point mutations. *Protein Eng.* 7:1203–8

50. Fine RM, Wang H, Shenkin PS, Yarmush DL, Levinthal C. 1986. Predicting antibody hypervariable loop conformations. II: Minimization and molecular dynamics studies of MCP603 from many randomly generated loop conformations. *Proteins* 1:342–62

51. Finkelstein AV, Reva BA. 1992. Search for the stable state of a short chain in a molecular field. *Protein Eng.* 5:617–24

52. Fischer D, Barret C, Bryson K, Elofsson A, Godzik A, Jones D, Karplus KJ, Kelley LA, MacCallum RM, Pawowski K, Rost B, Rychlewski L, Sternberg MJE. 1999. CAFASP-1: critical assessment of fully automated structure prediction methods. *Proteins.* Suppl. 3, pp. 209–17

53. Fischer D, Eisenberg D. 1996. Fold recognition using sequence-derived predictions. *Protein Sci.* 5:947–55

54. Fischer D, Eisenberg D. 1997. Assigning folds to the proteins encoded by the genome of *Mycoplasma genitalium*. *Proc. Natl. Acad. Sci. USA* 94:11929–34

55. Fiser A, Do RKG, Šali A. 2000. Modeling of loops in protein structures. Submitted

56. Fiser A, Sánchez R, Melo F, Šali A. 2000. Comparative protien structure modeling. In *Computational Biochemistry and Biophysics*, ed. M Watanabe, B Roux, A MacKerell, O Backer. New York: Marcel Dekker. In press

57. Flockner H, Braxenthaler M, Lackner P, Jaritz M, Ortner M, Sippl MJ. 1995. Progress in fold recognition. *Proteins* 23:376–86

58. Gerstein M, Levitt M. 1997. A structural census of the current population of protein sequences. *Proc. Natl. Acad. Sci. USA* 94:11911–16

59. Godzik A, Kolinski A, Skolnick J. 1992. Topology fingerprint approach to the

inverse protein folding problem. *J. Mol. Biol.* 227:227–38

60. Greer J. 1980. Model for haptoglobin heavy chain based upon structural homology. *Proc. Natl. Acad. Sci. USA* 77:3393–97

61. Greer J. 1990. Comparative modelling methods: application to the family of the mammalian serine proteases. *Proteins* 7:317–34

62. Gregoret LM, Cohen FE. 1991. Effect of packing density on chain conformation. *J. Mol. Biol.* 219:109–22

63. Gribskov M. 1994. Profile analysis. *Meth. Mol. Biol.* 25:247–66

64. Guenther B, Onrust R, Šali A, O'Donnell M, Kuriyan J. 1997. Crystal structure of the δ' subunit of the clamp-loader complex of *E. coli* DNA polymerase III. *Cell* 91:335–45

65. Harbury PB, Tidor B, Kim PS. 1995. Repacking proteins cores with backbone freedom: Structure prediction for coiled coils. *Proc. Natl. Acad. Sci. USA* 92:8408–12

66. Havel TF, Snow ME. 1991. A new method for building protein conformations from sequence alignments with homologues of known structure. *J. Mol. Biol.* 217:1–7

67. Henikoff S, Henikoff JG. 1994. Protein family classification based on searching a database of blocks. *Genomics* 19:97–107

68. Henikoff S, Henikoff JG, Alford WJ, Pietrokovski S. 1995. Automated construction and graphical presentation of protein blocks from unaligned sequences. *Gene* 163:17–26

69. Holm L, Sander C. 1991. Database algorithm for generating protein backbone and side-chain co-ordinates from C_α trace: application to model building and detection of co-ordinate errors. *J. Mol. Biol.* 218:183–94

70. Holm L, Sander C. 1996. Mapping the protein universe. *Science* 273:595–602

71. Holm L, Sander C. 1999. Protein folds and families: sequence and structure alignments. *Nucleic Acids Res.* 27:244–47

72. Hooft RWW, Sander C, Vriend G. 1996. Verification of protein structures: side-chain planarity. *J. Appl. Crystallogr.* 29:714–16

73. Hooft RWW, Vriend G, Sander C, Abola EE. 1996. Errors in protein structures. *Nature* 381:272

74. Howell PL, Almo SC, Parsons MR, Hajdu J, Petsko GA. 1992. Structure determination of turkey egg-white lysozyme using Laue diffraction data. *Acta Crystallogr. B* 48:200–7

75. Huang ES, Koehl P, Levitt M, Pappu RV, Ponder JW. 1998. Accuracy of side-chain prediction upon near-native protein backbones generated by ab initio folding methods. *Proteins* 33:204–17

76. Hubbard TJP, Ailey B, Brenner SE, Murzin AG, Chothia C. 1999. SCOP: A structural classification of proteins database. *Nucleic Acids Res.* 27:254–56

77. Huynen M, Doerks T, Eisenhaber F, Orengo C, Sunyaev S, Yuan Y, Bork P. 1998. Homology-based fold predictions for *Mycoplasma genitalium* proteins. *J. Mol. Biol.* 280:323–26

78. Jeanmougin F, Thompson JD, Gouy M, Gibson DG, Higgins TJ. 1998. Multiple sequence alignment with CLUSTAL X. *Trends Biochem. Sci.* 23:403–5

79. Johnson MS, Overington JP. 1993. A structural basis for sequence comparisons: an evaluation of scoring methodologies. *J. Mol. Biol.* 233:716–38

80. Johnson MS, Srinivasan N, Sowdhamini R, Blundell TL. 1994. Knowledge-based protein modelling. *CRC Crit. Rev. Biochem. Mol. Biol.* 29:1–68

81. Jones DT. 1999. GenTHREADER: An efficient and reliable protein fold recognition method for genomic sequences. *J. Mol. Biol.* 287:797–815

82. Jones DT, Taylor WR, Thornton JM. 1992. A new approach to protein fold recognition. *Nature* 358:86–89

83. Jones DT. 1997. Progress in protein struc-

ture prediction. *Curr. Opin. Struct. Biol.* 7:377–87

84. Jones S, Thornton JM. 1997. Prediction of protein-protein interaction sites using patch analysis. *J. Mol. Biol.* 272:133–43

85. Jones TH, Thirup S. 1986. Using known substructures in protein model building and crystallography. *EMBO J.* 5:819–22

86. Jung S-H, Pastan I, Lee B. 1994. Design of interchain disulfide bonds in the framework region of the Fv fragment of the monoclonal antibody B3. *Proteins* 19:35–47

87. Kick EK, Roe DC, Skillman AG, Liu G, Ewing TJ, Sun Y, Kuntz ID, Ellman JA. 1997. Structure-based design and combinatorial chemistry yield low nanomolar inhibitors of cathepsin D. *Chem. Biol.* 4:297–307

88. Kidera A. 1995. Enhanced conformational sampling in Monte Carlo simulations of proteins: applications to a constrained peptide. *Proc. Natl. Acad. Sci. USA* 92:9886–89

89. Koehl P, Delarue M. 1994. Application of a self-consistent mean field theory to predict protein side-chains conformation and estimate their conformational entropy. *J. Mol. Biol.* 239:249–75

90. Koehl P, Delarue M. 1994. Polar and nonpolar atomic environments in the protein core: implication for folding and binding. *Proteins* 20:264–78

91. Koehl P, Delarue M. 1995. A self consistent mean field approach to simultaneous gap closure and side-chain positioning in protein homology modelling. *Nat. Struct. Biol.* 2:163–70

92. Koehl P, Levitt M. 1999. A brighter future for protein structure prediction. *Nat. Struct. Biol.* 6:108–11

93. Koretke KK, Luthey-Schulten Z, Wolynes PG. 1996. Self-consistently optimized statistical mechanical energy functions for sequence structure alignment. *Protein Sci.* 5:1043–59

94. Krogh A, Brown M, Mian IS, Sjolander K,

Haussler D. 1994. Hidden Markov models in computational biology: applications to protein modeling. *J. Mol. Biol.* 235:1501–31

95. Lambert MH, Scheraga HA. 1989. Pattern recognition in the prediction of protein structure. I. Tripeptide conformational probabilities calculated from the amino acid sequence. *J. Comp. Chem.* 10:770–97

96. Laskowski RA, McArthur MW, Moss DS, Thornton JM. 1993. PROCHECK: a program to check the stereochemical quality of protein structures. *J. Appl. Crystalogr.* 26:283–91

97. Laskowski RA, MacArthur MW, Thornton JM. 1998. Validation of protein models derived from experiment. *Curr. Opin. Struct. Biol.* 5:631–39

98. Laskowski RA, Rullmann JAC, MacArthur MW, Kaptein R, Thornton JM. 1996. AQUA and PROCHECK-NMR: programs for checking the quality of protein structures solved by NMR. *J. Biomol. NMR* 8:477–86

99. Lazaridis T, Karplus M. 1999. Discrimination of the native from misfolded protein models with an energy function including implicit solvation. *J. Mol. Biol.* 288:477–87

100. Lee C. 1995. Testing homology modeling on mutant proteins: predicting structural and thermodynamic effects in the Ala98 → Val mutants of T4 lysozyme. *Folding Design* 1:1–12

101. Lesk AM, Chothia C. 1980. How different amino acid sequences determine similar protein structures: The structure and evolutionary dynamics of the globins. *J. Mol. Biol.* 136:225–70

102. Levitt M. 1992. Accurate modeling of protein conformation by automatic segment matching. *J. Mol. Biol.* 226:507–33

103. Levitt M. 1997. Competitive assessment of protein fold recognition and alignment accuracy. *Proteins* (Suppl.) 1:92–104

104. Levitt M, Gerstein M. 1998. A unified statistical framework for sequence

comparison and structure comparison. *Proc. Natl. Acad. Sci. USA* 95:5913–20

105. Lüthy R, Bowie JU, Eisenberg D. 1992. Assessment of protein models with three-dimensional profiles. *Nature* 356:83–85

106. MacKerell AD, Bashford D, Bellott M, Dunbrack RL Jr., Evanseck JD, Field MJ, Fischer S, Gao J, Guo H, Ha S, Joseph-McCarthy D, Kuchnir L, Kuczera K, Lau FTK, Mattos C, Michnick S, Ngo T, Nguyen DT, Prodhom B, Reiher WE, Roux M., Smith JC, Stote J, Watanabe M., Wiorkiewicz-Kuczera J, Yin D, Karplus M. 1998. All-atom empirical potential for molecular modeling and dynamics studies of proteins. *J. Phys. Chem. B* 102:3586–16

107. Martin ACR, Cheetham JC, Rees AR. 1989. Modeling antibody hypervariable loops: a combined algorithm. *Proc. Natl. Acad. Sci. USA* 86:9268–72

108. Martin ACR, MacArthur MW, Thornton JM. 1997. Assessment of comparative modeling in CASP2. *Proteins* (Suppl.) 1:14–28

109. Matsumoto R, Šali A, Ghildyal N, Karplus M, Stevens RL. 1995. Packaging of proteases and proteoglycans in the granules of mast cells and other hematopoietic cells. A cluster of histidines in mouse mast cell protease-7 regulates its binding to heparin serglycin proteoglycan. *J. Biol. Chem.* 270:19524–31

110. Mattos C, Petsko GA, Karplus M. 1994. Analysis of two-residue turns in proteins. *J. Mol. Biol.* 238:733–47

111. McGarrah DB, Judson RS. 1993. Analysis of the genetic algorithm method of molecular conformation determination. *J. Comp. Chem.* 14:1385–95

112. McGregor MJ, Islam SA, Sternberg MJE. 1987. Analysis of the relationship between side-chain conformation and secondary structure in globular proteins. *J. Mol. Biol.* 198:295–310

113. Melo F, Feytmans E. 1998. Assessing protein structures with a non-local atomic interaction energy. *J. Mol. Biol.* 277:1141–52

114. Mezei M. 1998. Chameleon sequences in the PDB. *Protein Eng.* 11:411–14

115. Miwa JM, Ibanez-Tallon I, Crabtree GW, Sánchez R, Šali A, Role LW, Heintz N. 1999. lynx1, an endogenous toxin-like modulator of nicotinic acetylcholine receptors in the mammalian CNS. *Neuron* 23:105–14

116. Modi S, Paine MJ, Sutcliffe MJ, Lian L-Y, Primrose WU, Wolfe CR, Roberts GCK. 1996. A model for human cytochrome P_{450} 2D6 based on homology modeling and NMR studies of substrate binding. *Biochemistry* 35:4540–50

117. Montelione GT, Anderson S. 1999. Structural genomics: keystone for a human proteome project. *Nat. Struct. Biol.* 6:11–12

118. Moult J, Hubbard T, Bryant SH, Fidelis K, Pedersen JT. 1997. Critical assessment of methods of protein structure prediction (CASP): round II. *Proteins* (Suppl.) 1:2–6

119. Moult J, James MNG. 1986. An algorithm for determining the conformation of polypeptide segments in proteins by systematic search. *Proteins* 1:146–63

120. Needleman SB, Wunsch CD. 1970. A general method applicable to the search for similarities in the amino acid sequence of two proteins. *J. Mol. Biol.* 48:443–53

121. Oldfield TJ. 1992. Squid: a program for the analysis and display of data from crystallography and molecular dynamics. *J. Mol. Graphics* 10:247–52

122. Oliva B, Bates PA, Querol E, Aviles FX, Sternberg MJE. 1997. An automated classification of the structure of protein loops. *J. Mol. Biol.* 266:814–30

123. Orengo CA, Jones DT, Thornton JM. 1994. Protein superfamilies and domain superfolds. *Nature* 372:631–34

124. Orengo CA, Pearl FMG, Bray JE, Todd AE, Martin AC, Conte L. Lo, Thornton JM. 1999. The CATH database provides insights into protein structure/function re-

lationship. *Nucleic Acids Res.* 27:275–79

125. Park J, Karplus K, Barret C, Hughey R, Haussler D, Hubbard T, Chothia C. 1998. Sequence comparisons using multiple sequences detect three times as many remote homologues as pairwise methods. *J. Mol. Biol.* 284:1201–10

126. Pawlowski K, Bierzyński A, Godzik A. 1996. Structural diversity in a family of homologous proteins. *J. Mol. Biol.* 258:349–66

127. Pearson WR. 1990. Rapid and sensitive comparison with FASTA and FASTP. *Methods Enzymol.* 183:63–98

128. Pearson WR. 1995. Comparison of methods for searching protein sequence databases. *Protein Sci.* 4:1145–60

129. Pearson WR. 1998. Empirical statistical estimates for sequence similarity searches. *J. Mol. Biol.* 276:71–84

130. Peitsch MC. 1996. PROMOD and SWISS-MODEL—Internet-based tools for automated comparative protein modeling. *Biochem. Soc. Trans* 24:274–79

131. Peitsch MC, Jongeneel CV. 1993. A 3-D model for the CD40 ligand predicts that it is a compact trimer similar to the tumor necrosis factors. *Int. Immunol.* 5:233–38

132. Peitsch MC, Wilkins MR, Tonella L, Sánchez JC, Appel RD, Hochstrasser DF. 1997. Large-scale protein modelling and integration with the SWISS-PROT and SWISS-2DPAGE databases: the example of *Escherichia coli. Electrophoresis* 18:498–501

133. Petrella RJ, Lazaridis T, Karplus M. 1998. Protein side chain conformer prediction: a test of the energy function. *Folding Design* 3:353–77

134. Pontius J, Richelle J, Wodak SJ. 1996. Deviations from standard atomic volumes as a quality measure for protein crystal structures. *J. Mol. Biol.* 264:121–36

135. Rapp CS, Friesner RA. 1999. Prediction of loop geometries using a generalized Born model of solvation effect. *Proteins* 35:173–83

136. Ring CS, Cohen FE. 1994. Conformational sampling of loop structures using genetic algorithm. *Isr. J. Chem.* 34:245–52

137. Ring CS, Sun E, McKerrow JH, Lee GK, Rosenthal PJ, Kuntz ID, Cohen FE. 1993. Structure-based inhibitor design by using protein models for the development of antiparasitic agents. *Proc. Natl. Acad. Sci. USA* 90:3583–87

138. Rosenbach D, Rosenfeld R. 1995. Simultaneous modeling of multiple loops in proteins. *Protein Sci.* 4:496–505

139. Rost B. 1995. Topits: Threading one-dimensional predictions into three-dimensional structures. In *The Third Int. Conf. on Intelligent Systems for Molecular Biology (ISMB)*, ed. C Rawlings, D Clark, R Altman, L Hunter, T Lengauer, S Wodak, pp. 314–21. Menlo Park, CA; AAAI Press

140. Rost B. 1999. Twilight zone of protein sequence alignments. *Protein Eng.* 12:85–94

141. Rost B, Sander C. 1993. Prediction of protein structure at better than 70% accuracy. *J. Mol. Biol.* 232:584–99

142. Rufino SD, Donate LE, Canard LHJ, Blundell TL. 1997. Predicting the conformational class of short and medium size loops connecting regular secondary structures: application to comparative modeling. *J. Mol. Biol.* 267:352–67

143. Russell RB, Barton GJ. 1994. Structural features can be unconserved in proteins with similar folds. An analysis of side-chain to side-chain contacts secondary structure and accessibility. *J. Mol. Biol.* 244:332–50

144. Rychlewski L, Zhang B, Godzik A. 1998. Fold and function predictions for *Mycoplasma genitalium* proteins. *Folding Design* 3:229–38

145. Šali A. 1995. Modelling mutations and homologous proteins. *Curr. Opin. Biotech.* 6:437–51

146. Šali A. 1995. Protein modeling by

satisfaction of spatial restraints. *Mol. Med. Today* 1:270–77

147. Šali A. 1998. 100,000 protein structures for the biologist. *Nat. Struct. Biol.* 5: 1029–32

148. Šali A, Blundell TL. 1993. Comparative protein modelling by satisfaction of spatial restraints. *J. Mol. Biol.* 234:779–815

149. Šali A, Matsumoto R, McNeil HP, Karplus M, Stevens RL. 1993. Three-dimensional models of four mouse mast cell chymases. Identification of proteoglycan-binding regions and protease-specific antigenic epitopes. *J. Biol. Chem.* 268:9023–34

150. Šali A, Overington JP. 1994. Derivation of rules for comparative protein modeling from a database of protein structure alignments. *Protein Sci.* 3:1582–96

151. Šali A, Potterton L, Yuan F, Vlijmen H, Karplus M. 1995. Evaluation of comparative protein structure modeling by MODELLER. *Proteins* 23:318–26

152. Šali A, Sánchez R, Badretdinov AY, Fiser A, Melo F, Overington JP, Feyfant E, Martí-Renom MA. 1999. *MODELLER, A Protein Structure Modeling Program, Release 5.* URL http://guitar.rockefeller.edu/

153. Samudrala R, Moult J. 1998. A graph-theoretic algorithm for comparative modeling of protein structure. *J. Mol. Biol.* 279:287–302

154. Sánchez R, Badretdinov A. Ya, Feyfant E, Šali A. 1997. Homology protein structure modeling. *Trans. Am. Cryst. Assoc.* 32:81–91

155. Sánchez R, Šali A. 1997. Advances in comparative protein-structure modeling. *Curr. Opin. Struct. Biol.* 7:206–14

156. Sánchez R, Šali A. 1997. Evaluation of comparative protein structure modeling by MODELLER-3. *Proteins* (Suppl.) 1:50–58

157. Sánchez R, Šali A. 1998. Large-scale protein structure modeling of the *Saccha-*

romyces cerevisiae genome. *Proc. Natl. Acad. Sci. USA* 95:13597–602

158. Sánchez R, Šali A. 1999. Comparative protein structure modeling in genomics. *J. Comp. Phys.* 151:388–401

159. Sánchez R, Šali A. 1999. The MODBASE database of comparative protein structure models. *Bioinformatics.* In press

160. Saqi MAS, Russell RB, Sternberg MJE. 1999. Misleading local sequence alignments: implications for comparative protein modelling. *Protein Eng.* 11:627–30

161. Schiffer CA, Caldwell JW, Kollman PA, Stroud RM. 1990. Prediction of homologous protein structures based on conformational searches and energetics. *Proteins* 8:30–43

162. Schrauber H, Eisenhaber F, Argos P. 1993. Rotamers: To be or not to be? An analysis of amino acid side-chain conformations in globular proteins. *J. Mol. Biol.* 230:592–612

163. Schuler GD. 1998. Sequence alignment and database searching. *Meth. Biochem. Anal.* 39:145–71

164. Sheng Y, Šali A, Herzog H, Lahnstein J, Krilis S. 1996. Modelling, expression and site-directed mutagenesis of human β_2-glycoprotein I. Identification of the major phospholipid binding site. *J. Immunol.* 157:3744–51

165. Shenkin PS, Yarmush DL, Fine RM, Wang H, Levinthal C. 1987. Predicting antibody hypervariable loop conformation. I. Ensembles of random conformations for ring-like structures. *Biopolymers* 26:2053–85

166. Shepherd AJ, Gorse D, Thornton JM. 1999. Prediction of the location and type of β-turns in proteins using neural networks. *Protein Sci.* 8:1045–55

167. Sibanda BL, Blundell TL, Thornton JM. 1989. Conformation of β-hairpins in protein structures: a systematic classification with applications to modelling by homology, electron deosity fitting and protein engineering. *J. Mol. Biol.* 206:759–77

168. Sippl MJ. 1990. Calculation of conformational ensembles from potentials of mean force. An approach to the knowledge-based prediction of local structures in globular proteins. *J. Mol. Biol.* 213:859–83

169. Sippl MJ. 1993. Recognition of errors in three-dimensional structures of proteins. *Proteins* 17:355–62

170. Smith RF, Wiese BA, Wojzynski MK, Davison DB, Worley KC. 1996. Bcm search launcher–an integrated interface to molecular biology data base search and analysis services available on the world wide web. *Genome Res.* 6:454–62

171. Smith TF. 1999. The art of matchmaking: sequence alignment methods and their structural implications. *Structure* 7:R7–R12

172. Smith TF, Waterman MS. 1981. Identification of common molecular subsequences. *J. Mol. Biol.* 147:195–97

173. Smith TF, Conte L. Lo, Bienkowska J, Gaitatzes C, Rogers RGJ, Lathrop R. 1997. Current limitations to protein threading approaches. *J. Comput. Biol.* 4:217–25

174. Srinivasan N, Blundell TL. 1993. An evaluation of the performance of an automated procedure for comparative modelling of protein tertiary structure. *Protein Eng.* 6:501–12

175. Srinivasan S, March CJ, Sudarsanam S. 1993. An automated method for modeling proteins on known templates using distance geometry. *Protein Sci.* 2:227–89

176. Sternberg MJE, Bates PA, Kelley LA, MacCallum RM. 1999. Progress in protein structure prediction: assessment of CASP3. *Curr. Opin. Struct. Biol.* 9:368–73

177. Sudarsanam S, DuBose RF, March CJ, Srinivasan S. 1995. Modeling protein loops using a ϕ_{i+1}, ψ_i dimer database. *Protein Sci.* 4:1412–20

178. Summers NL, Karplus M. 1990. Modeling of globular proteins: a distance-based search procedure for the construction of insertion/deletion regions and pro → nonpro mutations. *J. Mol. Biol.* 216:991–1016

179. Sutcliffe MJ, Haneef I, Carney D, Blundell TL. 1987. Knowledge based modelling of homologous proteins. Part I. Three dimensional frameworks derived from the simultaneous superposition of multiple structures. *Protein Eng.* 1:377–84

180. Taylor WR. 1996. Multiple protein sequence alignment: algorithms and gap insertion. *Methods Enzymol.* 266:343–67

181. Taylor WR, Flores TP, Orengo CA. 1994. Multiple protein structure alignment. *Protein Sci.* 3:1858–70

182. Terwilliger TC, Waldo G, Peat TS, Newman JM, Chu K, Berendzen J. 1998. Class-directed structure determination: foundation for a protein structure initiative. *Protein Sci.* 7:1851–56

183. Thanki N, Zeelen JP, Mathieu M, Jaenicke R, Abagyan RA, Wierenga RK, Schliebs W. 1997. Protein engineering with monomeric triosephosphate isomerase (monoTIM): the modelling and structure verification of a seven-residue loop. *Protein Eng.* 10:159–67

184. Topham CM, Srinivasan N, Thorpe CJ, Overington JP, Kalsheker NA. 1994. Comparative modelling of major house dust mite allergen *der p* I: structure validation using an extended environmental amino acid propensity table. *Protein Eng.* 7:869–94

185. Torda AE. 1997. Perspectives in protein-fold recognition. *Curr. Opin. Struct. Biol.* 7:200–5

186. Totrov M, Abagyan R. 1994. Detailed *ab initio* prediction of lysozyme-antibody complex with 1.6 Å accuracy. *Nat. Struct. Biol.* 1:259–63

187. Unger R, Harel D, Wherland S, Sussman JL. 1989. A 3-D building blocks approach to analyzing and predicting structure of proteins. *Proteins* 5:355–73

188. Vajda S, DeLisi C. 1990. Determining minimum energy conformations of polypeptides by dynamic programming. *Biopolymers* 29:1755–72

189. Vakser IA. 1997. Evaluation of GRAMM low-resolution docking methodology on the hemagglutinin-antibody complex. *Proteins* (Suppl.) 1:226–30

190. Gelder CWG, Leusen FJJ, Leunissen JAM, Noordik JH. 1994. A molecular dynamics approach for the generation of complete protein structures from limited coordinate data. *Proteins* 18:174–85

191. Vlijmen HWT, Karplus M. 1997. PDB-based protein loop prediction: parameters for selection and methods for optimization. *J. Mol. Biol.* 267:975–1001

192. Vasmatzis G, Brower RC, DeLisi C. 1994. Predicting immunoglobulin-like hypervariable loops. *Biopolymers* 34:1669–80

193. Vásquez M. 1996. Modeling side-chain conformation. *Curr. Opin. Struct. Biol.* 6:217–21

194. Vriend G. 1990. WHAT IF: A molecular modeling and drug design program. *J. Mol. Graph.* 8:52–56

195. Vriend G, Sander C, Stouten PFW. 1994. A novel search method for protein sequence-structure relations using property profiles. *Protein Eng.* 7:23–29

196. Wilson C, Gregoret LM, Agard DA. 1993. Modeling side-chain conformation for homologous proteins using an energy-based rotamer search. *J. Mol. Biol.* 229:996–1006

197. Wilson KS, Dauter Z, Lamsin VS, Walsh M, Wodak S, Richelle J, Pontius J, Vaguine A, Sander RWW Hooft, Vriend G, Thornton JM, Laskowski RA, MacArthur MW, Dodson EJ, Murshudov G, Oldfield TJ, Kaptein RR, Rullman JAC. 1998. Who checks the checkers? Four validation tools applied to eight atomic resolution structures. *J. Mol. Biol.* 276:417–36

198. Wojcik J, Mornon J-P, Chomilier J.

1999. New efficient statistical sequence-dependent structure prediction of short to medium-sized protein loops based on an exhaustive loop classification. *J. Mol. Biol.* 289:1469–90

199. Wolf E, Vassilev A, Makino Y, Šali A, Nakatani Y, Burley SK. 1998. Crystal structure of a GCN5-related N-acetyltransferase: *Serratia marcescens* aminoglycoside 3-N-acetyltransferase. *Cell* 94:51–61

200. Wu G, Fiser A, Kuile B, Šali A, Müller M. 1999. Convergent evolution of *Trichomonas vaginalis* lactate dehydrogenase from malate dehydrogenase. *Proc. Natl. Acad. Sci. USA* 96:6285–90

201. Xu LZ, Sánchez R, Šali A, Heintz N. 1996. Ligand specificity of brain lipid binding protein. *J. Biol. Chem.* 271:24711–19

202. Zarembinski TI, Hung LW, Mueller-Dieckmann HJ, Kim KK, Yokota H, Kim R, Kim SH. 1998. Structure-based assignment of the biochemical function of a hypothetical protein: a test case of structural genomics. *Proc. Nat. Acad. Sci. USA* 95:15189–93

203. Zhang B, Jaroszewski L, Rychlewski L, Godzik A. 1998. Similarities and differences between nonhomologous proteins with similar folds: evaluation of threading strategies. *Folding Design* 2:307–17

204. Zhang ZT. 1997. Relations of the numbers of protein sequences, families and folds. *Protein Eng.* 10:757–61

205. Zheng Q, Kyle DJ. 1996. Accuracy and reliability of the scaling-relaxation method for loop closure: an evaluation based on extensive and multiple copy conformational samplings. *Proteins* 24:209–17

206. Lund O, Frimand K, Gorodkiu J, Bohr H, Bohr J, Brunak S. 1997. Protein distance constraints predicted by neural networks and probability density functions. *Prot. Eng.* 10:1241–48

207. Šali A, Kuriyan J. 1999. Challenges at the frontiers of structural biology. *Trends Biochem. Sci.* 22:M20–M24

208. Burley SK, Almo SC, Bonanno JB, Capel M, Chance MR, Gaasterland T, Lin D, Šali A, Studier FW, Swaminathan S. 1999. Structural genomics: beyond the Human Genome Project. *Nat. Genet.* 23:151–57

209. Cort JR, Koonin EV, Bash PA, Kennedy MA. 1999. A phylogenetic approach to target selection for structural genomics: solution structure of YciH. *Nucl. Acids Res.* 27:4018–27

210. Sánchez R, Pieper U, Mirković N, de Bakker PIW, Wittenstein E, Šali A, 2000. MODBASE a database of annotated comparative protein structure models. *Nucl. Acids Res.* 28:250–53

211. Berman HM, Westbrook J, Feng Z, Gilliland G, Bhat TN, Weissig H, Shindyalov IN, Bourne PE. 2000. The Protein Data Bank. *Nucleic Acids Res.* 28:235–42

212. Jones TA, Kleywegt GJ. 1999. CASP3. Comperative modeling evoluation. *Proteins: Struct., Funct. & Gen.* Suppl. 3 pp. 30–46

213. Muller A. MacCallum RM, Sternberg MJ. 1999. Benchmarking PSI-BLAST in genome anotation *J. Mol. Biol.* 293:1257–41

Annu. Rev. Biophys. Biomol. Struct. 2000. 29:327–59

Fast Kinetics and Mechanisms in Protein Folding*

William A. Eaton, Victor Muñoz[1], Stephen J. Hagen[2], Gouri S. Jas, Lisa J. Lapidus, Eric R. Henry, and James Hofrichter

Laboratory of Chemical Physics, Building 5, National Institute of Diabetes and Digestive and Kidney Diseases, National Institutes of Health, Bethesda, Maryland 20892-0520; e-mail: eaton@helix.nih.gov

Key Words   laser-triggering, temperature-jump, fast mixing, secondary structure, kinetic models

■ **Abstract**   This review describes how kinetic experiments using techniques with dramatically improved time resolution have contributed to understanding mechanisms in protein folding. Optical triggering with nanosecond laser pulses has made it possible to study the fastest-folding proteins as well as fundamental processes in folding for the first time. These include formation of α-helices, β-sheets, and contacts between residues distant in sequence, as well as overall collapse of the polypeptide chain. Improvements in the time resolution of mixing experiments and the use of dynamic nuclear magnetic resonance methods have also allowed kinetic studies of proteins that fold too fast ($\gtrsim 10^3$ s^{-1}) to be observed by conventional methods. Simple statistical mechanical models have been extremely useful in interpreting the experimental results. One of the surprises is that models originally developed for explaining the fast kinetics of secondary structure formation in isolated peptides are also successful in calculating folding rates of single domain proteins from their native three-dimensional structure.

CONTENTS

*The US government holds a nonexclusive, royalty-free license in and to any copyright covering this paper.

[1]Present address: Department of Chemistry and Biochemistry, and Center for Biological Structure and Molecular Organization, University of Maryland, College Park, MD 20742.

[2]Present address: Department of Physics, University of Florida, Gainesville, FL 32611-8440.

INTRODUCTION AND OVERVIEW

Protein folding is a subject that is attracting scientists from a wide range of disciplines (34). The interest arises from the explosion of information on protein sequences and the challenge of understanding one of the most fundamental biochemical processes. The protein-folding problem is generally divided into two parts. In the first the goal is to predict the three-dimensional structure from the amino acid sequence. The second part is the no less daunting task of understanding the relation between protein sequences and mechanisms of folding. In protein folding, the mechanism is the distribution of microscopic pathways that connect the myriad of structures of the denatured state with the unique structure of the native state.

Over the past decade major advances have occurred in both theoretical (7, 19, 29, 37, 50, 83, 85, 103, 115) and experimental approaches to investigating protein-folding mechanisms. A turning point in experimental studies was the recognition that it is essential to first characterize the kinetics and thermodynamics of folding in the simplest systems. The idea of studying small, single domain proteins without additional chemical complexity from disulfide bridges, metals, or other cofactors began with the equilibrium and kinetic experiments on chymotrypsin inhibitor 2 (CI2) (56). CI2 was found to fold and unfold as a simple two-state system with no kinetic intermediates. In subsequent work, the participation of individual residues in the transition state for folding was investigated by studying the relative effects of mutations on folding rates and equilibrium constants (35, 54). The studies on CI2 sparked considerable interest among experimentalists in carefully characterizing the kinetics, thermodynamics, and effects of mutations in other small, single domain proteins (34, 55).

A second major advance in experimental studies has resulted from the introduction of a new generation of experiments with dramatically improved time resolution. The contribution of these studies to our understanding of protein folding is the subject of this review. Until just a few years ago, folding kinetics were studied almost exclusively using stopped-flow techniques. In this experiment, protein folding is initiated by rapidly mixing a chemically denatured protein solution with a buffer to dilute the denaturant. The kinetics of folding are then monitored with one of several optical spectroscopic methods. Similarly, unfolding can be initiated by mixing a native protein solution with concentrated denaturant. Stopped flow experiments have yielded an enormous amount of valuable information that has provided the basis for much of what we know about the kinetics of folding and unfolding. It does, however, have a fundamental limitation—poor time resolution. The time required to mix solutions and move them into an observation cuvette is generally at least a few milliseconds. This is the so-called "dead time" of the instrument. A typical observation in many experiments has been that much, and in some cases all, of the spectroscopic changes associated with folding already occur within this dead time (64, 72, 95, 98). Furthermore, it was known for some time from studies on synthetic polymers that elementary processes such as α-helix formation are too fast to be observed in stopped-flow experiments (44).

A second motivation for developing fast kinetic methods has been to provide a much-needed reality check on computer simulations, which are flooding the protein-folding literature. Our conceptualization of the folding process is strongly influenced by the results of simulations, so it is important to perform real experiments on time scales that can be directly compared with the computer experiments. So far the most important insights have come from simulations of simplified representations of proteins in lattice and off-lattice models (19, 29, 83, 85, 103, 115). Such models provide simple, concrete examples that can be extremely helpful in clarifying both theoretical and experimental issues. However, the most detailed and potentially realistic kinetic simulations employ all-atom molecular dynamics calculations. With few exceptions (23, 24, 75), these calculations have been restricted by computer time to one or just a few trajectories of tens of nanoseconds or less. They are therefore not yet capable of direct simulation of protein folding (see, however, Ref. 30) but are rapidly approaching time scales long enough to simulate secondary structure formation.

Finally, development of fast methods has been motivated by theoretical studies that have introduced an energy landscape approach to protein folding (9). A particularly interesting result from calculations of free energy surfaces is that the barriers to protein folding should be quite small, suggesting that for the fastest folding proteins the barrier might disappear altogether. This barrierless or so-called downhill folding could produce unusual (i.e. nonexponential) kinetics (8). The energy landscape perspective also suggested that in many proteins the multiphasic kinetics observed in stopped-flow experiments arise from the escape of misfolded or partially folded molecules from traps in the landscape and not from a stepwise formation of native structure (8, 9). For such proteins the fast productive routes to the native state were yet to be resolved (61). A notable example is cytochrome c in which folding is multiexponential and requires hundreds of milliseconds (33, 110). In this case kinetic complexity results from transient covalent binding to the heme iron of a nonnative histidine almost 50 residues distant along the sequence from the native methionine ligand. Once binding of this histidine is blocked, folding is submillisecond, too fast to be observed by the stopped-flow method (33, 110).

With this background several groups of biophysical scientists working in the area of time-resolved spectroscopy were attracted to the protein-folding problem. Time-resolved spectroscopy with pulsed lasers had been quite successful in functional studies on proteins, so it seemed natural to take advantage of this powerful technology to investigate protein folding. It was, moreover, apparent that finding ways to initiate protein folding with laser pulses would provide dramatically improved time resolution. Recognizing the importance of experiments in which the concentration of chemical denaturant is rapidly changed to initiate folding or unfolding, a second line of investigation has been directed toward the development of methods to improve the time resolution in mixing experiments. These new, fast-folding techniques have permitted the investigation of fundamental processes in protein folding, including formation of α-helices, β-sheets, and contacts between residues distant in sequence as well as overall collapse of the polypeptide chain and folding of the very fastest proteins.

Although these new techniques have allowed the study of previously unobserved processes in protein folding, it is only quite recently that they have provided major new insights into folding mechanisms. These include a much deeper understanding of the mechanism of secondary structure formation, the introduction of the notion of an upper limit on the rate of protein folding (a "speed limit"), the discovery of unusual kinetics suggesting that very fast folding is continuously downhill in free energy, and direct observation of polypeptide collapse prior to formation of the native structure. One of the surprises from this work is that simple statistical mechanical models, originally developed for explaining the fast kinetics of secondary structure formation in isolated peptides, are remarkably successful in quantitatively explaining the kinetic behavior of small proteins. This finding has several important implications, including the possibility that the underlying physics of folding may be much simpler than previously thought.

BASIC IDEAS OF FAST-FOLDING METHODS

There have been several recent reviews on fast-folding techniques, so here we only present a very brief description of the basic physical ideas underlying these methods (14, 43, 52, 99). Methods for rapid initiation of protein folding can be roughly classified into three categories—photochemical triggering, temperature or pressure jump, and ultrarapid mixing methods. The first fast-folding study employed a photochemical trigger—the photodissociation of carbon monoxide from denatured cytochrome c (17, 59). This experiment takes advantage of the fact that CO binds much more strongly to the heme of the denatured protein than to the heme of the native protein. Photodissociation of CO initiates folding because the CO-free protein is much more stable (Figure 1). The experiment has unlimited time resolution for folding experiments because photodissociation occurs in less than one picosecond. A conceptually similar, but more general, method utilizes a photo-induced electron transfer reaction to initiate folding (89) (Figure 1). The first such experiment was also performed on cytochrome c (20, 73, 89, 113). The reduced form of cytochrome c is more stable than the oxidized form, primarily due to the increased stability of the bond between methionine 80 and the heme

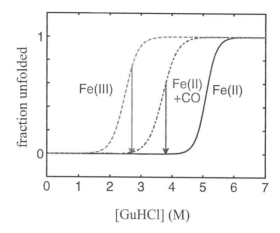

[GuHCl] (M)

Figure 1 Initiating the folding of reduced cytochrome c with photochemical triggers. Guanidinium chloride (GuHCl) unfolding curves for oxidized cytochrome c [Fe(III)], reduced cytochrome c [Fe(II)], and the carbon monoxide complex of reduced cytochrome c [Fe(II) + CO]. Folding can be initiated (*arrows*) by reduction of oxidized cytochrome c or dissociation of carbon monoxide in reduced cytochrome c. See text for additional description.

iron in the native protein. Optical excitation of a ruthenium bL-pyridine complex or NADH produces a long-lived excited state that is a powerful reductant. Injection of an electron reduces the heme iron of cytochrome c from ferric to ferrous in a few microseconds in a diffusion-limited bimolecular reaction and initiates folding. This technique has also been used to trigger folding of cytochrome b_{562} (121, 122) and myoglobin (123).

A different kind of photochemical trigger uses a photolabile disulfide (70, 118), which does not require a metal site, so in principle it can be used as a trigger for a much wider range of proteins. In this method, segments of a polypeptide chain are cross-linked by an aromatic disulfide. An appropriately engineered cross-link constrains the peptide or protein in a misfolded conformation, allowing folding to be triggered by sub-picosecond photo-cleavage of the disulfide bond.

A second class of optical triggers uses an intense laser pulse to produce a rapid temperature jump. This is a much more generally applicable method because it can be used to perturb the folding/unfolding equilibrium for any process that produces a significant enthalpy change. This was first done in a protein-folding experiment by heating a solution of a dye with a mode-locked picosecond laser operating at 532 nm (90). The time resolution of this experiment was $\sim$70 ps—the time required for thermal diffusion from the hot dye molecule to the solvent. A much more commonly employed method has been to directly heat water 10–20°C by shifting the fundamental of a Q-switched Nd:YAG laser at 1064 nm to a longer wavelength where water strongly absorbs (3, 4, 116, 120). The solution is heated during the $\sim$5 ns duration of the pulse by vibrational excitation of an O-H stretching overtone of water. The Eigen T-jump method of resistive heating with an electrical discharge has also been used to study folding kinetics with $\sim$10 μs time resolution (81, 82). Another perturbation method, pressure jump, has recently been employed to study folding kinetics (57). In this experiment, a stack of piezo-electric crystals is used to change the pressure 100–200 bar in 50–100 μs. The pressure change alters the folding/unfolding equilibrium because of the associated volume change.

Use of chemical denaturants, such as urea and guanidinium chloride, has played a central role in protein-folding experiments. Almost all proteins can be unfolded and remain soluble at sufficiently high denaturant concentrations, so dilution of denaturants continues to be an extremely important way of initiating protein folding. For this reason, there has been considerable effort to improve the time-resolution in mixing experiments by using continuous flow methods. Two such methods have recently been applied to protein folding, one based on turbulent mixing (18, 88, 104–106, 112, 124) and another based on hydrodynamic focusing (63, 93). In the turbulent mixing method liquids are forced through a small gap at high velocities (96). The turbulence created by the high shear forces "breaks" the liquids into very small volume elements called turbulent eddies. Mixing is rapid (1–10 μs) because diffusion of the denaturant occurs over short distances. In this experiment the mixed liquids flow continuously at constant velocity. The kinetics are monitored at various positions along the jet emerging from the mixer, time being measured by the distance from the mixing region and the flow velocity. The first time point in the kinetic measurements is significantly longer than the mixing time because the mixed solution must typically flow through a volume that is inaccessible to the monitoring probe. Nevertheless, the dead time of these instruments is only 50–200 μs, an improvement of more than an order of magnitude over the stopped flow method.

The second rapid mixing method employs hydrodynamic focusing to create a micron or submicron-wide stream of protein solution flowing at constant velocity in contact with a surrounding flowing reservoir (63, 93). Mixing occurs by diffusion into and out of the narrow stream. Solutions have been focused to diameters as small as 50 nm, corresponding to $\sim$1 μs mixing times (63). It should therefore be possible to obtain significant reduction in effective dead time compared to the turbulent mixing methods. An advantage of the hydrodynamic focusing method is that the flow is laminar. Consequently, the concentration of all species at all positions in the mixing device, including the mixing region, can in principle be calculated theoretically and also determined by experiments. This technique has allowed measurements of submillisecond, time-resolved small angle X-ray scattering for the determination of the radius of gyration of transient structures in protein folding (93).

Finally, protein-folding kinetics can be studied at equilibrium using dynamic nuclear magnetic resonance (nmr) methods (12, 13, 53). For a protein undergoing a simple two-state folding/unfolding transition, both the folding and unfolding rates can be derived from the measured lineshape if the resonant frequencies and transverse relaxation times for the two states are known. This method is useful for determining folding rates in the 10 μs–10 ms range under conditions where there is a significant population of both folded and unfolded states.

ELEMENTARY PROCESSES IN FOLDING

Contact Formation

Perhaps the simplest elementary process in protein folding is the formation of a contact between two residues of an unfolded polypeptide chain. In spite of its importance, this process was not investigated until the photodissociation experiments on cytochrome c (59). Time-resolved spectroscopy with nanosecond lasers was used to monitor heme absorption following photodissociation of the carbon monoxide complex of denatured reduced cytochrome c (Figure 1). The first change in absorption occurs with a relaxation time of $\sim$3 μs and was identified as binding of methionine to the heme. Detailed kinetic modeling led to an estimate of the time constant for methionine binding and dissociation of $\sim$40 μs and $\sim$4 μs, respectively. In subsequent experiments, the binding of free methionine to the heme attached to a small fragment of the cytochrome c polypeptide (the 11–21 undecapeptide) was studied, and it was found that the bimolecular rate is $\sim$2 $\times$ 10^8 M^{-1} s^{-1}, close to the diffusion limit (48, 49). Analysis of a simple two-step mechanism, in which binding occurs by first forming an encounter complex followed by formation of the heme-methionine covalent bond, showed that the observed unimolecular rate is almost purely diffusion limited. The heme iron is covalently bonded to a histidine at position 18, while the two methionines in the sequence are located at positions 65 and 80. The measured time of 40 μs is therefore the time required for diffusion-controlled contact between regions of the polypeptide separated by $\sim$50 residues. Together with the length scaling from polymer theory (15, 45, 111), this number could be used to estimate the formation rate of a contact between residues separated by any number of residues. For example, $\sim$3 μs was estimated for the formation of a short contact between residues separated by $\sim$10 peptide bonds using the $n^{-3/2}$ scaling for a random walk chain (see below). A second important result from these experiments was the calculation of the effective diffusion coefficient $\approx$5 $\times$ 10^{-7} cm^2 s^{-1} for the relative motion of heme and methionines, assuming a Gaussian distance distribution (111). This value is comparable to the diffusion constant $\approx$(1.5–8) $\times$ 10^{-7} cm^2 s^{-1} for the relative motion of a donor and acceptor in unfolded ribonuclease A, determined from the effect of Förster excitation energy transfer on the donor fluorescence decay kinetics (11).

The cytochrome c experiments indicated that it would be interesting to develop a more generic method for investigating contact formation in unfolded polypeptides. One approach to this problem has been to label the ends of small peptides with probes that undergo triplet-triplet energy transfer upon contact (5). In this experiment the triplet donor was a three-ring organic compound, thioxanthone, attached to the N-terminus of peptide, while the triplet acceptor was naphthalene attached

triplet-triplet energy transfer

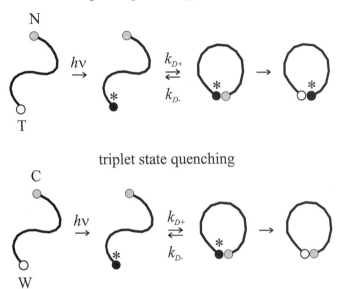

triplet state quenching

Figure 2   Using long-lived triplet states to measure rates of contact formation in peptides. In the triplet-triplet energy transfer experiment, an organic donor (thioxanthone, T) attached at one end of a peptide is optically excited to its long-lived triplet state. It remains in this state until it forms a contact in a diffusion limited process with an acceptor near the other end (naphthalene, N). Transfer of the excitation energy, raising the acceptor to its triplet state, is sufficiently fast that the diffusion-limited rate of contact formation is the same as the overall observed rate of energy transfer. In the triplet state quenching experiment tryptophan and cysteine are at two ends of the peptide. The optically-excited tryptophan (W) triplet is depopulated by transferring an electron to cysteine (C) when the two residues are close together, and the overall quenching rate is nearly the diffusion-limited rate of forming the tryptophan/cysteine contact. See text for additional description.

to the peptide as 1-naphthyl alanine (Figure 2). The triplet state of thioxanthone has a lifetime of ~ 30 μs and transfers its energy in a diffusion-limited process to the triplet state of naphthalene upon contact. A nice feature of this experiment is that energy transfer was clearly demonstrated by the disappearance of the thioxanthone triplet-triplet absorption spectrum simultaneously with the appearance of the naphthalene triplet-triplet absorption spectrum. Peptides were investigated that contain 1–4 glycine/serine pairs, corresponding to a spacing of 3–9 peptide bonds between the donor and acceptor. Exponential kinetics was found in all cases, with time constants varying from 20 ns for the shortest peptide to 50 ns for the longest.

One limitation of this triplet-triplet energy transfer method is that, with the current probes, positioning of the triplet states for efficient energy transfer requires the use of ethanol/water mixtures. Also, the use of extrinsic probes makes the study of proteins and the exploitation of site-directed mutagenesis more difficult. Another method has been developed for measuring contact formation rates that does not suffer from either of these limitations (67). In this method, contact formation was measured from the quenching of the triplet state of tryptophan at the C-terminus of a peptide by cysteine at the N-terminus (Figure 2). Earlier work had suggested that cysteine is a much more efficient triplet quencher than any other amino acid, exhibiting a near diffusion-limited bimolecular rate for the quenching of free tryptophan (42). The tryptophan triplet state is most probably depopulated by transfer of an electron to the sulfur of the quencher at distances close to van der Waals contact. The long lifetime ($>50~\mu$s) of the tryptophan triplet state, moreover, permits quenching rates to be measured over a relatively wide dynamic range by measuring the decay of the triplet-triplet absorption spectrum. The peptides studied contained the repeating amino acid triplet—alanine/glycine/glutamine—to avoid any specific secondary structure formation. Varying the number of peptide bonds between tryptophan and cysteine from 4 to 19 yielded contact time constants of 30 ns to 150 ns, consistent with the values found in the triplet-triplet energy transfer study.

Although both kinds of triplet state experiments yield times $\sim$50-fold smaller than the earlier estimate of $\sim$3 μs for contact between residues separated by $\sim$10 peptide bonds (49), they are not inconsistent with this prediction. At least two factors contribute to this difference. For an idealized chain with a Gaussian end-to-end equilibrium distribution, this rate is given by: $3Da/[(\pi/6)^{1/2}\langle r^2\rangle^{3/2}]$, where D is the effective relative diffusion constant of the two ends, a is the contact radius, and $\langle r^2\rangle$ is the mean squared end-to-end distance (111). The contact radius for the tryptophan-cysteine interaction is larger than for the methionine-heme encounter complex of cytochrome c, and the heme is only accessible to the methionine on one side, so the effective value of a is larger in the quenching experiments. Also, the peptides are rich in glycine and therefore have smaller $\langle r^2\rangle$ compared to cytochrome c, which has only an average of 1 glycine per 6–7 residues between the heme and methionines.

The above results suggest that tryptophan triplet lifetime measurements can provide a useful method for investigating the kinetics of forming a specific intramolecular contact in an unfolded or folding protein. They also show that this method can be used to address fundamental questions on the dynamical properties of polypeptides. Foremost among these are the length and composition dependence of contact formation rates. A maximum in the loop probability as a function of chain length has been predicted at about 10 residues for a generic polypeptide (15, 45, 114). In these calculations, formation of an end-to-end contact in longer chains is less probable because of the larger entropy decrease, while forming a contact in shorter chains is disfavored because of chain stiffness. In the simplest picture, the maximum in the loop probability should be reflected as a maximum in the contact formation rate [the rate of dissociation of the contacting polymer ends ($=3D/a^2$) is independent of chain length]. No such maximum was observed in the glycine-containing peptides, presumably because of their larger flexibility compared to the generic peptide considered in the theoretical calculations. This question is now being studied using less flexible peptides (LJ Lapidus, unpublished results). Another important aspect of studies of contact formation, at least in small glycine-containing peptides, is that it occurs on a time scale that can be directly simulated by all-atom molecular dynamics calculations, simulations that have yet to be performed.

Helix-Coil Transition

Although both the thermodynamics and kinetics of the helix-coil transition have been studied experimentally and theoretically for over 40 years, it was not until the late 1980s that a significant number of peptides of the size and composition found in proteins were shown to be helical in pure aqueous solvents. Since that time extensive equilibrium studies of α-helix formation in isolated peptides have been carried out and theoretically analyzed (16, 71, 78). Peptides rich in alanine are particularly suitable because of their high helix-forming propensity. This together with their ready availability have made them prime candidates for kinetic investigations using fast kinetic techniques.

In the first such study a 21-residue peptide having the sequence X-$(A)_5$ $(AAARA)_3$-A-NH_2 (X = succinyl) was investigated (120). A nanosecond laser temperature jump was used to perturb the helix-coil equilibrium, and infrared absorption measurements in the amide I region were used to monitor the decrease in helix content. The relaxation following the temperature jump was found to be biphasic with an unresolved (<10 ns) amplitude and a larger amplitude 160 ns relaxation. Subsequent laser T-jump measurements with a fluorescent probe at the N-terminus (methyl amino benzoic acid instead of the succinyl group) showed only a single fast relaxation at $\sim$20 ns (116). In this study a simple nucleation/propagation model was developed to explain both the infrared and fluorescence experiments. This model suggested that the fast relaxation results from helix propagation and partial melting of stretches of helix, while the slow relaxation corresponds to crossing a helix nucleation barrier (Figure 3). This barrier crossing occurs in both directions, corresponding to nucleation and growth of a new stretch of helix in one direction, and complete melting of a preexisting stretch of helix in the reverse direction. However, the model predicted that the N-terminal fluorescent probe would also show a comparable amplitude for the slow barrier crossing process, which was not observed.

This problem prompted further investigation of helix-coil transition kinetics in a very similar peptide, but one having an intrinsic fluorescent probe (117). In this peptide, with sequence Ac-WAAAH(AAARA)$_3$-A-NH$_2$, formation of the first turn of helix is signaled by quenching of tryptophan (W) fluorescence by the protonated histidine (H) (Figure 3). Both the temperature (117) and viscosity dependence (GS Jas, unpublished results) of the relaxation kinetics were studied. Again, only a single relaxation was observed, but with a rate (1/(220 ns)) very close

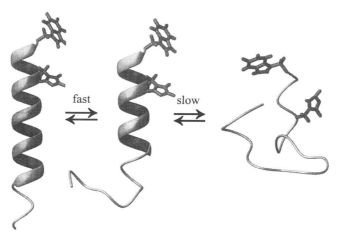

Figure 3 Processes contributing to temperature-dependent changes in the helix content of alanine peptides. An increase in temperature produces both an increased number of random coil peptides, shown on the *right*, and a decrease in the average helix length of helical peptides. The unzipping of the end of a helical peptide, shown schematically on the *left*, is predicted to be a rapid, diffusion-like process on a relatively flat free energy surface, with a characteristic time that is comparable to the relaxation time for removing a single residue from the helix ($\sim$100 ps). The melting and formation of helix-containing peptides requires formation of species that contain only a single helical turn. Since equilibrium models predict that such species are several kcal/mol less stable than either the random coil species or species that contain larger numbers of helical residues, these processes are slowed by crossing this (nucleation) free energy barrier. In a two-state picture of the helix-coil transition, it is the slower nucleation process that determines the overall relaxation time.

to the slower phase observed in the infrared experiments on a very similar peptide described above. To understand this result, the model developed in the study of a β-hairpin was used (77, 80) (Figure 4), which takes into account both the side chain interactions and the secondary structure propensities of individual residues (117). According to the model, in phases corresponding to both, helix propagation and partial melting are slowed in this peptide. The much lower helical propensities of histidine and tryptophan, together with the histidine-arginine ($i, i + 4$) repulsion, slow incorporation of the 5 N-terminal residues into a helix growing from the C-terminal side, while melting of the N-terminus is slowed by the stabilizing tryptophan-histidine ($i, i + 4$) interaction. The net result is that the fast relaxation is slower and with a much smaller amplitude, so that the observed kinetics are dominated by crossing the nucleation barrier (117).

A similar peptide without the tryptophan-histidine probe has also recently been studied using time-resolved resonance Raman spectra measured with far UV (204 nm) excitation to probe helix content (68). The Raman spectrum of the helical peptide exhibits much weaker intensities for the amide II, amide III, and Cα-H bending bands than does the random coil, so the Raman spectrum provides several independent measures of helical content. A single exponential relaxation was observed over the temperature range studied (310 K–337 K), with $\tau = 250$ ns at 300 K and an apparent activation energy of 7 kcal/mol. These results are very similar to those obtained from the fluorescence and infrared absorption experiments. No fast relaxation could be detected in these experiments even though the time resolution was ~3 ns.

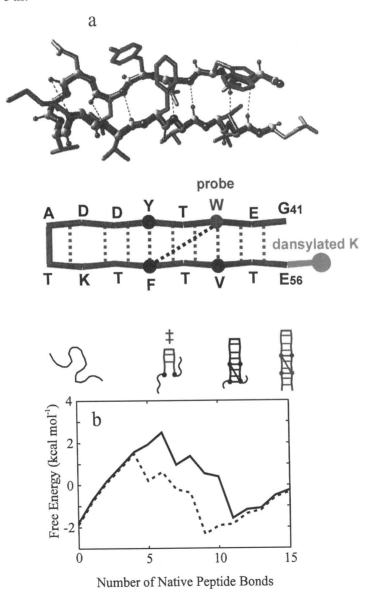

With a statistical mechanical model, quantitative predictions of helix-coil kinetics in other peptides are straightforward. Using the same parameters from fitting the equilibrium and kinetic data on the tryptophan/histidine peptide, the kinetics of the infrared experiments were simulated (117). Excellent agreement with experiment was obtained, with calculated relaxation times of 4 ns and 220 ns and an amplitude ratio for the fast and slow relaxations of approximately 1:4. More recently the model has been modified to predict the kinetics of peptides having the length and composition found in helices of proteins (V Muñoz, unpublished results) incorporating the more detailed equilibrium description of the helix-coil transition contained in the program AGADIR (78, 79). These calculations show that relaxation times for 15–20 residue peptides span the range from a few nanoseconds for peptides having less than 1% helix at equilibrium to ~1 μs for peptides containing >75% helix. The relaxation time is much shorter for very unstable peptides because melting, which is dominating the relaxation in these peptides, is downhill in free energy. On the other hand, the relaxation time for stable, protein-like sequences is longer than that of alanine-based peptides of comparable stability. This is a consequence of two factors. The entropy loss associated with forming a turn is greater for nonalanine peptides (alanine has the highest helical propensity), producing a larger nucleation barrier. To compensate for the lower helical propensity, stable helices require stronger side chain interactions, and these interactions must be broken for complete melting to occur, increasing the barrier in the reverse direction.

A surprising result has recently been reported from stopped-flow kinetic studies of helix formation monitored by circular dichroism (CD) in a 16-residue alanine-

---

Figure 4   Model for formation of β-hairpin from protein GB1. (*a*) Structure. (*b*) Free energy profile. The free energy calculated from a simple statistical mechanical model is plotted as a function of the number of native peptide bonds in the modified single sequence approximation (77, 80). The continuous curve is for the GB1 β-hairpin. The dashed curve is the profile predicted if the hydrophobic cluster is repositioned one residue closer to the turn (77). The model contains four basic ingredients. First, structures are classified according to backbone conformation, described by pairs of dihedral angles for each peptide bond. Two states for each peptide bond are considered—native and nonnative. By not allowing more than one stretch of native peptide bonds simultaneously in any molecule (the single sequence approximation) the number of conformations is markedly reduced, from 2^{15} to 121 for the 16-residue fragment containing 15 peptide bonds. This approximation is not as drastic as one might have suspected, as a comparison of the rates calculated by solving all 2^{15} kinetic equations yields only a threefold larger relaxation rate (77). Not native interactions are considered, and native interactions (either hydrophobic interactions or hydrogen bonds between strands) can only occur when all intervening peptide bonds have their native conformation. Finally, the free energy of each species can be obtained from the three adjustable thermodynamic parameters of the model—the entropy reduction upon forming a native peptide bond (taken as the same for all residues, including those in the turn), the stabilizing energy produced by hydrogen bonds, and the stabilizing (free) energy resulting from the hydrophobic interactions.

based peptide (21). In this study helix formation was initiated by dilution from 6 M guanidinium chloride. All of the equilibrium circular dichroism change was found to occur in a ~100 ms relaxation. To reconcile these results with the T-jump experiments, it was argued that at this high concentration of denaturant the peptide is completely unfolded and that the 100 ms relaxation corresponds to helix nucleation, while the much faster relaxation observed in the T-jump experiments arises from unzipping of existing helical sequences. If this explanation were correct, then the helix nucleation rate would be several orders of magnitude slower than previously thought. In an attempt to reconcile these discrepant observations, we reexamined the trypophan-histidine peptide using both stopped-flow and T-jump experiments. The stopped-flow experiments showed that helix formation as monitored by the tryptophan fluorescence is complete within the 3 millisecond dead time, while precise measurements of the kinetic amplitudes in T-jump experiments confirm that the fluorescence reaches its equilibrium value in less than a microsecond (117; GS Jas, unpublished results). Similar results were also obtained in the infrared (120) and Raman (68) studies. We should also point out that the statistical mechanical model predicts that the kinetics of helix formation from the completely unfolded state exhibit almost exactly the same relaxation time as that observed in the T-jump perturbation experiment. The origin of the 100 ms circular dichroism change remains unclear.

Helix-coil kinetics have also been observed in laser T-jump experiments on proteins. An interesting example is the study on apomyoglobin using infrared spectroscopy (31, 40, 41). By monitoring the infrared absorption at different wavelengths, it was possible not only to determine the change in total helix content, but also to distinguish between changes in solvent exposed helices and helices that are packed against other helices. Following a temperature jump, partially unfolded apomyoglobin exhibits a multiphasic relaxation. A rapid helix melting/formation relaxation at 50 ns has maximal amplitude at wavelengths characteristic of solvent-exposed helix (possibly helices C, D, or E in the denatured state). A slower relaxation at 120 μs has maximal amplitude at wavelengths for packed helices and may represent the cooperative unfolding and refolding of the core of the protein containing helices A, G, and H (31, 40, 41).

What is the relation between real and computer experiments on helix-coil kinetics? As mentioned in the introduction, one of the motivations for studying the kinetics of the helix-coil transition is that it occurs on time scales that are becoming accessible to all-atom molecular dynamics simulations. Ideally one would like to observe the helix form and completely melt many times in a single trajectory. To have adequate statistics to obtain equilibrium populations and rate constants, a large number of such trajectories would be required. Such simulations have recently been carried out on a β heptapeptide in methanol, which forms a left-handed 3_1-helix (in a β peptide a methylene group is inserted in the backbone between Cα and NH). The helix melts and reforms several times during the course of the 50 ns simulation (23, 24). The analysis of the residence time in helix and coil states yields an equilibrium constant close to the experimental value. Unfortunately, the kinetics of helix formation in this heptapeptide have not yet been studied experimentally.

No kinetic study by molecular dynamics is available yet for alanine peptides, but there is a hint from a single trajectory on a 13-residue alanine peptide in explicit water that accurate rates can be calculated (22). This alanine helix unfolds in the simulation at 373 K in 200 ps, compared to 700 ps obtained by extrapolating the experimental data to 373 K using the statistical mechanical model for this peptide (117). Another fundamental kinetic quantity that could be readily obtained by molecular dynamics is the time to add an alanine residue to a growing helix. This time comes directly from the modeling of the kinetic data and is found to be ~600 ps at 300 K, varying from ~50 ps at 373 K to ~2 ns at 273 K (117).

A number of important issues concerning the kinetics of the helix-coil transition remain to be resolved. These include the direct observation of the rate of helix growth and the exploration of the effects on the kinetics of amino acid substitution and chain length. While estimates of the growth rate can be obtained from models, it should be possible to directly observe this process by using time-resolved infrared or Raman measurements and a T-jump method with subnanosecond time resolution. Such studies might be facilitated by using peptides constrained by chemical modification to have prenucleated helices.

β-Hairpin Formation

Studies on β-sheets have not been nearly as extensive as those of the α-helix. The reason is that until recently it has not been possible to study β-sheets in isolation. The simplest β-sheet is one with just two antiparallel strands—a so-called β-hairpin. Isolated β-hairpins tend to aggregate at the high concentrations necessary to characterize their structure by nuclear magnetic resonance because the hydrophobic side chains that are required for stability also make them sticky. Over the past several years, however, several peptides have been shown to form β-hairpins that do not aggregate (38, 65). In the first kinetic investigation of β-hairpins, the 16-residue C-terminal fragment of the protein GB1 was studied (80) (Figure 4a). This peptide had been shown by nmr to have a high population of β-hairpin structure at room temperature (6). The folded conformation of the GB1 hairpin is stabilized by a hydrophobic cluster of 4 residues, including a tryptophan that can be used as an intrinsic fluorescent probe (Figure 4a). Upon formation of this cluster, the quantum yield of tryptophan fluorescence increases because the indole side chain becomes partially buried and is less accessible to quenching by water. To obtain an essentially independent probe, a dansylated lysine was attached to the C-terminus of the peptide, 13 residues distant in the sequence from the tryptophan. The absorption of the dansyl group occurs in the same wavelength range as the tryptophan emission and therefore acts as an efficient acceptor of excitation energy from the tryptophan. In the dansylated peptide, the tryptophan quantum yield is sharply reduced and changes in fluorescence are dominated by the energy transfer rate, which depends on the distance between the tryptophan and the dansyl groups.

Interestingly, the hairpin was found to fold in a few microseconds, more than an order of magnitude slower than α-helix formation in the alanine peptides (51). The surprising result was that, except for less cooperative thermal unfolding, the thermodynamic and kinetic behavior of this β-hairpin is very much like that of a small protein (80). In both the unmodified and dansylated peptide, the thermal unfolding curve could be explained with just two thermodynamic states—a folded state with an intact hydrophobic cluster and an unfolded state without the cluster and with a much larger average separation between the tryptophan and the dansyl group. In the laser temperature jump experiments, a single exponential relaxation was observed in both peptides with the same time constants of 3.5 μs at 288 K. The finding of single exponential progress curves with the same relaxation rates using essentially different probes is the hallmark of a two-state kinetic system. Another interesting finding in the kinetics was that the two-state analysis yields an apparently negative activation energy for hairpin folding (the observed relaxation rate, which is the sum of the folding and unfolding rates, shows a positive activation energy because unfolding of the hairpin has a positive and larger activation energy).

To explain these results a simple statistical mechanical model was developed (77, 80), which was subsequently used in the helix-coil study discussed above (117). An interesting aspect of the model is that it contains much of the underlying physics considered in the folding of a protein, i.e. the competition between loss of conformational entropy and stabilization from hydrophobic interactions and hydrogen bonds. Indeed, we shall see later that the model can be successfully applied to proteins. In this model, structures are classified according to their backbone conformation, with each peptide bond having either native or nonnative values for the ψ, ϕ dihedral angles. This idea was used previously in a simple model for protein folding (125). A natural reaction coordinate in such a model is the number of native peptide bonds (10). As can be readily seen from the free energy calculated as a function of this coordinate in the single sequence approximation (Figure 4b), there are only two regions of stability separated by a substantial barrier. One corresponds to the unfolded hairpin and one to the hairpin with the hydrophobic cluster intact but the ends frayed.

This immediately suggests that the peptide will behave like a two-state system both thermodynamically and kinetically. Indeed, solution of the differential equations with parameters that fit the experimental data shows a single exponential relaxation. This result is obtained with both the single sequence approximation (121 states) and the complete model (32,768 states). The projection of the free energy as a function of the number of native peptide bonds in the complete model also exhibits a barrier, showing the two-state behavior (ER Henry, V Muñoz, unpublished results). At the top of the free energy barrier, which is just before the transition state, the turn has formed, and the hairpin contains two of the seven hydrogen bonds connecting opposite strands (Figure 4*b*). The lower enthalpy of the transition state compared to the unfolded state (which has no stabilizing interactions in the model) explains the apparent negative activation energy for folding. Another interesting feature of the free energy profile (Figure 4*b*) is that hairpin formation is uphill in free energy until the onset of hydrophobic interaction between residues on opposite strands. Repositioning of the cluster closer to the turn would therefore be expected to speed up folding, without changing the difference in free energies between the unfolded and completely folded (i.e. unfrayed) peptide (Figure 4*b*). The idea of speeding up folding by decreasing the distance in sequence between stabilizing interactions will resurface when we discuss the calculation of protein folding rates (see above).

The statistical mechanical model developed to describe the β-hairpin kinetics imposes a mechanism in which the β-turn and proximal hydrogen bonds must form before the hydrophobic cluster. An alternative mechanism, which could also explain the data, was considered in the experimental study, but no detailed model was formulated (80). In this other mechanism, the molecule first forms a closed loop by docking of the hydrophobic cluster. The formation of the loop is rate-limiting and is followed by very fast formation of interstrand hydrogen bonds and the turn. Because the hairpin forms with two-state kinetics, it is not possible to distinguish between these two mechanisms experimentally. It may also not be realistic to answer this question with mutation experiments (ϕ analysis) because the stability of the hairpin is marginal ($\sim$1 kcal/mol at 273 K). All-atom molecular dynamics simulations might help to distinguish between the two mechanisms (27, 87). Two different strategies have been employed to overcome the limitation that folding and unfolding of the hairpin are too slow for currently available molecular dynamics simulations at experimental temperatures. In one, transition states found in high-temperature unfolding simulations were shown to behave like transition states at ambient temperature (87). The mechanism at the two temperatures was therefore assumed to be identical. In the other, Monte Carlo sampling was used to generate a large number of conformations that were then grouped according to their structure to produce free energy surfaces (27). In both studies, it was concluded that the hydrophobic cluster forms first. However, as with many simulation studies, structures were examined in great detail, but experimentally measured properties were not calculated. It was therefore not shown that the simulations are consistent with the major kinetic results, namely: the observation of a single exponential relaxation, the observed rates and apparent activation energies, and the observed changes in fluorescence quantum yields upon folding with and without Forster excitation energy transfer. It would also be important to know how the mechanism obtained from the simulations depends on the choice of force fields and parameters.

The laser temperature-jump experiments on the protein GB1 hairpin have provided the first glimpse of the time scales for formation of β-structure in isolation. These experimental results and their analysis with a simple statistical mechanical model, moreover, have exposed important issues that also arise in investigating the mechanism of protein folding. At this stage it is crucial to investigate other β-hairpin forming peptides to determine experimentally their range of kinetic and thermodynamic behavior. To this end a variant of a β-hairpin-forming peptide from ubiquitin (102) has been studied in which a tryptophan has been inserted in place of a tyrosine and a dansylated lysine added to the C-terminus. Folding in this system is more complex because of self-assembly into a trimer of hairpins (V Muñoz, FJ Blanco, R Ghirlando, unpublished results). However, at low concentrations where both the unfolded and folded peptide remain monomeric, the β-hairpin structure forms in $\sim$30 μs at 30°C, only five times slower than the GB1 hairpin.

FAST PROTEIN FOLDING

Speed Limit

An interesting issue raised from measurements of elementary processes in protein folding is the question of a speed limit (49). How fast can a protein possibly fold? Is there an upper limit for the rate of protein folding as there is for a bimolecular reaction in solution? For a bimolecular reaction, the upper limit is determined by the rate at which the reactants come together by diffusion. This problem was solved theoretically more than 80 years ago by Smoluchowski, who derived a simple analytical formula. No such theory has been developed yet for protein folding, so a semi-empirical approach was taken (49). It was reasoned that the rate of folding would be limited by the rate of polypeptide collapse, which would in turn be limited by the time required to form a small loop. From the experiment on cytochrome c discussed above, this minimum time for protein folding was estimated to be $\sim$1 μs (49). We now know that this is comparable to the time required to make a hairpin or a stable natural helix, so it remains a reasonable estimate. This notion of a speed limit for protein folding of $\sim$(1 μs)$^{-1}$ has stimulated experimentalists to look for fast folding proteins and redesign them to fold even faster.

Several proteins fold with rates approaching this speed limit. The single chain arc repressor folds with a rate of $\sim$10^4 s^{-1} obtained by extrapolating millisecond stopped flow data to zero denaturant concentration (97). Folding times as little as 600 μs were observed for oxidized cytochrome c (with misfolding blocked by binding to the extrinsic ligand, imidazole) using a rapid mixing, continuous flow method (18). The fastest measured folding rates have been determined for monomeric λ repressor using dynamic nmr methods (12, 13, 53). This small (80 residue), single domain protein exhibits two-state behavior (39). From lineshape analysis, rates were determined as a function of urea concentration, the shortest time constant being $\sim$1 ms in 1.4 M urea solution. In a later study (12), rates at lower urea concentration were measured using the contribution of the exchange between folded and unfolded structures to the transverse relaxation time, T_2. In the absence of urea, a folding rate of 5 × 10^3 s^{-1} was determined. This is the current speed record for a measured folding rate (from the denatured state, *vide infra*). A fast-folding mutant was also investigated (12), in which two of the glycine residues were replaced by alanine (G46A/G48A). In this case, however, even the T_2 measurements were limited by the lack of population of the unfolded state at low urea concentrations. In 2.1 M urea the folding rate was already 3×10^3 s^{-1}, with a rate extrapolated to zero urea concentration of $\sim 10^5$ s^{-1}.

The electron transfer triggering method has been used to show that several heme containing proteins fold very fast. Extrapolation to zero denaturant concentration has led to an estimate for reduced cytochrome c of $\sim 10^4$ s^{-1} (73, 89, 113). Cytochrome b_{562} is a particularly striking case. This protein consists of a bundle of four helices wrapped around a heme group. Reduction of the heme iron from ferric to ferrous leads to a marked increase in stability, the concentration of guanidinium chloride for 50% unfolding increasing from ~ 1.8 M to ~ 6 M. Triggering folding by reducing the oxidized protein, a folding rate of 1.5×10^3 s^{-1} in 2.2 M guanidinium chloride was measured (122). Extrapolation to zero denaturant yielded a folding time constant of 5 μs, very close to the speed limit!

Downhill Folding

Measurements of fast folding have additional physical significance. Theoretical calculations of free energy surfaces for folding predict that the barriers to folding are quite small. Barriers of only 5–7 $k_B T$ have been calculated for monomeric λ repressor (94) under conditions where folding occurs in ~ 1 ms. This indicates a pre-exponential factor k_0 in an expression $k_0 \exp(-\Delta G^{\ddagger}/k_B T)$ of only 10^5 s^{-1} to 10^6 s^{-1}, compared to $k_B T/h = 6 \times 10^{12}$ s^{-1} of gas phase chemical reaction kinetics. The calculation also suggests that, in the absence of a free energy barrier, the folding rate would be of the order of 10^6 s^{-1}, providing yet another estimate of an upper limit for protein folding. More importantly, the absence of a barrier could lead to non-exponential kinetics because folding is continuously downhill in free energy.

The ideal demonstration of downhill folding would be one in which the barrier of a two-state protein is made to decrease and then disappear as the stability of the native state is increased, switching the time course monotonically from exponential to non-exponential as folding speeds up. Conversion from exponential to non-exponential kinetics with an increased folding rate has recently been observed, but in a somewhat more complicated situation (32, 100). A nanosecond laser T-jump instrument was used to study the folding kinetics of a 76-residue protein, ubiquitin, from the cold denatured state (100). At 2°C, folding occurs with a relaxation time ≈ 5 ms ($\tau_{1/2} \approx 3$ ms), while at 8°C, where the protein is more stable, the half-time is dramatically reduced ($\tau_{1/2} \approx 100$ μs) and the time course becomes non-exponential. Interpretation of this result was not obvious because nmr data showed that ubiquitin exhibits two state equilibrium behavior at 8°C, indicating a barrier between cold-denatured and native states. An intriguing explanation of these results was proposed (100). It was suggested that the shape of the free energy surface changes with temperature, so that at 8°C the barrier is shifted significantly toward the unfolded state. In this way cold denatured molecules prior to the temperature jump find themselves on the native side of the barrier at the elevated temperature. Folding is now downhill in free energy, making it much faster and non-exponential. The movement of the barrier top is attributed to the strengthening of the hydrophobic interactions at the elevated temperature, overcoming the entropy decrease earlier along the reaction coordinate, reminiscent of our earlier discussion on the barrier to β-hairpin formation.

In this work the possible contribution of landscape ruggedness to the non-exponential kinetics was also discussed (100). In describing folding as diffusion on a low-dimensional free energy surface, the effective diffusion coefficient reflects the underlying energetic roughness that corresponds to transient trapping in local minima (108). Very hydrophobic sequences, for example, may cause transient formation of numerous nonnative interactions, resulting in a smaller effective diffusion coefficient. If this effective diffusion coefficient decreases as folding proceeds, the kinetics would become more extended in time—producing so-called "stretched" exponential kinetics having the form: $\exp[-(kt)^\beta]$) with $\beta < 1$ (46). One interesting speculation from these considerations is the possibility of observing a maximum in the folding rate as the free energy bias toward the native state is increased because of an even larger effect on the effective diffusion constant from increased ruggedness (32)

Downhill folding could be of great importance for obtaining the ultimate experimental description of protein folding, namely the microscopic paths that individual denatured molecules take to find the unique conformation of the native structure. In contrast to two-state folders, in which only the population of the native and denatured states can be observed, intermediate structures on the paths from the denatured to native state are populated in downhill folding. Downhill folders would be excellent candidates for study using the rapidly emerging technology of single molecule spectroscopy (32). There is the exciting prospect that by increasing the viscosity to slow the downhill kinetics, it will be possible to resolve the sequence of structural events as a single molecule progresses from a denatured to native conformation.

Polypeptide Collapse

If solvent conditions are changed from strongly denaturing to those that favor folding, i.e. from a good to a poor solvent, an unfolded protein is expected to collapse to form more compact structures. Collapse may occur simultaneously with folding, or it may occur in a prior phase that involves the formation of compact, but still-denatured structures. Resolving the kinetics of collapse has been one of the major objectives of fast-folding studies. The focus has initially been on cytochrome c because it has a readily accessible probe and is known to exhibit a collapse process that cannot be resolved by stopped flow methods (98, 109, 110). Horse cytochrome c contains a single tryptophan (W59) about 40 residues distant in sequence from the point of covalent attachment of the heme to the polypeptide chain (H18). In the native structure the fluorescence of this tryptophan is completely quenched by excitation energy transfer to the strongly absorbing heme chromophore. At high concentrations of chemical denaturant, the protein is unfolded and the tryptophan quantum yield is only 20–30% reduced compared to free tryptophan. Assuming that the heme-tryptophan distance reflects the overall size of the protein, the decrease in fluorescence is a sensitive indicator of polypeptide collapse.

Using a rapid mixing/continuous flow method with a dead time of $\sim$70 μs, the folding of cytochrome c complexed with imidazole was studied following dilution of guanidinium chloride (18). Imidazole blocks binding of nonnative ligands, with the result that folding becomes too fast to be observed by the stopped flow method (98, 110). Although submillisecond folding to the native conformation was completely resolved, the collapse process was still too fast for this technique (18). In a subsequent study using a continuous flow instrument with improved signal-to-noise and a dead time of only $\sim$45 μs, the collapse process was partially resolved and shown to have a time-constant of 40–60 μs (105). The partially resolved kinetic progress curve is consistent with an exponential form, suggesting a barrier crossing process. More recently, the collapse process has been completely resolved using nanosecond laser T-jump (47). These measurements confirm that collapse has an exponential time course and is an activated process.

A three-state analysis of the kinetics suggests that tryptophan fluorescence in the initial collapsed state is almost completely quenched, indicating that this state is compact (105). The radius of gyration of this transient state has been subsequently measured in a submillisecond, time-resolved small angle X-ray scattering experiment. These experiments used synchrotron radiation and a continuous flow method that employs hydrodynamic focusing to achieve rapid mixing (93). A value of R_g < 1.8 nm was determined, consistent with the fluorescence quenching and comparable to the equilibrium radius of gyration of cytochrome c at acid pH in the presence of high salt (the so-called "acid molten globule" state).

The finding of a free energy barrier between two denatured states in these experiments on cytochrome c may have greater significance than simply an interesting observation on a specific protein. Theoretical considerations suggest that proteins may generically have two denatured states—an expanded denatured state and a compact denatured state (25, 26, 86). If there is no barrier between expanded and compact denatured states, theoretical estimates suggest that collapse would be submicrosecond (91). It will be important to further investigate this question in other proteins using Förster excitation energy transfer and time-resolved X-ray scattering measurements. There are now several cases in which submillisecond kinetic processes have been attributed to polypeptide collapse (3, 4, 88), but the probes in these experiments prevent a completely unambiguous interpretation.

Another interesting aspect of the collapse process that merits further study by fast-folding methods is the question of the overall topology of transient compact denatured states. Is the overall topology similar to the final native conformation, as suggested for the compact denatured state which has been called the "molten globule state" (95), or is it widely distributed in a "random globule state" (26), as found in many lattice simulations? In the latter case, the slower process in protein folding corresponds to the search for the correct topology. In the former, the protein-folding problem, as far as overall topology is concerned, is "solved" in the very fast initial process, the slow process corresponding mainly to the annealing of side chains to reach the final native conformation.

PROTEIN-FOLDING RATES FROM A SIMPLE MODEL

What factors determine whether a protein will be a fast or slow folder? Is there any relation between folding rate and the final native structure? It is now possible to address these questions because of the availability of a sufficiently large set of data on the folding of small single domain proteins. We pointed out in the introduction to this review that the study of CI2 marked a turning point in experimental studies on protein folding (56). The 64-residue version of this protein, which has neither disulfide bridges nor *cis*-prolines, behaves like a perfect two-state system. For a two-state protein, only two populations of molecules are detected in both equilibrium and kinetic experiments (126). One state corresponds to molecules having the native structure and the second to the ensemble of conformations that make up the denatured state. Over 20 proteins are now known to exhibit two-state behavior, and the results of these studies have been summarized in a recent review (55). Their folding rates span more than four orders of magnitude, from $(200\ \mu s)^{-1}$ for monomeric λ repressor to $(4\ s)^{-1}$ for muscle acyl phosphatase (Figure 5).

In searching for empirical correlations in this set of kinetic data, a key observation was made: The rates of folding show a significant correlation with a simple measure of protein topology, the so-called "contact order" (1, 92). The relative contact order is the mean separation in sequence between residues that are in contact in the three-dimensional structure, normalized by the total number of amino acids in the protein. For proteins with many long-range interactions, such as muscle acyl phosphatase, the contact order is large and folding is relatively slow. For α-helical proteins, such as monomeric λ repressor, local $(i, i + 4)$ interactions are

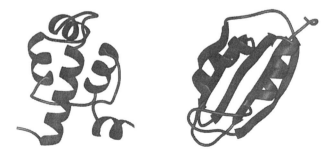

Figure 5   Schematic structures of monomeric λ repressor (left) and muscle acyl phosphatase (right).

much more abundant The contact order is therefore small and folding is observed to be relatively much faster.

The observation of a correlation between folding rates and such a simple measure of structure suggested that a simple physical model may be capable of calculating the rates of protein folding. A simple statistical mechanical model had already been developed for explaining the kinetics of β-hairpin formation, which as pointed out earlier, contains most of the basic features of folding a small protein. It was therefore logical to apply this model to two-state proteins (76). The analysis of the β-hairpin revealed that for this molecule the single sequence approximation, which allows only one stretch of native structure simultaneously in each molecule, produces results very close to the complete model, which imposes no restrictions on the number of stretches (125). To account for the larger size of the molecule in applying the model to proteins, this approximation was relaxed to allow two and three simultaneous stretches. For 18 proteins that exhibit two-state behavior experimentally the free energy as a function of the number of native peptide bonds, the natural reaction coordinate in this model, shows only two deep minima separated by a free energy barrier. Furthermore, free energy profiles for four other proteins, known to populate more than two states in kinetic experiments, show additional deep minima. The striking finding was that the calculated free energy barriers to folding are small for fast-folding proteins and large for slow-folding proteins (Figure 6a,b). The rates calculated for the 18 two-state proteins from diffusion on these free energy profiles, moreover, show a remarkably good correlation with the experimentally determined rates (Figure 6c). It is perhaps surprising that even approximate relative rates can be calculated using a single reaction coordinate for such a complex system. However, the absolute folding rate of a lattice protein with $\sim 10^{16}$ possible structures was accurately calculated from diffusion on a one-dimensional free energy profile (108).

In addition to ignoring much polymer physics, there are several obvious weaknesses to these simple calculations. One is a restrictive assumption of the model that does not allow native interactions between residues unless the intervening chain has its native conformation. A second is the naive treatment of the entropy of the denatured state. The denatured state appears as a sharp minimum in the free energy profiles (Figure 6a,b), instead of the broad minimum that would appear with no restriction on the distribution of native peptide bonds (125). Other weaknesses are the use of a simplified free energy function in which native propensities and contact energies are sequence independent and solvation effects are ignored. Nevertheless, the success of the simple model in calculating rates is an important result, for it suggests that the underlying physics determining folding rates is simpler than previously thought. It appears that the folding rate is determined largely by the distribution and strength of contacts in the native three-dimensional structure. As pointed out earlier in our discussion of β-hairpin formation (Figure 4b), compensation of the conformational entropy loss by strong stabilizing interactions earlier along the reaction coordinate lowers the free energy barrier and allows faster folding.

What about mechanism? Calculations with this simple model contain an enormous amount of detail on microscopic structural pathways between the native and denatured state. For these pathways it is possible to identify the structures that, once formed, rapidly proceed to the native state. This is the so-called transition state ensemble. Detailed structural information on this transition state ensemble can in principle be obtained from experimental measurements of the relative effects of mutations on the rates and equilibrium constants for folding (so-called ϕ values, defined as $\Delta \ln k_{\text{folding}} / \Delta \ln K_{\text{equilibrium}}$) (34, 35, 54, 84). This model, like two other simple models with similar approximations (2, 36), shows qualitative agreement with mutation experiments. However, thus far, these simple models do not give good quantitative agreement between the observed and calculated ϕ values, so it is somewhat premature to use them to describe structural pathways in

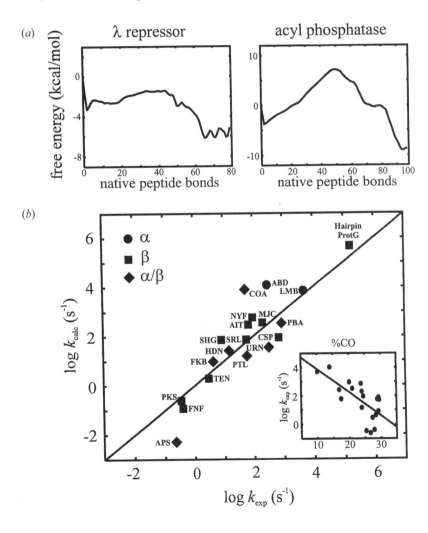

any detail. Accurate calculation of ϕ values remains an important goal, and more realistic theoretical models (107) as well as knowledge of the detailed structure of the mutated protein may be necessary. The task would also be made easier by experimental studies in which there are several different mutations at each of the studied positions. Predicting ϕ values theoretically is a crucial issue because the mutation experiments probably hold the key to elucidating mechanism in structural detail.

BIOLOGICAL RELEVANCE OF FOLDING KINETICS

From the preceding discussion we have seen that kinetics is important for a physical understanding of how proteins fold. However, is there any direct biological implication of folding kinetics? We should say at the outset that there are no answers to this question that can be rigorously supported, but there are a number of interesting speculations. One subject under study is whether proteins with similar structure but no sequence homology have the same folding mechanism. This is, in principle, independent of whether these proteins are products of divergent or convergent evolution. To explore this idea, sequence and structure alignments have

---

Figure 6   A simple statistical model for protein folding (from 76). As with the hairpin, structures are classified by the backbone conformation in which each peptide bond can adopt either a native or nonnative conformation as defined by the pair of flanking ψ, ϕ dihedral angles. To reduce the number of conformations to allow for complete enumeration, it is assumed that native structure can be simultaneously present in just a few regions of the polypeptide as it folds and that two residues interact only if all intervening peptide bonds have the native conformation. In the single sequence approximation, which yields $\sim 5 \times 10^3$ conformations for 100 peptide bonds, no more than one contiguous stretch may be present. That is, *..ccnnnnc...* is allowed, but not *...cnncnnc....* In the double sequence approximation, no more than two stretches are allowed ($\sim 4 \times 10^6$ conformations), and in the triple no more than three ($\sim 10^9$ conformations). The free energy for each species is calculated in these three approximations using a simple free energy function consisting of a contact energy term derived from the atomic coordinates of the native structure and the entropy loss associated with fixing the peptide bonds in their native conformation. With this simplistic energy function, it is unrealistic to expect that the equilibrium constant for folding can be accurately reproduced, so the contact energy is treated as an adjustable parameter to get the experimentally observed equilibrium stability. Folding rates were calculated from the profiles of the free energy as a function of the number of native peptide bonds, the natural reaction coordinate in this model. (*a*) Free energy profiles (kcal/mol) using the double sequence approximation for monomeric λ repressor and muscle acyl phosphatase. (*b*) Correlation between calculated and observed rates for 18 two-state proteins and the β-hairpin forming fragment from protein GB1. The three letters correspond to those of the PDB file name. Circles correspond to α proteins, squares to β proteins, and diamonds to $\alpha\beta$ proteins. The correlation coefficient is 0.85. Inset: correlation of experimental rates and contact order for the same set of proteins (correlation coefficient = 0.64).

been used to search for clusters of conserved residues that are not necessary for either function or stability. The assumption is that these residues, if they appear, correspond to "nuclei" that determine the folding rate (74).

A more general question is whether there is any pressure on folding rates other than that required for the appropriate stability. There must be some constraint, for newly synthesized polypeptide chains must be able to fold within a certain time to be able to perform their biological function and to avoid proteolysis and aggregation. What is the minimal folding time required for biological function? In *Escherichia coli*, proteins are synthesized at a rate of 10–15 amino-acids per second. Assuming an average molecular mass of 40,000 daltons (~350 amino-acids) for *E. coli* proteins, the ribosomes require on average 30 sec to synthesize a protein molecule (69). One could argue that folding speed will not be a limiting factor as long as it is comparable to the rate of protein synthesis. If there is indeed biological pressure, we should expect proteins to fold no slower than 1/minute. All known folding rates for two-state proteins are faster than this minimum speed (55) (Figure 6). Other processes coupled to protein folding, such as proline isomerization and disulfide formation, could slow folding considerably, but specialized enzymes catalyze these reactions in vivo (101). The role of molecular chaperones, such as GroEL and GroES, can also be rationalized in this light. Theoretical estimates indicate that the known chaperones only assist folding of ~5% of the existing proteins (69). One of their roles might be to ensure folding of a small subset of biologically critical proteins that would otherwise fold with rates slower than the one-minute biological minimum.

A still open issue, however, is whether it is difficult for evolution to find sequences that can form stable 3-D structures faster than this biological minimum speed. This question has been approached using combinatorial chemistry. Heavily mutated variants of the IgG binding domain of protein L were found to fold at similar, or even faster, rates than the wild-type protein (62). This result has been used to suggest that for single domain proteins, it is not difficult to find sequences that fold "biologically fast." It would be important to further pursue this idea with experiments on other proteins, and, ideally, to explore large regions of sequence space that are not limited to the neighborhood of naturally occurring sequences. A potential drawback of combinatorial methods is that they generally involve biological selection. It is therefore possible that the method is finding fast folding proteins because they are the only ones that are biologically viable.

Does protein function ever require folding much faster than one minute? For λ repressor, which folds in 200 μs, it has been argued that very fast folding is required for stability to compensate fast unfolding, fast unfolding being required for efficient regulation by proteolysis (13). We do not know the rate of protease binding to unfolded states of proteins, but it could be argued that what really determines the rate of proteolysis of a target protein is the residence time in the unfolded state. Fast folding could then be a strategy to avoid proteolysis while maintaining the low stability necessary for its function (e.g. binding to DNA). Related to this is the interesting suggestion that there is evolutionary pressure for proteins to be marginally stable in order to have the conformational flexibility required for function (58).

A corollary to the idea of folding speed as an evolutionary pressure is the suggestion that to avoid aggregation in the cell, compact states may be required to form much more quickly than the final native structure (49). This idea is consistent with the finding that polypeptide collapse is submillisecond (see above). In a typical *E. coli* cell in logarithmic phase with a volume of $\sim10^{-15}$ liter, there are $\sim$35,000 ribosomes (69), which are producing $\sim$1000 protein molecules per second. We can make a rough estimate of the maximum folding time that is compatible with minimal aggregation. If we assume that aggregation is nonspecific, irreversible, and diffusion limited ($\sim10^8$ M^{-1} s^{-1}) (119), folding in less than $\sim$10 milliseconds would result in aggregation of less than $\sim$1% of newly synthesized proteins. Although this calculation is very approximate for many reasons, it does support the idea that competition between aggregation and folding may provide additional selection pressure for fast-folding sequences or for sequences that collapse quickly to form compact denatured states that do not aggregate. Understanding this competition in more detail may be important for investigations of the pathophysiology of several human diseases (28, 60, 66).

Finally, is there any connection between evolutionary pressure on folding speed and the catalogue of naturally occurring protein structures? The model for protein folding discussed above would suggest that topologically simple structures are expected to fold faster than complicated structures. A large number of geometrically feasible and stable structures may not be observed in nature because they would fold too slowly to be consistent with the constraints of synthesis and aggregation discussed above. This could be a factor responsible for the limited number and distribution of distinct protein folds that have been observed so far (74, 127, 128).

Visit the Annual Reviews home page at www.AnnualReviews.org

LITERATURE CITED

1. Alm E, Baker D. 1999. Matching theory and experiment in protein folding. *Curr. Opin. Struct. Biol.* 9:189–96
2. Alm E, Baker D. 1999. Prediction of protein-folding mechanisms from free-energy landscapes derived from native structures. *Proc. Natl. Acad. Sci. USA* 96:11305–10
3. Ballew RM, Sabelko J, Gruebele M. 1996. Direct observation of fast protein folding: the initial collapse of apomyoglobin. *Proc. Natl. Acad. Sci. USA* 93:5759–64
4. Ballew RM, Sabelko J, Gruebele M. 1996. Observation of distinct nanosecond and microsecond protein folding events. *Nat. Struct. Biol.* 3:923–26
5. Bieri O, Wirz J, Hellrung B, Schutkowski M, Drewello M, Kiefhaber T. 1999. The speed limit for protein folding measured by triplet-triplet energy transfer. *Proc. Natl. Acad. Sci. USA* 96:9597–601
6. Blanco FJ, Rivas G, Serrano L. 1994. A short linear peptide that folds into a β-hairpin in aqueous solution. *Nature Struct. Biol.* 1:584–90
7. Brooks CL. 1998. Simulations of protein

folding and unfolding. *Curr. Opin. Struct. Biol.* 8:222–26

8. Bryngelson JD, Onuchic JN, Socci ND, Wolynes PG. 1995. Funnels, pathways, and the energy landscape of protein folding: a synthesis. *Proteins: Struct. Funct. Genet.* 21:167–95

9. Bryngelson JD, Wolynes PG. 1987. Spin glasses and the statistical mechanics of protein folding. *Proc. Natl. Acad. Sci. USA* 84: 7524–28

10. Bryngelson JD, Wolynes PG. 1989. Intermediates and barrier crossing in a random energy model (with applications to protein folding). *J. Phys. Chem.* 93:6902–15

11. Buckler DR, Haas E, Scheraga HA. 1995. Analysis of the structure of ribonuclease A in native and partially denatured states by time-resolved nonradiative dynamic excitation energy transfer. *Biochemistry* 24: 15965–78

12. Burton RE, Huang GS, Daugherty MA, Calderone TL, Oas TG. 1997. The energy landscape of a fast-folding protein mapped by Ala → Gly substitutions. *Nat. Struct. Biol.* 4:305–10

13. Burton RE, Huang GS, Daugherty MA, Fullbright PW, Oas TG. 1996. Microsecond protein folding through a compact transition state. *J. Mol. Biol.* 263311–22

14. Callender RH, Dyer RB, Gilmanshin R, Woodruff WH. 1998. Fast events in protein folding: the time evolution of primary processes. *Annu. Rev. Phys. Chem.* 49:173–202

15. Camacho J, Thirumalai D. 1995. Theoretical predictions of folding pathways by using the proximity rule, with applications to bovine pancreatic trypsin inhibitor. *Proc. Natl. Acad. Sci. USA* 92:1277–81

16. Chakrabartty A, Baldwin RL. 1995. Stability of α-helices. *Adv. Prot. Chem.* 46:141–76

17. Chan C-K, Hofrichter J, Eaton WA. 1996. Optical triggers in protein folding. *Science* 274:628–29

18. Chan C-K, Hu Y, Takahashi S, Rousseau DL, Eaton WA, Hofrichter J. 1997. Submillisecond protein folding kinetics studied by ultrarapid mixing. *Proc. Natl. Acad. Sci. USA* 94:1779–84

19. Chan HS, Dill KA. 1998. Protein folding in the landscape perspective: chevron plots and non-arrhenius kinetics. *Proteins* 30:2–33

20. Chen E, Wittung-Stafshede P, Kliger DS. 1999. Far-UV time-resolved circular dichroism detection of electron-transfer-triggered cytochrome *c* folding. *J. Am. Chem. Soc.* 121:3811–17

21. Clarke DT, Doig AJ, Stapley BJ, Jones GR. 1999. The alpha-helix folds on the millisecond time scale. *Proc. Natl. Acad. Sci. USA* 96:7232–37

22. Daggett V, Levitt M. 1992. Molecular-dynamics simulation of helix denaturation. *J. Mol. Biol.* 223:1121–38

23. Daura X, Jaun B, Seebach D, van Gunsteren WF, Mark AE. 1998. Reversible peptide folding in solution by molecular dynamics simulation. *J. Mol. Biol.* 280: 925–32

24. Daura X, van Gunsteren WF, Mark AE. 1999. Folding-unfolding thermodynamics of a beta-heptapeptide from equilibrium simulations. *Proteins* 34:269–80

25. Dill KA, Shortle D. 1991. Denatured states of proteins. *Annu. Rev. Biochem.* 60:795–825

26. Dill KA, Stigter D. 1995. Modeling protein stability as heteropolymer collapse. *Adv. Prot. Chem.* 46:59–104

27. Dinner AR, Lazaridis T, Karplus M. 1999. Understanding β-hairpin formation. *Proc. Natl. Acad. Sci. USA* 96:9068–73

28. Dobson CM. 1999. Protein misfolding, evolution and disease. *Trends Biochem. Sci.* 24:329–32

29. Dobson CM, Sali A, Karplus M. 1998. Protein folding: a perspective from theory and experiment. *Angew. Chem. Int. Edit.* 37:868–93

30. Duan Y, Kollman PA. 1998. Pathways to a protein folding intermediate observed in a

1-microsecond simulation in aqueous solution. *Science* 282:740–44

31. Dyer RB, Gai F, Woodruff WH, Gilmanshin R, Callender RH. 1998. Infrared studies of fast events in protein folding. *Accts. Chem. Res.* 31:709–16

32. Eaton WA. 1999. Commentary: searching for "downhill scenarios" in protein folding. *Proc. Natl. Acad. Sci. USA* 96:5897–99

33. Elöve GA, Bhuyan AK, Roder H. 1994. Kinetic mechanism of cytochrome *c* folding: involvement of the heme and its ligands. *Biochemistry* 33:6925–35

34. Fersht AR. 1998. *Structure and Mechanism in Protein Science: A Guide to Enzyme Catalysis and Protein Folding.* San Francisco: Freeman

35. Fersht AR, Matouschek A, Serrano L. 1992. The folding of an enzyme. I. Theory of protein engineering analysis of stability and pathway of protein folding. *J. Mol. Biol.* 224:771–82

36. Galzitskaya OV, Finkelstein A. 1999. A theoretical search for folding/unfolding nuclei in three-dimensional protein structures. *Proc. Natl. Acad. Sci. USA* 96: 11299–304

37. Garel T, Orland H, Pitard E. 1998. Protein folding and heteropolymers. In *Spin Glasses and Random Fields*, ed. AP Young, pp. 387–443. Singapore: World Scientific

38. Gellman SH. 1998. Minimal model systems for beta sheet secondary structure in proteins. *Curr. Opin. Chem. Biol.* 2:717–25

39. Ghaemmaghami S, Word JM, Burton RE, Richardson JS, Oas TG. 1998. Folding kinetics of a fluorescent variant of monomeric lambda repressor. *Biochemistry* 37:9179–85

40. Gilmanshin R, Callender RH, Dyer RB. 1998. The core of apomyoglobin E-form folds at the diffusion limit. *Nat. Struc. Biol.* 5:363–65

41. Gilmanshin R, Williams S, Callender RH, Woodruff WH, Dyer RB. 1997. Fast events in protein folding: relaxation dynamics of secondary and tertiary structure in native

apomyoglobin. *Proc. Natl. Acad. Sci. USA* 94:3709–13

42. Gonnelli M, Strambini G. 1995. Phosphorescence lifetime of tryptophan in proteins. *Biochemistry* 34:13847–57

43. Gruebele M. 1999. The fast protein folding problem. *Annu. Rev. Phys. Chem.* 50:485–516

44. Gruenewald B, Nicola CU, Lustig A, Schwarz G, Klump H. 1979. Kinetics of the helix-coil transition of a polypeptide with non-ionic side groups, derived from ultrasonic relaxation measurements. *Biophys. Chem.* 9:137–47

45. Guo Z, Thirumalai D. 1995. Kinetics of protein folding—nucleation mechanism, time scales, and pathways. *Biopolymers* 36:83–102

46. Hagen SJ, Eaton WA. 1996. Nonexponential structural relaxations in proteins. *J. Chem. Phys.* 104:3395–98

47. Hagen SJ, Eaton WA. 2000. Two-state expansion and collapse of a polypeptide. *J. Mol. Biol.* In press

48. Hagen SJ, Hofrichter J, Eaton WA. 1997. Rate of intrachain diffusion of unfolded cytochrome-*c*. *J. Phys. Chem. B* 101:2352–65

49. Hagen SJ, Hofrichter J, Szabo A, Eaton WA. 1996. Diffusion-limited contact formation in unfolded cytochrome *c*: estimating the maximum rate of protein folding. *Proc. Natl. Acad. Sci. USA* 93:11615–17

50. Hao M-H, Scheraga HA. 1998. Theory of two-state cooperative folding of proteins. *Accts. Chem. Res.* 31:433–40

51. Hardin C, Luthey-Schulten Z, Wolynes PG. 1999. Backbone dynamics, fast folding, and secondary structure formation in helical proteins and peptides. *Proteins* 34:281–94

52. Hofrichter J, Thompson PA. 2000. Laser temperature jump methods for studying folding dynamics. In *Protein Stability and Folding*, ed. KP Murphy. Totowa, NJ: Humana. 2nd ed. In press

53. Huang GS, Oas TG. 1995. Submillisecond

folding of monomeric λ repressor. *Proc. Natl. Acad. Sci. USA* 92:6878–82

54. Itzhaki LS, Otzen DE, Fersht AR. 1995. The structure of the transition state for folding of chymotrypsin inhibitor-2 analyzed by protein engineering methods— evidence for a nucleation condensation mechanism for protein folding. *J. Mol. Biol.* 254:260–88

55. Jackson SE. 1998. How do small single-domain proteins fold? *Folding Design* 3: R81–R91

56. Jackson SE, Fersht AR. 1991. Folding of chymotrypsin inhibitor 2. 1. Evidence for a two-state transition. *Biochemistry* 30: 10428–35

57. Jacob M, Holterman G, Perl D, Reinsten J, Schindler T, Geeves, Schmid FX. 1999. Microsecond folding of the cold shock protein measured by a pressure-jump technique. *Biochemistry* 38:2882–91

58. Jaenicke J. 1991. Protein stability and molecular adaptation to extreme conditions. *Eur. J. Biochem.* 202:715–28

59. Jones CM, Henry ER, Hu Y, Chan CK, Luck SD, Bhuyan A, Roder H, Hofrichter J, Eaton WA. 1993. Fast events in protein folding initiated by nanosecond laser photolysis. *Proc. Natl. Acad. Sci. USA* 90:11860–64

60. Kelly JW. 1998. The alternative conformations of amyloidogenic proteins and their multi-step assembly pathways. *Curr. Opin. Struct. Biol.* 8:101–6.

61. Kiefhaber T. 1995. Kinetic traps in lysozyme folding. *Proc. Natl. Acad. Sci. USA* 92:9029–33

62. Kim DE, Gu HD, Baker D. 1998. The sequences of small proteins are not extensively optimized for rapid folding by natural selection. *Proc. Natl. Acad. Sci. USA* 95:4982–86

63. Knight JB, Vishwanath A, Brody JP, Austin RH. 1998. Hydrodynamic focusing on a silicon chip: mixing nanoliters in microseconds. *Phys. Rev. Lett.* 80:3863–66

64. Kuwajima K. 1989. The molten globule

state as a clue for understanding the folding and cooperativity of globular-protein structure. *Proteins* 6:87–103

65. Lacroix E, Kortemme T, de la Paz ML, Serrano L. 1999. The design of linear peptides that fold as monomeric beta-sheet structures. *Curr. Opin. Struct. Biol.* 9:487–93

66. Lansbury PT. 1999. Evolution of amyloid: What normal protein folding may tell us about fibrillogenesis and disease. *Proc. Natl. Acad. Sci. USA* 96:3342–44

67. Lapidus LJ, Eaton WA, Hofrichter J. Measuring the rate of intramolecular contact formation in unfolded polypeptides. Submitted

68. Lednev IK, Karnoup AS, Sparrow MC, Asher SA. 1999. Alpha-helix peptide folding and unfolding activation barriers: a nanosecond UV resonance raman study. *J. Am. Chem. Soc.* 121:8074–86

69. Lorimer GH. 1996. A quantitative assessment of the role of chaperonin proteins in protein folding in vivo. *FASEB J.* 10:5–9

70. Lu HSM, Volk M, Kholodenko Y, Gooding E, Hochstrasser RM, DeGrado WF. 1997. Aminothiotyrosine disulfide, an optical trigger for initiation of protein folding. *J. Am. Chem. Soc.* 119:7173–80

71. Marqusee S, Robbins VH, Baldwin RL. 1989. Unusually stable helix formation in short alanine based peptides. *Proc. Natl. Acad. Sci. USA* 86:5286–90

72. Matthews CR. 1993. Pathways of protein folding. *Annu. Rev. Biochem.* 62:653–83

73. Mines GA, Pascher T, Lee SC, Winkler JR, Gray HB. 1996. Cytochrome *c* folding triggered by electron transfer. *Chem. Biol.* 3:491–97

74. Mirny LA, Shakhnovich EI. 1999. Universally conserved positions in protein folds: Reading evolutionary signals about stability, folding kinetics and function. *J. Mol. Biol.* 291:177–96.

75. Mohanty D, Elber R, Thirumalai D, Beglov D, Roux B. 1997. Kinetics of peptide folding: Computer simulations of SYPFDV

and peptide variants in water. *J. Mol. Biol.* 272:423–42

76. Muñoz V, Eaton WA. 1999. A simple model for calculating the kinetics of protein folding from three-dimensional structures. *Proc. Natl. Acad. Sci. USA* 96:11311–16

77. Muñoz V, Henry ER, Hofrichter J, Eaton WA. 1998. A statistical mechanical model for β-hairpin kinetics. *Proc. Natl. Acad. Sci. USA* 95:5872–79

78. Muñoz V, Serrano L. 1994. Elucidating the folding problem of helical peptides using empirical parameters. *Nat. Struct. Biol.* 1:399–409

79. Muñoz V, Serrano L. 1995. Elucidating the folding problem of helical peptides using empirical parameters. II. Helix macrodipole effects and rational modification of the helical content of natural peptides. *J. Mol. Biol.* 245:275–296

80. Muñoz V, Thompson PA, Hofrichter J, Eaton WA. 1997. Folding dynamics and mechanism of β-hairpin formation. *Nature* 390:196–99

81. Nölting B. 1996. Temperature-jump induced fast refolding of cold-unfolded protein. *Biochem. Biophys. Res. Commun.* 227:903–8

82. Nölting B, Golbik R, Fersht AR. 1995. Submillisecond events in protein folding. *Proc. Natl. Acad. Sci. USA* 92:10668–72

83. Onuchic J, Luthey-Schulten A, Wolynes PG. 1997. Theory of protein folding: the energy landscape perspective. *Annu. Rev. Phys. Chem.* 48:545–600

84. Onuchic J, Socci ND, Luthey-Schulten Z, Wolynes PG. 1996. Protein folding funnels: the nature of the transition state ensemble. *Folding Design* 1:441–50

85. Pande VS, Grosberg AY, Tanaka T, Rokhsar DS. 1998. Pathways for protein folding: Is a new view needed? *Curr. Opin. Struct. Biol.* 8:68–79

86. Pande VS, Rokhsar DS. 1998. Is the molten globule a third phase of proteins? *Proc. Natl. Acad. Sci. USA* 95:1490–94

87. Pande VS, Rokhsar DS. 1999. Molecular dynamics simulations of unfolding and refolding of a β-hairpin fragment of protein G. *Proc. Natl. Acad. Sci. USA* 96:9062–67

88. Park S-H, Shastry MCR, Roder H. 1999. Folding dynamics of the B1 domain of protein G explored by ultrarapid mixing. *Nature Struct. Biol.* 6:943–47

89. Pascher T, Chesick JP, Winkler JR, Gray HB. 1996. Protein folding triggered by electron transfer. *Science* 271:1558–60

90. Phillips CM, Mizutani Y, Hochstrasser RM. 1995. Ultrafast thermally induced unfolding of RNase A. *Proc. Natl. Acad. Sci. USA* 92:7292–96

91. Pitard E, Orland H. 1998. Dynamics of the swelling or collapse of a homopolymer. *Europhys. Lett.* 41:467–72

92. Plaxco KW, Simons KT, Baker D. 1998. Contact order, transition state placement and the refolding rates of single domain proteins. *J. Mol. Biol.* 277:985–94

93. Pollack L, Tate MW, Darnton NC, Knight JB, Gruner S, Eaton WA, Austin RH. 1999. Compactness of the denatured state of a fast-folding protein measured by submillisecond small-angle x-ray scattering. *Proc. Natl. Acad. Sci. USA* 96:10115–17

94. Portman JJ, Takada S, Wolynes PG. 1998. Variational theory for site resolved protein folding free energy surfaces. *Phys. Rev. Lett.* 81:5237–40

95. Ptitsyn OB. 1995. Molten globule and protein folding. *Adv. Prot. Chem.* 47:83–229

96. Regenfuss P, Clegg RM, Fulwyler MJ, Barrantes FJ, Jovin TM. 1985. Mixing liquids in microseconds. *Rev. Sci. Instrum.* 56:283–90

97. Robinson CR, Sauer RT. 1996. Equilibrium stability and sub-millisecond refolding of a designed single-chain arc repressor. *Biochemistry* 35:13878–84

98. Roder H, Colón W. 1997. Kinetic role of early intermediates in protein folding. *Curr. Opin. Struct. Biol.* 7:15–28

99. Roder H, Shastry MCR. 1999. Methods for

exploring early events in protein folding. *Curr. Opin. Struct. Biol.* 9:620–26

100. Sabelko J, Ervin J, Gruebele M. 1999. Observation of strange kinetics in protein folding. *Proc. Natl. Acad. Sci. USA* 96:6031–36

101. Schmid FX. 1995. Protein-folding–prolyl isomerases join the fold. *Curr. Biol.* 5:993–94

102. Searle MS, Williams DH, Packman LC. 1995. A short linear peptide derived from the N-terminal sequence of ubiquitin folds into a water-stable non-native β-hairpin. *Nature Struct. Biol.* 2:999–1006

103. Shakhnovich EI. 1997. Theoretical studies of protein-folding thermodynamics and kinetics. *Curr. Opin. Struct. Biol.* 7:29–40

104. Shastry MCR, Luck SD, Roder H. 1998. A continuous-flow capillary mixing method to monitor reactions on the microsecond time scale. *Biophys. J.* 74:2714–21

105. Shastry MCR, Roder H. 1998. Evidence for barrier-limited protein folding kinetics on the microsecond time scale. *Nat. Struc. Biol.* 5:385–92

106. Shastry MCR, Sauder JM, Roder H. 1998. Kinetic and structural analysis of submillisecond folding events in cytochrome-*c*. *Acc. Chem. Res.* 31:717–25

107. Shoemaker BA, Wang J, Wolynes PG. 1999. Exploring structures in protein folding funnels with free energy functionals: the transition state ensemble. *J. Mol. Biol.* 287:657–94

108. Socci ND, Onuchic JN, Wolynes PG. 1996. Diffusive dynamics of the reaction coordinate for protein folding funnels. *J. Chem. Phys.* 104:5860–68

109. Sosnick TR, Mayne L, Englander SW. 1996. Molecular collapse: the rate-limiting step in two-state cytochrome *c* folding. *Proteins* 24:413–26

110. Sosnick TR, Mayne L, Hiller R, Englander SW. 1994. The barriers in protein folding. *Nat. Struct Biol.* 1:149–56

111. Szabo A, Schulten K, Schulten Z. 1980. The first passage time approach to diffusion-controlled reactions. *J. Chem. Phys.* 72:4350–57

112. Takahashi S, Yeh SR, Das TK, Chan CK, Gottfried DS, Rousseau DL. 1997. Folding of cytochrome *c* initiated by submillisecond mixing. *Nat. Struct. Biol.* 4:44–50

113. Telford JR, Tezcan A, Gray HB, Winkler JR. 1999. Role of ligand substitution in ferrocytochrome *c* folding. *Biochemistry* 38:1944–49

114. Thirumalai D. 1999. Time scales for the formation of the most probable tertiary contacts in proteins with applications to cytochrome *c*. *J. Phys. Chem. B* 103:608–10

115. Thirumalai D, Klimov D. 1999. Deciphering the time scales and mechanisms of protein folding using minimal off-lattice models. *Curr. Opin. Struct. Biol.* 9:197–207

116. Thompson PA, Eaton WA, Hofrichter J. 1997. Laser temperature-jump study of the helix-coil kinetics of an alanine peptide interpreted with a 'kinetic zipper' model. *Biochemistry* 36:9200–10

117. Thompson PA, Muñoz V, Jas GS, Henry ER, Eaton WA. 2000. The helix-coil kinetics of a heteropeptide. *J. Phys. Chem. B.* 104:378–89

118. Volk M, Lu HSM, Kholodenko Y, Gooding E, DeGrado WF, Hochstrasser RM. 1997. Peptide conformational dynamics and vibrational Stark effects following photinitiated disulfide cleavage. *J. Phys. Chem. B* 101:8607–16

119. Waldburger CD, Jonsson T, Sauer RT. 1996. Barriers to protein folding: formation of buried polar interactions is a slow step in acquisition of structure. *Proc. Natl. Acad. Sci. USA* 93:2629–34

120. Williams K, Causgrove TP, Gilmanshin R, Fang KS, Callender RH, Woodruff WH, Dyer RB. 1996. Fast events in protein folding: helix melting and formation

in a small peptide. *Biochemistry* 35:691–97

121. Wittung-Stafshede P, Gray HB, Winkler JR. 1997. Rapid formation of a four-helix bundle. Cytochrome b_{562} folding triggered by electron transfer. *J. Am. Chem. Soc.* 119:9562–63

122. Wittung-Stafshede P, Lee JC, Winkler JR, Gray HB. 1999. Cytochrome b_{562} folding triggered by electron transfer: approaching the speed limit for formation of a four-helix-bundle protein. *Proc. Natl. Acad. Sci. USA* 96:6587–90

123. Wittung-Stafshede P, Malmström BG, Winkler JR, Gray HB. 1998. Folding of deoxymyoglobin triggered by electron transfer. *J. Phys. Chem. A.* 102:5599–1

124. Yeh SR, Takahashi S, Fan B, Rousseau DL. 1997. Ligand exchange during cytochrome *c* folding. *Nat. Struct. Biol.* 4:51–56

125. Zwanzig R. 1995. A simple model of protein folding kinetics. *Proc. Natl. Acad. Sci. USA* 92:9801–4

126. Zwanzig R. 1997. Two-state models of protein folding kinetics. *Proc. Natl. Acad. Sci. USA* 94:148–50

127. Thirumalai D, Klimov DK. 2000. Emergence of stable and fast folding protein structures. In *Stochastic Dynamics and Pattern Formation in Biological and Complex Systems*, eds. S Kim, KJ Lee, W. Sung. pp. 95–111. Proceedings #501 American Institute of Physics, Melvelle, New York.

128. Govindarajan S. Recabarren R., Goldstein RA. 1999. Estimating the total number of protein folds. *Proteins: Struct. Funct. Gen.* 35:408–14

Annu. Rev. Biophys. Biomol. Struct. 2000. 29:361–410

ATOMIC FORCE MICROSCOPY IN THE STUDY OF MACROMOLECULAR CRYSTAL GROWTH

A. McPherson, A. J. Malkin, and Yu. G. Kuznetsov

Department of Molecular Biology and Biochemistry, University of California, Irvine, California 92697-3900; e-mail: amcphers@uci.edu

Key Words protein crystals, virus crystals, crystal defects, growth mechanisms, X-ray crystallography

■ **Abstract** Atomic force microscopy (AFM) has been used to study protein, nucleic acid, and virus crystals *in situ*, in their mother liquors, as they grow. From sequential AFM images taken at brief intervals over many hours, or even days, the mechanisms and kinetics of the growth process can be defined. the appearance of both two- and three-dimensional nuclei on crystal surfaces have been visualized, defect structures of crystals were clearly evident, and defect densities of crystals were also determined. The incorporation of a wide range of impurities, ranging in size from molecules to microns or larger microcrystals, and even foreign particles were visually recorded. From these observations and measurements, a more complex understanding of the detailed character of macromolecular crystals is emerging, one that reveals levels of complexity previously unsuspected. The unique features of these crystals, apparently in AFM images, undoubtedly influence the diffraction properties of the crystals and the quality of the molecular images obtained by X-ray crystallography.

CONTENTS

INTRODUCTION

The technique of atomic force microscopy (AFM), also known as scanning force microscopy (SFM), is relatively recent, having been invented in the early 1980s (3), but it has already had a major impact in the characterization of surface structures in both material science and biology. Early applications were principally in vacuum or in air; thus the study of the structure and formation of hard materials initially

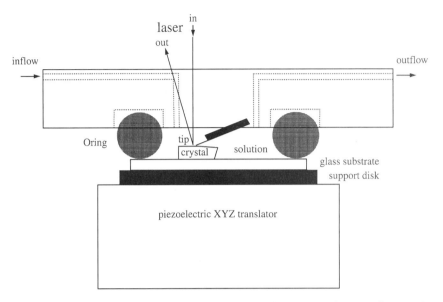

Figure 1   A simplified schematic diagram showing the fundamental features of an atomic force microscope useful in the analysis and direct visualization of the surface features, development, and growth kinetics of macromolecular crystals.

received the most benefit. Increasingly, however, the method is being applied in fluid cells in liquid media; hence, successes in the analysis of biological structure, where rigorously specified conditions are essential, have begun appearing with increasing frequency (1, 7, 21). Its potential in the sphere of biological research, though, has hardly been tapped.

All AFM instruments, one of which is shown schematically in Figure 1 and in actuality in Figure 2, are quite simple in design and construction as compared to, say, X-ray diffraction systems. There is a probe that is brought into close proximity to the surface of interest and then scanned in a systematic manner over the surface. The probe in AFM is a very sharp stylus, similar to a minute phonograph needle, with a tip radius of about 5 to 60 nm. Even sharper tips are currently under development leased on carbon nanotube technology (53, 19). The probe is mounted at the end of a short cantilever, typically 100–250 μm in length. The cantilever has a low spring constant (<1 N/m) to minimize the force between the tip and the sample during imaging. Scanning is accomplished by moving the probe, which is under piezoelectric control, along a series of raster lines. As the probe tip moves over the surface, it interacts through aggregate atomic forces with features on the surface. As a consequence of the interactions, the probe is deflected, the deflections are amplified by corresponding deflections of a laser beam, which is reflected from the upper surface of the probe, and photoelectric circuitry converts these fluctuations into height information. The resulting data can then be presented in a number of different visual formats as well as recorded as a digital image.

Figure 2   A commercially available atomic force microscope, the Nanoscope III (Digital Instruments Corp., Santa Barbara, CA) suitable for imaging growing macromolecular crystals in situ, and that was used to record most of the AFM images presented in this review. The microscope itself, which contains the fluid cell, cantilever, optics system, and piezzo driven positioners is seen in the lower right. It is usually mounted on an optics table, marble stand, or in some arrangement that minimizes ambient vibration.

Microfabricated cantilevers exert a force on the substrate surface of about 10^{-9} to 10^{-12} N/m, and as one might anticipate, the resolution of the technique depends on the degree of force employed. The greater the force between probe and surface, the more sensitive the probe is to surface variations. On the other hand, the greater the force, the more the probe will perturb the surface. While this may not be a severe limitation for hard surfaces such as minerals or metals, it is a major consideration when dealing with relatively soft biological materials. The sharper the tip, the greater the resolution, but the more concentrated is the force on the surface under study. Thus surface damage again becomes a consideration.

Problems arising from unfavorable probe—surface interactions, particularly lateral force—have been overcome to some extent by the development of what are known as tapping mode instruments (20). With tapping mode, the probe tip is not in continuous contact with the surface (referred to as contact mode) but oscillates up and down as it is scanned over the surface, essentially "tapping" its way gently and sensing the heights of features it encounters. This "tapping mode" approach has proven a significant boon to biological researchers as it has allowed the characterization of samples that would otherwise be too soft or too fragile to withstand contact mode examination. Operating in a fluid environment presents some complications due to fluid dynamics, but these are not severe. One constraint that sometimes presents obstacles is that the specimen under study must be fixed to, or adhere firmly to, the substrate surface of the fluid cell, which may be glass, cleaved mica, plastic, or any other hard material. If this condition is not met, then the specimen will move due to interaction with the probe and no useful information is gathered. For the macromolecular crystals discussed here, both contact and tapping mode were used, a variety of substrate materials employed, and all operations, unless specifically noted otherwise, were carried out in a fluid cell containing mother liquor.

AFM often yields images of extraordinary clarity and detail of complex surfaces and objects. It can be applied to scan fields ranging in size from less than 20 nm up to about 150 μm, and with a spatial resolution on biological soft materials of about 1 nm, with a height resolution as great as 0.1 nm. Thus, it provides precise visual detail over a size range that is impossible for most other techniques. Its application extends over the range lying between individual macromolecules that are accessible by X-ray crystallography, macromolecular assemblies amenable to electron microscopy, to living cells, which can just be seen using light microscopy. Because visualization is carried out in a fluid environment, the specimens suffer no dehydration, as is generally necessary with electron microscopy. They require no fixing or staining; indeed living specimens can be observed over long periods so long as they stay relatively well put. And for the most part, the specimen seems in most cases oblivious even to the presence of the probe tip poking about its surface.

The great power of AFM, however, does not lie just in its imaging capability but arises from the nonperturbing nature of the probe interaction with the surface under study. Because the specimen ignores the presence of the probe, its natural processes, such as growth, continue uninhibited. This allows the investigator to record not simply a single image, but a series of images that may extend over hours or even days. This is ideal of course for the study of the growth of macromolecular crystals, which develop over such periods of time. Imaging frequency depends on the scan rate of the probe, and images may be gathered rapidly, within a few seconds or more slowly. Because image quality often deteriorates with increased scan speed, generally images are collected within a period of one to five minutes. For macromolecular crystal growth, a relatively slow process, events on the surface, at low supersaturations, impose no requirement for high scan speed. Thus, a long series of high quality images are generally accessible to the investigator.

A further property of AFM carried out in fluid cells is that the fluid can be changed during the course of experiments without appreciably disturbing the specimen. This is of great value in the study of macromolecular crystal growth because it is often desirable to study the growth process under different conditions of supersaturation. This can be done repeatedly with a single growing crystal because the mother liquor can be exchanged. Growth steps, as seen below, are often clearly visible on the surfaces of crystals, and because their advancement is relatively slow, their rate of progression over the surface can be readily recorded in a temporal sequence of images. When rates are measured as a function of temperature, salt concentration, supersaturation, or some other influence, then growth step velocities can be used to deduce other important thermodynamic and kinetic parameters such as the step free energy, and the kinetic coefficient (6, 9, 11). As illustrated below, in the best of cases, individual virus particles, and even single protein molecules, can be observed as they are recruited into advancing step edges.

Finally, before proceeding to examine some of the early returns from the AFM analysis of macromolecular crystal growth, it is necessary to call attention to some of the practical problems that are often encountered, and to some obstacles that prevent achieving the level of quality seen in the images below. First, because biological crystals are extremely fragile and difficult to manipulate, and because the analysis takes place in an aqueous environment, it may be difficult to fasten or fix the crystals to the substrate. This has been overcome by nucleating and growing the crystals directly on the substrate, i.e. in situ analysis (25, 27, 33), or by devising ways of essentially "clamping" larger crystals down to the substrate with flexible carbon fibers. The greatest difficulty in obtaining images is the fragility of the crystals and their susceptibility to damage or scarring by the AFM tip. As noted above, tapping mode operation can obviate this problem in some instances, but even then softness may prove the limit to resolution. Some crystals such as lysozyme or thaumatin (see below) are relatively hard and resistant to probe damage, and they yield unusually detailed images. Others such as most virus crystals are extremely fragile and difficult to deal with, though the large particle size of the incorporating unit pays great dividends to the patient investigator.

Of course, other technical points must be addressed, but most of these can be addressed through trial and error, and prudent adjustments to technique. Among these are identifying the optimal cantilever length (long and soft for contact mode, short and stiff for tapping mode), probe tip, and particularly finding a well-made tip among a wafer of many. Tips are, at the nanometer level, irregular and often have two or more contact points with the surface under study. As a consequence, double images, multiple images, convoluted images, and other types of artifacts are frequently obtained. Image artifacts are common in AFM work. Probe tips are also easily fouled by extraneous material, such as precipitate, which dramatically lessens their ability to sense surface detail. Mother liquors, therefore, must be scrupulously clean and well filtered. Vibration can affect high magnification and high resolution analyses and obviously need to be eliminated as best as possible. Thus, AFM instruments are usually situated on an optics table or a marble slab.

Analysis of Macromolecular Crystals by AFM

Application of AFM to the study of protein crystals was pioneered by Steve Durbin in 1992 (12, 13) using crystals of lysozyme. He clearly showed not only that two dimensional islands and growth steps could be directly visualized in single images, but that a series of images could be obtained in the native mother liquor that permitted quantitative description of their movement. Additional early work, again on lysozyme, was carried out by Konnert et al (23), who compared simulated images computed from the X-ray crystallographic structure with experimental images. In these studies, they achieved near molecular resolution and demonstrated the influence of probe tip properties on the resultant image. The first work on virus crystals was reported by Malkin et al (38) using crystals of satellite tobacco mosaic virus. Images of the growth of tRNA crystals, the first nucleic acid crystals studied, were achieved by Ng et al (46) who demonstrated the acute temperature sensitivity of the growth mechanisms responsible for these crystals.

In the past few years a number of studies from several different laboratories reported using AFM to study protein crystal growth. Insulin crystallization, for example, was studied in the laboratory of Ward (54–56); an excellent study of rhombohedral canavalin crystals was reported by Land et al (26), apoferritin by Vekilov et al (51a), and lysozyme in the laboratory of Komatsu (45) and Li et al (28–30). Investigations of numerous protein crystals were reported from our own laboratory (24, 25, 32, 33, 35–37). It is reasonable to expect that the number of applications to protein and virus crystal growth will likely proliferate in the future, as the amount of new information that can be obtained from such studies is vast and rich in content.[1]

The properties of macromolecular crystals, including protein, nucleic acid, and virus crystals, have been described previously (39–41), as have the methods and procedures for their growth (39, 41, 52), and these aspects of the research are not addressed further here. A few properties relevant to the AFM approach are, however, worth emphasizing. First among these is the fragility of macromolecular crystals as physical materials. Compared to conventional crystals, and even many other biological materials, they are extremely soft (10) and sensitive to damage by pressure. This, as noted above, can be the ultimate limitation to their study by AFM. They also must be maintained fully hydrated. Because of capillary and surface tension effects, samples cannot be studied in thin films of fluid as is done with capillary mounts in X-ray diffraction analysis. Thus, the crystals can only be studied fully submerged in mother liquor, in the fluid cell.

On the other side of the ledger, however, macromolecular crystals are almost ideal systems for studying crystal growth as a general phenomenon. The particle size is relatively large, 3 to 10 nm diameters for most proteins, several times that for viruses, which is an order of magnitude or more larger than conventional molecules that crystallize. Thus their aggregates can be seen on the surfaces of crystals; even the incorporation of single molecules can be observed. The kinetics

---

[1]Most of the illustrations presented in this review are from our own laboratory's work. This is so only for the sake of expediency, as images were therefore available and cataloged that illustrated the specific points, events, or processes discussed in the text. We apologize to our colleagues whose images are frequently of equal quality and intend no disrespect for their work.

of the growth processes of macromolecular crystals are several orders of magnitude slower than for conventional crystals; thus, the course of events during growth is fully compatible with the temporal resolution of the instrument. Unit cells are one to two orders of magnitude larger than for conventional crystals, and this enhances the definition of growth steps, dislocations, the incorporation of large impurities, and the defect structure. For virus crystals, where softness allows, these advantages of size and speed are increased by an additional order of magnitude.

Macromolecular crystals are, of course, periodic in structure. This is useful because the eye averages when their images are examined, and otherwise minor features become pronounced. In addition, the underlying periodicity makes possible the application of Fourier filtering and averaging processes that can yield appreciably improved images for measurement. These methods are less useful than in X-ray crystallography, however, because what are often of most interest are nonperiodic features such as step edges or defects that occur against the periodic background. These are precisely what are eliminated by Fourier methods.

As described more fully below, macromolecular crystals appear to grow by using a variety of mechanisms, some of which are familiar to conventional crystal growth (5, 6, 8), but also by another mechanism, which may be unique. Although the kinetic parameters are strikingly different, the underlying physics of the growth processes and the thermodynamic principles are the same as for other crystals (see 4, 14–16). Because of the nature of the building units, and the density of their interactions, defects and their causes may be different than otherwise, but nonetheless they are more or less the same as for small molecule crystals. Again, the major differences between macromolecule and conventional crystal growth arise almost entirely from the large sizes and lower density of interactions of the macromolecules, the liquid environment and the consequent role of water, and the generally higher level of impurities that we find in macromolecular preparations.

Mechanisms of Macromolecular Crystal Growth

A feature that strikes the investigator using AFM to image macromolecular crystals is the complexity, diversity, and variability of crystal surfaces. These arise from the different mechanisms and growth processes, their combinations, in operation, the spectrum of defects and dislocations, the roughness of the surfaces produced by impurities and multiple conformers, and the asymmetries and shapes arising from the bonding energies of molecules in different directions in the lattice. Some crystals are relatively smooth and unperturbed; others, like those illustrated in Figure 3, are highly varied in surface character. AFM has been used to analyze the growth and dissolution of protein, nucleic acid, and virus crystals, to delineate the causes and factors that produce and influence this diversity. AFM has been used to suggest explanations that are unavailable from other methods, and to provide quantitative kinetic and thermodynamic measurements essential to a detailed understanding of the crystallization process. Chief among these are the surface

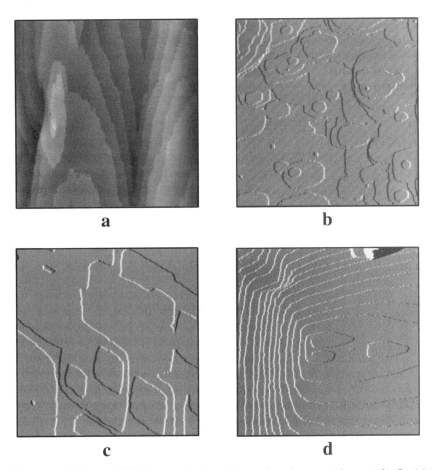

a

b

c

d

Figure 3 Arbitrary AFM images of the surfaces of various protein crystals. In (a) lysozyme, (b) and (d) thaumatin, and (c) glucose isomerase. Scan areas are (a) $6 \times 6 \ \mu m^2$, (b) $12 \times 12 \ \mu m^2$, (c) $11 \times 11 \ \mu m^2$, (d) $13 \times 13 \ \mu m^2$.

free energy of the step edge and the kinetic coefficient measures of growth rates compared with conventional crystals, and the types and distribution of defects and dislocations throughout the crystal.

The purpose of most AFM studies is, first of all, to advance understanding of the fundamental physics and chemistry underlying the crystallization process. Second, however, is the objective of improving the crystallization process in support of macromolecular X-ray crystallography, a keystone of modern molecular biology. It is fair to assume that increased understanding of the process may be translated into more effective and efficient crystallization approaches and methods, and these, ultimately, into larger crystals of more and more proteins—crystals that diffract to higher resolution, have reduced mosaic spread, and withstand the rigors of cryocrystallography (18) and data collection in a more robust fashion.

There is also at least some likelihood that AFM may be able to contribute in other ways to X-ray diffraction analyses. Because height information is preserved, the handedness of molecular arrangements arising from screw axes can be deduced. Thus, AFM may provide a means of discriminating screw axes from their enantiomorph, as was done for crystals of fungal lipase (25), something difficult early in a structure analysis. As illustrated by the example seen in Figure 4, packing arrangements of molecules within unit cell are sometimes visible, which may assist in molecular replacement structure solutions. In the case of virus crystallography, the value may be even greater. As Figure 5 illustrates, with AFM the orientations of individual virus particles and the capsomere structure of their surfaces may be clearly visible in images. These may then be used for constructing initial models at low resolution for phase extension. It is important to bear in mind that images are obtained under fully hydrated and unperturbed conditions; thus the images represent the molecules or virus particles as they actually exist in the crystal used for data collection.

As illustrated in Figure 6, there are two processes that must occur for the growth of any crystal; we refer to these as crystal face growth and tangential growth. Growth normal to the surface proceeds by the creation of new nascent layers, or islands in most cases, which exhibit step edges to which new molecules can be added. Because addition of new layers requires, in the absence of dislocations (see below), the appearance of a new, ordered arrangement where none previously existed, i.e. atop the surface layer, it is a nucleation event. Nucleation events, which represent a phase transition, generally occur with difficulty and require surmounting an energy barrier. Thus, they are usually the rate-limiting step in most physical and chemical processes, including crystal growth. The initiation of new layers, then, is the slower, more difficult process in crystal growth.

Tangential growth refers to the recruitment of molecules into step edges and the extension of new layers over the surface. This is, relatively, a much easier process because the incorporation of a new individual is essentially a cooperative process favored by both molecules composing the existing step edge and the new recruit. The energetics of the situation for incorporation favors the union. Thus, once a nascent layer appears, its two-dimensional expansion may proceed unimpeded. Indeed, if we look at the surfaces of a crystal that has stopped growing in the absence of impurities, we see that there are no islands or step edges remaining on the surface—it is flat. While the last available step edge has expanded over the surface to the very edges of the crystal, the barrier to the formation of new layers cannot be overcome.

A principle that dominates virtually all aspects of crystal growth, macromolecular and otherwise, is the degree of supersaturation of the mother liquor. Virtually all kinetic and thermodynamic variables vary with supersaturation. This includes the probability of forming critical nuclei, that is the birth of a new crystal, initiation of new layers on an existing surface, the velocity of step movement on the surface (tangential growth), the incorporation of impurities (8, 11, 47, 48), and a host of lesser properties. Even the particular kind of mechanism employed in

Figure 4 (*a*) A 200 × 200 nm² scan area image of the (100) face of a hexagonal crystal of fungal lipase, with space group $P6_1$ (or $P6_5$) and cell dimensions a = b = 142.9 Å, and c = 80.4 Å. The lattice, and even individual molecules, are clearly evident in this raw image. (*b*) Fourier transform (diffraction pattern) of the raw image, with a resolution of ~12–14 Å. It was subsequently filtered using the program ICE, and the Fourier-filtered image obtained from a is presented in c. (*d*) Fourier-filtered image (5 × 5 unit cells) of the lipase crystal. Light features are above and dark features below the mean plane of the crystal surface.

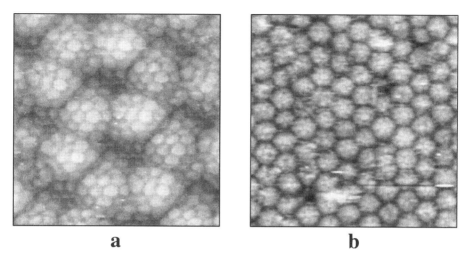

a   **b**

Figure 5 AFM images of areas on the surfaces of (*a*) turnip yellow mosaic virus crystals, and (*b*) brome grass mosaic virus (BMV) crystals. In (*a*) the TYMV particles can be seen to pack in hexagonal groups about central solvent channels that permeate the crystals, and the capsomeres on the surfaces of the virions are clearly visible. In (*b*) capsomeres are again observable on the virion surfaces, and in some cases indentations at the centers of the capsomeres are even evident. Both TYMV and BMV have diameters of 28 nm. Scan areas are (*a*) $140 \times 140 \ nm^2$, (*b*) $275 \times 275 \ nm^2$.

growth on a crystal surface is dependent on supersaturation. Supersaturation in turn may, of course, be a function of an array of experimental variables such as salt concentration, macromolecule concentration, temperature, or other physical and chemical factors. It is also dependent on the underlying physical and chemical properties of the macromolecules and the manner by which they interact with one another.

Four principal mechanisms have been described for the development of faces of macromolecular crystals (38). It should be noted, however, that different faces of a single crystal, being nonidentical, might simultaneously employ different mechanisms for development. A single face may use more than one mechanism at the same time, and the type of mechanism may change as some experimental variable, such as temperature, is altered. Thus, when only one or a few observations of growth mechanism is available for a particular crystal, this by no means implies that other mechanisms are not involved at other times or under other conditions. Most crystals, it seems, utilize all mechanisms at one time or another, though some one mechanism may be strongly favored.

Over a broad range of supersaturation, most protein and virus crystals appear to generate step edges, new growth layers, through a process of two-dimensional nucleation. Guided undoubtedly by the underlying lattice, molecules from solution adhere to the surface and organize themselves into similarly ordered arrays consistent with the underlying surface. These molecules are also free to leave the surface as well, but when the organized array reaches some critical size, the balance

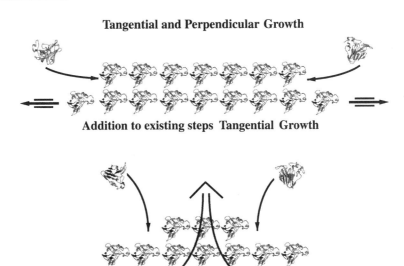

Figure 6   Tangential and face growth. Schematic diagram showing tangential growth by addition of molecules to step edges causing their lateral extension, and face growth proceeding by the addition of nascent layers atop those already grown. Diagram showing tangential and face growth may require two-dimensional nucleation on the surface of a crystal and, therefore, must overcome an energy barrier of some significance. Thus, face growth may cease well before tangential growth.

changes to favor addition, and it persists and expands as a growth island by recruitment of additional molecules into its step edges. The first event, two-dimensional nucleation, provides growth normal to the surface; the latter events, tangential growth. Crystal surfaces growing by this process of two-dimensional nucleation often appear to be littered with growth islands as seen in Figure 7. In many cases, the shapes of the growth islands reflect the geometries of the morphological face on which they are present, as in Figure 8. AFM allows the investigator to observe the changes in the islands as a function of time, as in Figure 9. This permits the direct calculation of step movement rates, which at specified supersaturations, then allow deduction of important thermodynamic parameters (14, 32).

Using AFM, the heights of the steps on the surfaces can easily be measured to a precision of a few angstroms, and almost invariably they correspond to a single unit cell dimension. This implies that, in general, crystals grow by initiating and completing discrete crystallographic unit cells, rather than starting and filling cells here and there on the island. The question as to whether molecules add individually

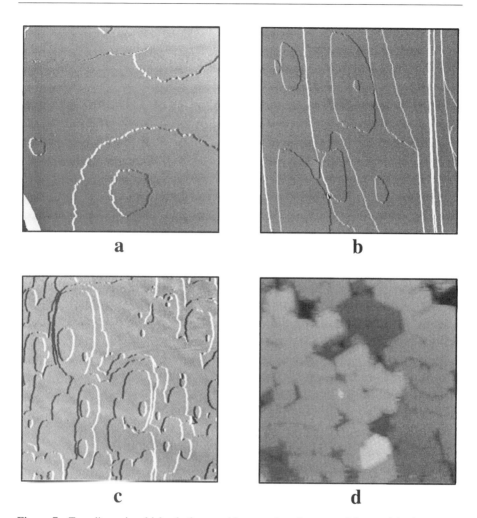

Figure 7 Two-dimensional islands that provide step edges for tangential growth by incorporation of new molecules from solution are seen here on the surfaces of (*a*) cubic satellite tobacco mosaic virus (STMV) crystals, (*b*) beef liver catalase crystals, (*c*) thaumatin crystals, and (*d*) orthorhombic STMV crystals. Scan areas are (*a*) 12 × 12 μm^2, (*b*) 32.5 × 32.5 μm^2, (*c*) 13.5 × 13.5 μm^2, (*d*) 800 × nm^2.

to the advancing step edge, or as ordered aggregates corresponding to entire or discreet portions of a unit cell, can be answered by examining changes in the fine structure of step edges in high magnification, high resolution images. This has been done in the case of thaumatin crystals, as illustrated in Figure 10 and reveals that the step edges do indeed advance by addition of individual molecules, and not by the addition of preformed assemblies or clusters (24). This latter process could occur in rare instances, but it is not a dominant process.

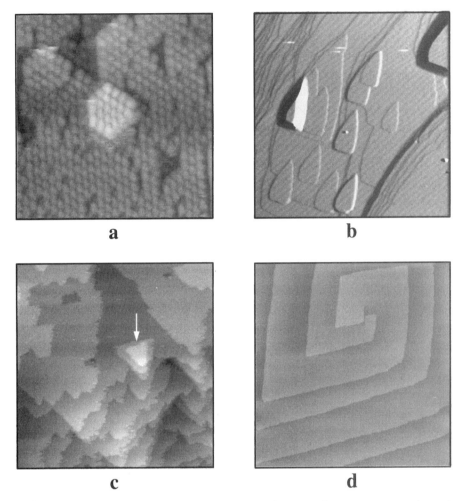

Figure 8   In many cases two-dimensional growth islands or growth centers assume anisotropic or geometric shapes characteristic of the morphology of the particular crystal of which they are a part. Shown here are islands on the surfaces of (*a*) STMV, (*b*) thaumatin, (*c*) TYMV, and (*d*) glucose isomerase crystals. Scan areas are (*a*) 470 × 470 nm^2, (*b*) 21 × 21 μm^2, (*c*) 4 × 4 μm^2, (*d*) 27 × 27 μm^2.

Thermodynamic considerations would suggest that, for mixed solid and fluid phases, molecules would be expected to leave the crystalline state and return to the solution phase, while others do the opposite. If the system is undersaturated, the first process would dominate and crystals would dissolve, while dominance of the latter process would lead to net growth. At equilibrium, no net change would occur. Kinetic considerations, however, could prevail, as they frequently do in chemical systems, depending on how difficult it is to add molecules to or remove

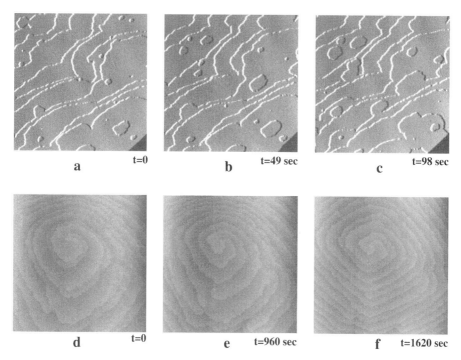

Figure 9   (*a*) through (*c*) show the time-dependent development of two-dimensional growth islands on the surface of a thaumatin crystal. In (*d*) through (*e*) is seen the continuous spiral generation of new step edge over time by a right-handed double screw dislocation on the surface of a growing canavalin crystal. Scan areas are (*a*)–(*c*) 4.8 × 4.8 μm^2, (*d*)–(*f*) 20 × 20 μm^2.

them from the lattice. Because the molecules at step edges make fewer contacts with neighbors, most of the coming and going would be expected to occur there. Studies of surface development and step edge movement of a number of protein crystals under a variety of conditions, however, suggest that once a molecule joins the lattice at a step edge, if the solution is at all supersaturated, it virtually never leaves (24). There is, in fact, no coming and going. For some crystals this is extreme. Catalase crystals grown from PEG, and STMV crystals grown from ammonium sulfate, for example, remain completely insoluble, once grown, even when placed in distilled water. AFM suggests that it is, in many cases, indeed difficult to pull a macromolecule free of its crystal lattice, and that the energy barrier to doing so is substantial.

The heights of growth islands are not always a single crystallographic unit cell in height, however, and some interesting exceptions have been recorded. Orthorhombic crystals of beef liver catalase, for example, shown in the series of images in Figure 11, develop by formation of growth islands corresponding in height to exactly one half-unit cell (37). Examination of the X-ray crystallographically determined structure provides an explanation. Molecules in the **ab** plane

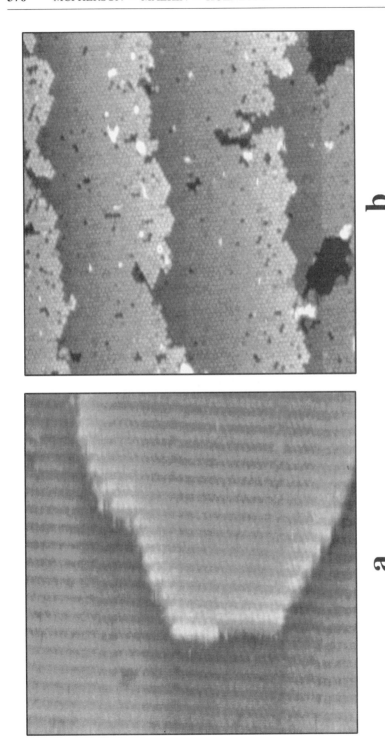

Figure 10 The fine structure of growth step edges like those shown here on (*a*) thaumatin, and (*b*) BMV crystals can be recorded over time as they accumulate new molecules, allowing the investigator to model the sequence of addition of individual molecules to unit cells under formation. Scan areas are (*a*) 330 × 330 nm^2, (*b*) 2 × 2 μm^2.

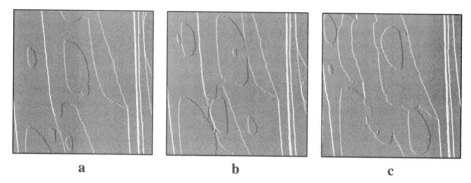

a   **b**   **c**

Figure 11   A second sequence of AFM images a different area on the $\langle 001 \rangle$ face of a beef liver catalase crystal. The area is $32.5 \times 32.5 \ \mu m^2$, and the interval between images is 12 min. Again, note the sequence of right- and left-handed islands that alternately appears on successive growth layers of the crystal.

interact closely with one another to form tight arrangements related by 2_1 screw axes along a and b. Molecules related by the 2_1 axes along c, however, are separated by solvent from one another and interact only weakly. Thus, layers of molecules corresponding to the "bottom halves" and "top halves" of unit cells are deposited alternately along c. Because the "bottoms" and "tops" have different hands (note the curved and flat sides) they can be readily identified in the images.

Two-dimensional islands generally do not advance at equal rates in all directions. This is so because the step edges present a different appearance, that is, display different bonding possibilities in different directions. Thus, new molecules are recruited differentially into step edges at different points on the island boundaries and therefore at different rates. Impurities, which also affect the rate of step advancement, are incorporated with different affinities around the growth islands, and these too affect recruitment rates, leading in turn to asymmetric shapes for the islands. Growth island asymmetry was apparent in the catalase crystals in Figure 11 but can be seen for those macromolecular crystals earlier presented in Figure 8.

An interesting question in all areas of crystal growth, including that of macromolecules, is what size a nucleus must be in order to persist, to develop. Nucleation, of course, represents a phase transition and is, therefore, significant even beyond crystallization. Nuclear size is dependent on the particular molecule and the intermolecular interactions driving crystallization, and also upon the degree of supersaturation. While it is difficult to use AFM to study the formation of three-dimensional "critical nuclei" directly from solution, the two-dimensional nuclei that form on existing crystal surfaces and give rise to new growth layers are readily visualized. Examples are shown for thaumatin crystals, in Figure 12. Because these share the properties of nuclei that initiate new crystals, their analysis is of substantial interest. Using AFM and simply observing the number of unit cells comprising that two-dimensional nuclei, whether they persist over time

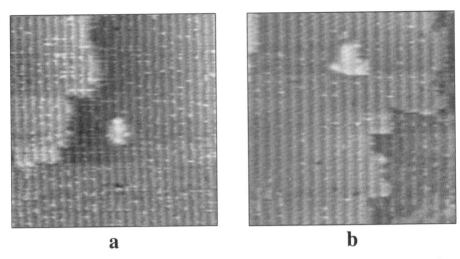

a   **b**

Figure 12   Small organized nuclei greater than the minimum critical nuclear size are seen here on the surfaces of thaumatin crystals. These small clusters of 20 to 50 molecules later develop into two-dimensional islands and further into new growth layers. Scan areas are (*a*) 470×470 nm^2, (*b*) 390×390 nm^2.

or disappear, and carrying out these observations at different supersaturations, we can obtain the sizes of critical nuclei as a function of supersaturation. This has been done for several crystals and has yielded some important quantitative information related to the bonding energies and assembly properties that govern the formation of nuclei (38).

Another mechanism, very common to crystals of conventional molecules, is growth through the creation of step edges at dislocations in the lattice (6, 17). These arise when, for one reason or another, perhaps incorporation of a contaminant or misincorporation of one or several molecules, a displacement occurs along the direction normal to the surface. At such points, steps are continuously propagated in a spiral about the dislocation; hence their name, screw dislocations. The salient difference between growth by this mechanism and growth through formation of two-dimensional islands is that face growth is more readily facilitated because no nucleation step is necessary to initiate a new layer. The spirally produced step edges provide nascent layers, and the crystal grows almost exclusively by tangential addition of molecules to step edges.

Arrays of screw dislocations from various crystals are shown in Figures 13 and 14. Note that in most cases, the spirals, like the growth islands discussed above, are asymmetric in shape, for the same reasons again. Spirals may be left-handed or right-handed, and a single crystal surface will often exhibit both. Spirals may also be single or double at the dislocation, and similarly, these more complex spirals may be either handed. Although screw dislocations have been observed on the surfaces of nearly all protein and nucleic acid crystals examined, they have not been identified on any virus crystal to date. Not all of the former kinds of

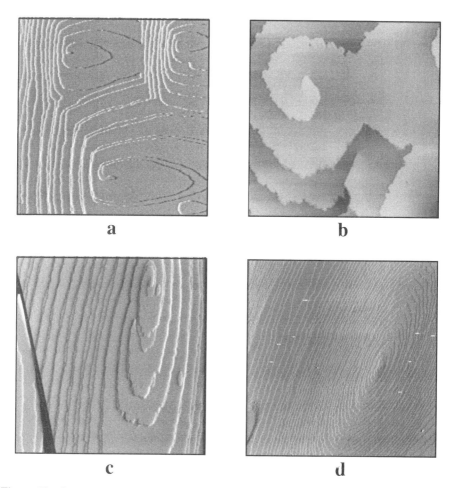

Figure 13 Screw dislocations of different sorts on the surfaces of protein crystals. In (*a*) two single and one double screw dislocations on a thaumatin crystal, (*b*) a single right-handed spiral on the surface of a canavalin crystal, (*c*) a left-handed double screw dislocation on a lysozyme crystal, and in (*d*) a steep vicinal hillock formed by a screw dislocation source on a lysozyme crystal. Scan areas are (*a*) $15 \times 15 \ \mu m^2$, (*b*) $15 \times 15 \ \mu m^2$, (*c*) $12 \times 12 \ \mu m^2$, (*d*) $2 \times 2 \ \mu m^2$.

crystals have an equal propensity to form screw dislocations, presumably due to differences in mechanical properties. Some crystals, like those of beef liver catalase, have none at all, while the surfaces of rhombohedral canavalin crystals are crowded with them. The appearance of screw dislocations is crystal dependent, a function of its mechanical properties, rather than molecule dependent as it seems. While rhombohedral canavalin is thick with screw dislocations, the orthorhombic and hexagonal forms are virtually dislocation free.

On many crystals, particularly at higher supersaturations where growth is rapid and tends to become somewhat disorganized, large macrosteps, like those

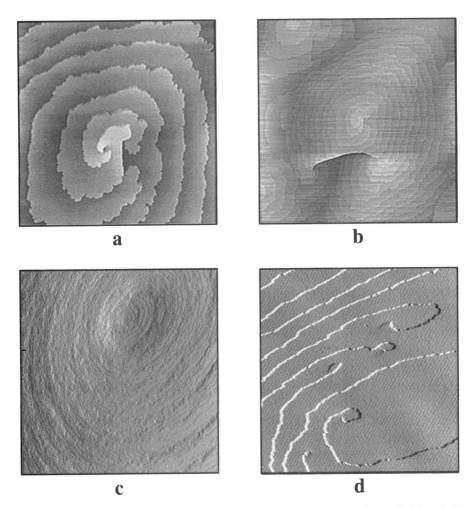

a   b

c   d

Figure 14 Additional screw dislocations are shown here on the surfaces of (*a*) and (*b*) canavalin crystals, (*c*) lysozyme, and (*d*) thaumatin crystals. Scan areas are (*a*) 10×10 μm^2, (*b*) 30×30 μm^2, (*c*) 2.5×2.5 μm^2, (*d*) 2×2 μm^2.

illustrated in Figure 15, consisting of stacks of growth layers are common. Although individual layers grow independently by molecular addition to their step edges, except through competition of their diffusion fields, the macrosteps tend to move like organized waves over the surface of crystals. The remarkable thing is that when the growth layers of one macrostep encounter those of another, the corresponding individual layers of the two macrosteps seem to merge and form a flawless union. Occasionally, some unusual events are observed on the steep slopes of the macrosteps, or vicinal hillocks. In the image of the surface of a bromegrass mosaic virus crystal seen in Figure 16, some adjacent growth layers have merged

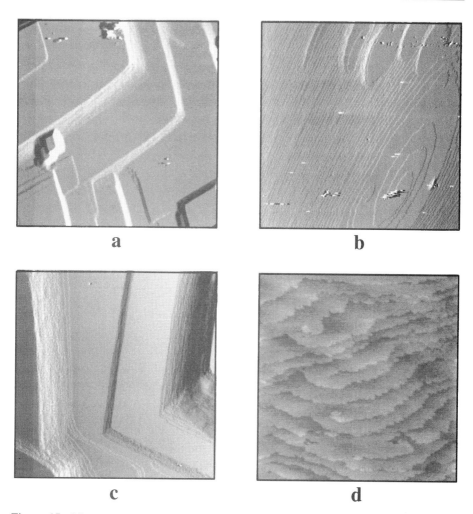

Figure 15   Macrosteps are common on the surfaces of most protein crystals caused by step bunching produced by defects and physical fluctuations. Those seen here are on the surfaces of (*a*) and (*c*) glucose isomerase, (*b*) lysozyme, and (*d*) lysozyme crystals. Scan areas are (*a*) $70 \times 70 \ \mu m^2$, (*b*) $40 \times 40 \ \mu m^2$, (*c*) $45 \times 45 \ \mu m^2$, (*d*) $3 \times 3 \ \mu m^2$.

to form double steps, which then advance as a single step of double height. This has been the only observation of such a phenomenon.

Most crystals, including macromolecular crystals, grow by addition of smooth layers, one atop another, through addition of molecules to the edges of the layers. As described above, these layers may be generated by two-dimensional nucleation or by screw dislocations. Another mechanism for crystal development, called normal growth, does not proceed by layer addition, but by random recruitment of molecules at arbitrary sites on the surface. In a sense, molecules are joining the

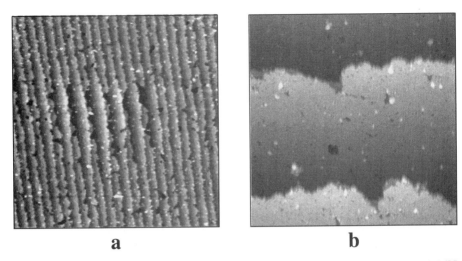

a   **b**

Figure 16   Step doubling, a rare occurance, is shown here for bromegrass mosaic virus (BMV) crystals. Note in the center of (*a*) where a series of steps have coupled and merged so that two adjacent steps develop as one, shown at higher magnification in (*b*). Scan areas are (*a*) 17.25 × 17.25 μm^2, (*b*) 3 × 3 μm^2.

lattice everywhere on the surface at once. This kind of crystallization is characteristic, for example, of crystals grown from the melt. This leads to an atomically "rough" surface as opposed to the atomically "smooth" surface yielded by layer growth.

Macromolecular crystals have been observed by AFM to grow by a normal mechanism, in which case the surface appearance becomes extremely rough and irregular as shown for the apo ferritin crystals in Figure 17*a*. Growth by this mechanism in the regime of high supersaturation is completely disorganized and produces, as one might anticipate, crystals of very poor quality, though ultimate size is not necessarily restricted. Apoferritin crystals grow to very large size.

A mechanism that may be unique to macromolecular crystals is illustrated in Figure 18, as it has not been described for conventional crystal growth, and it may arise as a consequence of the unique properties of concentrated macromolecular solutions. For virtually all of the protein, nucleic acid, and virus crystals investigated, the sudden appearance of vast, multiple stacks of growth layers has been observed (examples are presented in Figure 19). Often these hillocks, whose characteristic shape frequently reflects the gross morphology of the entire crystal, are ten to a hundred or more layers in height. Each layer of the stack provides a step edge and, therefore, a source for tangential growth. Growth by this mechanism, which has been termed growth by three-dimensional nucleation, can in some cases be the dominant growth mechanism (33). It is noteworthy that when tangential growth of layers proceeds simultaneously from proximal several multilayer stacks on the surface of a crystal, the corresponding layers from the various stacks ultimately

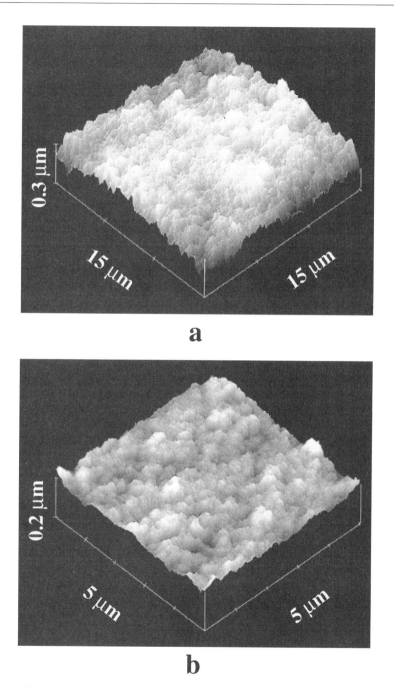

Figure 17   Normal growth is illustrated here by two AFM images of areas on the surfaces of growing horse spleen apoferritin crystals.

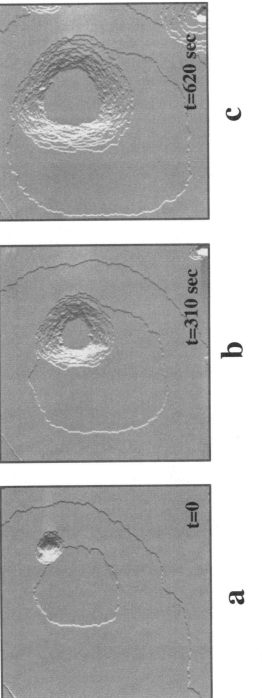

Figure 18

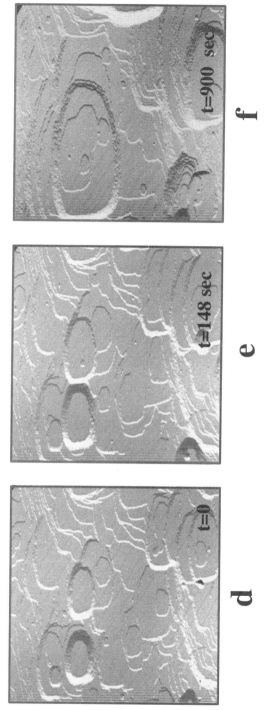

Figure 18 The sudden appearance of a prominent multilayered stack of several tens of growth layers on the surface of a crystal of STMV is seen to develop tangentially in (b) and (c). A large number of three-dimensional, multilayered stacks of growth steps, here in the range of several up to a dozen or more, are seen to appear and develop on the surface of a thaumatin crystal. Scan areas are (a)–(c) 15×15 μm^2, (d)–(f) 11.4×11.4 μm^2.

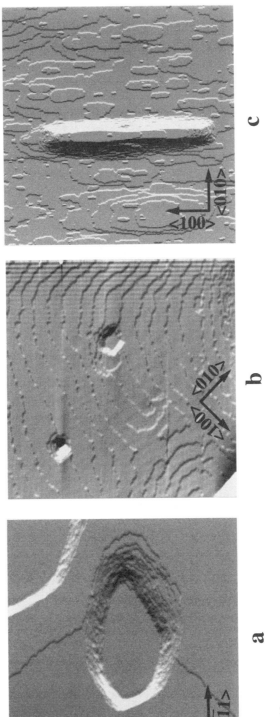

Figure 19

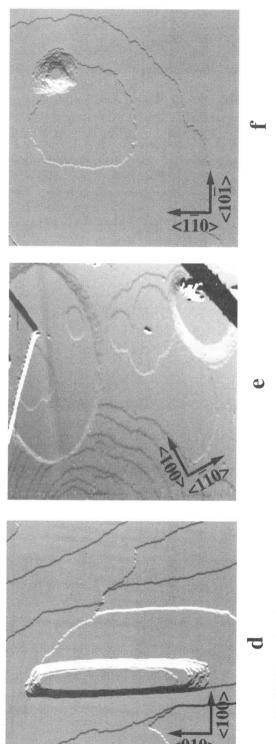

d

e

f

Figure 19 Multilayered stacks of growth layers often assume a morphology characteristic to a particular kind of crystal. Multilayer stacks formed after sedimentation of liquid protein aggregates on the crystal surfaces of (*a*) thaumatin, scan size 10×10 μm^2, (*b*) canavalin, scan size 25×25 μm^2, (*c*) lipase, scan size 15×15 μm^2, (*d*) catalase, scan size 25×25 μm^2, (*e*) lysozyme, scan size 40×40 μm^2, and (*f*) STMV, scan size 15×15 μm^2, crystals. The average height of stacks was 8–10 growth layers. Stacks with heights in the range of only two layers up to those of several hundred growth layers were observed in various experiments. The shape of the multilayer stacks depended on the anisotropic velocities of the growth steps at the edges of the two-dimensional islands.

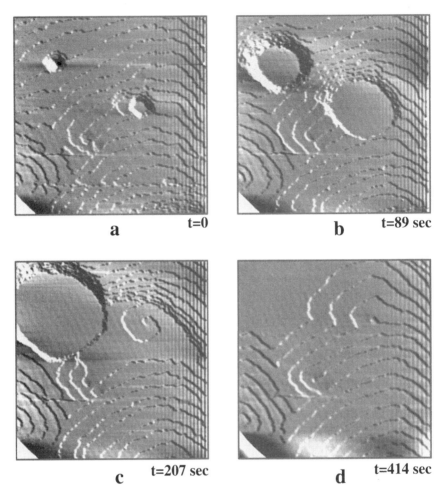

Figure 20   These AFM images show the sedimentation of two small three-dimensional nuclei on the surface of a growing canavalin crystal. The nuclei give rise to multilayered stacks whose step edges extend over the surrounding surface. The three-dimensional nuclei are undoubtedly perfectly aligned with the underlying lattice since their growth steps can be seen, ultimately, to merge in a contiguous manner with step edges arising from the substrate crystal. Scan areas are 30×30 μm^2.

encounter one another, merge, and knit with one another in a completely contiguous manner. An example, canavalin, is shown in Figure 20.

The intriguing question is the origin of these multilayer stacks. One possibility is that they arose from microcrystals preformed in solution that sedimented on the surface and continued to grow. Such a phenomenon fails, however, to explain the perfect alignment of all of the stacks with the underlying lattice and with one another. Other evidence casts further doubt on this idea (23a). A second explanation, for which there is now substantial and persuasive evidence, suggests that they arise from liquid protein phase droplets that exist in concentrated macro-molecular solutions (2, 24, 31), particularly mother liquors. These liquid protein phase droplets are composed of hundreds to thousands of molecules exhibiting short-range order mediated principally by nonspecific hydrophobic interactions and random arrangements of hydrogen bonds. They are in a sense very large disor-dered protein aggregates. Because of the extraordinary concentration of molecules in the droplets, they are locally hypersaturated. When the droplets sediment upon existing crystal surfaces, the lattice serves as an epitaxial substrate to guide and promote crystallization in the molecules above. As described schematically in Figure 21, these form a crystal layer, inspire crystallinity in the molecules above them, and so forth, propagating a continuous series of growth layers, a multilayer stack. In some cases, like those shown in Figure 22, this process has been visually recorded. In some other cases, they form independent microcrystals, which are discontinuous with the underlying lattice. An extreme example of the appearance of a three-dimensional nucleus is shown in Figure 23. On the steep slope of a macrostep on the surface of a thaumatin crystal, a liquid protein droplet (see be-low) gives rise to a large three-dimensional nucleus, another nascent macrostep atop the first.

The existence of a liquid protein phase in concentrated protein solutions (the multilayer stacks discussed here being one manifestation) has been dealt with in greater detail elsewhere, and it is the source of much current interest in the field of colloids as well as crystal growth (2, 24, 31, 49). It was one of the more unexpected results to emerge from AFM studies of macromolecular crystal growth (23a), and it may have consequences for the physical chemistry and structure of concentrated macromolecular solutions, such as occur inside living cells, far outside the area of crystallization. The existence of this liquid protein phase does, it should be noted, also provide an explanation or a pathway, not only for the mechanism of crystal growth through three-dimensional nucleation, but also for the spontaneous formation in solution of crystal nuclei having critical size (49).

DEFECTS, DISLOCATIONS, AND IMPURITY INCORPORATION

One fact that seems unequivocal is that the levels of impurities and contami-nants in macromolecular solutions, despite the greatest care, vastly exceed those in conventional crystal growth solutions (43). This is unavoidable and unlikely ever to change, as it arises as a natural consequence of the complexity of the macromolecules, their sources, and the accessory molecules that may be needed to sustain them. Although there is no systematic evidence to support it, intuitively we might conclude that the kinds of impurities most detrimental to macromolecu-lar crystal growth are impurities of large size, in the range of the nutrient molecules or larger. This seems reasonable because these, if incorporated into a developing

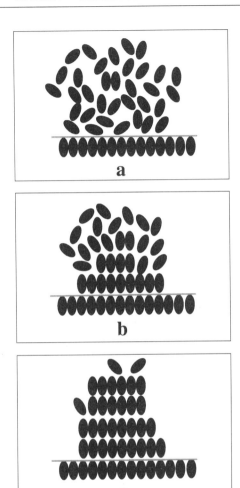

Figure 21   A large aggregate of molecules having short-range order adsorbs to the surface of a growing crystal in (*a*), promoted by the lattice in which they are in contact; the molecules in immediate contact begin to assume a congruent arrangement above to form a new growth layer in (*b*). Molecules above are promoted to do the same, and the development of new growth layers propagates upward to the top of the locally hypersaturated ensemble, thereby giving rise to the multilayered stacks of growth layers seen in the AFM images.

lattice, would most likely produce dislocations, and the kinds of defects that we can clearly see using AFM. That is, the most probably damaging impurities to the crystal are misoriented, improperly folded, or molecules having alternative conformations. They would also include clusters or aggregates of the nutrient molecules, foreign particles such as dust, microcrystals, and other contaminating macromolecules. Evidence exists from AFM that all of these types of impurities can and do become incorporated into crystal lattices.

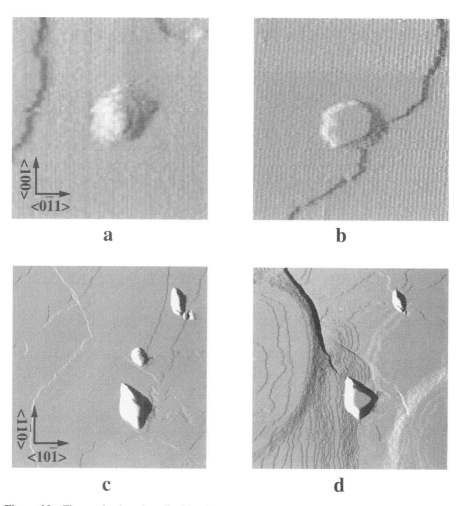

Figure 22 The mechanism described in Figure 20 is recorded in fact occurring on the surfaces of (*a* and *b*) a thaumatin crystal, and (*c* and *d*) on the surface of an STMV crystal. In (*a*) and (*c*) disordered aggregates are seen transforming into the crystalline multilayered stacks of growth layers in (*b*) and (*d*) respectively. Scan areas are (*a*)–(*b*) 4 × 4 μm^2, (*c*)–(*d*) 25 × 25 μm^2.

It is important to recognize that the incorporation of impurities into the lattice, and the defects that they produce, may not be confined to their immediate local but may have long-range effects on the structure of the crystal. In some cases, of course, only the molecules adjacent to the incorporated impurity may be jostled or perturbed by the elbows of their neighbor, but often not. Frequently, impurity incorporation is accompanied by large inclusions or voids, or their resultant dislocation is propagated great distances through the lattice, affecting enormous numbers of otherwise uninvolved molecules. Figure 24 is a record, for example of the incorporation of a large foreign particle into the lattice of a growing crystal

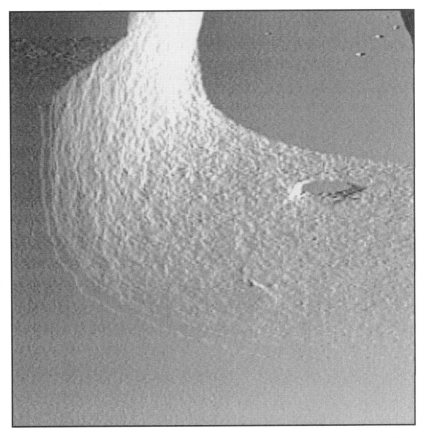

Figure 23 Sedimentation of a liquid protein droplet and its development into a multilayer stack (height 104 nm) on the 20° slope of another, much larger multilayer stack (height 750 nm) on a thaumatin crystal surface. Scan size $12.5 \times 12.5 \ \mu m^2$.

and illustrates how deep inclusions that pass through many layers of the crystal form as a consequence.

In the mother liquor in which a crystal grows, there are not only liquid protein-rich phase droplets and aggregate, as discussed above, but the spontaneous nucleation of other crystals as well. These can sediment on the surfaces of larger crystals, adhere, and be incorporated. Figure 25 is an illustration of this phenomenon in the case of a rhombohedral canavalin crystal. The microcrystal is clearly misoriented with respect to the underlying crystal lattice, but it is consumed by the larger crystal nonetheless. This occurs, however, not without cost, as screw dislocations that propagate long distances through the crystal result along with a host of stacking faults (see below). In Figure 26 is another example, this time involving a crystal of the virus STMV. Again the microcrystal is accepted into the bulk of the crystal, but only with a subsequent formation of defects.

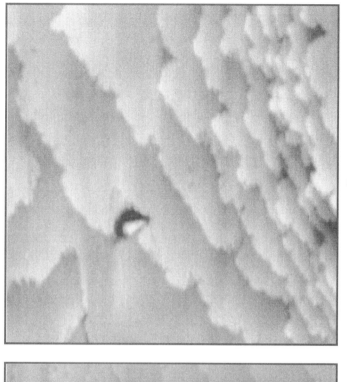

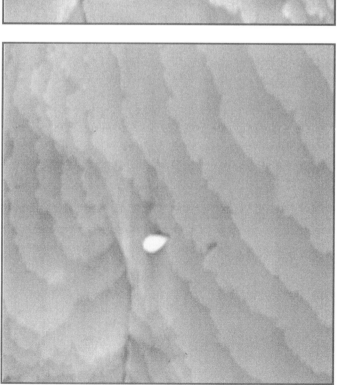

Figure 24 A large foreign particle sediments on the surface of a growing canavalin crystal at $t = 0$ in (a) and is overwhelmed by growth steps in (b) to be fully incorporated into the crystal at $t = 420$ seconds. Incorporation results in the formation of a vast liquid inclusion surrounding the embedded particle. Scan areas are (a) 10×10 μm^2, (b) 5×5 μm^2.

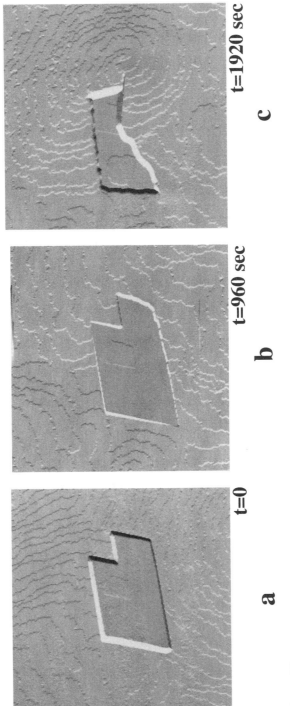

Figure 25

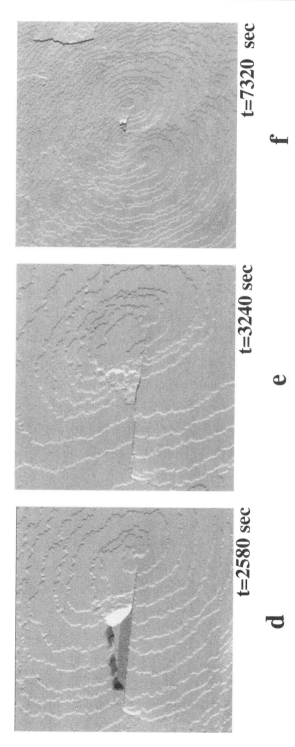

Figure 25 A series of six AFM images showing the direct incorporation of a microcrystal of 15 μm × 8 μm into a larger, growing crystal of the protein canavalin. A lattice mismatch clearly exists for the two crystals. As the sequence progresses and the small crystal is consumed by the larger, both a planar defect and spiral dislocations form and propagate in the larger crystal. Scan areas are (a) 28 × 28 μm^2, (b) 25 × 25 μm^2, (c) 20 × 20 μm^2, (d) and (e) 50 × 50 μm^2.

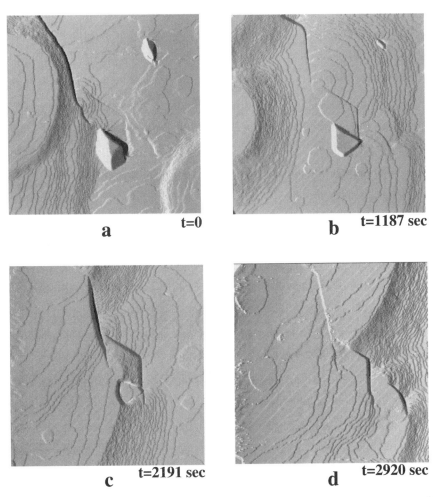

Figure 26   Incorporation of small microcrystals into a growing STMV crystal (25 × 25 a μm^2 in situ AFM images). In (*a*) two microcrystals have sedimented on the (111) face of a growing, cubic satellite tobacco mosaic virus (STMV) crystal. The surface structure of the larger crystal is very complex and step trains, two-dimensional nuclei, macrosteps, planar defects, and growth plateau are everywhere evident. In (*b*) the smallest of the two nuclei has virtually disappeared leaving in (*c*) a cavity above its incorporation site. The same process occurs for the larger of the two as well. A cavity can be seen forming around it in (*d*) due to step retardation, and it too has completely disappeared by frame (*d*).

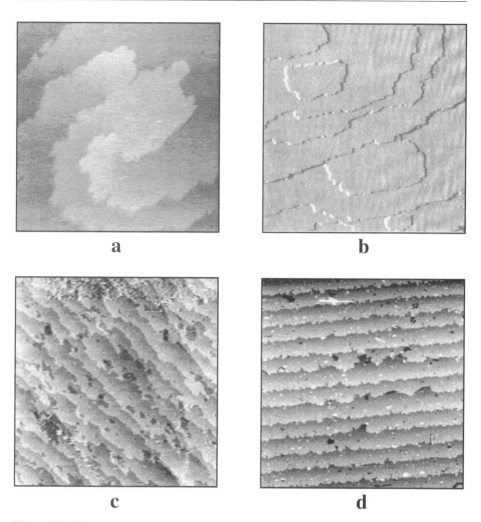

Figure 27 The extreme roughness and irregularity of the growth step edges suggest the presence of a high level of impurities, most probably macromolecular in origin, in the mother liquors of these growing crystals. In (*a*) rhombohedral canavalin, (*b*) beef liver catalase, (*c*) an intact monoclonal antibody, and (*d*) bromegrass mosaic virus crystals. Scan areas are (*a*) 2.5 × 2.5 μm^2, (*b*) 17 × 17 μm^2, (*c*) 5 × 5 μm^2, (*d*) 10 × 10 μm^2.

Evidence for the extensive incorporation of impurities more on the size scale of the nutrient molecules, perhaps representing misoriented individual, clusters, or other macromolecular impurities, is illustrated in Figure 27. There, step edges generated by screw dislocations or two dimensional islands on the surface of crystals are seen to be extraordinarily rough and ragged. The irregular appearance of the step edges arises either directly from the incorporation of impurities or from pushing ahead impurities in their paths.

Individual defects and the overall defect structures (51) present in macromolecular crystals are particularly amenable to visualization by AFM (35). These show considerable variety but taken as an ensemble of faults, they suggest the basis of what gives rise to the effect known to X-ray crystallographers as mosaicity. They also suggest why some crystals may appear far more ordered and diffract to higher resolution than do others. One important finding from AFM studies, which allows one to simply count defects and dislocations directly, is that macromolecular crystals contain two to four orders of magnitude more faults than do most conventional crystals (35, 43).

Figure 28 presents examples of the most commonly observed defects in macromolecular crystals. Examination of the surfaces of thaumatin crystals in Figure 28*a* and *b* shows that it is strewn with vacancies corresponding to one or more unit cells. These are not filled later, as etching experiments (see below) demonstrate. Vacant unit cells may account for as much as one percent of all the cells in a crystal. Their effects, however, appear to be fairly localized, and only a marginal diminution of order and quality results. In Figure 28*c* and *d* crystals of viruses are similarly permeated by empty lattice sites.

Defects of a considerably more serious nature are dislocations. These are devastating to long-range order because they extend great distances through the crystals. Screw dislocations have already been discussed above, but an even more common type of defect is the stacking fault. Figure 29 provides examples of stacking faults on the surfaces of several different types of crystals. Stacking faults arise from partial unit cell displacements of an entire row of unit cells. As shown in Figure 30, when advancing steps encounter the faults, they are unable to continue and must flow around the fault and up the other side. Thus, molecules may be affected near the fault extending hundreds of layers through the crystal, and clearly, a block structure is imposed on the crystal by the propagating displacement.

ETCHING AND DISSOLUTION

Just as the observation and recording of crystal growth is valuable for the mechanistic information it yields, experiments on the dissolution of crystals can also be revealing. In particular, if dissolution occurs in a slow and controlled manner, then it becomes useful too for delineating the defect structure of the crystal and identifying sites of impurity incorporation (5, 35, 44). At defect and impurity sites, because of strain introduced into the lattice, the chemical potential is higher than in ordered areas. As a consequence of this lattice stress, dissolution, loss of molecules from the crystals, occurs first at these sites. Point defects due to absences, improper molecules, misoriented molecules, or foreign molecules produce what are called etch pits at undersaturated conditions. In Figure 31, the surface of a dissolving thaumatin crystal exhibits a field of etch pits that grows wider and deeper with time as the crystal proceeds to dissolve. This provides a record of the

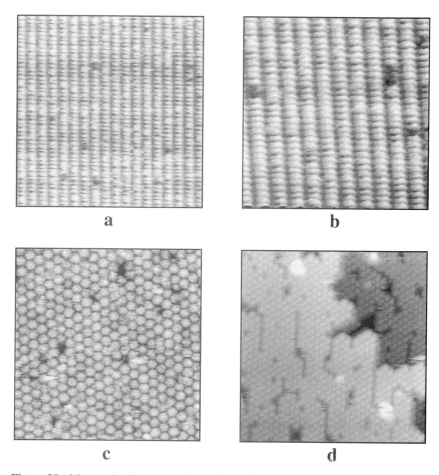

Figure 28 Many unit cells seen on the surfaces of growing macromolecular crystals are partially unfilled or entirely vacant, sometimes over several or even many consecutive cells. These remain unfilled as new layers form over them as revealed by etching experiments. In (*a*) and (*b*) are surfaces of thaumatin crystals, in (*c*) a crystal of BMV, and in (*d*) an orthorhombic crystal of STMV. Scan areas are (*a*) 28 × 280 nm^2, (*b*) 225 × 225 nm^2, (*c*) 540 × 540 nm^2, (*d*) 600 × 600 nm^2.

mistakes made and contaminants added during the growth process. In some cases, larger contaminants can even be recovered from the etch pits and identified. In Figures 31*b* and 32 for example, a foreign particle is found at the bottom of an etch pit.

Etching reveals not only particles and point defects, but larger objects that have been incorporated as well. In Figure 33 etching of a crystal of beef catalase produces a remarkable record of microcrystal incorporation by a larger crystal. The

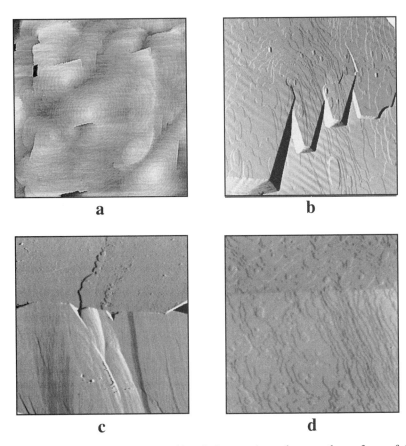

a

b

c

d

Figure 29 A variety of severe stacking faults are shown here on the surfaces of (a) canavalin, (b) and (d) thaumatin, and (c) a lysozyme crystal. Scan areas are (a) $80 \times 80 \ \mu m^2$, (b) $20 \times 20 \ \mu m^2$, (c) $55 \times 55 \ \mu m^2$, (d) $30 \times 30 \ \mu m^2$.

rectangular microcrystals, some more than a micron in length and having a variety of orientations inconsistent with the underlying lattice, are strewn everywhere below the top surface. Orthorhombic beef catalase crystals do not, in general, diffract well. The forgiving nature of the crystals to microcrystal incorporation may very well suggest why. It is also interesting that microcrystal incorporation into catalase crystals does not seem to produce either screw dislocations or stacking faults. Presumably, crystals have varying degrees of tolerance for microcrystal and other contaminant incorporation and different mechanical properties, some accommodating it without undue stress, and others not.

Figure 34 shows examples of etching in the neighborhood of a stacking fault where local dissolution is pronounced. Etching has the effect of emphasizing the lines of the fault and suggests as well the extent of local stress that it produces. In light of the fact that the defect density in macromolecular crystals is so great,

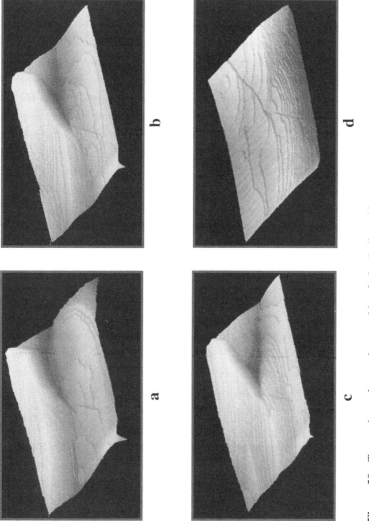

Figure 30 Two major and one minor stacking faults (indicated by arrows) are seen in (*a*) at *t* = 0 among a field of moving steps on the surface of a growing STMV crystal. In (*b*) at *t* = 240 sec through (*c*) at *t* = 420 sec the macrosteps progress around the ends of the faults and continue to expand. In (*d*) at *t* = 780 sec, however, it is clear that the faults, including the minor fault, have propagated through the layers in the normal direction. The area of the in situ AFM images is 23 × 23 μm².

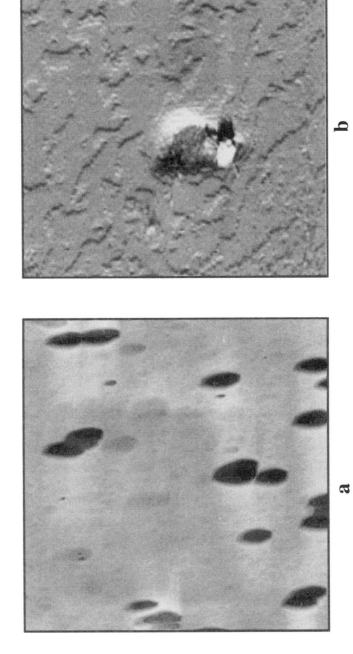

Figure 31 In (*a*) a field of etch pits is observed on the dissolving surface of a thaumatin crystal. In (*b*) an etch pit is found to contain an impurity particle at its bottom that was responsible for the formation of the defect and the consequent pit. Scan areas are (*a*) 18 × 18 μm², (*b*) 4 × 4 μm².

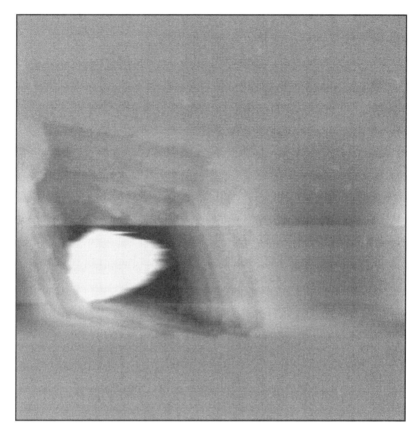

Figure 32   A large foreign particle is found here at the bottom of an etch pit on the surface of a glucose isomerase crystal. Scan area is $4.8 \times 4.8 \ \mu m^2$.

it is again not surprising that they exhibit such fragility, sensitivity to X-rays, and limited diffraction resolution.

In some AFM investigations of macromolecular crystals, evidence for surface restructuring has emerged (34). In Figure 35, for example, a crystal close to equilibrium conditions of the virus TYMV is seen as a function of time. In the time interval between scans, no more than a few minutes, the distribution of virus particles in the surface lattice changes completely. Using X-ray structural evidence and packing models, it was possible to show that the changes occur by the sudden, coordinated, and complete loss of an entire layer of virus particles from the crystal. A given pattern reappears on this crystal face every three layers as expected from the known X-ray crystal structure. The massive loss of virus particles from a surface illustrated here represents some cooperative phenomenon among the particles, and the loss is quite different from the dissolution process seen above for thaumatin.

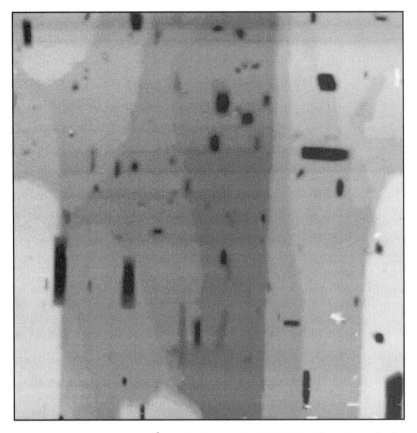

Figure 33 An area $42 \times 42 \ \mu m^2$ recorded by AFM on the $\langle 001 \rangle$ surface of an orthorhombic catalase crystal that has been slightly etched near equilibrium conditions. This procedure reveals defects and incorporated impurities including incorporated microcrystals that are misoriented with respect to the underlying lattice. Here it can be seen that there is a striking number of such misoriented microcrystals dispersed throughout the crystal, some as long as $10 \ \mu m$.

A chronic problem of crystallographers is the failure of crystals to reach sizes adequate for X-ray data collection. As Kam, Shore, and Feher pointed out (22), crystals often seem to reach a fixed "terminal size" and further development ceases. Explanations have varied from defect accumulation to surface contamination. AFM studies have suggested two likely causes. First, the degree of supersaturation required to support growth normal to the surface is considerably greater that is necessary to promote tangential growth. Thus, a solution, after significant crystal growth has already taken place, may still be supersaturated, but insufficient to sustain formation of two-dimensional nuclei. Thus, crystal growth ceases, and the last growth island fills out to the edge of the face to yield a final flat surface. This is, in fact, exactly what is observed.

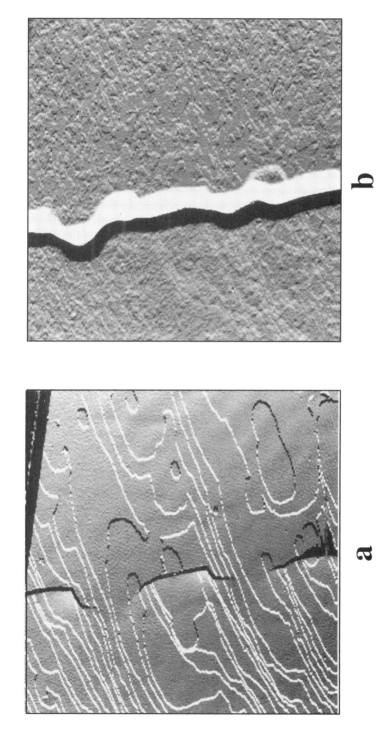

Figure 34 A large stacking fault, visible but obscured by growth steps in (*a*), is revealed dramatically by etching in (*b*) on the surface of a thaumatin crystal. Scan area are (*a*) 10 × 10 μm^2.

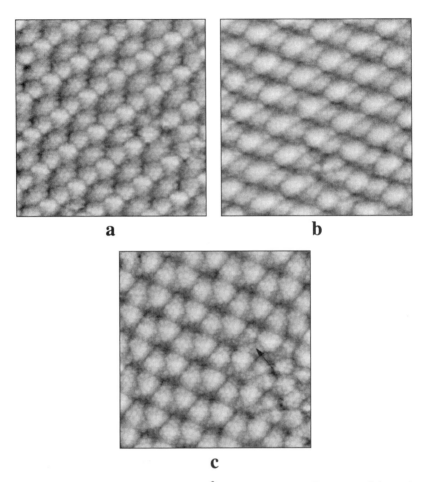

Figure 35   (a)–(c) In situ, 300×300 nm^2 AFM images recording sequential transformations of the surface layer of the (101) face of the TYMV crystals when exposed to equilibrium conditions.

In addition to supersaturation conditions, contamination also appears to be a principal cause not only of terminal size but also of the failure of many seeding attempts (50). What has been observed using AFM is that crystals that have stopped growing sometimes have a thick, rather hard shell of material coating their surfaces. As illustrated in Figure 36, if an area of this shell is scratched away to create a fresh surface below, then almost immediately new growth islands appear on the revealed surface and begin to expand tangentially. There is no inherent property of the crystal as a whole that inhibits further growth, but only the fouling of surface layer. So far as defect accumulation is concerned, AFM shows that, perhaps counterintuitively, some of the very largest, most rapidly growing crystals that have

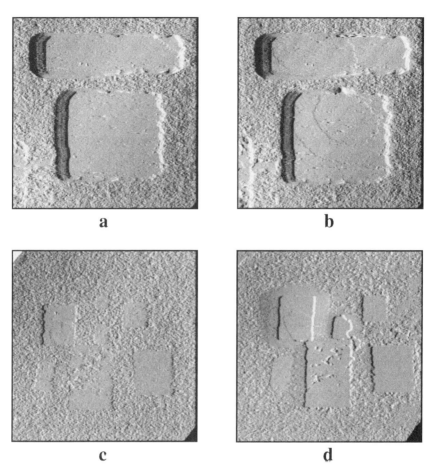

Figure 36   Surface of a lysozyme crystal was completely covered by the impurity adsorption layer, resulting in a cessation of growth. This layer was partially scratched by the AFM tip, which resulted in resumption of growth. The scan areas for the AFM images are (*a*) and (*b*) 7.5 × 7.5 μm^2 (*c*) and (*d*) 8 × 8 μm^2.

been investigated are also those that exhibit the highest defect density. While this may be a determinant of crystal quality and diffraction resolution, it does not seem to be a factor in ultimate size.

ACKNOWLEDGMENTS

Research summarized here was supported by grants and contracts from the National Aeronautics and Space Administration and the National Institutes of Health. The authors wish to thank Mr. Aaron Greenwood for help in producing the figures.

Visit the Annual Reviews home page at www.AnnualReviews.org

LITERATURE CITED

1. Allen S, Davies MC, Roberts CJ, Tendler SJB, Williams PM. 1997. Atomic force microscopy in analytical biotechnology. *TIBTECH* 15

2. Asherie N, Lomakin A, Benedek GB. 1996. Phase diagram of colloidal solutions. *Phys. Rev. Lett.* 77:4832–35

3. Binning G, Quate CF, Gerber C. 1986. Atomic force microscope. *Phys. Rev. Lett* 56:930–33

4. Boistelle R, Astier JP. 1988. Crystallization mechanisms in solution. *J. Cryst. Growth* 90:14–30

5. Buckley HE. 1951. *Crystal Growth*, London: Wiley & Sons

6. Burton WK, Cabrera N, Frank FC. 1951. The growth of crystals and the equilibrium structure of their surfaces. *Philos. Trans. R. Soc.* London, Ser. A 243:299

7. Bustamante C, Keller D. 1995. Scanning force microscopy in biology. *Phys. Today* 48(12):32–38

8. Chernov AA. 1984. *Modern Crystallography*. Vol. III. *Crystal Growth*. Berlin: Springer-Verlag

9. Chernov AA. 1993. Roughening and melting of crystalline surfaces. *Prog. Cryst. Growth.* 26:195–218

10. Chernov AA, Komatsu H. 1995. Topics in crystal growth kinetics. In *Science and Technology of Crystal Growth*, ed. JP van der Eerden, OSL Bruinsma, p. 67–79. Dordrecht, The Netherlands: Kluwer

11. Chernov AA, Rashkovich LN, Smolískii IL, Kuznetsov Yu G, Mkrtchyan AA, Malkin AI. 1988. *Growth of Crystals*. Vol. 15:43–91, ed. EI Givargizov, SA Grinberg. New York: Consultant Bur.

12. Durbin SD, Carlson WE. 1992. Lysozyme crystal growth studied by atomic force microscopy. *J. Crystal Growth* 122:71–79

13. Durbin SD, Carlson WE, Saros MT. 1993. In situ studies of protein crystallization by atomic force microscopy. *J. Phys. D Appl. Phys.* 26:128–32

14. Durbin SD, Feher G. 1996. Protein crystallization. *Annu. Rev. Phys. Chem.* 47, 171–204

15. Feher G. 1986. Mechanisms of nucleation and growth of protein crystals. *J. Cryst. Growth* 76:545–46

16. Feigelson RS. 1988. The relevance of small molecule crystal growth theories and techniques to the growth of biological macromolecules *J. Cryst. Growth* 90:1–13

17. Frank FC. 1949. The influence of dislocations on crystal growth. *Discussions Faraday Soc.* 5:48–54

18. Garman EF, Schneider TR. 1997. Macromolecular cryocrystallography. *J. Appl. Cryst.* 30:211–37

19. Hafner JH, Cheung CL, Lieber CM. 1999. Growth of nanotubes for probe microscopy tips. *Nature* 398:761–62

20. Hansma PK, Cleveland JP, Radmacher M, Walters DA, Hillner PE, Bezanilla M, Fritz M, Vie D, Hansma HG, Prater CB, Massie J, Fukunage L, Gurley J, Elings V. 1994. Tapping mode atomic force microscopy in liquids. *Appl. Phys. Lett,* 64:1738–40

21. Hok JH, Hansma PK. 1992. Atomic force microscopy for high resolution imaging in cell biology. *Trends Cell Biol.* 2:208–13

22. Kam Z, Shore HB, Feher G. 1978. On the crystallization of proteins. *J. Mol. Biol.* 123:539–55

23. Konnert JH, D'Antonio P, Ward KB. 1994. Observation of growth steps, spiral dislocations and molecular packing on the surface of lysozyme crystals with the atomic force microscope. *Acta Cryst.* D 50:603–13

23a. Kuznetsov Yu G, Malkin AJ, McPherson A. 19??. Atomic Force mocroscopy studies of phase separation in macromolecular systems. *Phys Rev. B* 58(10):6097–6103

24. Kuznetsov Yu G, Konnert J, Malkin AJ, McPherson A. 1999. The advancement and structure of growth steps on thaumatin crystals visualized by atomic force microscopy at molecular resolution. *Surface Sci.* 440:69–80

25. Kuznetsov Yu G, Malkin AJ, Land TA, DeYoreo JJ, Barba de la Rosa AP, Konnert J, McPherson A. 1997. Molecular resolution imaging of macromolecular crystals by atomic force microscopy. *Biophys. J.* 72:2357

26. Land TA, DeYoreo JJ, Lee JD. 1997. An *in situ* AFM investigation of canavalin crystallization kinetics. *Surface Sci.* 384:136–55

27. Land TA, Malkin AJ, Kuznetsov Yu G, McPherson A, DeYoreo JJ. 1995. Mechanisms of protein crystal growth: An atomic force microscopy study of Canavalin crystallization. *Phys. Rev. Lett.* 75(13):2774–77

28. Li MR, Nadarajah A, Pusey ML. 1999. Growth of (101) faces of tetragonal lysozyme crystals: determination of the growth mechanism. *Acta. Cryst.* D 55:1012–22

29. Li HY, Perozzo MA, Konnert JH, Nadarajah A, Pusey ML. 1999. Determining the molecular-packing arrangements on protein crystal faces by atomic force microscopy. *Acta. Cryst.* D 55:1023–35

30. Li MR, Nadarajah A, Pusey ML. 1999. Determining the molecular growth mechanisms of protein crystal faces by atomic force microscopy. *Acta. Cryst.* D 55:1036–45

31. Lui C, Lomakin A, Thurston GM, Hayden D, Pande A, Pande J, Ogun O, Asherie N, Benedek GB. 1995. Phase separation in multicomponent aqueous-protein solutions. *J. Phys. Chem.* 99:454–61

32. Malkin AJ, Kuznetsov Yu G, Glantz W, McPherson A. 1996. Atomic force microscopy studies of surface morphology and growth kinetics in thaumatin crystallization. *J. Phys. Chem.* 100:11736–43

33. Malkin AJ, Kuznetsov Yu G, Land TA, DeYoreo JJ, McPherson A. 1995. Mechanisms of growth for protein and virus crystals. *Nature Struct. Biol.* 2(11):956–59

34. Malkin AJ, Kuznetsov Yu G, Lucas RW, McPherson A. 1999. Surface processes in the crystallization of turnip yellow mosaic virus visualized by atomic force microscopy. *J. Struct. Biol.* 127:35–43

35. Malkin AJ, Kuznetsov Yu G, McPherson A. 1996. Defect structure of macromolecular crystals. *J. Struc. Biol.* 117:124–37

36. Malkin AJ, Kuznetsov Yu G, McPherson A. 1996. Incorporation of microcrystals by growing protein and virus crystals. *Proteins: Struc., Func. Gen.* 24:247–52

37. Malkin AJ, Kuznetsov Yu G, McPherson A. 1997. An in situ AFM investigation of catalase crystallization. *Surface Sci.* 393:95

38. Malkin AJ, Land TA, Kuznetsov Yu G, McPherson A, DeYoreo JJ. 1995. Investigation of virus crystal growth by *in situ* atomic force microscopy. *Phys. Rev. Lett.* 75(13):2778–81

39. McPherson A. 1982. *The Preparation and Analysis of Protein Crystals*, New York: Wiley & Sons

40. McPherson A. 1989. Macromolecular crystals. *Sci. Am.* 260(3):62–69

41. McPherson A. 1998. *Crystallization of Biological Macromolecules*, New York: Cold Spring Harbor Lab. Press

42. McPherson A, Malkin AJ, Kuznetsov Yu G. 1995. The science of macromolecular crystallization. *Structure* 3(8):759–68

43. McPherson A, Malkin A, Kuznetsov Yu G, Koszelak S. 1996. Incorporation of Impurities into Macromolecular Crystals. *J. Cryst. Growth.* 168:74–92

44. Monaco LA, Rosenberger F. 1993. Growth and etching kinetics of tetragonal lysozyme. *J. Cryst. Growth.* 129:465–84

45. Nakada T, Sazaki G, Miyashita S, Durbin SD, Komatsu H. 1999. Direct AFM observations of impurity effects on a lysozyme crystal. *J. Cryst. Growth* 196:503–10

46. Ng JD, Kuznetsov Yu G, Malkin AJ, Keith G, Giege R, McPherson A. 1997. Visualizaton of nucleic acid cyrstal growth by atomic microscopy. *Nucleic Acids Res.* 25(13):2582–88

47. Rosenberger F, Vekilov PG, Muschol M, Thomas BR. 1996. Nucleation and crystallization of globular proteins—what we know and what is missing. *J. Cryst. Growth.* 168:1–27

48. Schlichtkrull ??. 1957. Growth rates of protein crystals. *Acta Chem. Scand.* 11:439–48

49. Ten Wolde PR, Frenkel D. 1997. Enhancement of protein crystal nucleation by critical density fluctuations. *Science* 277:1975

50. Thaller C, Weaver LH, Eichele G, Wilson E, Karlson R, Jansonius JN. 1981. Repeated seeding technique for growing large single crystals of proteins. *J. Mol. Biol.* 147:465

51. Tiller WA. 1991. *The Science of Crystallization: Macroscopic Phenomena and Defect Generation.* Melbourne, Sydney: Cambridge Univ. Press

51a. Yau S-T, Thmas BR, Vekilov PG. 2000. Molecular mechanisms of crystallization and defect formation. *Phys. Rev. Lett.* Submitted

52. Weber PC. 1997. Overview of protein crystallization methods: macromolecular crystallography. *Methods Enzymol.* 276A

53. Wong SS, Woolley AT, Odom TW, Huang JL, Kim P, Vezenov DV, Lieber CM. 1998. Single-walled carbon nanotube probes for high-resolution nanostructure imaging. *Appl. Phys. Lett.* 73:3465–67

54. Yip CM, Brader ML, DeFelippis MR, Ward MD. 1998. Atomic force microscopy of crystalline insulins: the influence of sequence variation on crystallization and interfacial structure. 74:2199–9

55. Yip CM, DeFelippis MR, Frank BH, Brader ML, Ward MD. 1998. Structural and morphological characterization of ultralente insulin crystals by atomic force microscopy: evidence of hydrophobically driven assembly. *Biophys. J.* 75:1172–79

56. Yip CM, Ward MD. 1998. Atomic force microscopy of insulin single crystals—direct visualization of molecules and crystal growth. *Biophys. J.* 71:1071–78

Annu. Rev. Biophys. Biomol. Struct. 2000. 29:411–38

A DECADE OF CLC CHLORIDE CHANNELS: Structure, Mechanism, and Many Unsettled Questions

Merritt Maduke, Christopher Miller, and Joseph A. Mindell

Department of Biochemistry, Howard Hughes Medical Institute, Brandeis University, Waltham, Massachusetts 02454; e-mail: cmiller@brandeis.edu

Key Words   ion channel, membrane protein, structure-function

■ **Abstract**   ClC-type chloride channels are ubiquitous throughout the biological world. Expressed in nearly every cell type, these proteins have a host of biological functions. With nine distinct homologues known in eukaryotes, the ClCs represent the only molecularly defined family of chloride channels. ClC channels exhibit features of molecular architecture and gating mechanisms unprecedented in other types of ion channels. They form two-pore homodimers, and their voltage-dependence arises not from charged residues in the protein, but rather via coupling of gating to the movement of chloride ions within the pore. Because the functional characteristics of only a few ClC channels have been studied in detail, we are still learning which properties are general to the whole family. New approaches, including structural analyses, will be crucial to an understanding of ClC architecture and function.

CONTENTS

INTRODUCTION

Chloride is the most abundant aqueous ion on earth. All living organisms have accordingly evolved membrane transport and ion channel proteins to exploit Cl^- toward varied physiological ends. Despite their biological ubiquity, Cl^- channels have been relegated to the sidelines in the grand trajectory of ion channel studies of the past fifty years, mainly because their specific biological roles have been, until recently, only vaguely glimpsed. In their seminal discovery, Hodgkin & Huxley (31) described three conductances–Na^+, K^+, and "leak"–underlying neuronal action potentials. As the research they inspired progressed, complex collections of cellular currents were dissected into components consisting of many K^+, Na^+, and Ca^{++} channels. These and other cation-conducting ion channels became a central focus for research on the molecular foundations of neurobiology, while the inescapable leak languished as an experimental irritant. It is now appreciated, however, that "leaks" are largely mediated by Cl^- channels and that these channels play diverse functional roles, belying their original pejorative label, from regulation of blood pressure, muscle tone, and cell volume to control of synaptic transmission and cellular excitability.

While Cl^- currents were recognized electrophysiologically long ago, an understanding of their molecular underpinnings has only recently begun to emerge. The key breakthrough occurred when Jentsch and colleagues (35) cloned a voltage-gated Cl^- channel from an electric fish. This result led swiftly to the discovery of an abundant, widespread, and ancient molecular family of Cl^- channels (35, 66). These "ClC" genes are found in virtually all organisms, from humans and invertebrates to plants, protists, and prokaryotes. In mammals, nine ClC homologues have been identified, and these fall into three subfamilies (Figure 1). In addition to sequence similarity (30–80% within, ~20% between subfamilies), subfamily members share some general functional features such as anion selectivity, voltage-dependent gating, and macroscopic current rectification.

With some reluctance, we suggest an updated nomenclature for ClC channels from multicellular organisms, which heretofore have been named on an ad hoc basis, mostly by sequential numbering without reference to subfamily. It is awkward and unappealing to refer to the "0/1/2" or "3/4/5" subfamily (Figure 1), and so we propose a supplementary subfamily designation α, β, γ–to be inserted within the current nomenclature; thus, ClC-0 and ClC-6 become ClCα-0 and ClCγ-6, respectively. This naming is timely because it is likely that all ClC subfamilies from higher organisms have now been identified; the three subfamilies encompass

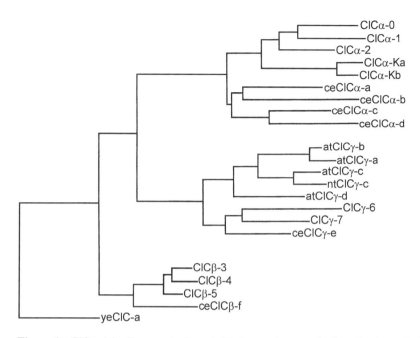

Figure 1 ClC subfamily organization. A. Phylogenetic tree of selected eukaryotic ClC genes, derived by Clustal analysis of aligned sequences, is shown. The α, β, γ subfamilies are indicated in the nomenclature introduced here. Nonvertebrate genes are annotated with lowercase species prefixes "ce" (*C. elegans*), "ye" (*S. cerivisiae*), "at" (*A. thaliana*), "nt" (*N. tabacum*). B. A table translating old nomenclatures of ClC channels into the naming format used here. The plant channel ntClCγ-c is so classified because it is a close orthologue of atClCγ-c.

all known ClC genes from animals and plants, the latter of which are so far exclusively of the type γ (29, 48). The six ClC channels from the complete *C. elegans* genome fall into all three subfamilies (81). We further suggest that as new orthologues are identified in nonvertebrate organisms, they should in addition be labeled by a species prefix and denoted by letters so as not to be confused with the numeral denotation of the vertebrate ClC genes. ClC channels from unicellular organisms cannot be classified in this way; the single ClC channel in the yeast genome (32) and all prokaryotic ClC genes are too distant in sequence to be shoehorned into the above subfamilies. Table 1 provides a nomenclature translation scheme for all eukaryotic ClC channels reported to date.

The ClCs make up the only recognized molecular family of Cl^- channels, and several excellent reviews have recently dealt with them from different viewpoints (33, 93). In this review, a recurrent theme will be that ClC channels differ utterly in form and function from "conventional" ion channel proteins such as S4-type voltage-gated channels, neurotransmitter-activated channels, and gap junctions. These familiar channel proteins are all constructed according to a barrel-stave plan in which the ion-conducting pore lies along the axis of symmetry formed by

TABLE 1   Translation of existing ClC names into proposed nomenclature

	Old name	New name
Vertebrate species		
	ClC-0	ClCα-0
	ClC-1	ClCα-1
	ClC-2	ClCα-2
	ClC-Ka	ClCα-Ka
	ClC-Kb	ClCα-Kb
	ClC-3	ClCβ-3
	ClC-4	ClCβ-4
	ClC-5	ClCβ-5
	ClC-6	ClCγ-6
	ClC-7	ClCγ-7
Plants		
	atClC-a	atClCγ-a
	atClC-b	atClCγ-b
	atClC-c	atClCγ-c
	atClC-d	atClCγ-d
	Ntl	ntClCγ-c (orthologue of atClC-c)
S. cerivisiae		
	GEF-1	yeClC-a
C. elegans		
	CeClC-1	ceClCα-a
	CeClC-2	ceClCα-b
	CeClC-3	ceClCα-c
	CeClC-4	ceClCα-d
	CeClC-5	ceClCβ-f
	CeClC-6	ceClCγ-g

the conjunction of four, five, or six identical or similar subunits. In contrast, ClC pores are formed from a single subunit, and therefore they must be lined by regions of protein scattered throughout the primary sequence. Also in contrast to conventional channels, the voltage-dependence of gating in ClC channels arises not from movement of charge on the protein but from movement of the permeant ion through the transmembrane electric field. Together, the unique features of the ClCs foreshadow an entirely new structure-function paradigm for this family of ion channels, one in which the vast experience gained from mutagenesis and analysis of familiar cation-conducting channels will be of little use in guiding experiments.

PHYSIOLOGICAL ROLES OF CLC CHANNELS

ClC channels act in many different biological contexts for numerous physiological purposes. Despite their widespread distribution in virtually all cells, or perhaps because of it, the functions of most of these channels remain obscure. In a few cases, though, we have a good understanding of ClC physiology. Other reviews (33, 93) have discussed this topic in some detail, and our purpose here is only to outline the few examples of known ClC functions.

Skeletal Muscle Excitability

The most thoroughly studied example of ClC biology is found in mammalian skeletal muscle, where ClCα-1 provides the preponderance of the resting conductance. In contrast to most cells, which are K^+-selective at rest, vertebrate skeletal muscle is Cl^- selective, a circumstance that allows it to maintain an unusually high resting potential (-90 mV). The resting conductance to Cl^- is mediated by ClCα-1, as was originally demonstrated from analyzing the genetic defect in a line of myotonic mice (90). These animals, which along with ClCα-1-defective goats (4, 6) provide models for certain human myotonias (24, 90), have muscle cells that are hyperexcitable because they lack the outward currents (inward Cl^- flux) carried by ClCα-1. In addition to stabilizing the resting membrane, this channel also provides repolarization current to help terminate the action potential in skeletal muscle; however, this effect is probably small compared to the action of voltage-gated K^+ channels in repolarization, since ClCα-1 is approximately 50% open at the resting potential (18, 74), and consequently Cl^- conductance can increase only about twofold in response to depolarization.

A similar physiology in a very different cellular context is illustrated by ClCα-0, the first ClC channel to be identified at the molecular level. This is a close homologue of ClCα-1 and is found in the specialized electroplax organ of marine electric rays. The electric organ is laid out as a series of disc-shaped cells piled on top of each other; the cells are polarized, with the negative, innervated side of the disc richly endowed with nicotinic acetylcholine receptors, and the positive side loaded with ClCα-0. As in skeletal muscle, the Cl^- channel establishes a high-voltage, low-resistance pathway across the resting membrane. When a nerve signal activates the acetylcholine receptors in all the electroplax cells simultaneously, the stacked structure causes the individual cellular voltages (-90 mV for each cell in the stack) generated by ClCα-0 to add in series, generating 50–100 V across the entire organ and producing the fish's lethal jolt. This physiology is actually close to that of skeletal muscle (from which the electroplax is evolutionarily derived); the main difference is the absence of regenerative action potentials in the electroplax. Indeed, skeletal muscles of electric rays express ClCα-0 (34), possibly for the same purpose as ClCα-1 in higher vertebrates.

Renal and Intravesicular Ion Transport

Investigations of human genetic diseases of blood pressure regulation have led to deeper understanding of two other ClC genes, both involved in renal function. Bartter's syndrome is an inherited disorder of NaCl reabsorption, the salt-concentrating process of the mammalian kidney. Lifton's group (85) has shown that Bartter's is caused by defects in any one of three separate transport proteins involved in salt resorption: the Na-K-Cl cotransporter, a K^+ channel, and a Cl^-

channel recently identified as ClCα-Kb. A detailed analysis of NaCl transport defects in patients with Bartter's localized the physiological disruption to the thick ascending limb of the loop of Henle. This nephron segment is known to bring about NaCl reuptake (86), with the Na-K-Cl cotransporter and K^+ channel cohabiting the apical membrane to clear NaCl from the lumen, and the Cl^- channel allowing the accumulated cytoplasmic Cl^- to flow "downhill" across the basolateral membrane back into the blood. The fact that mutations in any one of these transporter genes indeed cause Bartter's syndrome provides elegant support for this physiological mechanism, even in the absence of direct measurements of ClC-mediated Cl^- currents in kidney tubules.

The second human renal disease associated with a ClC channel is Dent's disease, caused by mutations in the ClCβ-5 gene, which is prominently expressed in kidney (42,91). Dent's disease is a polymorphic disorder associated with kidney stones, elevated urinary protein, and chronic depletion of phosphate and vitamin C. No unifying physiological principle has been definitively identified to tie these defects together. However, Günther and coworkers (27) noticed that ClCβ-5 is predominantly localized to intracellular vesicles, and they proposed that ClCβ-5 is normally involved in the physiology of endosomal ion transport, in particular intravesicular acidification. This idea makes sense: Many intracellular compartments, including lysosomes and endosomes, are maintained at acidic pH by H^+-ATPases, which utilize Cl^- conductance to shunt the membrane and thereby allow mass transport of protons (1, 95).

Genetic studies of *Saccharomyces cerivisiae* frequently produce insight into the functions of mammalian genes, and the case of ClC channels is no exception. The yeast genome contains a single ClC gene (yeClC-a) originally called GEF1, mutants of which are impaired for aerobic growth because of a limitation in Fe transport (25). Gaxiola and coworkers (23) posed the question: Why should a Cl^- channel defect lead to a requirement for Fe? They tracked down a rather complex pathway in which defective Cl^- conductance inhibits intravesicular acidification as above, and this in turn suppresses the ATP-dependent transport of Cu^{2+} into post-golgi vesicles; since Cu is a cofactor for the high-affinity Fe-uptake system, GEF1 mutants require high levels of Fe to grow. Moreover, disruptions of either GEF1, which is localized in golgi membranes, or of the vacuolar H^+-ATPase produce similar phenotypes (82). These experiments, along with the rescue of GEF1 mutant phenotypes by ClC genes from vertebrates or green plants (23, 29, 56), strongly imply that this yeast ClC gene provides a Cl^- shunt pathway accompanying proton uptake into intracellular compartments. However, no direct electrophysiological demonstration of this channel's Cl^- transport function has been reported.

Cell Volume Regulation

When exposed to osmotically altered bathing solutions, many cells counteract swelling or shrinkage by dumping KCl or taking up NaCl and thus maintain their original cell volume. Cl^- channels activated or inhibited by hyper- or hypo-osmotic challenge have been observed in numerous cell-types as rate-determining components of this process (59). The molecular identities of these channels have been extremely difficult to deduce, but recent results suggest that at least two ClC channels, $ClC\alpha$-2 and $ClC\beta$-3, may be involved in cell volume regulation. $ClC\alpha$-2 is found ubiquitously in mammalian tissues, and when expressed in Xenopus oocytes, this channel induces Cl^--selective currents that increase upon applying hypo-osmotic condition leading to cell swelling (26). The appearance of similar currents in many $ClC\alpha$-2-expressing native tissues suggests by correlation that this is a volume-sensing channel in native tissue. However, the currents observed in physiological preparations differ in detail from those observed with heterologous expression of $ClC\alpha$-2. This raises several possibilities: that the native osmotically sensitive currents are mediated by a different ClC isoform (or an unknown non-ClC channel), that the channels in native systems are functionally modulated by accessory subunits, or that they result from heteromers of different ClC isotypes. The dearth of specific high-affinity blockers for ClC channels has frustrated attempts to convincingly associate native channels with ClC genes, and in fact the very involvement of ClC channels in physiological volume-regulated anion currents remains controversial (60).

$ClC\beta$-3 has also been tied to volume regulation. Duan and colleagues (12, 13) observed that guinea pig $ClC\beta$-3 produces an osmosensitive current when expressed in NIH-3T3 cells. As monitored by whole-cell recording, $ClC\beta$-3 induces an outwardly rectifying Cl^- current that increases when the cells are exposed to hypotonic solutions and decreases in hypertonic media. Remarkably, phosphorylation of $ClC\beta$-3 by protein kinase C (PKC) is a critical element in the osmotic regulation pathway. Hypotonic exposure leads to inhibition of endogenous PKC and thereby to net dephosphorylation of $ClC\beta$-3, a modification that increases channel activity (13, 37); conversely, hypertonic conditions activate PKC and downregulate the channel. The site of osmoregulatory phosphorylation has been identified: Ser51, located in the cytoplasmic N-terminal domain of $ClC\beta$-3 (12). These results provide a real breakthrough in dissecting the molecular foundations of volume regulation, which has been a persistently murky area of investigation (10). Nevertheless, even in this case there are major differences between volume regulated currents in native tissues and those arising from heterologous expression of $ClC\beta$-3 (93).

Control of GABA-ergic Neurons

An important and novel neurophysiological function has been proposed for $ClC\alpha$-2 in central neurons: to ensure that $GABA_A$ receptors produce the classic inhibitory response. Cytoplasmic Cl^- concentrations are maintained differently in different types of neurons. In some, Cl^- is actively accumulated in the cytoplasm, thereby establishing an equilibrium potential (E_{Cl}) positive to the cell's resting potential. Other neurons are constitutively more permeable to Cl^- and have passively distributed Cl^- and resting potentials closer to E_{Cl}. These differences in Cl^- handling can lead to dramatic differences in GABA synaptic physiology. In cells where $E_{Cl} \sim V_{rest}$, $GABA_A$ receptors (Cl^- channels themselves) are inhibitory; their activation stabilizes the resting potential and counteracts action potential generation. In contrast, in cells of low resting Cl^- conductance and high Cl^- content, $GABA_A$ receptors are excitatory (62). GABA-inhibitory neurons often contain a hyperpolarization-activated Cl^- current, which provides the relevant Cl^- conductance near the resting potential (89). Staley's group (87) noticed that this current is similar to heterologously expressed ClCα-2. They demonstrated that ClCα-2 is expressed in neurons with inhibitory $GABA_A$ responses, but not in those with excitatory $GABA_A$ responses; accordingly they proposed that ClCα-2 expression provides a key molecular control on the qualitative character of a given neuron's $GABA_A$ response. Staley and colleagues (88) elegantly tested this hypothesis by genetically introducing ClCα-2 into rat dorsal root ganglion neurons, which lack the hyperpolarization-activated Cl^- current and normally show an excitatory $GABA_A$ response. This maneuver resulted in the appearance of the hyperpolarization-activated Cl^- current and concomitantly converted the cells into GABA-inhibitory neurons. The combination of in situ and heterologous expression results thus makes a convincing case for this proposed function of ClCα-2 in GABA-ergic neurons.

MOLECULAR ARCHITECTURE OF CLC CHANNELS

Transmembrane Topology

The first glimpse of ClC primary sequence provided by the cloning of ClCα-0 (35) revealed a protein of roughly 800 residues with 12-13 transmembrane helical stretches, D1-D13, a feature present in all eukaryotic orthologues subsequently discovered (Figure 2). The following topological characteristics are definitively known from work on the ClCα subfamily. The N- and C-termini are both cytoplasmic (26, 50), as is the residue (K519 in ClCα-0) just following D12 (52); the D8-D9 loop carrying the single N-linked glycosylation site is extracellular (51), and D13 is part of the cytoplasmic C-terminal domain, not a transmembrane sequence (26, 36, 50). The extracellular location of the D8-D9 loop presents a conundrum as to the exact number of transmembrane crossings, since it constrains the polypeptide chain to cross the membrane an odd number of times from D1 to D8 and from D9 to D12; in each of these regions, therefore, the number of actual membrane crossings is probably one less than the number of transmembrane sequences assigned by hydropathy analysis. All eukaryotic ClC channels so far examined contain in the C-terminal region two copies of a CBS domain, a $\sim$50-residue sequence motif of known structure but unknown function originally recognized in various globular proteins (63).

By 1997, a consensus (Figure 2) had been reached for ClC transmembrane topology on the basis of the above facts, combined with a determined assault on

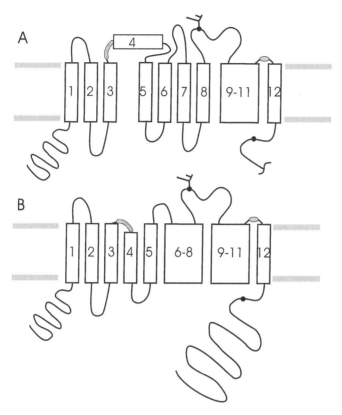

Figure 2 Alternative views of ClC transmembrane topology. The figure presents (A) Schmidt-Rose & Jentsch (79) and (B) Fahlke et al (20) models of ClC topology, with extracellular side up. Definitively established positions that are not in contention are explicitly indicated. Residues N365 and K519 (dark circles, ClCα-0 numbering) are singled out as solidly established in membrane sidedness, as is the conserved EXT sequence in the D11-D12 linker (shaded patch). The striped patch near D4 represents the conserved sequence GKEGP, which has been located near the center of twofold symmetry of homodimeric ClCα-1.

the problem by glycosylation-mapping, protease-protection, and cysteine-modification studies (79). However, additional data have recently called this picture into question in the region around D4 and D5. In particular, Fahlke and colleagues (20) showed that a cysteine substitution at the C-terminal end of D5 could be modified by a thiol-reactive reagent only when the reagent was added to the external side of the membrane. This result starkly clashes with Schmidt-Rose & Jentsch's (79) demonstration that an asparagine residue engineered in the D4-D5 loop can be glycosylated in truncated constructs. We do not know how to reconcile the straightforward interpretations of these two results, but they cannot both be correct, at least when extended to wild-type ClC channels. Until this question is resolved, our view of ClC transmembrane topology will remain seriously blurred.

Quaternary Structure

In contrast to the prevailing uncertainty over transmembrane topology, ClC quaternary structure is not in contention; all ClC channels examined are dimeric. Indeed, quaternary structure is one of the few properties that has been studied in widely divergent ClC family members. The effects of dominant negative mutations indicated early on that ClCα-1 is multimeric (24, 90), and sedimentation studies on ClCα-0 and ClCα-1 suggested that these channels are homodimers (16, 51). Examination of single ClCα-0 channels formed by co-expression of wild-type and point mutants with altered unitary conductance definitively confirmed this channel's dimeric architecture (46, 52).

Recently, an *E. coli* ClC homologue–the product of the yadQ gene only 15% identical in sequence to any eukaryotic ClC channel–was overexpressed and purified (49). Functional reconstitution has been so far limited to Cl$^-$ fluxes in liposomes, but even in the absence of direct electrical recordings it is clear that the protein acts as a Cl$^-$ channel with ion selectivity properties expected from the eukaryotic homologues. The functional channel is readily produced in large quantities (1–5 mg/L culture) and thus is amenable to protein-level biochemical analysis. Three complementary experimental techniques–chemical cross-linking, gel filtration, and analytical ultracentrifugation–confirmed the dimeric structure of this prokaryotic ClC channel. Since this result applies to a ClC channel so distant from the eukaryotic homologues, it suggests that dimeric architecture is a general hallmark of all ClC channels and not merely an idiosyncracy of ClCα-0 and ClCα-1.

BASIC FUNCTIONAL PROPERTIES OF CLC CHANNELS

Anion Permeation

The prominent functional characteristics of the S4 family of Na$^+$, K$^+$, and Ca^{2+} channels can be succinctly stated: strongly voltage-dependent opening upon depolarization, and specific selectivity for the appropriate cation. (Cyclic nucleotide gated channels, however, lack strong voltage dependence although they are formally within the S4 family.) Likewise, the defining properties of classic neurotransmitter-activated channels are easily summarized: activation by binding of multiple ligands, desensitization upon sustained application of neurotransmitters, and ionic selectivity on the basis of electrical valence. In contrast, only a single functional property is common to all ClC channels studied so far: strong selectivity for inorganic anions. All ClC channels studied selectively conduct Cl$^-$, Br$^-$, and NO$_3^-$, and some are also permeable to the low-conductance blockers I$^-$ and SCN$^-$. No universal "signature" ion selectivity sequence is known, possibly because no single set of ionic conditions has been used for selectivity measurements on all the ClC channels. This situation is unhelpful to the electrophysiologist hoping to identify the molecular identity of a cellular Cl^- current, especially since many anion currents have been described–some the products of known non-ClC genes, and some molecularly unidentified–and all of them display roughly similar interanionic selectivities.

A careful and extensive examination of ClC selectivity (75) shows that ClCα-1 is not a simple anion sieve. Although interanionic permeability values (measured by macroscopic reversal potential) generally decrease with ion size, there are striking exceptions; ClO_4^- and SCN^- are more permeant than Br^-, NO_3^-, or ClO_3^-, and hydrophobic acids like benzoate and hexanoate are more permeant than much smaller anions BrO_3^-, formate, and bicarbonate. If the "anomalous" permeabilities of the larger hydrophobic anions are ignored, the size-dependence of permeability shows a cutoff at about 5 Å ionic diameter, similar to the values for the anion-selective $GABA_A$ and glycine receptor channels (5). In other ion channels, such size cutoffs have been taken as empirical measures of the narrowest constriction along the conduction pathway (30), and this has now been directly verified in the case of a bacterial K^+ channel (11).

Very little is understood about the actual mechanism of anion permeation and selectivity of ClC channels. Our ignorance of this most basic process is mainly the consequence of a technical problem: the difficulty of making direct measurements of anion permeation through ClC channels. Since ion permeation is so tightly coupled to gating (see below), interpretation of the effects of ion substitution on macroscopic currents are nearly always ambiguous. In principle, this ambiguity can be resolved by direct single-channel studies of permeation, but because of the small conductances of ClC channels, very few such studies have been made. Early work (94) on the variation of single-channel conductance with Cl^- concentration showed that ClCα-0 saturates in a simple Michaelis-Menten fashion, as expected for a channel that can accommodate only one Cl^- ion at a time. More recently, experiments showing complex dependence of macroscopic currents in ionic mixtures led to proposals that ClC pores allow two ions simultaneous occupancy (15, 69).

Voltage-Dependent Activation

The most thoroughly studied ClC channels–ClCα-0 and ClCα-1–are voltage dependent. They display fast activation gating upon depolarization, with weak voltage-sensitivity (e-fold increase in opening for $\sim$25 mV, five- to tenfold weaker than in S4-type channels). The position of the voltage-activation curve, i.e., the set-point along the voltage axis, is strongly modulated by cytoplasmic pH and extracellular Cl^- (9, 28, 69, 74), for physiological reasons that remain completely unknown. ClCα-2 gating is also voltage-dependent, but with polarity opposite of that of ClCα-0 and ClCα-1 (92). Remarkably, the voltage dependence of ClCα-0 and ClCα-1 is "plastic," with many mutations of these channels producing reversed-polarity gating (19, 44, 45, 50). All three mammalian ClCβ channels show outward rectification of macroscopic currents (13, 22), but it is not known how much of this reflects voltage-dependent gating and how much open-channel permeation. No mammalian members of the ClCγ subfamily have been functionally expressed, so their electrophysiological properties are unknown. However, strong inward rectification was observed in ntClCγ-c, a γ-subfamily channel from a green plant, tobacco (48).

Inactivation Gating

Upon maintained depolarization, ClCα-0 inactivates. Qualitatively, this gating process is similar to inactivation observed in many voltage-dependent channels, but there are differences in detail that warrant discussion. Inactivation of ClCα-0 is extremely slow (10–100 sec timescale) and astonishingly temperature-dependent, with a 10-degree temperature increase leading to a 40-fold rate enhancement (8, 21, 53, 68). The biological purpose of inactivation–if there is one–is unknown. Like fast activation, inactivation is favored by depolarization, but the set-point of the equilibrium inactivation curve is about 60 mV displaced in the positive direction along the voltage axis from the activation curve. For this reason, there is a wide voltage window in which the channel is often open at equilibrium, in contrast to S4-type channels, where inactivation curves typically lie negative to the activation curve, and the open state is in consequence only transient. At this time, it is not known whether inactivation is intrinsically voltage-dependent, or whether its voltage dependence arises from coupling to activation gating, as in some S4 channels. Like activation, inactivation is also modulated by cytoplasmic pH and extracellular Cl$^-$ (9, 54, 67).

The mechanism of inactivation is unknown, and there is no reason to suppose that a K$^+$channel-like ball-and-chain mechanism (97) is involved. Extensive chimera studies aiming to localize determinants of inactivation in the ClCα-0 sequence showed that the process can be affected by manipulations of numerous regions (21), much like C-type inactivation in K$^+$ channels. Recently Chen (8), following up on the known "block" of ClC channels by transition metal cations (39), showed that extracellular Zn^{2+} or Cd^{2+} inhibits ClCα-0 by promoting inactivation, not by pore plugging, most likely by coordination with a cysteine residue. Chen's group went on to locate a cysteine in D5, C212, whose replacement by serine eliminates all traces of inactivation without affecting activation gating (41). The mechanism by which C212 exerts its influence on inactivation is unknown.

Single-Channel Gating Behavior of ClCα-0

General mechanisms of ClC gating remain obscure for a simple reason: the scarcity of information at the single-channel level. Most ClC channels that have been functionally expressed are very low in conductance (<5 pS) and therefore inaccessible to detailed microscopic examination (70, 75). The only exception is ClCα-0, which is large enough ($\sim$10 pS) to allow such measurements. For this reason, nearly everything we know about single ClC channels comes from ClCα-0, and

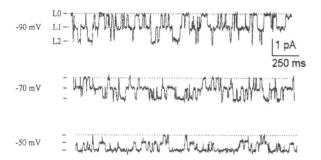

Figure 3   Fast activation gating in ClCα-0. A single inactivation-removed ClCα-0 channel is shown in a Xenopus oocyte membrane patch. The three substate levels are labeled, and opening is downward. Data taken from Lin et al (41).

it is uncertain whether the conclusions reached for this one channel apply to the entire molecular family. Nevertheless, it is worth reviewing the single-channel behavior of ClCα-0, which has provided unique insight into both gating mechanism and molecular structure.

In Figure 3, records of a single inactivation-removed ClCα-0 channel are shown at several voltages. The striking feature of these recordings is their multistate character. Simple inspection shows the channel fluctuating among three levels of current: a nonconducting level (L0) and two conducting levels (L1, L2), of which one appears to be about twice the current of the other. At hyperpolarized voltages, transitions among the substates are frequent; at more depolarized voltages, the channel spends more of its time in L2, and excursions into L0 and L1 become short-lived and less frequent. This is the microscopic manifestation of ClCα-0 activation gating: a depolarization-promoted shift from the low to the high substates. The channel's open probability levels off at a nonzero value at very hyperpolarized voltages (9), as is also seen in ClCα-1 (18). Not shown in this figure is the single-channel symptom of inactivation at depolarized voltages: long-lived nonconducting intervals that segment the channel record into "bursts" of activity (53). Recently, in a series of heroic experiments (77), single ClCα-1 channels were observed directly. Although at 1 pS the channels are much lower in conductance than ClCα-0, the qualitative features of ClCα-0 are all present in ClCα-1: three substates involved in voltage-dependent activation gating and sojourns into a longer-lived nonconducting state analogous to the inactivated intervals of ClCα-0.

A great deal of discussion and controversy has been expended on the underlying molecular meaning of the ClCα-0 (and now ClCα-1) substates. On one side (2, 53), the substates are seen as a direct reflection of an unusual molecular architecture: a double-barreled construction in which the functional channel carries two identical Cl⁻ conduction pores that gate independently on the fast timescale of activation, but are coupled together in an obligatory dimeric complex. These two pores inactivate via a slower "common gate" that occludes or exposes both pores simultaneously. On the other side (17), the substates represent multiple conformations of a single pore. Since this controversy is so fundamental to all molecular understanding of these channels, we review below the experimental evidence on which the two views of ClC proteins are based.

Experimental Support for Double-Barreled Architecture

To recapitulate the fundamental fact: ClCα-0 shows multistate bursting behavior. When the channel leaves the long-lived inactivated state, it engages in a burst of transitions among three substates, L0, L1, L2, distinguishable by their different conductances (0, ~10, and ~20 pS, respectively, in symmetrical 200 mM Cl^-). There are three experimental lines of evidence that these substates reflect the independent random opening and closing of two separate, distinct, and identical Cl^- diffusion pores.

1. Equally spaced conductance. An obvious property of ClCα-0 substates is their equal spacing in the single-channel record, a feature observed with native Torpedo membranes, heterologous expression systems, and the purified protein (2, 28, 51, 53). L0 is nonconducting, and L2 is twice the conductance of L1 to a precision better than ±2%. This twofold ratio holds across a 250 mV voltage span and under diverse ionic conditions, where absolute single-channel currents vary nearly tenfold. Moreover, the Cl-Br-selectivity and the blocking potency of SCN^- are identical in L1 and L2. These properties are obviously demanded of a double-barreled channel with independent permeation pores. They have never been observed together in single-pore channels showing substates. In cyclic nucleotide-gated channels, for example, in which different protonation states of a single pore give rise to three substates, the conductances are unequal (58, 72), and the spacing depends strongly on ionic conditions (M Root, R MacKinnon, unpublished results). Likewise, Kv channel substates, which reveal partially open conformations along the voltage-activation pathway, are unequally spaced in conductance and display different ion selectivities (98).

2. Binomial gating. Another remarkable property arguing for two independent, identical structures in substate gating is strict adherence to a binomial distribution (2, 9, 28, 41, 53). As long as the inactivated states are long-lived enough to be unambiguously distinguishable from the brief closed states, the probabilities, f_i, of substate appearance can be predicted without any adjustable parameters:

$$f_0 = (1 - p_o)^2 \quad f_1 = 2\,p_o(1 - p_o) \quad f_2 = p_o^2$$

where p_o is the fundamental open probability obtained measured directly from the integrated channel record. In addition to this equilibrium behavior, the kinetics of the three substates are tightly constrained by the double-barreled channel assumptions. Specifically, the time constants of the single-exponential dwell-time distributions of the three substates are obligatorily related to each other:

$$2/\tau_1 = 1/\tau_0 + 1/\tau_2 \quad \tau_2/\tau_0 = p_o/(1 - p_o)$$

The fact that these quantitative relations have all been repeatedly confirmed (2, 9, 28, 41, 47, 51, 53) over a wide set of conditions is a powerful argument for any model invoking independence and equivalence. In the cyclic nucleotide-gated channel, a binomial distribution of substates was observed (72), and this result argued compellingly for the equivalence and independence of the substate-generating mechanism, in that case two protonation reactions in a single pore.

A further experimental feature of substate gating is demanded of this picture: forbidden transitions between L0 and L2. In terms of the binomial model, this is a simple consequence of the fact that the closing of two open pores requires two independent events, which cannot happen at exactly the same time. This predicted feature of ClCα-0 gating has also been confirmed (53). Forbidden transitions like this are consistent with multistate models in single-pore channels, but they are not required of them; for example, in a K$^+$ channel from sarcoplasmic reticulum, all possible transitions among the three conductance levels were observed (40).

3. Independent behaviors of the substates. Another argument that the substates represent separate pores, each with its own activation gate, is based on experiments in which the substates are independently manipulated. There are now four such examples. First, the effect of DIDS, an irreversible inhibitor of ClCα-0, was examined at the single-channel level (55). The reagent caused disappearance of the channel in a two-hit process, each hit apparently occurring on a separate pore. The first hit converted the three-substate bursts into conventional two-state open-closed channel gating, as in a single-pore channel; the second hit eliminated all channel activity. Moreover, the putative single-barreled channel gating in the interval after the first hit but before the second was quantitatively as predicted from the binomial kinetics observed before inhibitor was added. These facts are easy to understand in terms of two independent gating entities, each inhibited separately by DIDS, but would be difficult to reconcile with a single pore fluctuating among multiple conducting conformations.

Second, point mutations were made at various positions that influence single-channel conductance, and mixed-subunit channels were examined (46, 52). Heterodimers containing one wild-type and one mutant subunit display a striking new property: bursts with four substates instead of the usual three. This result is demanded by the double-barreled picture, since in this case L1 loses the degeneracy of the homodimer: the value of L1 conductance now depends on which of the pores is open–the wild-type or mutant pore. Most importantly, the values of the single-pore conductances of the heterodimers are identical to those in the "parental" homodimers; again, the individual pores behave independently of one another. This kind of behavior is nearly incomprehensible in terms of a single pore.

Third, a pore-counting experiment was performed using a chemically reactive cysteine residue substituted at a position that electrostatically influences single-channel conductance (52). While recording the single channel, the cysteine was modified with a positively charged thiosulfonate reagent, a maneuver that places a lysine-like moiety at this position. The experiment demonstrated conversion of a low-conductance "double-cysteine" channel to a high-conductance "double lysine-like" channel in exactly two chemical steps, one acting on each substate.

Finally, heterodimeric channels were constructed from parental channels with different activation-gating properties (47). In this case, the substate behavior was no longer binomial; instead, the gating could be quantitatively modeled by two nonequivalent, but independently gating pores, each with gating characteristics observed in the parental homodimers. None of these results rigorously rules out single-pore construction for ClCα-0. Only direct structure determination can do that. However, these independent lines of evidence force upon any single-pore model contortions so extreme as to cast it into great doubt. In contrast, all of the results cited are not only interpretable in terms of a double-pore structure of the channel dimer, they are required of it a priori. It is this feature of prediction before the experiment that makes the case for a double-barreled construction of ClCα-0 so compelling.

Experimental Support for Single-Pore Architecture

The usual explanation of substates in a single-channel record invokes multiple conformations of a single pore. This idea is well supported for numerous cases of substate behavior in channels known to consist of a single pore: voltage-gated and Ca^{2+}-activated K^+ channels (7, 43, 98), Na^+ and Ca^{2+} channels (38, 65, 78), cyclic nucleotide-gated channels (72, 73), and NMDA receptors (64). Fahlke and colleagues (17) recently argued that ClCα-1 is a homodimer containing a single pore. This conclusion is based on a series of experiments employing cysteine replacements in the vicinity of transmembrane sequence D4. The experiments first argued that D4 lines a major part of the anion conduction pathway (20), since MTS reagents applied to channels cysteine-substituted in this area cause inhibition of macroscopic currents, depending on which side of the membrane the reagent is added. With the stage thus set, MTS inhibition at several such positions was carefully compared in tandem homo- and heterodimers. If the cysteine side chains project into two separate and independent pores, they should react independently with MTS reagents and give additive effects of modification; on the other hand, if the two side chains project into a single pore, strong interactions between them might be expected.

Several examples of such strong interactions were indeed observed. The tandem homodimer K231C-K231C, for example, is inhibited by externally applied reagent at rates >20-fold higher than the single-cysteine heterodimer K231C-K231A. Moreover, the final extent of inhibition (~75%) is identical in the two constructs; this result is simply inconsistent with the idea that the cysteine side chains project into separate and independent pores because in that case, the heterodimeric channel should suffer only half the inhibition of the homodimer. Another dramatic experiment demonstrated disulfide cross-linking between the two K231C residues. With this cysteine-substituted channel, current was virtually abolished by mild oxidation conditions, and inhibition was reversed by DTT; in contrast, the tandem C-A heterodimer was insensitive to the same oxidation conditions. This experiment implies forcefully that a disulfide bridge forms between the two 231C residues. Again, the results are harmonious with a link between the residues across a single pore, but they clash with a double-barreled picture in which the two cysteines project into separate pores distant enough to act independently in ion permeation. Further indicators of cysteine-cysteine interaction–MTS reactivity and Cd^{2+} block–were presented at several other positions in D4.

These experiments were taken to show that $ClC\alpha$-1 does not adopt a double-barreled structure (17). Instead, the side chains of these residues were proposed to line a single pore in the homodimeric complex. According to this picture, the pore of this twofold symmetric homodimer would lie on the unique axis of symmetry, as in conventional channel architecture. $ClC\alpha$-0 would have to be built likewise, given its close similarity to $ClC\alpha$-1 in both sequence and function.

What Does It All Mean?

How can we reconcile these two fundamentally different pictures of ClC channel structure? The single-channel properties of $ClC\alpha$ 0 outlined above, and their recapitulation in $ClC\alpha$-1, point inexorably to two Cl^--permeation pathways operating in parallel, at least for the $ClC\alpha$ subfamily. But the strong interactions between the substituted cysteine groups, especially the striking disulfide cross-linking experiment, imply that these D4 residues lie close in space near the twofold symmetry axis of the channel dimer.

These two sets of facts may be straightforwardly reconciled by questioning the central premise leading to the single-pore conclusion: that the D4 cysteine side chains project into the Cl^- conduction pathway. The experimental evidence supporting this premise is weak. It is based on a cysteine-scanning study (20) showing inhibition of macroscopic $ClC\alpha$-1 currents upon adding MTS reagents to channels substituted with cysteine in and near the highly conserved "GKEGP" sequence preceding D4. The key argument that these side chains project into the pore is that, in some cases, MTS modification alters selectivity or that cysteine substitution leads to block by Cd^{2+}. This is a fallacious argument. In cases with firm structural foundations, channel pores are known to be tightly constructed, and their permeation properties are easily altered by secondary effects of distant molecular manipulations. For instance, in Shaker K^+ channels, mutations at a residue in the sixth transmembrane segment produce very large changes in ion selectivity (61), even though this is known, from analogy to the bacterial K^+ channel structure (11), not to be a pore-lining position. (One reason that mutagenesis work on K^+ channels has been so successful in visualizing structure is the standard of extreme caution employed in that field in assigning local effects to point mutations.) Moreover, Cd^{2+} is known to block the pores of certain cation-conducting channels, but there is neither evidence nor reason to suspect that Cd^{2+} inhibition of an anion-conducting ClC channel would reflect pore-block; indeed, Cd^{2+} inhibition of ClCα-1 via gating is more plausible in light of the fact (8) that transition metal cations inhibit ClCα-0 by binding preferentially to a nonconducting conformation (see above), not by plugging the pore.

We suspect that MTS inhibition of the D4 cysteine mutants is a consequence of secondary structural rearrangements, not of chemical modification of side chains lining the anion conduction pore. Certainly, a case for pore-locality of the mutations could not be made in these studies, since changes in gating behavior as profound as a reversal of voltage dependence in some cases occur in these cysteine substitutions (17, 20), as has been seen with many other "permeation mutants" of ClC channels (14, 15, 44, 69). For these reasons, we consider that the cysteine-modification experiments argue only for the location of these residues somewhere near the dimer's axis of twofold symmetry; they imply nothing about the location or character of the pore. In contrast, two-pore architecture naturally accounts for all the experimental results thus far.

So, let us summarize our current opinions on ClC architecture. First, we view ClCα channels as two-pore, symmetric homodimers. In such a complex, the twin conduction pores must necessarily both be removed from the axis of twofold symmetry, and indeed must be sufficiently distant from each other to permit independent, noninteracting operation (farther, say, than 20 Å, the Debye length at 25 mM ionic strength). We admit to paralysis in choosing between the two mutually exclusive proposals about transmembrane topology in the D4-D5 region; the experimental evidence is fairly split on whether D4 spans the membrane or remains formally on the extracellular side (but perhaps buried within the protein). We accept the contention (17) that the conserved D4 residues are located close to the homodimer's axis of symmetry. To us, this means that this functionally important sequence cannot be directly associated with the pores; instead, we imagine that it is intimately involved (whatever that means!) in inactivation gating, a process known to act on both pores simultaneously. In this view, we would also have to assert that these D4 residues do not act only locally, that mutation leads to global alterations of channel structure and disruption of the channel's linked functions.

The question still remains: Does double-barreled structure apply generally to all ClC channels, or is it a peculiarity of ClCα-0 and ClCα-1? Although pore construction would seem to be a property so fundamental to a molecular family as to be general, this is nevertheless a serious and urgent question. Several sightings of single ClCα-2 and ClCβ-3 channels have been reported in the literature, with records devoid of the double-barreled substate behavior seen with ClCα-0 and ClCα-1. At this point, however, we remain unconvinced that these single-channel recordings correspond to the ClC channels claimed. The recordings of the two reports (13, 37) on ClCβ-3 do not resemble each other, and the single channels identified as ClCα-2 (83) were not connected to any expressed macroscopic ClCα-2 currents. We therefore consider the question about the generality of ClC double-barreled construction to be entirely unresolved and very compelling.

UNPRECEDENTED GATING MECHANISMS OF CLC CHANNELS

ClC channels present the researcher with a collection of unusual gating behaviors that have been encountered only rarely, if at all, in the huge literature on gating of familiar voltage-dependent and neurotransmitter-activated channels. Because of their novelty and unprecedented character, these phenomena are not yet understood in mechanistic depth, and consequently they pose many fascinating challenges for future work. The three such mechanisms discussed here are (*a*) the source of gating charge in voltage-dependent ClC channels, (*b*) coupling of gating to ion permeation, and (*c*) sensitivity of gating to osmotic conditions.

Mechanism of Voltage Dependence: Coupling of Gating to Conduction

The fundamental thermodynamic requirement for voltage-dependence of channel gating is that the conformational changes between open and closed states must be linked to the transmembrane movement of electrical charge (84). In electrically excitable membranes, the strong voltage-dependence of Na^+, Ca^{2+}, and K^+ channels is achieved mainly by the outward movement of arginine and lysine residues on the fourth transmembrane segment as the channel opens (96). This movement leads by unknown mechanisms to the actual opening of the ion-conduction pore. For classic channels, the processes of gating and ion permeation are independent to a first-order approximation; the gating charge-moving events are similar regardless of the ionic species carrying current through the open channel.

The two voltage-gated ClC channels that have been closely examined—ClCα-0 and ClCα-1—sense transmembrane voltage in strikingly different ways. Here, gating charge is carried by Cl^- ion itself, not by charged residues on the protein. The first suggestion for this idea emerged from studies of the effects of external Cl^- concentration on ClCα-0 gating. Pusch and colleagues (69) showed that an increase in extracellular Cl^- opens the channel by shifting the voltage-activation curve to the left (favoring the open state), while minimally affecting its slope. In other words, ClCα-0 is a Cl^--activated Cl^- channel. They offered the idea that the pore of the closed channel is anion-accessible exclusively from the external solution and that only when Cl^- ions occupy the pore can the channel open. Furthermore, the pore-associated activation site was postulated to be located deep within the membrane field, so that binding of external Cl^- to that site—and hence channel opening—would be promoted by depolarization. This was a surprising suggestion, especially in light of previous gating models that invoked a particular carboxyl group on ClCα-1 as the gating charge (19).

Because of the unprecedented nature of this proposal, Pusch and colleagues (69) built a case for direct involvement of pore-associated anions in gating. They showed that only channel-permeant ions, including Br^-, NO_3^-, and (less effectively) I^-, cause this shift in activation. Moreover, they exploited mixtures of permeant ions to correlate a pore property with a gating shift; in Cl^--NO_3^- mixtures, current through the open channel depends nonmonotonically on the external anion composition, with a minimum at $\sim 30\%$ NO_3^-/70% Cl^-. This "anomalous mole-fraction effect," usually considered indicative of multi-ion conduction (30), is mirrored by a similar minimum in the voltage of half-maximal activation. These results make a strong argument that anion occupancy of the pore is in some way linked to channel opening, but they do not by themselves finger the permeant anion as the gating charge; for example, Cl^- occupancy might be required only for a conformational change leading to opening, while gating charge is carried by the movement of protein residues, as in a conventional mechanism.

To approach the gating mechanism in more detail, Chen & Miller (9) examined the Cl^- dependence of ClCα-0 activation gating at the single-channel level. Using purified ClCα-0 reconstituted into planar lipid bilayer membranes, they verified that single ClCα-0 channels are strongly activated by external Cl^-. This Cl^- activation results predominantly from an increase in the rate of channel opening, with a much weaker effect on closing rate. Thus, external Cl^- acts upon the not-yet-open channel. Moreover, the study showed that as external Cl^- is reduced toward zero, the channel approaches a state in which it can still open, albeit with very low probability. Most significantly, in this Cl^--starved condition, channel opening loses nearly all its voltage-dependence. Thus, just as proposed initially (69), Cl^- ion is indeed the gating charge; its movement within pre-open states of the channel confers voltage-dependence to ClCα-0 gating. The number of Cl^- ions involved in channel activation is still uncertain. The small gating charge of ~ 1 could reflect a single Cl^- ion moving through the entire transmembrane voltage drop, or several ions moving partway. The anomalous mole fraction effects mentioned above would seem to favor the latter possibility, but data on this question are still too sparse for a firm conclusion.

These studies could be carried out only because of the technical feasibility of single-channel studies with ClCα-0 over a wide range of experimental conditions, a capability not yet available with other ClC channels. Nevertheless, it is likely that the gating mechanism of ClCα-1 adheres to the same principles established for ClCα-0. At the macroscopic level, ClCα-1 activation responds to both voltage and Cl^- in ways strongly reminiscent of ClCα-0 (74), and the single-channel behavior is qualitatively similar to that of ClCα-0 in the limited range of conditions so far examined (77).

Recently, Rychkov and co-workers (75) extensively examined the effects of anion substitution on ClCα-1 permeation and gating. They studied a broad series of anions and found several distinct classes of behavior: Some anions had minimal effects on either gating or permeation when substituted for Cl⁻, while others affected both properties in similar ways. Interestingly, though, a third group of anions including cyclamate and methansulfonate had strong effects on channel gating despite negligible permeability.

Gating Is a Nonequilibrium Process

One immediate consequence of the above Cl⁻ activation mechanism is that the gating of these channels cannot be at thermodynamic equilibrium. Opening of the channel is inherently coupled to the movement of Cl⁻ ions across the membrane; the free energy of Cl⁻ entering the closed channel from the external solution and leaving the open channel to the internal solution–an irreversible process–is an intrinsic part of the gating reaction. For this reason, the usual conformational equilibrium treatments of gating are inapplicable here. Instead, the kinetic mechanism by which Cl⁻ permeates the pore becomes an inextricable part of any gating model (96), and since details of ClC permeation mechanisms are unknown, satisfactorily quantitative gating models of these channels are a long way off.

Given the mechanism of ClC voltage dependence, the above conclusions about gating irreversibility can be asserted with certainty on thermodynamic grounds alone. But how does nonequilibrium gating show itself experimentally? The distinctive substate behavior of ClCα-0 allows irreversible gating to be observed unambiguously. Because the channel has three distinguishable conductance levels–two open states (L1 and L2) and a long-lived inactivated state (I)–single-channel recordings reveal the life history of the channel as it undergoes state-transitions around a cycle (Figure 4). If channel gating were at thermodynamic equilibrium, then microscopic reversibility would require equal rates of transitions around

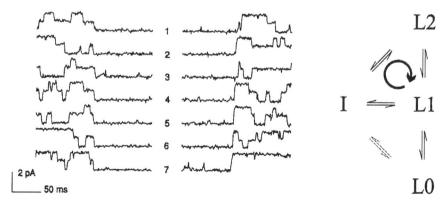

Figure 4 ClC gating violates microscopic reversibility. Left panel: 7 sequential examples of a single ClCα-0 channel (opening upward) entering and leaving the long-lived inactivated state. Right panel: State diagram indicating a clockwise cycle, as in traces 2-7. Data taken from Richard & Miller (71).

the cycle in clockwise and counterclockwise directions. But when Richard & Miller (71) examined these cycles for ClCα-0, they found that in general clockwise cycles (L1 → I → L2 → L1) predominate over counterclockwise cycles (L2 → I→ L1 → L2). In other words, the channel tends to enter the inactivated state from the low-conductance open state L1, but to leave the inactivated state into the high-conductance state L2. This fact means that channel gating is not at equilibrium; gating must obtain energy from an external source. In the reconstituted system used, the only energy source external to the channel resides in the gradients of transported ions, specifically Cl^-. Indeed, the ratio of clockwise to counterclockwise transition rates, a direct measure of external energy input, varies with the magnitude of the Cl^- gradient. Other channels are now known to display nonequilibrium gating cycles as well; CFTR channels derive external free energy from ATP hydrolysis coupled to gating (3), and coupling of gating to ion permeation in a mutant NMDA receptor was elegantly modeled by Schneggenburger & Ascher (80).

Coupling of Gating to Osmotic Conditions

Another novel form of gating has been observed in ClCα-2, one of the ClC isoforms implicated in cell volume–regulation. As discussed above, when expressed in Xenopus oocytes, ClCα-2 currents respond to the osmotic strength of the medium bathing the oocytes–activating in hypotonic media. The pathway by which the channel senses solution tonicity is unknown, but Grunder and colleagues (26) uncovered a remarkable molecular aspect of the phenomenon: that the cytoplasmic N-terminal domain is necessary for osmosensitive gating. When the N-terminus of ClCα-2 was replaced with those of either ClCα-0 or ClCα-1, basic conduction properties were retained, but osmotic sensitivity was completely lost. Likewise, deletion of 62 N-terminal residues in ClCα-2 resulted in a constitutively open channel unresponsive to osmotic conditions. Surprisingly, osmosensitivity could be partially restored by transplanting a large portion of the N-terminal region onto the C-terminal cytoplasmic domain! This unexpected result elicited the suggestion that, in analogy to K^+ channel inactivation (97), the N-terminal domain acts by a ball-and-chain mechanism, in which the N-terminal "ball" domain occludes the pore, and exposure to low osmotic strength (or downstream consequences of such exposure) removes the ball from its blocking site. This suggestion proceeds from the observation that the osmosensory domain exerts its channel-closing effect regardless of where it resides in the channel sequence, just as the K^+ channel's N-terminal peptide plugs the pore regardless of whether it is tethered to the rest of the protein sequence or dissolved free in solution. This logic is understandable, but in our opinion, the absence of any evidence that the ClCα-2 N-terminal domain interacts with the channel's conduction pathway makes this mechanistic proposal premature. We remain similarly skeptical that the cytoplasmic loop connecting D7 and D8 acts as the "receptor" for the N-terminal domain, as proposed from the observation that mutations in this region also abolish osmotically sensitive gating of ClCα-2 (36).

CONCLUSION

We conclude by listing several standing questions about ClC channels. All of these are intrinsically compelling in understanding the unprecedented features of the ClC family.

1. What are the physiological functions of ClC channels?

   The ubiquitous expression of ClC channels attests to the many different ends to which cells use these proteins. But except for a small handful of examples, these uses are undocumented. This sparsity of information makes ClC channels attractive targets for investigating the biological consequences of directed gene deletions. The central role of ClCα-0 and ClCα-1 in the excitability of muscle or muscle-derived tissue is firmly established, and ClCα-Kb almost certainly provides a major salt resorption pathway in mammalian kidney. The osmotic sensitivities of ClCα-2 and ClCβ-3 are clearly established in heterologous expression systems, and it will now be important to discover the physiological contexts in which this unusual property is actually used. The involvement of ClCβ-5 in acid transport by intracellular vesicles is suggested by recent results; if this role for ClCβ-5 and perhaps for its close homologue ClCβ-4 (22) is confirmed by follow-up studies, it is likely to be found well beyond the epithelial setting in which it was first revealed. At this time, we know nothing about the functional properties of any ClCγ subfamily members, either in heterologous or endogenous systems. Beyond the simple questions of which ClC channels are "involved in" which functions, we have no information whatever about heterodimeric assembly of ClC homologues, a common means of functional fine-tuning many other types of ion channels.

2. Are all ClC channels double barreled?

   The two-pore property is established in the ClCα subfamily, but we have no information for other ClC channels. From a structure-function standpoint, this question is of obvious importance. There have been several reports of single Cl$^-$ channels that appear double-barreled, but with conductances much higher than that of ClCα-0 (57, 76); so far, efforts to identify these channels at the molecular level have been fruitless. On the other hand, it will be very important to test the claim (13) that ClCβ-3 forms a conventional single-barreled channel; verification of this assertion would unequivocally eliminate two-pore construction as a fundamental characteristic of ClC proteins.

3. What do ClC proteins look like?

   Until last year, the direct structural investigation of any ClC channel was far out of the realm of possibility. Even the abundantly expressed ClCα-0 could be purified in only minuscule quantities (51). Today's torrent of prokaryotic genome sequences, however, changes this situation dramatically. ClC genes are represented in about half the prokaryotic genomes examined so far, and overexpression of ClC channels in bacterial expression systems is consequently a plausible experimental goal. Indeed, the first ClC channel for which bacterial overexpression was attempted, the yadQ gene of *E. coli*, produced large quantities of pure, functionally active ClC protein. While it is too early to embrace a positive optimism about ClC structure, the dismal feelings of structural hopelessness that have long pervaded the field are no longer warranted. The availability of high-milligram amounts of diverse ClC homologues will soon open the way to protein-level work with an eye toward direct structural information, by solution physical-chemical techniques, spectroscopic probes, and–dare we say it?–crystallization.

Visit the Annual Reviews home page at www.AnnualReviews.org

LITERATURE CITED

1. Al-Awqati Q. 1995. Chloride channels of intracellular organelles. *Curr. Opin. Cell Biol.* 7:504–8
2. Bauer CK, Steinmeyer K, Schwarz JR, Jentsch TJ. 1991. Completely functional double-barreled chloride channel expressed from a single Torpedo cDNA. *Proc. Natl. Acad. Sci. USA* 88:11052–56
3. Baukrowitz T, Hwang T-C, Nairn AC, Gadsby DC. 1994. Coupling of CFTR Cl⁻ channel gating to an ATP hydrolysis cycle. *Neuron* 12:473–82
4. Beck CL, Fahlke C, George AL. 1996. Molecular basis for decreased muscle chloride conductance in the myotonic goat. *Proc. Natl. Acad. Sci. USA* 93:11248–52
5. Bormann J, Hamill OP, Sakmann B. 1987. Mechanism of anion permeation through channels gated by glycine and gamma-aminobutyric acid in mouse cultured spinal neurones. *J. Physiol.* 385:243–86
6. Bryant SH, Morales-Aguilera A. 1971. Chloride conductance in normal and myotonic muscle fibres and the action of monocarboxylic aromatic acids. *J. Physiol.* 219:367–83
7. Chapman ML, VanDongen HM, VanDongen AM. 1997. Activation-dependent subconductance levels in the drk1 K channel suggest a subunit basis for ion permeation and gating. *Biophys. J.* 72:708–19
8. Chen T-Y. 1998. Extracellular zinc ion inhibits ClC-0 chloride channels by facilitating slow gating. *J. Gen. Physiol.* 112:715–26
9. Chen T-Y, Miller C. 1996. Nonequilibrium gating and voltage dependence of the ClC-0 Cl⁻ channel. *J. Gen. Physiol.* 108:237–50
10. Clapham DE. 1998. The list of potential volume-sensitive chloride currents continues to swell (and shrink). *J. Gen. Physiol.* 111:623–24
11. Doyle DA, Cabral JM, Pfuetzner A, Kuo JM, Gulbis JM, et al. 1998. The structure of the potassium channel: molecular basis of K⁺ conduction and selectivity. *Science* 280:69–76
12. Duan D, Cowley S, Horowitz B, Hume JR. 1999. A serine residue in CLC-3 links phosphorylation-dephosphorylation to chloride channel regulation by cell volume. *J. Gen. Physiol.* 113:57–70
13. Duan D, Winter C, Cowley S, Hume JR, Horowitz B. 1997. Molecular identification of a volume-regulated chloride channel. *Nature* 390:417–21
14. Fahlke C, Beck CL, George AL. 1997. A mutation in autosomal dominant myotonia congenita affects pore properties of the

muscle chloride channel. *Proc. Natl. Acad. Sci. USA* 94:2729–34

15. Fahlke C, Durr C, George AL. 1997. Mechanism of ion permeation in skeletal muscle chloride channels. *J. Gen. Physiol.* 110:551–64

16. Fahlke C, Knittle T, Gurnett CA, Campbell KP, George AL. 1997. Subunit stoichiometry of human muscle chloride channels. *J. Gen. Physiol.* 109:93–104

17. Fahlke C, Rhodes TH, Desai RR, George AL. 1998. Pore stoichiometry of a voltage-gated chloride channel. *Nature* 394:687–90

18. Fahlke C, Rosenbohm A, Mitrovic N, George AL, Rudel R. 1996. Mechanism of voltage-dependent gating in skeletal muscle chloride channels. *Biophys. J.* 71:695–706

19. Fahlke C, Rudel R, Mitrovic N, Zhou M, George AL. 1995. An aspartic acid residue important for voltage-dependent gating of human muscle chloride channels. *Neuron* 15:463–72

20. Fahlke C, Yu HT, Beck CL, Rhodes TH, George AL. 1997. Pore-forming segments in voltage-gated chloride channels. *Nature* 390:529–32

21. Fong P, Rehfeldt A, Jentsch TJ. 1998. Determinants of slow gating in ClC-0, the voltage-gated chloride channel of Torpedo marmorata. *Am. J. Physiol.* 274:C966–73

22. Friedrich T, Breiderhoff T, Jentsch TJ. 1999. Mutational analysis demonstrates that ClC-4 and ClC-5 directly mediate plasma membrane currents. *J. Biol. Chem.* 274:896–902

23. Gaxiola RA, Yuan DS, Klausner RD, Fink GR. 1998. The yeast ClC chloride channel functions in cation homeostasis. *Proc. Natl. Acad. Sci. USA* 95:4046–50

24. George AL, Carackower MA, Abdalla JA, Hudson AJ, Ebers GC. 1993. Molecular basis of Thomsen's disease (autosomal dominant myotonia congenita). *Nat. Genet.* 3:305–10

25. Greene JR, Brown NH, DiDomenico BJ, Kaplan J, Eide DJ. 1993. The GEF1 gene of *Saccharomyces cerevisiae* encodes an integral membrane protein; mutations in which have effects on respiration and iron-limited growth. *Mol. Gen. Genet.* 241:542–53

26. Grunder S, Thiemann A, Pusch M, Jentsch TJ. 1992. Regions involved in the opening of ClC-2 chloride channel by voltage and cell volume. *Nature* 360:759–62

27. Günther W, Luchow A, Cluzeaud F, Vandewalle A, Jentsch TJ. 1998. ClC-5, the chloride channel mutated in Dent's disease, colocalizes with the proton pump in endocytotically active kidney cells. *Proc. Natl. Acad. Sci. USA* 95:8075–80

28. Hanke W, Miller C. 1983. Single chloride channels from Torpedo electroplax: activation by protons. *J. Gen. Physiol.* 82:25–45

29. Hechenberger M, Schwappach B, Fischer WN, Frommer WB, Jentsch TJ, Steinmeyer K. 1996. A family of putative chloride channels from Arabidopsis and functional complementation of a yeast strain with a CLC gene disruption. *J. Biol. Chem.* 271:33632–38

30. Hille B. 1992. *Ionic Channels of Excitable Membranes*. Sunderland, MA: Sinauer. 2nd ed.

31. Hodgkin AL, Huxley AF. 1952. A quantitative description of membrane current and its application to conduction and excitation in nerve. *J. Physiol.* 117:500–44

32. Huang ME, Chaut JC, Galibert F. 1994. A voltage-gated chloride channel in the yeast *Saccharomyces cerevisiae*. *J. Mol. Biol.* 242:595–98

33. Jentsch TJ, Friedrich T, Schriever A, Yamada H. 1999. The CLC channel family. *Pflügers Arch.* 437:783–95

34. Jentsch TJ, Gunther W, Pusch M, Schwappach B. 1995. Properties of voltage-gated chloride channels of the ClC gene family. *J. Physiol.* 482:S19–S25

35. Jentsch TJ, Steinmeyer K, Schwarz G. 1990. Primary structure of Torpedo marmorata chloride channel isolated by expression cloning in *Xenopus* oocytes. *Nature* 348:510–14

36. Jordt S-V, Jentsch TJ. 1997. Molecular

dissection of gating in the ClC-2 chloride channel. *EMBO J.* 16:1582–92

37. Kawasaki M, Uchida S, Monkawa T, Miyawaki A, Mikoshiba K, et al. 1994. Cloning and expression of a protein kinase C-regulated chloride channel abundantly expressed in rat brain neuronal cells. *Neuron* 12:597–604

38. Klöckner U, Mikala G, Schwartz A, Varadi G. 1996. Molecular studies of the asymmetric pore structure of the human cardiac voltage-dependent Ca^{2+} channel. Conserved residue, Glu1086, regulates proton-dependent ion permeation. *J. Biol. Chem.* 271:22293–96

39. Kürz LL, Wagner S, George AL, Rüdel R. 1997. Probing the major skeletal muscle chloride channel with Zn2+ and other sulfhydryl-reactive compounds. *Pflügers Arch.* 433:357–63

40. Labarca PP, Miller C. 1981. A K^{+}-selective, three-state channel from fragmented sarcoplasmic reticulum of frog leg muscle. *J. Membr. Biol.* 61:31–38

41. Lin Y-W, Lin C-W, Chen T-Y. 1999. Elimination of the slow gating of ClC-0 chloride channel by a point mutation. *J. Gen. Physiol.* 114:1–12

42. Lloyd SE, Pearce SHS, Fisher SE, Steinmeyer K, Schwappach B, et al. 1996. A common molecular basis for three inherited kidney stone diseases. *Nature* 379:445–49

43. Lucchesi K, Moczydlowski E. 1990. Subconductance behavior in a maxi Ca^{2+}-activated K^{+} channel induced by dendrotoxin-I. *Neuron* 4:141–48

44. Ludewig U, Jentsch TJ, Pusch M. 1997. Inward rectification on ClC-0 chloride channels caused by mutations in several protein regions. *J. Gen. Physiol.* 110:165–71

45. Ludewig U, Jentsch TJ, Pusch M. 1997. Analysis of a protein region involved in permeation and gating of the voltage-gated Torpedo chloride channel ClC-0. *J. Physiol.* 498:691–702

46. Ludewig U, Pusch M, Jentsch TJ. 1996.

Two physically distinct pores in the dimeric ClC-0 chloride channel. *Nature* 383:340–43

47. Ludewig U, Pusch M, Jentsch TJ. 1997. Independent gating of single pores in CLC-0 chloride channels. *Biophys. J.* 73:789–97

48. Lurin C, Geelen D, Barbier-Brygoo H, Guern J, Maurel C. 1996. Cloning and functional expression of a plant voltage-dependent chloride channel. *Plant Cell* 8:701–11

49. Maduke M, Pheasant DJ, Miller C. 1999. High-level expression, functional reconstitution, and quaternary structure of a prokaryotic ClC-type Cl^- channel. *J. Gen. Physiol.* 114:713–22

50. Maduke M, Williams C, Miller C. 1998. Formation of CLC-0 chloride channels from separated transmembrane and cytoplasmic domains. *Biochemistry* 37:1315–21

51. Middleton RE, Pheasant DJ, Miller C. 1994. Purification, reconstitution, and subunit composition of a voltage-gated chloride channel from *Torpedo* electroplax. *Biochemistry* 33:13189–98

52. Middleton RE, Pheasant DJ, Miller C. 1996. Homodimeric architecture of a ClC-type chloride ion channel. *Nature* 383:337–40

53. Miller C. 1982. Open-state substructure of single chloride channels from *Torpedo* electroplax. *Philos. Trans. R. Soc. B* 299:401–11

54. Miller C, White MM. 1980. A voltage-dependent chloride channel from *Torpedo* electroplax membrane. *Ann. NY Acad. Sci.* 341:534–51

55. Miller C, White MM. 1984. Dimeric structure of C^l-channels from *Torpedo* electroplax. *Proc. Natl. Acad. Sci. USA* 81:2772–75

56. Miyazaki H, Uchida S, Takei Y, Hirano T, Marumo F, Sasaki S. 1999. Molecular cloning of CLC chloride channels in *Oreochromis mossambicus* and their functional complementation of yeast CLC gene

mutant. *Biochem. Biophys. Res. Commun.* 255:175–81

57. Morier N, Sauve R. 1994. Analysis of a novel double-barreled anion channels from rat liver rough endoplasmic reticulum. *Biophys. J.* 67:590–602

58. Morrill JA, MacKinnon R. 1999. Isolation of a single carboxyl-carboxylate proton binding site in the pore of a cyclic nucleotide-gated channel. *J. Gen. Physiol.* 114:71–83

59. Nilius B, Eggermont J, Voets T, Buyse G, Manolopoulos V, et al. 1997. Properties of volume-regulated anion channels in mammalian cells. *Prog. Biophys. Mol. Biol.* 68:69–119

60. Nilius B, Eggermont J, Voets T, Droogmans G. 1996. Volume-activated Cl^- channels. *Gen. Pharmacol.* 27:1131–40

61. Ogielska EM, Aldrich RW. 1998. A mutation in S6 of Shaker potassium channels decreases the K+ affinity of an ion binding site revealing ion-ion interactions in the pore. *J. Gen. Physiol.* 112:243–57

62. Perkins KL, Wong RK. 1997. The depolarizing GABA response. *Can. J. Physiol. Pharmacol.* 75:516–19

63. Ponting CP. 1997. CBS domains in ClC chloride channels implicated in myotonia and nephrolithiasis (kidney stones). *J. Mol. Med.* 75:160–63

64. Premkumar LS, Qin F, Auerbach A. 1997. Subconductance states of a mutant NMDA receptor channel kinetics, calcium, and voltage dependence. *J. Gen. Physiol.* 109:181–89

65. Prod'hom B, Pietrobon D, Hess P. 1987. Direct measurement of proton transfer rates to a group controlling the dihydropyridine-sensitive Ca^{2+} channel. *Nature* 329:243–46

66. Pusch M, Jentsch TJ. 1994. Molecular physiology of voltage-gated chloride channels. *Physiol. Rev.* 74:813–25

67. Pusch M, Jordt SE, Stein V, Jentsch TJ. 1999. Chloride dependence of hyperpolarization-activated chloride

channel gates. *J. Physiol.* 515:341–53

68. Pusch M, Ludewig U, Jentsch TJ. 1997. Temperature dependence of fast and slow gating relaxations of ClC-0 chloride channels. *J. Gen. Physiol.* 109:105–16

69. Pusch M, Ludewig U, Rehfeldt A, Jentsch TJ. 1995. Gating of the voltage-dependent chloride channel ClC-0 by the permeant anion. *Nature* 373:527–31

70. Pusch M, Steinmeyer K, Jentsch TJ. 1994. Low single channel conductance of the major skeletal muscle chloride channel, ClC-1. *Biophys. J.* 66:149–52

71. Richard EA, Miller C. 1990. Steady-state coupling of ion-channel conformations to a transmembrane ion gradient. *Science* 247:1208–10

72. Root MJ, MacKinnon R. 1994. Two identical noninteracting sites in an ion channel revealed by proton transfer. *Science* 265:1852–56

73. Ruiz ML, Karpen JW. 1997. Single cyclic nucleotide-gated channels locked in different ligand-bound states. *Nature* 389:389–92

74. Rychkov GY, Pusch M, Astill DSJ, Roberts ML, Jentsch TJ, et al. 1996. Concentration and pH dependence of skeletal muscle chloride channel ClC-1. *J. Physiol.* 497:423–35

75. Rychkov GY, Pusch M, Roberts ML, Jentsch TJ, Bretag AH. 1998. Permeation and block of the skeletal muscle chloride channel, ClC-1, by foreign anions. *J. Gen. Physiol.* 111:653–65

76. Sansom SC, La B, Carosi SL. 1990. Double-barreled chloride channels of collecting duct basolateral membrane. *Am. J. Physiol.* 259:F46–F52

77. Saviane C, Conti F, Pusch M. 1999. The muscle chloride channel ClC-1 has a double-barreled appearance that is differentially affected in dominant and recessive myotonia. *J. Gen. Physiol.* 113:457–68

78. Schild L, Ravindran A, Moczydlowski E. 1991. Zn^{2+}-induced subconductance events in cardiac Na^+ channels

prolonged by batrachotoxin. Current-voltage behavior and single-channel kinetics. *J. Gen. Physiol.* 97:117–42

79. Schmidt-Rose T, Jentsch TJ. 1997. Transmembrane topology of a CLC chloride channel. *Proc. Natl. Acad. Sci. USA* 94: 7633–38

80. Schneggenburger R, Ascher P. 1997. Coupling of permeation and gating in an NMDA-channel pore mutant. *Neuron* 18:167–77

81. Schriever AM, Friedrich T, Pusch M, Jentsch TJ. 1999. CLC chloride channels in *Caenorhabditis elegans*. *J. Biol. Chem.* 274:34238–44

82. Schwappach B, Stobrawa S, Hechenberger M, Steinmeyer K, Jentsch TJ. 1998. Golgi localization and functionally important domains in the NH_2 and COOH terminus of the yeast CLC putative chloride channel Gef1p. *J. Biol. Chem.* 273:15110–18

83. Sherry AM, Stroffekova K, Knapp LM, Kupert EY, Cuppoletti J, et al. 1997. Characterization of the human pH- and PKA-activated ClC2G(2α) Cl^- channel. *Am. J. Physiol.* 273:C384–93

84. Sigworth FJ. 1994. Voltage gating of ion channels. *Q. Rev. Biophys.* 27:1–40

85. Simon DB, Bindra RS, Mansfield TA, Nelson-Williams C, Mendonca E, et al. 1997. Mutations in the chloride channel gene CLCNKB cause Bartter's syndrome type III. *Nat. Genet.* 17:171–78

86. Simon DB, Lifton RP. 1998. Mutations in Na(K)Cl transporters in Gitelman's and Bartter's syndromes. *Curr. Opin. Cell Biol.* 10:450–54

87. Smith RL, Clayton GH, Wilcox CL, Escudero KW, Staley KJ. 1995. Differential expression of an inwardly rectifying chloride conductance in rat brain neurons: a potential mechanism for cell-specific modulation of postsynaptic inhibition. *J. Neurosci.* 15:4057–67

88. Staley KJ, Smith R, Schaack J, Wilcox C, Jentsch TJ. 1996. Alteration of GABA-A receptor function following gene transfer of the ClC-2 chloride channel. *Neuron* 17:543–51

89. Staley KJ, Soldo BL, Proctor WR. 1995. Ionic mechanisms of neuronal excitation by inhibitory $GABA_A$ receptors. *Science* 269:977–81

90. Steinmeyer K, Lorenz C, Pusch M, Koch MC, Jentsch TJ. 1994. Multimeric structure of ClC-1 chloride channel revealed by mutations in dominant myotonia congenita (Thomsen). *EMBO J.* 13:737–43

91. Steinmeyer K, Schwappach B, Bens M, Vandewalle A, Jentsch TJ. 1995. Cloning and functional expression of rat CLC-5, a chloride channel related to kidney disease. *J. Biol. Chem.* 270:31172–77

92. Thiemann A, Grunder S, Pusch M, Jentsch TJ. 1992. A chloride channel widely expressed in epithelial and non-epithelial cells. *Nature* 356:57–60

93. Valverde MA. 1999. ClC channels: leaving the dark ages on the verge of a new millennium. *Curr. Opin. Cell Biol.* 11:509–16

94. White MM, Miller C. 1981. Probes of the conduction process of a voltage-gated chloride channel from *Torpedo* electroplax. *J. Gen. Physiol.* 78:1–19

95. Xie XS, Crider BP, Stone DK. 1989. Isolation and reconstitution of the chloride transporter of clathrin-coated vesicles. *J. Biol. Chem.* 264:18870–73

96. Yellen G. 1998. The moving parts of voltage-gated ion channels. *Q. Rev. Biophys.* 31:239–95

97. Zagotta WN, Hoshi T, Aldrich RW. 1990. Restoration of inactivation in mutants of *Shaker* potassium channels by a peptide derived from ShB. *Science* 250:568–71

98. Zheng J, Sigworth FJ. 1998. Intermediate conductances during deactivation of heteromultimeric Shaker potassium channels. *J. Gen. Physiol.* 112:457–74

Annu. Rev. Biophys. Biomol. Struct. 2000. 29:439–61

DESIGNED SEQUENCE-SPECIFIC MINOR GROOVE LIGANDS

David E. Wemmer

Department of Chemistry, University of California, and Physical Biosciences Division, Lawrence Berkeley Laboratory, Berkeley California; e-mail: DEWemmer@LBL.gov

Key Words   molecular recognition, drug design, DNA recognition

■ **Abstract**   In the past decade, a general design for sequence-specific minor groove ligands has evolved, based on the natural products distamycin and netropsin. By utilizing a basic set of design rules for connecting pyrrole, imidazole, and hydroxypyrrole modules, new ligands can be prepared to target almost any sequence of interest with both high affinity and specificity. In this review we present the design rules with a brief history of how they evolved. The structural basis for sequence-specific recognition is explained, together with developments that allow linking of recognition modules that enable targeting of long DNA sequences. Examples of the affinity and specificity that can be achieved with a number of variations on the basic design are given. Recently these molecules have been used to compete with proteins both in vitro and in vivo, and a brief description of the experimental results are given.

CONTENTS

A BRIEF OVERVIEW OF DNA RECOGNITION

Over the past two decades, the techniques of structural biology have provided a great deal of insight into how the molecules of nature (proteins and small molecule ligands) achieve sequence-specific binding to DNA. Early X-ray structures of phage repressors (1, 50) showed a relatively simple binding motif. The dimeric protein structure positioned α-helices so that they fit neatly into two successive major grooves, with little distortion of either protein or DNA in the process. Sequence specificity seemed to be generated, in large part, by contacts of amino acid side chains with the edges of the bases. Just considering the structure of DNA and the functionality of the bases, it had been suggested that protein recognition would be primarily through the major groove (60), and this has held true to a reasonable extent. From these early structures one might have hoped that there was an underlying code—particular amino acids in a specific secondary structure recognizing particular base pairs. In fact for zinc-finger-containing proteins, this idea does seem to hold to some extent, and proteins from combinatorial Zn-finger libraries have been created to recognize new target sequences using this framework (29, 30). However these "simple" cases seem to be the exception rather than the rule. As more and more structures have been determined, the situation has gotten ever more complex (54). Some proteins distort the DNA tremendously in the process of recognition, and they can do this through either the major or minor groove. Some proteins become structured only upon binding DNA, while others combine rigid cores with flexible tails wrapped around the DNA to recognize both grooves. Bridging water molecules seem to be important in some cases, and the sequence-specific structure of the DNA can also play a role.

With smaller ligands there are also examples of recognition in both grooves; however, the preference for sequence-specific binders seems to be the minor groove rather than the major (76). This is likely because it is easier to generate a large contact interface in the narrower minor groove. In the cases in which major groove recognition occurs, it is accompanied by intercalation, which provides a good deal of the binding energy. There is considerable variation in mechanisms for generating sequence specificity, including hydrogen bonds, hydrophobic contacts, and shape complementarity (21). The chemical functionality in ligands can be more diverse than in amino acids. As is the case for proteins binding DNA, ligand binding is sometimes close to rigid body docking, but in other cases it occurs with substantial distortion of the DNA. The diversity of structures and functionality means that, as for proteins, in general it has been difficult to design ligands to target new sequences. However, there is now one "framework" that can be used to prepare ligands to bind almost any sequence desired, retaining both high binding affinity and good sequence discrimination. This review focuses on this specific design, describing its evolution, present status, and a few of the applications for such molecules. Broader reviews of minor groove ligands in general have appeared in the last few years (2, 21, 41, 43, 75).

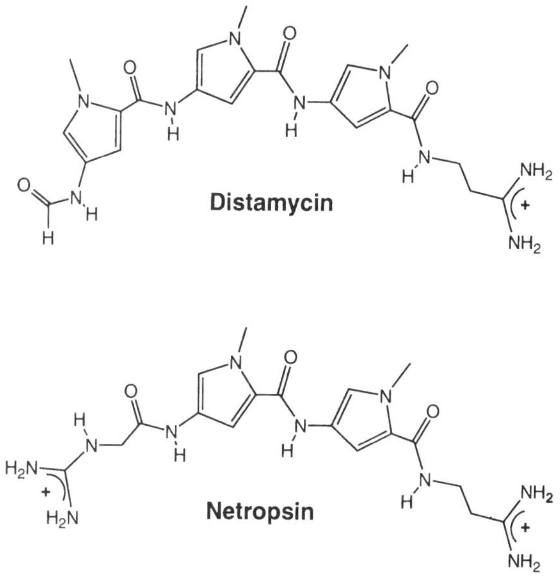

Figure 1 The structures of the natural products distamycin-A and netropsin are shown. For distamycin (and analogs) the N-terminus (formylated) is referred to as the head, and the C-terminus (with the propylamidine) as the tail.

THE ORIGINS: Distamycin and Netropsin

The class of ligands to be discussed here, the pyrrole/imidazole polyamides (called lexitropsins by some), evolved from the streptomycete natural products distamycin and netropsin, shown in Figure 1. These contain pyrrole rings linked by amide bonds, with either a formyl group or a guanidine at the N-terminus (which is termed the head henceforth) and a propylamidine at the C-terminus (the tail). Both bind at A-T rich sequences (four or more consecutive A-T pairs), discriminating fairly strongly against sequences containing any G-C pairs. Early physical studies demonstrated they did not intercalate (4, 87), and NMR first showed directly that they bound in the minor groove (53). A detailed picture of the binding came first from crystallographic studies on netropsin (9, 35, 36) followed later by both NMR and crystallographic structures of distamycin complexes (8, 34, 55). All of these showed clearly that the ligands bind snugly in the minor groove, taking advantage of the relatively deep, narrow minor groove at the A-T rich sequences (an intrinsic feature of such sequences as it is observed in free DNA structures as well as complexes) (Figure 2). The crescent shape of the ligand matches well the curvature of the minor groove, and the N-Hs of the amides point into the groove, hydrogen bonding to acceptors on

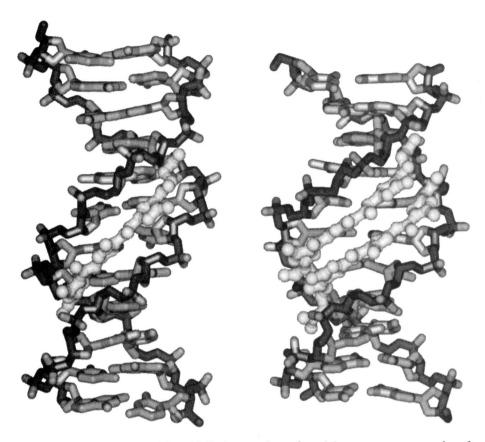

Figure 2 Structures derived from NMR data are shown for a 1:1, narrow groove complex of distamycin bound at an AATT site (left) and a 2:1, wide groove complex also of distamycin, bound at an AAATT site (right). The backbone atoms of the DNA are shaded dark to stress the groove;ligands are shown as ball and stick shaded light.

the base pairs. The positively charged tail(s) are positioned deep in the groove where the electrostatic potential is highest. It is apparent that a combination of dispersion forces (van der Waals), electrostatics and hydrogen bonding contribute to the binding energy. Many other curved aromatic molecules bind in a similar fashion.

It was noted through affinity cleavage (71) and NMR studies (77) that the binding of distamycin on nonsymmetric sequences was orientational, the N-terminus of the molecule binding at the 5′ end of any stretch with multiple A residues. Netropsin does not show this behavior; the two orientations are essentially equivalent energetically on any combination of A-T base pairs (78).

THE FIRST DESIGNED ELABORATIONS

The first work in modifying the natural ligands to change their binding properties came through covalently linking distamycin or netropsin modules through their ends (for examples, see 11, 37). As might be anticipated, this increased both the affinity and the length of the preferred A-T sequence. An alternative approach was to synthesize homologs with larger numbers of pyrrole rings (85). This also increased affinity (up to five rings; the implications of this are discussed further in subsequent sections) and again target sequence length. By combining these two approaches, a ligand that bound a sequence of sixteen consecutive A-T pairs was created (86). In addition to polypyrrole extensions, a variety of other known DNA ligands were also attached, and while they added functionality, none created a significant new sequence specificity.

When the first crystal structure of a netropsin complex was solved, the complementarity of the ligand and groove was noted. Comparing A-T and G-C base pairs, the important difference in the minor groove is the amino group of G, and it was suggested that this group protruding into the groove was what inhibited binding at G-C-containing sequences. A modification of the ligand, replacing pyrrole with imidazole, was suggested by the groups of Dickerson (36) and Lown (42) as a mechanism for converting the specificity from A-T to G-C at the contacted base pair. Removing the C-H of the pyrrole and replacing it with N: in the imidazole corrects the steric conflict and at the same time provides the opportunity for a hydrogen bond. Lown's group synthesized such molecules, initially based upon netropsin (38–40). The first results were disappointing; the ligands with one or two imidazoles did show more G-C tolerance, but they bound A-T sequences as well, and the affinity was modest.

A NEW TYPE OF COMPLEX

While studying distamycin complexes with A-T sequences that contained more than the minimum four A-T pairs, a new type of complex was discovered that contained two molecules of distamycin bound at the sequence AAATT (56). The two ligands were fully overlapped, running antiparallel, one in contact with each wall of the groove (Figure 2). The same features of good contact to the groove walls and hydrogen bonds to the edges of the base pairs seen in the 1:1 complexes were also observed for the 2:1. Since tails extended from either end of the complex, each contacting the DNA, a minimum of five A-T base pairs was required for formation of such a complex. The most obvious difference from the previously characterized complexes is the substantially wider groove of the DNA, which is closer to the "normal" B-DNA width than that seen in A-T rich sequences alone. In titrations of the AAATT sequence with distamycin, it was apparent that at low stoichiometries 1:1 complexes formed, being replaced by the 2:1 complex as more ligand was added. From the relative amounts, it was estimated that the binding constant for the first ligand was about 10 times higher than the second, a value later confirmed by titration calorimetry (59). This indicated that the groove was in fact quite flexible, capable of changing width to accommodate a second ligand after the first was bound. Further studies on different combinations of A-T and T-A base pairs showed that the relative affinity of binding in the two complexes was in fact highly sequence dependent. With more consecutive A residues on one strand, the 1:1 complex was preferred; with more A-T alternations, the 2:1 complex became highly preferred (16). Going from AAAAA to ATATA, the ratio of the binding constants for the first and second molecules binding changed by $>10^4$. It is important to note that in all of the complexes studied there was strong orientational character. The N-terminus of the distamycin ligand was always at the 5′ end of the contacted strand, with the positively charged C-terminus at the 3′ end. To date the only 2:1 structures of distamycin on A-T sequences have been determined by NMR, though crystallographic structures of it bound to alternating IC (5), and mixed A-T/I-C sequences have been determined.

SUCCESS IN G-C RECOGNITION

In thinking about groove width and how it would affect ligand binding, it seemed that there should be a strong preference for the 2:1 complex in sequences with an intrinsically wide groove. Inspection of crystallographic data on groove widths seemed to indicate that only A-T rich sequences showed the unusually narrow groove seen in the crystallographic structures of netropsin and distamycin complexes (excluding the 2:1 complex), and that G-C rich, or mixed A-T/G-C sequence had approximately the normal B-DNA groove width (25). It seemed that a wide groove would not bind a single ligand well, since it is not thick enough to contact both groove walls. This seemed to explain the observations made with the imidazole containing netropsin analogs—when binding in an all A-T, site there is unsatisfied hydrogen bonding of the imidazole but good contact with the groove walls; on the other hand, in a G-C sequence, hydrogen bonding of the imidazole could occur, but then there would be poor contact to the groove. Since the netropsin-like ligands carry a positively charged group on each end, binding in the 2:1 mode is strongly disfavored as it would require the charges to be immediately adjacent in the groove. This leads to the observed characteristics of low sequence preference and moderate affinity. These observations suggested that the basic idea of having an amino-imidazole pairing might work better using the distamycin framework with binding in a 2:1 mode. Keeping close to the initial observation of the 2:1 complex, a ligand with rings pyrrole-imidazole-pyrrole (PyImPy-) was made to bind to a target sequence AAGTT, also in the 2:1 mode. Lown's group synthesized this molecule, and NMR studies showed (14) that indeed it bound AAGTT in preference to AAATT, with a high cooperativity of the two molecules binding. A model of the complex generated from the NMR data showed that the imidazole rings did indeed bind over the G-C base pair. However, it also showed that the imidazole ring against the C containing strand was in a poor position to hydrogen bond, while that bound near the G was in a good hydrogen bonding geometry.

Dervan's group had also synthesized ligands containing hydrogen bond acceptors, and they had demonstrated that a ligand in which the first ring was pyridine did show specificity for G-C containing sequences (72). Using footprinting and affinity cleavage methods, they found this ligand, and a related one with imidazole as the first ring (73), bound to sites of the type W G W C W, where W represents A or T. While the first G made sense to bind to the hydrogen bond acceptor imidazole, it was unclear why there was specificity for the second C-G pair. However, in light of the 2:1 complex of distamycin, it seemed likely that this ligand was adopting a similar binding motif, and each G-C pair was being recognized by a combination of one pyridine or imidazole ring and one pyrrole ring on the opposite strand. NMR studies of these ligands showed that this was indeed precisely correct (49). A heterodimer of ImPyPy with PyPyPy was shown to target a single G-C pair (18, 44).

The preference for an imidazole/pyrrole pair relative to imidazole/imidazole was tested by addition of distamycin to the 2:1 complex of PyImPy on AAGTT. Indeed a heterocomplex with one PyImPy and one distamycin was the preferred complex (17). Free energy perturbation calculations also predicted this and helped establish that the desolvation of the imidazole required to insert it into the groove without a compensating hydrogen bond from the DNA was the primary source of the energetic preference for G-C over A-T (61). Essentially all other features of these complexes were identical to the original 2:1 distamycin complex, including the orientational preference of the ligands. A crystal structure of the ligand ImImPyPy bound at its cognate GGCC target sequence was later solved (32), providing better high resolution detail than the NMR studies had. The basic features of the complexes deduced from the NMR derived structures held up well.

GENERALITY OF G-C RECOGNITION

With the two initial examples of successful recognition of G-C base pairs, there seemed to be a fairly simple set of rules for generating a ligand combination, to target a specific desired sequence:

1. To bind a mixed A-T/G-C sequence use the 2:1 binding motif.
2. Connect rings from N to C-terminus to read 5′ to 3′ along the contacted strand;
    (a) to target a G-C pair put an imidazole against the G-containing strand and pyrrole opposite it on the C-containing strand;
    (b) to target an A-T or T-A pair use pyrrole on both strands.
3. The tails of the molecules must be at A-T base pairs.

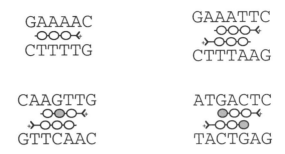

Figure 3 Schematic drawings of polyamide complexes. The DNA duplex is indicated by normal four letter code, with the top strand written 5′ to 3′. Ligands are indicated by circles for each ring (open circle for pyrrole, shaded for imidazole), with a branched line for the tail of each ligand. The top two structures are for distamycin, with structures shown in Figure 2. The bottom three are complexes with G-C specific recognition.

As a test of these ideas, a ligand was designed to bind to a symmetric sequence with an all G-C core in the 2:1 mode: ImPyImPy with W G C G C W (Figure 3). The ligand was synthesized by Dervan's group. NMR (19) and footprinting (47) verified that binding was to the desired target sequence with good specificity and affinity. This success indicated that the approach did indeed seem to be general and capable of targeting G-C rich sequences—a considerable step from the original A-T specificity of distamycin. Although these rules for specificity work well, there is some sequence-dependent variation in the absolute binding affinity. This issue is discussed further below.

BREAKING THE A-T/T-A DEGENERACY

Although the contact between imidazole and a G-C pair was strand specific, the Py/Py combination used initially for A-T and T-A pairs was intrinsically degenerate. Expanding the idea of a strand-specific hydrogen bond, Dervan's lab introduced hydroxypyrrole (Hp) to introduce a new functional group for interaction (82). Examination of an A-T base pair shows that there are hydrogen bond acceptors on both strands, the thymine carbonyl oxygen and the ring N3 of adenosine. In spite of this, the detailed geometry makes the affinity significantly higher when the hydroxypyrrole ring is against the T containing strand. This breakthrough completes the recognition code for base pairs (Figure 4). The details of the hydroxypyrrole-T interaction were shown in a crystal structure of the ligand ImHpPyPy bound in a

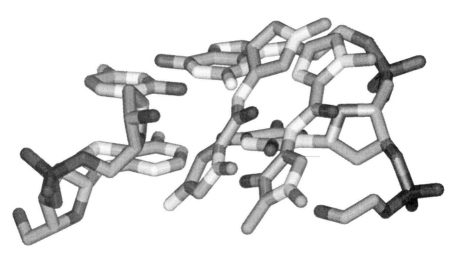

Figure 4   A blowup of a portion of the structure of ImHpPyPy-β-Dp complexed to AGTACT, PDB 407D, showing sequence-specific recognition of a C-G pair (top) by a pyrrole/imidazole ring pair, and an A-T pair (bottom) by a pyrrole/hydroxypyrrole pair.

classic 2:1 motif (33). Multiple Hp rings can be used together to recognize specific sequences of A-T pairs.

LINKING THE MODULES

Even as the first heterocomplex of PyImPy with distamycin was made, it was clear that in long DNAs there would be binding sites, in addition to the desired one. These sites would compete for the ligands, for example distamycin binding at a site with all A-T pairs—an undesirable feature with respect to generating sequence-specific binding. The obvious solution was to link the two halves of the ligand covalently so that they could not bind at separate sites. Two mechanisms for linking were apparent; the first exploited the N-methyls of the pyrrole/imidazole rings, making them N-alkyl with one end of the alkyl chain attached to each ligand (Figure 5). Dervan's group made a homodimer series (45) with different length linkers, ranging from three to six methylene groups in the connector. They all bound with similar affinity and did show the expected increase in specificity, and a significant increase of affinity as well. NMR showed that they seemed to bind in the expected manner (15). A heterodimer version was also prepared (46). Lown's group synthesized such ligands as well and disputed the ability for short linkers to bind in the intended mode (6), but in the end it does appear that linkers as short as three carbons do bind "folded back" as intended.

The second linking mechanism was to attach the head of one molecule to the tail of the other (Figure 5), with a group to make a tight turn preserving the antiparallel

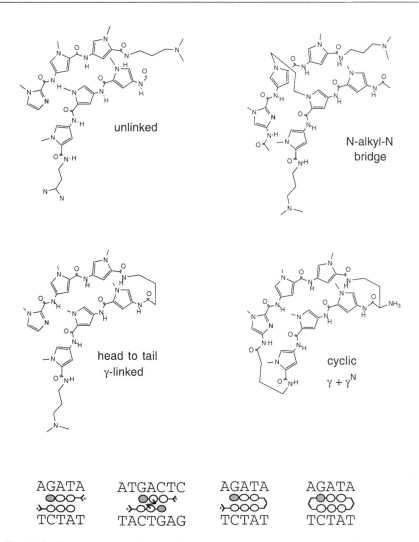

Figure 5 The structures of side-by-side ligands with various degrees of linking are shown at the top. The schematic drawings of complexes of these are shown below.

binding, a hairpin motif. Dervan's group synthesized a series (48, 52), again varying in linker length—in this case ranging from one to four methylene carbons attached via amine and carboxylate as usual. Footprinting showed that only the three carbon linker (gamma amino butyric acid—shortened to γ henceforth) gave high affinity, though both the two and four carbon linkers could fold back to bind the targeted sequence with reduced affinity. Strain in the two carbon linker (beta alanine, β for short) seemed to be the reason for decreased affinity, while NMR suggested that steric conflict with the groove seemed to occur for the longest linker (10). The γ linker is capable of forming a tight turn, which fits well at the bottom of the minor groove. Footprinting has shown that this linker has a strong preference for binding at an A-T pair (65), probably because of steric conflict with the amino group of G-C pairs, but it might also interfere with the amino group hydrogen bonding to solvent. The affinity of ligands with the γ linker increased by even more than those with the ring-alkyl-ring linkers. General considerations and design methods for linking have been discussed (74).

To explore other ways of increasing affinity, Dervan's group also derivatized the γ hairpin forming linker (26). They found that addition of an amino group at the C-terminal methylene, $-\gamma^N-$, increased both the affinity and the sequence specificity. As one might expect in the chiral environment of the DNA groove, one enantiomer (the R form in this case) was much better than the other. The R-isomer has the amino group pointed up and along the groove, while the S would be pointed toward the side wall of the groove in the same ligand binding configuration. If the ligand folded in the opposite way, then the S-isomer would have the amino group up but would read the DNA sequence backward relative to the design rules. Footprinting indicated that this does occur, but the affinity is reduced relative to the R-isomer and forward reading. All of the general characteristics of binding of the hairpin ligands were preserved. Conversion of the free amine to an acetamido group did not alter affinity or specificity relative to the underivatized hairpin, which indicated that this site could be used for further linking, as discussed below.

The most extreme case of linkage is connecting both ends of the ligand to generate a cyclic compound (7) (Figure 5). Although synthetically more challenging this has also been accomplished. The first ligand of this sort, $-ImPyPy-\gamma-PyPy^*Py-\gamma$, had very high binding affinity, putting the dissociation constant below the nanomolar level. However, this ligand had somewhat reduced specificity; that is, the discrimination against sequences containing mismatches with respect to the design rules was reduced. Recently the cyclic ligands $-ImPyPyPy-\gamma^N-ImPyPyPy-\gamma-$ and $-ImPyPyPy-\gamma^N-PyPyPyPy-\gamma-$ were made (28) (utilizing the amino-γ linker on one end). These bound to matched target sites with dissociation constants of 0.013 nM and 0.32 nM, respectively. They also showed good sequence discrimination.

EXTENDING TARGET SEQUENCE LENGTH

In the early days of making analogs of distamycin, extending the target sequence length had been accomplished through two means. The first was increasing the number of pyrrole rings in the compound. Affinity and target sequence length both increased in going to four and five pyrrole rings, but then affinity decreased if more were added (85). This was rationalized as a mismatch between the curvature of the ligand and that of the minor groove (32), or a mismatch in length that would lead to a mispositioning of hydrogen bond partners of the ligand and DNA (22), with the recent crystallographic work supporting the former. Addition of rings was tested in the context of the hairpin ligands, with very similar findings (70). As the length of each half of the hairpin is increased to four rings, affinity increases, and again marginally, going to five rings. For ligands of this length, the dissociation constants are routinely in the nanomolar range for matched target sequences. Beyond five rings there is again a decrease in affinity and specificity. The same conclusion was reached for unlinked ligands binding in the 2:1 motif (31). To push the target length further, the flexible linker approach (as had been used in extending 1:1 complexes) was again employed. The short linkers, glycine (G) and beta alanine (β), which were too short for hairpin turn formation, were in fact effective when used as flexible insertions to allow extended side-by-side binding (63), or transitions between 2:1 and 1:1 binding regions (20) (Figure 6). Whereas

CTGATATACAC

GACTATATGTG

TTGTTAACAG

AACAATTGTC

TTGTTAACAG

AACAATTGTC

AGCCATTAGA

TCGGTAATCT

CTTTTAGACAAATTC

GAAAATCTGTTTAAG

AAAAGCAGCTGCTTAT

TTTTCGTCGACGAATA

ATTGTTATTGTTAGC

TAACAATAACAATCG

Figure 6   Schematic drawings of various extended linked ligand complexes are shown schematically. In these the flexible β-alanine linkers are shown as a wavy line.

ImPyPy-Py-PyPyPy had modest affinity and poor specificity when binding in the 2:1 motif, ImPyPy-β-PyPyPy showed both good affinity and specificity. The equivalent ligand with G was better than that with Py, but not as good as that with β. The β linker has also been used in extended hairpins.

In addition to having two β linkers next to each other in the groove, pairings of β/Py and β/Im have been explored in the context of extended hairpins as well (70). A series of hairpins was prepared that were derivatives of a twelve-ring ligand: ImPyPyPyPyPy-γ-ImPyPyPyPyPy-β-Dp, which was tested for binding to a matched target site of TGTTAACA. This parent ligand bound the target site, forming a complex with a dissociation constant of 0.4 nM. Replacing any of the Py/Py pairs with a β/β increased affinity, moving across the ligand, the relative affinities were determined to be 2.9 (first Py/Py), 48 (second), 6.8 (third) and 1.9 (fourth). There is clearly a rather strong preference for the second position—this ligand showing a K_d of 0.008 nM (8 pM!). When the β residues were staggered, they also increased affinity; with the outside Py/Py pairs converted to β/Py and Py/β, the relative affinity was 18, and with the inside pairs it was 11. An increase in specificity was shown by comparing affinity for a single G-C mismatch site (discussed in the section on specificity below). In a slightly different context the rigid ligand Im-**Py**-ImPyPyPy-γ-ImPyPyPy-**Py**-Py-β-Dp was compared with Im-β-ImPyPyPy-γ-ImPyPyPy-**Py**-Py-β-Dp, the β/Py pair again yielding an increase in affinity by a factor of about five for the matched site, and going from no sequence specificity for the internal Im/Py pair to ~50-fold preference for G-C in the Im/β ligand. Finally, the ligand Im**Py**ImPy-γ-Im**Py**ImPy-β-Dp was compared with Im-β-ImPy-γ-Im-β-ImPy-β-Dp. In this case the introduction of the flexible linkers as β/Im pairs led to an increase in affinity of a factor of 100. These studies indicate clearly that rigid/flexible pairs can be effective in counteracting the affinity (and specificity) loss with longer ligands. However, it is also apparent that this effect is somewhat context dependent. As further exploration is done, it seems likely that the basis for such effects will become apparent, allowing prediction of the gains available through different linking mechanisms.

Flexible linkers also allow binding at sites that exploit both the 2:1 and 1:1 motifs (Figure 6). The flexibility is important to facilitate repositioning of the rings into the proper part of the groove on either side of the junction. Cooperative binding of two linked ligands extended the recognized sequence to 13 base pairs (20, 68). A longer ligand with four two-ring modules and four β linkers was demonstrated to bind a targeted site of 16 base pairs with very high affinity (67). A hairpin ligand, with a γ linker to make the foldback turn and a β linker to attach a 1:1 binding module, has also been used to target a sequence of 9 base pairs (66).

Linking has also now been done at the level of whole hairpin units, utilizing the modified amino-γ in the hairpin turn. A "tandem hairpin" ligand was made (27) by coupling a carboxylate in the tail of one hairpin to the amino γ in the other (Figure 6), making an amide bond and either a two- or four-carbon chain. The highest affinity was obtained with the four-carbon linker of the hairpins, binding a direct repeat of the matched target for each hairpin, separated by one A-T base pair.

The dissociation constant of this tandem ligand-DNA complex was subpicomolar. This ligand also showed good sequence discrimination, including a strong A-T preference at the base pair under the bridging chain.

SYNTHESIS

All of the early synthetic ligands were made using a stepwise solution coupling approach, with purification between steps. This chemistry could be adapted to include the desired end groups, including N-terminal formylation and a C-terminal tail with an amidine. For both synthetic convenience and chemical stability, these were sometimes converted to an N-terminal acetyl and a C-terminal dimethylamine. These introduce no major changes in shape; however, the amidine gives slightly higher affinity than the dimethyl amine, and, as discussed further below, the acetyl can alter specificity.

As the length of ligands increased dramatically, this synthetic approach became limiting both in time required and in the losses during each round of coupling/purification. Since there are amide bonds between the pyrrole and imidazole rings in these molecules, as in peptides, it was possible to adapt solid phase methods that had become so successful in peptide synthesis to the aromatic amino acids required for the polyamide ligands (3). The implementation of this approach has made preparation of new molecules much more efficient, enabling a wide exploration of modified structures. For the solid phase approach, it is necessary to have a linker to the solid resin; a natural choice for the polyamide ligands was an amino acid. Initially glycine was used, but soon it was determined that β-alanine was better in most contexts (52) and contributed to the binding affinity. After coupling all of the desired rings, release of the ligand from the resin is accomplished by reaction with an amine, generally dimethylaminopropylamine (Dp). This leaves the tail of the molecule extended by the initially coupled amino acid relative to the original versions. NMR studies have shown that the extended tail contacts slightly more than one additional base pair, and footprinting showed that it (as expected from previous experience) has A-T base pair specificity. It has also been possible to adapt solid phase methods for the synthesis of cyclic ligands.

A NEW TWIST

In the course of studying hairpin ligands with different "head" and "tail" functionality, it was recognized that some particular ligands were binding at sequences that did not obey the consensus rules (81). Both NMR and affinity cleavage studies indicated that these specific ligands were binding "backwards," that is, the N-terminus of the ligand was contacting the 3' end of the recognized sequence at some sites. Such binding occurred when there was an acetyl group at the

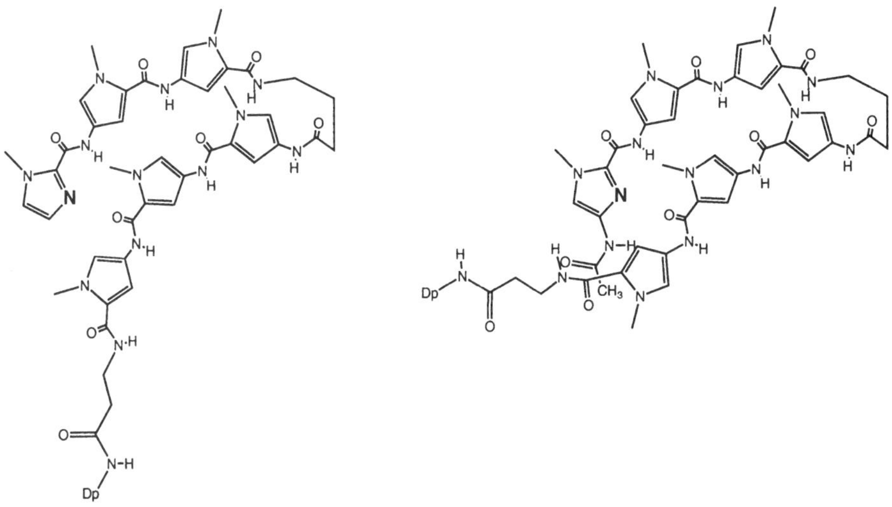

Figure 7   The structure of a tail in hairpin ligand (left), and a tail out hairpin ligand (right) are shown. The interactions of the tail with the groove significantly affect binding orientation preferences.

N-terminus, or with a glycine linker in the tail, but the effect was clearest when these two modifications were combined. NMR studies showed that whenever binding occurred in the backward mode, there were no contacts between the tail of the ligand and the groove (24). A careful analysis of intraligand NOEs in the acetyl/Gly complex showed that the last (C-terminal) ring was inverted, positioning the pyrrole N-methyl group along the groove and pointing the tail out away from the DNA (Figure 7). With ligands that had just Gly in the tail, there was evidence for flipping of the last ring on a millisecond time scale, indicating that both the normal and inverted conformations were being sampled by the last ring. Although having the tail out of the groove lowers affinity, this binding mode suggests a new approach to allow cooperative binding of two hairpin ligands, which was previously hindered by the long tails.

SEQUENCE-DEPENDENT AFFINITY AND SPECIFICITY

With the development of new variant ligands and finding of new binding modes, it has been important to characterize affinity and specificity of ligand-DNA interactions. Titration calorimetry was used to examine the energetics of 2:1 binding of distamycin to the AAATT sequence (59). It was found that the binding constant of the second molecule was tenfold less than the first (in agreement with the NMR titration data) but had a larger enthalpic contribution than the first. This approach has also been used to characterize hairpin ligands (57, 58), demonstrating that discrimination of matched target sites from mismatched ones is largely enthalpic.

For exploring a wide range of ligands and sequences, a powerful approach has been quantitative footprinting. When done carefully this method can provide binding constants at a number of different binding sites simultaneously by including them in restriction fragments used. The rules used to predict binding sites have been very well obeyed, with the backward binding discussed above the only clear exception. When binding at different sequences was quantitatively examined, some patterns of variation in affinity were noted. For example, in spite of the fact that A-T and T-A are considered as degenerate when recognized by a Py/Py pair, the precise sequence on each strand can make an affinity difference of up to a factor of 10 (79). In the case of the heterocomplex of ImPyPy with distamycin, NMR competition titrations were also used to examine sequence-specific differences, the results being in good agreement with those from footprinting. It is easy to invoke sequence-dependent differences in groove width, hydration, or position of hydrogen bond acceptors to explain the observations, but in fact these cannot be independently manipulated. It is thus very hard to verify the source of the variation in affinity.

A great deal of footprinting has been done with hairpin ligands as well, defining the ring pairing rules (80). Quantitative binding studies were done with a related pair of ligands, ImImPy-γ-PyPyPy-β-Dp and PyPyPy-γ-ImImPy-β-Dp (51). These bind the same basic target sequences, W G G W W. For the specific target ATGGTTT the first ligand had a dissociation constant of 10 nM, while for the second ligand it was 60 nM. On a mismatched target sequence, missing one of the G-C pairs (TTGTTAT), the affinity was a factor of 60 lower for the first ligand and more than 160 for the second. A target-ligand mismatch with an extra G-C pair (TGGGTAG) had affinities reduced by over a factor of 100 for both ligands. These affinity differences are a measure of the specificity of the ligand—the preference for binding the matched site over mismatches.

Both affinity and sequence discrimination were demonstrated to be high in ligands with a total of eight (62) and ten (68) rings as well. A related pair of ligands was again made, ImPyPyPyPy-γ-ImPyPyPyPy-β-Dp, and ImImPyPyPy-γ-ImPyPyPyPy-β-Dp (69). The affinities were determined for two target sites differing by a single base pair: TGTAACA and TGGAACA. The dissociation constants for the matched pairs, ligand 1-site 1 and ligand 2-site 2, were 0.08 nM and 0.3 nM respectively. For the mismatched pairs, ligand 1-site 2 and ligand 2-site 1, the affinities were 1.5 nM and >100 nM. Thus the single T-A to G-C change lowers the affinity of ligand 1 by a factor of about 20, while it increases that of ligand 2 by over 100, again demonstrating good sequence selectivity of ligands.

Specific combinations of rings can yield lower affinity than others. In general, imidazole-rich ligands have somewhat lower affinity than pyrrole-rich ligands of the same length. In looking at the structures of imidazole-containing ligands, it is easy to think that the hydrogen bond from the guanosine amino group to the ligands should contribute to the stability. However, when the ligand is not bound to DNA, it is hydrogen bonded to water, and the important parameter is the energy difference between the hydrogen bond to the DNA and that to water. Hence, while these hydrogen bonds do not dominate stability, they are still the critical feature contributing to the specificity.

Even among ligands that have the same Im/Py composition, but different target sequences, there is a good deal of variation in affinity (64). For example the ligand ImImPyPy-γ-ImImPyPy binds TGGCCA with a K_d of 0.1 nM, while ImPyImPy-γ-ImPyImPy binding TGCGCA and ImImImIm-γ-PyPyPyPy binding TGGGGA have K_d values of 30 nM, weaker by two orders of magnitude. The reasons for such differences are not readily apparent. Some interesting observations were made when the flexible β linker was paired with a pyrrole or imidazole ring in the context of a 12-ring hairpin ligand. As noted above, the addition of a sixth ring to both halves lowers specificity relative to shorter ligands.

The behavior of hydroxypyrrole is similar to imidazole in having slightly lower affinity than pyrrole. The effect of multiple Hp rings was tested recently in a ten-ring hairpin ligand, ImXXXPy-γ-ImXXXPy with X either Py or Hp (83). The target sequences compared were TGTTACA and TGTATCA. When all Xs were Py, the dissociation constant of the first complex was 0.1 nM, and that of the second was 0.4 nM. When hydroxypyrrole (112) was used to target each T, ImHpHpPyPy-γ-PyHpPyPyPy, the affinity was increased to 1.1 nM for the matched TTA sequence but was > 100 nM for the TAT sequence. This clearly demonstrates there is only a modest decrease in affinity relative for Hp-rich ligands relative to Py, but a very dramatic increase in specificity.

It is important to note that a change in the absolute affinity of binding does not necessarily correlate with loss of specificity—that is, the decrease in affinity when an incorrect sequence (relative to the consensus rules for recognition) is bound. Because there are a huge number of incorrect sequences, it has been possible to sample only a few using footprinting methods. The sequence discrimination (ratio of affinity at the correct site divided by that of the mismatched site) can reach a factor of 100. It is usually of the order of 10, but in the worst cases it is as low as 2–3. For uses in specific contexts, it may be important to test both affinity and specificity for particular ligand-sequence combinations of interest.

USING LIGANDS IN VIVO

Although a variety of modified polyamide ligands have been tested in vivo, in only a small number of cases has the high sequence specificity as well as affinity been exploited. Distamycin itself is cytotoxic to many cells types. The mechanism of action remains uncertain, although there are data which indicate that ternary complexes of distamycin with DNA and a topoisomerase may play an important role (84). The first real test of high specificity binding was done with a ligand designed to target a specific binding site for the transcription factor TFIIIA in a 5S RNA gene in frog kidney cells (23). Control ligands were made that had exactly the same composition of imidazole and pyrrole, but different target sequences. An in vitro transcription assay, the designed ligand reduced the level of 5S RNA produced. More importantly, when added to the culture medium around growing cells, the designed ligand showed a clear, dose-dependent reduction in the level of 5S RNA produced, but the control ligands did not. This demonstrated that there was selectivity (the 5S RNA production was reduced with the correct ligand, and none of them were cytotoxic), that there was high enough affinity for the ligand to bind in vivo (a 1 μM concentration in the medium was sufficient for a substantial response), and that the ligand was taken up by the cells. In another study the binding sites for several cellular transcription factors (LEF-1, Ets-1, and TBP), which are important for HIV RNA synthesis, were selected as targets (13). Ligands were designed to target each site and were demonstrated to bind the correct target sequences and also to inhibit viral transcription by RNA Pol-II. The combination of ligands was very effective at inhibiting viral replication in isolated lymphocytes, and it showed no detectable cell toxicity. The effects of ligands directed to Ets-1 sites with flanking NF-κB sites have also been explored in detail (12). The activities explored to date are very encouraging that these will become useful as agents in molecular biology at least, and perhaps as drugs as well.

Visit the Annual Reviews home page at www.AnnualReviews.org

LITERATURE CITED

1. Anderson WF, Ohlendorf DH, Takeda Y, Matthews BW. 1981. Structure of the cro repressor from bacteriophage λ and its interaction with DNA. *Nature* 290:754–58

2. Bailly C, Chaires JB. 1998. Sequence-specific DNA minor groove binders. Design and synthesis of netropsin and distamycin analogs. *Bioconj. Chem.* 9:513–38

3. Baird EE, Dervan PB. 1996. Solid phase synthesis of polyamides containing imidazole and pyrrole amino acids. *J. Am. Chem. Soc.* 118:6141–46

4. Braithwaite AW, Baguley BC. 1980. Existence of an extended series of antitumor compounds which bind to DNA by non-intercalative means. *Biochemistry* 19:1101–6

5. Chen X, Ramakrishnan B, Rao ST, Sundaralingam M. 1994. Binding of two distamycin A molecules in the minor groove of an alternating B-DNA duplex. *Nat. Struct. Biol.* 1:169–75

6. Chen Y-H, Yanwu Y, Lown JW. 1996. Optimization of cross-linked lexitropsins. *J. Biomol. Struct. Dyn.* 14:341–55

7. Cho J, Parks ME, Dervan PB. 1995. Cyclic polyamides for recognition in the minor groove of DNA. *Proc. Natl. Acad. Sci. USA* 92:10389–92

8. Coll M, Fredrick CA, Wang AH-J, Rich A. 1987. A bifurcated hydrogen-bonded conformation in the d(AT) base pairs of the DNA dodecamer d(CGCAAATTTGCG) and its complex with distamycin. *Proc. Natl. Acad. Sci. USA* 84:8385–89

9. Coll M, Aymami J, van der Marel GA, van Boom JH, Rich A, Wang AH-J. 1989. Molecular structure of the netropsin-d(CGCGATATCGCG) complex: DNA conformation in an alternating AT segment. *Biochemistry* 28:310–20

10. de Clairac RPL, Geierstanger BH, Mrksich M, Dervan PB, Wemmer DE. 1997. NMR characterization of hairpin polyamide complexes with the minor groove of DNA.

J. Am. Chem. Soc. 119(34):7909–16

11. Dervan PB. 1986.Design of sequence-specific DNA binding molecules. *Science* 232:464–71

12. Dickinson LA, Trauger JW, Baird EE, Dervan PB, Graves BJ, et al. 1999. Inhibition of Ets-1 DNA binding and ternary complex formation between Ets-1, NF-κB, and DNA by a designed DNA-binding ligand. *J. Biol. Chem.* 274(18):12765–73

13. Dickinson LA, Gulizia RJ, Trauger JW, Baird EE, Mosier DE, et al. 1998. Inhibition of RNA polymerase II transcription in human cells by synthetic DNA-binding ligands. *Proc. Natl. Acad. Sci. USA* 95:12890–95

14. Dwyer TJ, Geierstanger BH, Bathini Y, Lown JW, Wemmer DE. 1992. Design and binding of a distamycin A analog to d(CGCAAGTTGGC)·d(GCCAACTTGC-G): synthesis, NMR studies, and implications for the design of sequence-specific minor groove binding oligopeptides. *J. Am. Chem. Soc.* 114:5911–19

15. Dwyer TJ, Geierstanger BH, Mrksich M, Dervan PB, Wemmer DE. 1993. Structural analysis of covalent peptide dimers, bis(pyridine-2-carboxamidonetropsin) $(CH_2)_{3-6}$, in complex with 5'-TGACT-3' sites by two-dimensional NMR. *J. Am. Chem. Soc.* 115:9900–6

16. Fagan PA, Wemmer DE. 1992. Cooperative binding of distamycin-A to DNA in the 2:1 mode. *J. Am. Chem. Soc.* 114:1080–81

17. Geierstanger BH, Dwyer TJ, Bathini Y, Lown JW, Wemmer DE. 1993. NMR characterization of a heterocomplex formed by distamycin and its analog 2-ImD with d(CGCAAGTTGGC):d(GCCAACT-TGCG): preference for the 1:1:1 2-ImD: Dst:DNA complex over the 2:1 2-Im D: DNA and the 2:1 Dst:DNA complexes. *J. Am. Chem. Soc.* 115:4474–82

18. Geierstanger BH, Jacobsen JP, Mrksich M, Dervan PB, Wemmer DE. 1994. Structural and dynamic characterization of the heterodimeric and homodimeric complexes of distamycin and 1-methylimidazole-2-carboxamide-netropsin bound to the minor groove of DNA. *Biochemistry* 33:3055–62

19. Geierstanger BH, Mrksich M, Dervan PB, Wemmer DE. 1994. Design of a G·C-specific DNA minor groove binding peptide. *Science* 266:646–50

20. Geierstanger BH, Mrksich M, Dervan PB, Wemmer DE. 1996. Extending the recognition site of designed minor groove binding molecules. *Nat. Struct. Biol.* 3:321–24

21. Geierstanger BH, Wemmer DE. 1995. Complexes of the minor groove of DNA. *Annu. Rev. Biophys. Biomol. Struct,* 24: 463–93

22. Goodsell D, Dickerson RE. 1986. Isohelical analysis of DNA groove-binding drugs. *J. Med. Chem.* 29:727–33

23. Gottesfeld JM, Neely L, Trauger JW, Baird EE, Dervan PB. 1997. Regulation of gene expression by small molecules. *Nature* 387:202–5

24. Hawkins CA, de Clairac RP, Parks ME, Dervan PB, Wemmer DE. 1999. Reversed binding of polyamide ligands. Submitted

25. Heinemann U, Alings C, Bansal M. 1992. Double helix conformation, groove dimensions and ligand binding potential of a G/C stretch in B-DNA. *EMBO J.* 11:1931–39

26. Herman DM, Baird EE, Dervan PB. 1998. Stereochemical control of the DNA binding affinity, sequence specificity, and orientation preference of chiral hairpin polyamides in the minor groove. *J. Am. Chem. Soc.* 120:1382–91

27. Herman DM, Baird EE, Dervan PB. 1999. Tandem hairpin motif for recognition in the minor groove of DNA by pyrrole-imidazole polyamides. *Chem. Eur. J.* 5:975–83

28. Herman DM, Turner JM, Baird EE, and Dervan PB. 1999. Cycle polyamide motif for recognition of the minor groove of DNA. *J. Am. Chem. Soc.* 121:1121–29

29. Isalan M, Klug A, Choo Y. 1998. Comprehensive DNA recognition through concerted interactions from adjacent zinc

fingers. *Biochemistry* 37:12026–33
30. Jamieson AC, Wang H, Kim S-H. 1996. A zinc finger directory for high affinity DNA recognition. *Proc. Natl. Acad. Sci. USA* 93:12834–39
31. Kelly JJ, Baird EE, Dervan PB. 1996. Binding site size limit of the 2:1 pyrrole-imidazole polyamide-DNA motif. *Proc. Natl. Acad. Sci. USA* 93:6981–85
32. Kielkopf CL, Baird EE, Dervan PB, Rees DC. 1997. Structural basis for G · C recognition in the DNA minor groove. *Nat. Struct. Biol.* 5:104–9
33. Kielkopf CL, White S, Szewczyk JW, Turner JM, Baird EE, et al. 1998. A structural basis for recognition of A · T and T · A base pairs in the minor groove of B-DNA. *Science* 282:111–15
34. Klevit RE, Wemmer D, Reid BR. 1986. ^{1}HNMR studies on the interaction between distamycin A and a symmetrical DNA dodecamer. *Biochemistry* 25:3296–03
35. Kopka ML, Yoon C, Goodsell D, Pjura P, Dickerson RE. 1985. Binding of an antitumor drug to DNA: netropsin and CGCGAATT[Br]CGCG. *J. Mol. Biol.* 183: 553–63
36. Kopka ML, Yoon C, Goodsell D, Pjura P, Dickerson RE. 1985. The molecular origin of DNA-drug specificity in netropsin and distamycin. *Proc. Natl. Acad. Sci. USA* 82:1376–80
37. Kopka ML, Larsen TA. 1992. Netropsin and the lexitropsins. The search for sequence-specific minor-groove-binding ligands. In *Nucleic Acid Targeted Drug Design*, ed. CL Propst, TJ Perun, pp.303–374. New York: Marcel Dekker
38. Lee M, Chang DK, Hartley JA, Pon RT, Krowicki K, Lown JW. 1988. Structural and dynamic aspects of binding of a prototype lexitropsin to a decadeoxyribonucleotide d(CGCAATTGCG)$_2$ deduced from high-resolution ^{1}H NMR studies. *Biochemistry* 27:445–55
39. Lee M, Coulter DM, Pon RT, Krowicki K, Lown JW. 1988. Sequence specific

molecular recognition and binding of a monocationic Bis-imidazole lexitropsin to the decadeoxyribonucleotide d-(GATCC-GTATG) · (CATACGGATC).: structural and dynamic aspects of intermolecular exchange studied by ^{1}H-NMR. *J. Biomol. Struct. Dyn.* 5:1059–87
40. Lee M, Hartley JA, Pon RT, Krowicki K, Lown JW. 1988. Sequence specific molecular recognition by a monocationic lexitropsin of the decadeoxyribonucleotide d-CATGGCCATG.$_2$: structural and dynamic aspects deduced from high field ^{1}H-NMR studies. *Nucleic Acids Res.* 16:665–84
41. Lida H, Jia G, Lown WJ. 1999. Rational recognition of nucleic acid sequences. *Curr. Opin. Biotech.* 10:29–33
42. Lown JW, Krowicki K, Bhat UG, Skorobogaty A, Ward B, Dabrowiak JC. 1986. Molecular recognition between oligopeptides and nucleic acids: novel imidazole-containing oligopeptides related to netropsin that exhibit altered DNA sequence specificity. *Biochemistry* 25:7408–16
43. Lown JW. 1994. DNA recognition by lexitropsins, minor groove binding agents. *J. Molec. Recog.* 7:79–88
44. Mrksich M, Dervan PB. 1993. Antiparallel side-by-side heterodimer for sequence-specific recognition in the minor groove of DNA by a distamycin/1-methylimidazole-2-carboxamide-netropsin pair. *J. Am. Chem. Soc.* 115:2572–76
45. Mrksich M, Dervan PB. 1993. Enhanced sequence specific recognition in the minor groove of DNA by covalent peptide dimers: bis(pyridine-2-carboxamidonetropsin)(CH$_2$)$_{3–6}$. *J. Am. Chem. Soc.* 115:9892–99
46. Mrksich M, Dervan PB. 1994. Design of a covalent peptide heterodimer for sequence-specific recognition in the minor groove of double-helical DNA. *J. Am. Chem. Soc.* 116:3663–64
47. Mrksich M, Dervan PB. 1995. Recognition in the minor groove of DNA at 5′

(A,T)GCGC(A,T)3' by a four ring tripeptide dimer. Reversal of the specificity of the natural product distamycin. *J. Am. Chem. Soc.* 117:3325–32

48. Mrksich M, Parks ME, Dervan PB. 1994. Hairpin peptide motif. A new class of oligopeptides for sequence-specific recognition in the minor groove of double-helical DNA. *J. Am. Chem. Soc.* 116:7983–88

49. Mrksich M, Wade WS, Dwyer TJ, Geierstanger BH, Wemmer DE, et al. 1992. Antiparallel side-by-side dimeric motif for sequence-specific recognition in the minor groove of DNA by the designed peptide 1-methylimidazole-2-carboxamide netropsin. *Proc. Natl. Acad. Sci. USA* 89:7586–90

50. Pabo CO, Lewis M. 1982. The operator-binding domain of λ repressor: structure and DNA recognition. *Nature* 298:443–47

51. Parks ME, Baird EE, Dervan PB. 1996. Recognition of 5'-(A,T)GG(A,T)$_2$-3' sequences in the minor groove of DNA by hairpin polyamides. *J. Am. Chem. Soc.* 118:6153–59

52. Parks ME, Baird EE, Dervan PB. 1996. Optimization of the hairpin polyamide design for recognition of the minor groove of DNA. *J. Am. Chem. Soc.* 118:6147–52

53. Patel DJ. 1982. Antibiotic-DNA interactions: intermolecular nuclear Overhauser effects in the netropsin-d(C-G-C-G-A-A-T-T-C-G-C-G) complex in solution. *Proc. Natl. Acad. Sci. USA* 79:6424–28

54. Patikoglou G, Burley SK. 1997. Eukaryotic transcription factor-DNA complexes. *Annu. Rev. Biophys. Biomol. Struct.* 26:289–325

55. Pelton JG, Wemmer DE. 1988. Structural modeling of the distamycin A-d(CGCGAATTCGCG)$_2$ complex using 2D NMR and molecular mechanics. *Biochemistry* 27:8088–96

56. Pelton JG, Wemmer DE. 1989. Structural characterization of a 2:1 distamycin A · d(CGCAAATTGGC) complex by two-dimensional NMR. *Proc. Natl. Acad. Sci. USA* 86:5723–27

57. Pilch DS, Poklar N, Baird EE, Dervan PB, Breslauer KJ. 1999. The thermodynamics of polyamide-DNA recognition: hairpin polyamide binding in the minor groove of duplex DNA. *Biochemistry* 38:2143–51

58. Pilch DS, Poklar N, Gelfand CA, Law SM, Breslauer KJ, et al. 1996. Binding of a hairpin polyamide in the minor groove of DNA: sequence-specific enthalpic discrimination. *Proc. Natl. Acad. Sci. USA* 93:8306–11

59. Rentzeperis D, Marky LA, Dwyer TJ, Geierstanger BH, Pelton JG, Wemmer DE. 1995. Interaction of minor groove ligands to an AAATT/AATTT site: correlation of thermodynamic characterization and solution structure. *Biochemistry* 34:2937–45

60. Seeman NC, Rosenberg JM, Rich A. 1976. Sequence-specific recognition of double helical nucleic acids by proteins. *Proc. Natl. Acad. Sci. USA* 73:804–8

61. Singh SB, Ajay, Wemmer DE, Kollman PA. 1994. Relative binding affinities of distamycin and its analog to d(CGCAAGTTGGC)·d(GCCAACTTGC-G): comparison of simulation results with experiment *Proc. Natl. Acad. Sci. USA* 91:7673–77

62. Swalley SE, Baird EE, Dervan PB. 1996. Recognition of a 5'-(A,T)GGG(A,T)$_2$-3' sequence in the minor groove of DNA by an eight-ring hairpin polyamide. *J. Am. Chem. Soc.* 118:8198–6

63. Swalley SE, Baird EE, Dervan PB. 1997. A pyrrole-imidazole polyamide motif for recognition of eleven base pair sequences in the minor groove of DNA. *Chem. Eur. J.* 3:1600–7

64. Swalley SE, Baird EE, Dervan PB. 1997. Discrimination of 5'-GGGG-3', 5'-GCGC-3', and 5'-GGCC-3' sequences in the minor groove of DNA by eight-ring hairpin polyamides. *J. Am. Chem. Soc.* 119:6953–61

65. Swalley SE, Baird EE, Dervan PB. 1998. Effects of γ-turn and β-tail amino acids on sequence-specific recognition of DNA by hairpin polyamides. *J. Am. Chem. Soc.* 121:1113–20

66. Trauger JW, Baird EE, Dervan PB.1996. Extended hairpin polyamide motif for sequence-specific recognition in the minor groove of DNA. *Chem. Biol.* 3:369–77

67. Trauger JW, Baird EE, and Dervan PB. 1998. Recognition of 16 base pairs in the minor groove of DNA by a pyrrole-imidazole polyamide dimer. *J. Am. Chem. Soc.* 120:3534–35

68. Trauger JW, Baird EE, Mrksich M, Dervan PB. 1996. Extension of sequence-specific recognition in the minor groove of DNA by pyrrole-imidazole polyamides to 9–13 base pairs. *J. Am. Chem. Soc.* 118:6160–66

69. Turner JM, Baird EE, Dervan PB. 1997. Recognition of seven base pair sequences in the minor groove of DNA by ten-ring pyrrole-imidazole polyamide hairpins. *J. Am. Chem. Soc.* 119:7636–44

70. Turner JM, Swalley SE, Baird EE, and Dervan PB. 1998. Aliphatic/aromatic amino acid pairings for polyamide recognition in the minor groove of DNA. *J. Am. Chem. Soc.* 120:6219–26

71. Van Dyke MW, Hertzberg RP, Dervan PB. 1982. Map of distamycin, netropsin, and actionmycin binding sites on heterogeneous DNA: DNA cleavage-inhibition patterns with methidiumpropyl-EDTA · Fe(II). *Proc. Natl. Acad. Sci. USA* 79:5470–74

72. Wade WS, Dervan PB. 1987. Alteration of the sequence specificity of distamycin on DNA by replacement of an N-methylpyrrolecarboxamide with pyridine-2-carboxamide. *J. Am. Chem. Soc.* 109:1574–75

73. Wade WS, Mrksich M, Dervan PB. 1992. Design of peptides that bind in the minor groove of DNA at 5'-(A,T)G(A,T)C(A,T)-3' sequences by a dimeric side-by-side motif. *J. Am. Chem. Soc.* 114:8783–94

74. Walker WL, Kopka ML, Filipowsky ME, Dickerson RE, Goodsell DS. 1995. Desgin of B-DNA cross-linking and sequence-reading molecules. *Biopolymers* 35:543–53

75. Walker WL, Kopka ML, Goodsell DS. 1997. Progress in the design of DNA sequence-specific lexitropsins. *Biopolymers (Nuc. Acids Sci.)* 44:323–34

76. Wemmer DE, Dervan PB. 1997. Targeting the minor groove of DNA. 1997. *Curr. Op. Struct. Biol.* 7:355–61

77. Wemmer DE, Fagan P, Pelton JG. 1995. Determination of distamycin-A binding modes by NMR. In *Molecular Basis of Specificity in Nucleic Acid-Drug Interactions,* ed. B Pullman and JJ Jortner, P. 95–102

78. Wemmer DE, Geierstanger BH, Fagan PA, Dwyer TJ, Jacobsen JP, Pelton JG, et al. 1994. Minor groove recognition of DNA by distamycin and its analogs. In *Structural Biology: The State of the Art, Proceedings of the Eighth Conversation on Biomolecular Stereodynamics,* ed. Sarma RH, Sarma MH, 2:301–323. Guilderland: Adenine

79. White S, Baird EE, Dervan PB. 1996. Effects of the A T/T A degeneracy of pyrrole-imidazole polyamide recognition in the minor groove of DNA. *Biochemistry* 35:12532–37

80. White S, Baird EE, Dervan PB. 1997. On the pairing rules for recognition in the minor groove of DNA by pyrrole-imidazole ployamides. *Chem. Biol.* 4:569–78

81. White S, Baird EE, Dervan PB. 1997. Orientation preferences of pyrrole-imidazole polyamides in the minor groove of DNA. *J. Am. Chem. Soc.* 119:8756–65

82. White S, Szewczyk JW, Turner JM, Baird EE, Dervan PB. 1998. Recognition of the four Watson-Crick base pairs in the DNA minor groove by synthetic ligands. *Nature* 391:468–71

83. White S, Turner JM, Szewczyk JW, Baird EE, Dervan PB. 1999. Affinity

and specificity of multiple hydroxypy-role/pyrrole ring pairings for coded recognition of DNA. *J. Am. Chem. Soc.* 121:260–61

84. Woynarowski JM, McHugh M, Sigmund RD, Beerman TA. 1989. Modulation of topoisomerase II catalytic activity by DNA minor groove binding agents distamycin, Hoeschst 33258, and 4'-6-diamidine-2-phenylimidazole. *Mol. Pharm.* 35:177–82

85. Youngquist RS, Dervan PB. 1985. Sequence-specific recognition of B-DNA by Oligo(N-methylpyrrole-carboxamide)s. *Proc. Natl. Acad. Sci. USA* 82:2565–69

86. Youngquist RS, Dervan PB. 1987. A synthetic peptide binding 16 base pairs of A,T double helical DNA. *J. Am. Chem. Soc.* 109:7564–66

87. Zimmer C, Wähnert U. 1986. Nonintercalating DNA-binding ligands: specificity of the interaction and their use as tools in biophysical, biochemical and biological investigations of the genetic material. *Prog. Biophys. Mol. Biol.* 47:31–112

Annu. Rev. Biophy. Biomol. Struct. 2000. 29:463–95

PULSED AND PARALLEL-POLARIZATION EPR CHARACTERIZATION OF THE PHOTOSYSTEM II OXYGEN-EVOLVING COMPLEX

R. David Britt, Jeffrey M. Peloquin, and Kristy A. Campbell

Department of Chemistry, University of California, Davis, California 95616;
e-mail: rdbritt@ucdavis.edu

Key Words manganese cluster, photoactivation, oxygen evolution, ENDOR

■ **Abstract** Photosystem II uses visible light to drive the oxidation of water, resulting in bioactivated electrons and protons, with the production of molecular oxygen as a byproduct. This water-splitting reaction is carried out by a manganese cluster/tyrosine radical ensemble, the oxygen-evolving complex. Although conventional continuous-wave, perpendicular-polarization electron paramagnetic resonance (EPR) spectroscopy has significantly advanced our knowledge of the structure and function of the oxygen-evolving complex, significant additional information can be obtained with the application of additional EPR methodologies. Specifically, parallel-polarization EPR spectroscopy can be used to obtain highly resolved EPR spectra of integer spin Mn species, and pulsed EPR spectroscopy with electron spin echo-based sequences, such as electron spin echo envelope modulation and electron spin echo-electron nuclear double resonance, can be used to measure weak interactions obscured in continuous-wave spectroscopy by inhomogeneous broadening.

CONTENTS

1056-8700/00/0610-0463$14.00

PERSPECTIVES AND OVERVIEW

The photosystem II (PSII) component of the photosynthetic apparatus of chloroplasts and cyanobacteria uses light energy (wavelengths ≤ 680 nm) to drive electron transfer reactions that result in the oxidation of water and the reduction of membrane-diffusable plastoquinone (29). Because the oxidation of two water molecules to one molecule of molecular oxygen is a four-electron process, whereas the primary photochemistry drives single-electron transfers, an oxygen-evolving complex (OEC) is used to sequentially accumulate the four oxidation equivalents, as well as to position the substrate water molecules to facilitate the final O–O bond formation (12, 24, 91). The OEC contains a tetranuclear Mn cluster, a redox-active tyrosine, and required cofactors Ca^{2+} and Cl^-.

The oxygen evolution/water oxidation process is cyclic (55), with five intermediate states of the OEC designated S_0 through S_4, as displayed in Figure 1. The light-driven transitions of the cycle begin with the photooxidation of the Chl "special pair" P_{680} (12, 24, 29, 91). The resulting Chl cation, P_{680}^+, in turn oxidizes the phenolic side chain of tyrosine-161 of the PSII D1 protein. This tyrosine, designated $Y_Z^\bullet$, undergoes deprotonation coupled to its oxidation, forming a neutral radical $Y_Z^\bullet$. (A symmetry-related tyrosine, Y_D, which is typically present as a dark-stable neutral radical, does not participate in the fast electron transfer between Mn and P_{680}^+). The $Y_Z^\bullet$ tyrosine radical in turn oxidizes Mn ions (or alternatively substrate or amino acid ligands) to drive the intermediate S-state transitions. Molecular oxygen is released on the 1-ms timescale after S_4 state formation, resulting in the return of the OEC to its most reduced state, S_0.

Given that the Kok S-state cycle involves a series of single-electron transfers, one would anticipate that electron paramagnetic resonance (EPR) should provide a very useful spectroscopic tool for the study of the oxygen evolution cycle intermediates. This is indeed correct, as illustrated by Figure 2, which displays the Mn "multiline" EPR signals so far characterized through the S-state cycle. The most reduced state, S_0, has an odd-electron configuration and exhibits a $g = 2$ multiline signal (at least in the presence of added methanol) with partially resolved ^{55}Mn hyperfine features (4, 62, 63). The integer spin S_1 state exhibits a multiline EPR signal in parallel-polarization mode (17, 18). This multiline signal is observed in cyanobacterial PSII preparations or in spinach preparations in which extrinsic polypeptides of 17- and 23-kDa molecular masses have been removed. The S_2 state exhibits the longest known and most studied signals, a well-resolved $g = 2$ multiline signal (31) and a high-spin $g = 4.1$ signal (20, 97). The latter is featureless in unoriented preparations, but reveals ^{55}Mn hyperfine structure in oriented PSII membranes (54). Multiline signals have not yet been observed from the S_3 state or the transient S_4 state, but an interesting "split" EPR signal is observed under

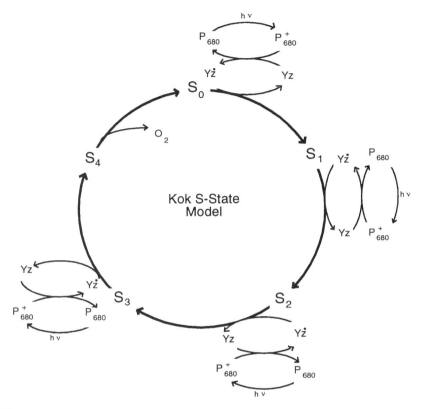

Figure 1   The Kok S-state cycle (55) describing the kinetic intermediates in photosynthetic oxygen evolution.

PSII inhibition conditions that block the $S_2 \rightarrow S_3$ transition (9, 10, 43). This split signal is now known to arise from the magnetic interaction of the the $Y_Z^\bullet$ tyrosine, stabilized beyond its normal lifetime by the lesion in the S-state cycle, and the S_2-state–trapped Mn cluster (32, 38, 57, 69, 86).

Although conventional perpendicular-polarization EPR spectroscopy has been very useful in the study of photosynthetic oxygen evolution, for example, in the detection and characterization of the S_0 and S_2 state EPR signals, important additional information has been gained by further exploiting the range of modern EPR methods. In this review, we discuss advances obtained by parallel-polarization EPR spectroscopy, which allows detection of integer spin signals that may be unobservable with conventional perpendicular-mode spectroscopy, and pulsed EPR spectroscopy, in which electron spin echo (ESE) sequences can be used to measure weak interactions masked by spectral inhomogeneity in continuous-wave (CW) spectroscopy.

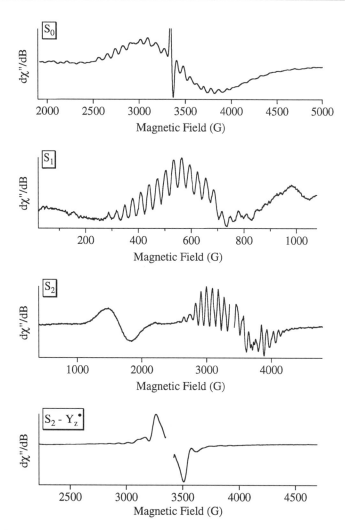

Figure 2 The Mn electron paramagnetic resonance signals of the oxygen evolution cycle, labeled by S state.

PARALLEL-POLARIZATION ELECTRON PARAMAGNETIC RESONANCE SPECTROSCOPY OF Mn COMPLEXES

Parallel-Polarization EPR

EPR performed with the oscillating-magnetic-field component $\vec{B}_1$ applied parallel to the static $\vec{B}_0$ field provides for sensitive detection of electron spin transitions of integer spin systems (1, 41, 46). There are a number of such "non-Kramers" integer spin biological metal complexes that have been fruitfully studied with parallel-polarization EPR (see 47 for a recent review from a historical perspective). The most basic Hamiltonian needed to describe an integer electron spin system includes axial (D) and rhombic (E) zero field-splitting (ZFS) terms along with the g-matrix–characterized electron Zeeman interaction:

$$H = D\left(S_z^2 - S(S+1)/3\right) + E\left(S_x^2 - S_y^2\right) + \beta \vec{B} \cdot \tilde{g} \cdot \vec{S}. \qquad (1)$$

The $S = 2$ case, relevant, for example, for high-spin Mn(III), has been treated quite explicitly in the limit in which the Zeeman interaction is a perturbation to the ZFS interaction (1, 41). The zero field eigenenergies are $E_{|2^+>} = 2D + 3E^2/D$, $E_{|2^->} = 2D$, $E_{|1^+>} = -D + 3E$, $E_{|1^->} = -D - 3E$, and $E_{|0>} = -2D - 3E^2/D$. The zero-field energy gaps between levels separated by $\Delta m_s = \pm 1$ are relatively large. However for modest D values and E/D ratios, the separation $3E^2/D$ between the $|2^+>$ and $|2^->$ states is relatively small, and we can think of these states as a "non-Kramers doublet," nondegenerate in the absence of an applied field, but with a splitting much smaller than the separation between any of the other states (see Figure 3). These energies split further with an applied magnetic field, as shown in Figure 3, which also includes the effect of a hyperfine term $(\hat{S} \cdot \tilde{A} \cdot \hat{I})$ to account for the magnetic interaction between the net electron spin and the spin $I = 5/2$ ^{55}Mn nucleus. For an oscillating $\vec{B}_1$ field applied parallel to the static $\vec{B}_0$ field, the matrix elements connecting the two relevant doublet states are nonzero. Thus, as long as the microwave photon energy $h\nu$ is $> 3E^2/D$, such transitions may be observed via parallel-polarization EPR spectroscopy. Because these transitions are of lower energy than the $\Delta m_s = \pm 1$ transitions probed with conventional perpendicular-polarization EPR, for many cases with moderate values of D, parallel-polarization experiments with the relatively low microwave frequency of an X-band spectrometer ($h\nu \approx 0.3$ cm^{-1}) will reveal the transitions, whereas conventional perpendicular-polarization EPR performed at the same frequency would fail to observe the $\Delta m_s = \pm 1$ transitions. Of course, another approach to observe non-Kramers ions is to use very high-frequency EPR spectroscopy to bring the $\Delta m_s = \pm 1$ transitions into resonance. However the expense and complication of a high-frequency (≥ 94 GHz) EPR spectrometer are appreciably greater than those of a dual-mode X-band cavity capable of both parallel- and perpendicular-mode EPR spectroscopy.

Mn(III) Superoxide Dismutase and Synthetic Mn(III) Complexes

Our recent investigation of the oxidized form of manganese superoxide dismutase provides an excellent example of the use of parallel-mode EPR to observe integer spin Mn species with well-resolved ^{55}Mn hyperfine splittings (19). In this enzyme, the redox-active Mn ion catalyzes disproportionation of superoxide as it cycles between Mn(II) and Mn(III) oxidation states. The Mn(III) form of the oxidized enzyme is high-spin $S = 2$. Figure 4a shows the experimental parallel-polarization EPR signature of this monomeric integer spin Mn complex, along with a spectral simulation. The six hyperfine lines, centered at an effective g value of 8.17, with hyperfine splitting of 100 G, correspond to the six transitions

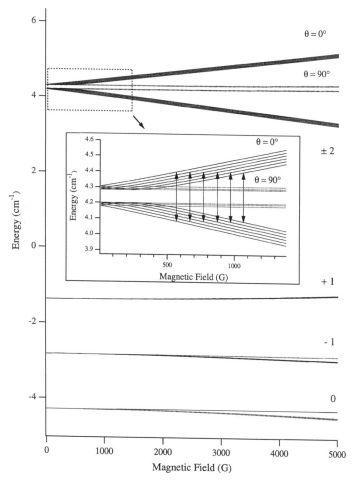

Figure 3 Energy vs magnetic field diagram for the $S=2$, $I=5/2$ spin system with a positive D value.

between the ± 2 states displayed in the inset of Figure 3. In this case the spectrum is simulated with ZFS parameters of $D = 2.10\ \text{cm}^{-1}$ and $E = 0.24\ \text{cm}^{-1}$. No distribution of D or E parameters is required to simulate this highly hyperfine-resolved spectrum. As shown in Figure 3, for a positive value of D, the parallel-polarization EPR–detectable non-Kramers doublet is highest in energy, and therefore one would expect a non-Curie law temperature dependence, which is indeed observed (Figure 4b). The temperature dependence is perfectly fit with the same ZFS values used in the EPR simulation.

Parallel-polarization EPR can also be used to study synthetic Mn(III) coordination complexes. For example, Dexheimer et al (27) reported spectra of Mn(III) tris(acetylacetonate) and tris(picolinate) complexes. However, the ^{55}Mn hyperfine resolution of this study was poor at best. Such limited resolution is not a general

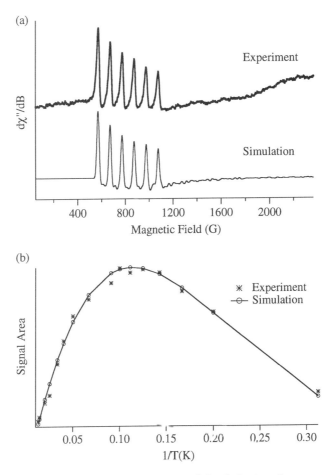

Figure 4 *a.* Mn(III) superoxide dismutase parallel-polarization electron paramagnetic resonance experimental spectrum and simulation. *b.* Temperature dependence of this signal and a simulation. (Adapted from 19).

property of synthetic clusters however; we have observed highly resolved [55]Mn hyperfine structure in several synthetic Mn(III) complexes.

The First "Photoactivation" Intermediate of Photosystem II

The same photochemistry that drives oxygen evolution in PSII is used to assemble the Mn cluster through a process termed "photoactivation" (84, 93), in which bioavailable Mn(II) ions are oxidized to the higher Mn(III)-Mn(IV) valencies of the cluster. The first photooxidation event occurs at a unique high-affinity Mn(II)-binding site, where Mn(II) is oxidized to Mn(III) by the $Y_Z^\bullet$ radical. Mutagenesis studies have implicated the D1 protein residue aspartate-170 in high-affinity binding of this photooxidizable Mn(II) (68). We have used parallel-polarization EPR to detect the spectroscopic signature of the Mn(III) ion formed by photooxidation of Mn(II) bound at the high-affinity site of PSII (Figure 5) (16). This species corresponds to the first photoactivation intermediate formed on the pathway to assembly of the water-splitting Mn cluster of PSII. The spectrum of this photooxidation product of 1.2/1-stoichiometry Mn(II)-Mn–depleted wild-type *Synechocystis* PSII particles reveals a well-resolved Mn(III) EPR spectrum with relatively small ^{55}Mn hyperfine splittings (45 G). This spectral signature is absent in photooxidized Mn(II)/-apo-PSII complexes prepared from D1-D170E and D1-D170H mutants (not shown), providing direct spectral evidence for a role for this specific D1–aspartate-170 residue in the initial photoactivation chemistry. This signal exhibits a Curie law temperature dependence, corresponding to a negative *D* value

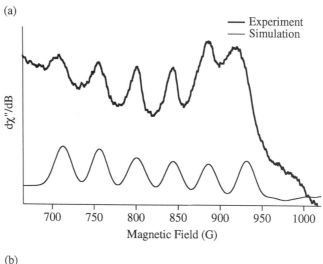

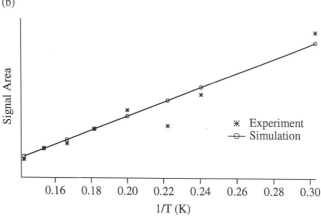

Figure 5   *a.* Mn(III) parallel-polarization electron paramagnetic resonance experimental spectrum and simulation for the initial photoactivation intermediate of photosystem II. *b.* Temperature dependence of this signal and a simulation. (Adapted from 16).

(the spectrum is simulated with ZFS parameters of $D = -2.6$ cm^{-1} and $E = 0.275$ cm^{-1}), which inverts the level scheme displayed in Figure 3. The change of the sign of D and the much reduced ^{55}Mn hyperfine splitting indicate a much different Mn(III)-binding-site environment than for the Mn(III) of oxidized Mn Superoxide dismutase.

Higher-Nuclearity Complexes

Partial ^{55}Mn hyperfine resolution has also been observed in parallel-polarization EPR spectra of weakly exchange-coupled Mn(III)-Mn(III) dimers (27; KA Campbell, WH Armstrong, RD Britt, unpublished observations). For example, the parallel-mode spectrum of the Mn dimer [Mn(III)$_2$(OAc)$_2$(bpta)$_2$](ClO$_4$) (Figure 6) shows a 10- to 1 1-line spectrum centered at $g_{eff} \approx 13$, arising from an excited spin state of the symmetric antiferromagnetically coupled dimer. The ≈ 11-line spectrum is produced by two equivalent, hyperfine-coupled $I = 5/2$ ^{55}Mn nuclei, as expected for this symmetric dimer. Chan & Armstrong (21) reported a $g_{eff} \approx 4.8$ signal from a tetranuclear 2 Mn(III)-2 Mn(IV) complex ([Mn$_2$O$_2$)$_2$ (tphpn)$_2$]$^{4+}$), which bears a strong resemblance to a parallel-mode signal attributed by Dexheimer & Klein (28) to the S$_1$ state of the PSII cluster. Unfortunately, neither the tetranuclear model cluster nor the PSII signal exhibits any ^{55}Mn hyperfine structure.

The S$_1$ State of the Oxygen-Evolving Complex

The Dexheimer & Klein PSII signal (28, 92), observed in spinach PSII membrane preparations, is correlated with the dark-stable S$_1$ state, which must be integer spin

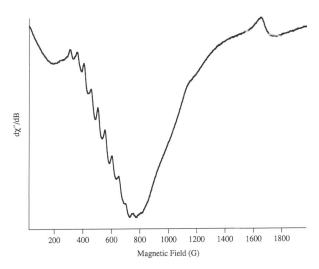

Figure 6 Parallel-polarization electron paramagnetic resonance spectrum of an antiferromagnetically coupled Mn(III)-Mn(III) complex {[Mn(III)$_2$(OAc)$_2$(bpta)$_2$](ClO$_4$)} (in collaboration with WH Armstrong).

(including the diamagnetic $S = 0$ possibility) given the half-integral spin of the S_2 state. This relatively weak signal, centered at $g_{eff} \approx 4.8$, with a broad featureless line shape of $\sim$600-G width, is observed as a "dark-minus-light" difference spectrum under illumination conditions that drive the $S_1 \to S_2$ state advancement. It is not observed in the difference spectrum generated with illumination at 77 K, a temperature too low for S_2 state formation, and it is not observed in Mn-depleted preparations. Conclusive evidence that it is actually a signal arising from the Mn cluster is lacking given the absence of [55]Mn hyperfine features. On the other hand, this does not rule out an Mn origin, given the similarity to the synthetic tetranuclear Mn cluster signal (21), which also is featureless, and the lack of observed hyperfine structure on the $g = 4.1$ signal in unoriented samples. Additional hyperfine-free parallel-mode signals have recently been attributed to the S_3 state (60).

Fortunately, a hyperfine-rich, parallel-polarization multiline signal presents itself in cyanobacterial PSII particles (Figure 7a) (18). This signal can also be observed in spinach membrane preparations when extrinsic proteins of apparent molecular masses of 17 and 23 kDa are removed (these are not present in cyanobacteria) (17). This signal and its temperature dependence can be simulated for higher integer spin states ($S \geq 2$) of the cluster (Figure 7), using a positive D value and four equivalent [55]Mn hyperfine matrices. The spectral simulation in Figure 7a uses $S = 2$ with $A_{\|} = 59.3$ G for each [55]Mn nucleus and with a D value of 0.805 cm^{-1}, the same value used for the temperature dependence curve for $S = 2$ in Figure 7b (KA Campbell, RJ Debus, RD Britt, unpublished observations). On the other hand, D values that match the temperature dependence with $S = 1$ fail to give proper spectral simulations. The simulations of this hyperfine resolved parallel-polarization signal provide strong evidence for a magnetically coupled Mn tetramer in the S_1 state.

We do not yet have a unique answer to the question of how the extrinsic proteins modulate the magnetic properties of the Mn cluster such that the S_1 state multiline signal is seen only in their absence. One possibility is that they affect a spin state change. The Dexheimer & Klein signal has been modeled as a spin $S = 1$ signal (28, 92), whereas line shape and temperature dependence of the multiline S_1 state signal are best modeled with spin $S \geq 2$. Alternatively, the actual spin state may not change, but instead the D and E values could be altered such that we detect the multiline signal only in the absence of these proteins. Another possibility is that these extrinsic proteins somehow induce "strain" in the D and E parameters, resulting in appreciable spectral broadening and a loss of hyperfine resolution.

PULSED EPR SPECTROSCOPY OF Mn COMPLEXES

Electron Spin Echo Methods

Conventional CW EPR has provided a very powerful tool in research on the PSII Mn cluster (Figure 2). However, CW EPR spectroscopy has limitations that can be overcome by performing pulsed EPR experiments with multipulse electron spin

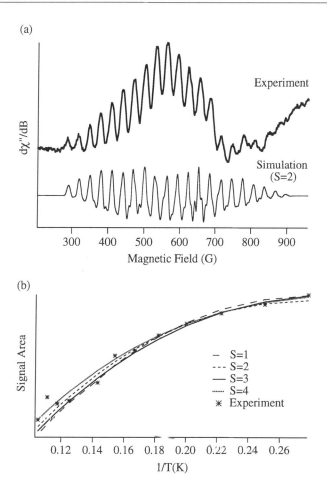

Figure 7 *a.* Cyanobacterial S_1-state electron paramagnetic resonance experimental spectrum and simulation. *b.* Temperature dependence of this signal and simulation for various integer spin states.

echo (ESE) sequences. These ESE methods are useful because EPR line shapes of biological paramagnetic entities are typically dominated by inhomogeneous broadening (65). The inhomogeneously broadened line shape arises from the overlap of resonances ("spin packets") resulting from a near continuum of magnetic environments. One source of inhomogeneous broadening is the unresolved overlap of hyperfine lines from many coupled nuclei, because the number of hyperfine lines increases multiplicatively with the number of classes of coupled nuclei. If the spectral density becomes sufficiently high, the spacing between individual hyperfine lines will become less than the intrinsic lifetime-broadened line width of each spin packet, and the EPR line shape will become dominated by the resulting

Gaussian line shape, such as the case of the $g = 4.1$ signal in unoriented PSII membranes. Even for a partially resolved signal such as the S_2-state multiline, much spectral information is buried by the inhomogeneous broadening; only 18–21 peaks are resolved out of the 1296 transitions resulting from four $I = 5/2$ ^{55}Mn couplings, in addition to unresolved hyperfine, inhomogeneous broadening results from orientational distribution of anisotropic hyperfine and g-matrix interactions, as well as site-to-site "strain" of g and A terms.

The negation of inhomogeneous broadening by the simplest spin echo sequence, that of the 2-pulse Hahn echo (42), is illustrated in Figure 8. At point a illustrated in the sequence and in the underlying rotating frame vector picture, a resonant H_1 field is applied along the x-axis to rotate magnetization from its initial equilibrium direction (along the z-axis coincident with the static H_0 field). By point b, the magnetization has been rotated by $\pi/2$ onto the rotating frame y-axis, and the H_1 field is removed. In the subsequent interval before the second microwave pulse, individual spin packets, of which a select set of five are displayed (Figure 8) will precess at different frequencies owing to the effect of inhomogeneous broadening. Spin packet 0 has a resonance frequency equal to the rotating-frame frequency relative to the laboratory frame, and therefore it remains fixed along the y-axis. The remaining spin packets have higher or lower resonant frequencies and therefore precess away from the y-axis during the free induction (c) after the $\pi/2$ pulse. At time τ (d), a π pulse is applied to the spin system. The spin packets are rotated into the positions displayed at point e. After this second pulse, each spin continues to precess with its original sense and rate relative to the y-axis, and, at a time τ

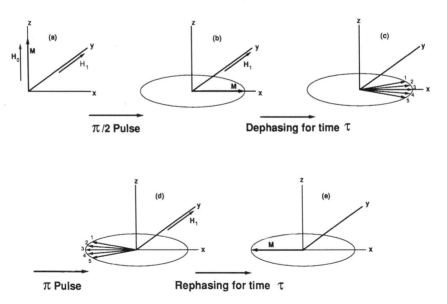

Figure 8   The two-pulse electron spin echo sequence.

after this π pulse, all spin packets refocus simultaneously onto the $-y$-axis. This evanescent magnetization coherence is referred to as a spin echo, and it manifests itself as a burst of radiation that can be detected with the spectrometer.

The detected echo can be used to generate a field-swept EPR spectrum analogous to the conventional CW EPR spectrum. Field modulation is not used, so the spectrum generated is a measure of the direct absorption rather than the field derivative. This can be beneficial for the detection of signals with broad, relatively featureless line shapes in which the field derivative is everywhere small (see for example 96). More importantly, by overcoming the deleterious effects of inhomogeneous broadening obscuring hyperfine interactions with magnetic nuclei, ESE methods can introduce much new spectral information. Specifically, the techniques of ESE envelope modulation (ESEEM) and ESE–electron nuclear double resonance (ENDOR) can be used to detect the nuclear spin transitions of such nuclei that are in magnetic contact with electron spins (13, 48). In these experiments, the spin echo is the carrier onto which nuclear spin information is encoded, either by time domain interference (ESEEM) or through radio frequency (RF)-driven magnetization transfer (ESE-ENDOR). In addition, because ESE experiments are performed in the time domain, they can be used to accurately measure relaxation times of electron spin systems (see, e.g., 59).

Electron Spin Echo–Envelope Modulation   In the ESEEM experiment, ESEs are formed by the application of two or more resonant microwave pulses. In addition to inducing the electron spin transitions, the microwave pulses may also induce "semiforbidden" transitions of nuclear spins magnetically coupled to the electron spins, resulting in quantum mechanical coherences in the nuclear spin sublevels associated with the electron spin levels (53, 65–67). These coherences create interference effects that can be measured by varying the ESE pulse timing. Fourier analysis of the resulting time domain ESEEM pattern reveals the frequencies of the nuclear spin transitions. The frequencies and amplitudes of the Fourier peaks can be interpreted to determine hyperfine and electric quadrupolar interactions of the coupled nuclei. Time domain simulations may also be used to determine the number of coupled nuclei of a given class. In general, ESEEM excels for relatively weakly coupled nuclei. ESEEM experiments with two-pulse Hahn echo (Figure 9a) or three-pulse "stimulated" echo (Figure 9b) sequences have been applied to the study of the PSII Mn cluster.

Electron Spin Echo–Electron Nuclear Double Resonance   Unlike ESEEM, the ESE-ENDOR experiments do not rely on semi forbidden nuclear spin transitions during the microwave pulses. Rather, the nuclear transitions are driven directly with separate high-power RF pulses. In an ESE-ENDOR experiment, an alteration of the initial electron spin magnetization is created by one or more high-power resonant microwave pulses. Application of the RF pulse further perturbs the electron magnetization if the RF pulse induces spin transitions of nuclei magnetically coupled to the electron spins. The nuclear spin transition frequencies are measured

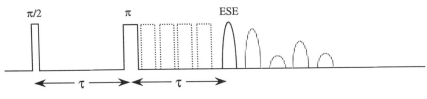

(a) Two-Pulse ESEEM Sequence

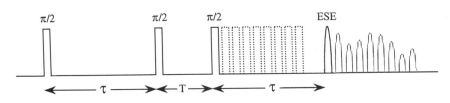

(b) Three-Pulse ESEEM Sequence

Figure 9   The two-pulse (*a*) and three-pulse (*b*) electron spin echo envelope modulation (ESEEM) sequences.

by varying the RF while monitoring the effect of the RF pulse on a subsequent ESE (48, 88). The ESE-ENDOR sequences are capable of detecting nuclei that are too strongly coupled for ESEEM detection. Pulse sequences introduced by Davies (23) and by Mims (64) have been applied to the PSII Mn cluster (Figure 10). The Davies sequence is preferable for large couplings, whereas the Mims sequence provides ESE-ENDOR access to smaller couplings. Both ESEEM and Mims ENDOR are often useful for measurements of weakly coupled nuclei, where the quantitative aspect of ESEEM complements the often superior spectral resolution of Mims ENDOR.

Mn Model Complexes

EPR studies of "model" synthetic Mn clusters have provided a useful base for investigating the EPR signals of the Mn cluster of PSII. For example, the multiline spectra of strongly antiferromagnetically coupled Mn(III)-Mn(IV) species bear a passing resemblence to the S_2-state multiline, although they present fewer resolved hyperfine peaks ($\approx$16), and the overall line width is not as large (30). After developing high-frequency ESE-ENDOR capabilities to investigate strongly coupled [55]Mn nuclei (82), we applied this pulsed EPR technique to accurately measure the hyperfine matrices of such Mn(III)-Mn(IV) clusters (73, 75). Although these dinuclear complexes are relatively simple, there is appreciable loss of information in the conventional CW EPR spectra. The two inequivalent [55]Mn nuclei provide for 36 distinct EPR transitions (compared with 1296 for a tetranuclear cluster), yet only

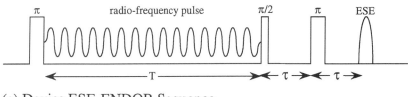

(a) Davies ESE-ENDOR Sequence

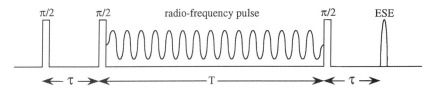

(b) Mims ESE-ENDOR Sequence

Figure 10   The Mims (*a*) & Davies (*b*) electron spin echo-electron nuclear double resonance (ESE-ENDOR) sequences.

≈ 16 are resolved (Figure 11*a*). Thus, even with only two ^{55}Mn nuclei, there is appreciable spectral overlap. We find that the ESE-ENDOR spectra are appreciably simpler, because the spin transitions of the Mn(IV) and Mn(III) nuclei occur in distinct spectral regions (Figure 11*b*) (73, 75). Specifically, because of the $2:-1$ ratio of spin projection factors that take into account the effects on the observed hyperfine interactions in making the transition from describing the system as two separate Mn ions with an exchange interaction to describing the system as a net $S = 1/2$ spin coupled to two inequivalent ^{55}Mn nuclei (8, 30), the ^{55}Mn nucleus associated with the Mn(III) ion has approximately twice the observed hyperfine coupling of the Mn(IV) ion. The ENDOR resonance frequencies, which are dominated by the Mn hyperfine interaction, occur at ~ 200 MHz for the ^{55}Mn of the Mn(III) ion, but only ~ 100 MHz for the ^{55}Mn of the Mn(IV) ion. The Mn(III) hyperfine coupling is much more anisotropic, leading to broader ENDOR line widths. A careful analysis of the ENDOR line shapes measured across the EPR spectrum provides an excellent measure of the ^{55}Mn quadrupolar coupling parameter e^2qQ for each nucleus (73, 75), information that is inaccessible from analysis of the CW EPR spectra. ^{55}Mn ENDOR can also be used for Mn(III)-Mn(IV) clusters with weaker exchange coupling such that the Mn ion ZFS interactions [particularly for the Mn(III)] are not negligible compared with the exchange interaction between ions (95). In this case the effective anisotropy of the Mn(IV) ion is increased, leading to broad ENDOR line shapes for the ^{55}Mn nuclei of both the Mn(III) and Mn(IV) ions (70, 72).

Although the ^{55}Mn hyperfine interactions for dinuclear clusters are partially obscured in CW EPR spectra, the situation with the weaker ligand superhyperfine

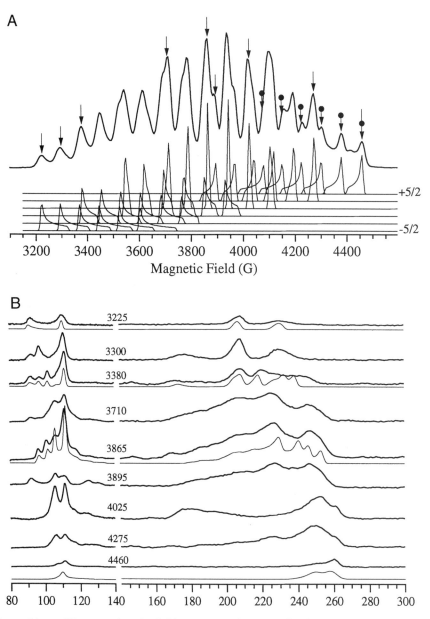

Figure 11   *a*. Electron spin echo-field sweep and simulation for the Mn(III)-Mn(IV) complex [(phen)$_2$Mn(III)O$_2$Mn(IV)(phen)$_2$](ClO$_4$)$_3$. *b*. Davies electron spin echo-electron nuclear double resonance spectra and simulations. Data were recorded at the field positions marked in *a*. (Adapted from 73).

interactions is far worse; such interactions are completely masked. ESEEM can be used to measure superhyperfine and quadrupolar couplings of ^{14}N nuclei of nitrogen-coordinated ligands (11, 14, 52, 72, 79, 81), and these serve as comparison points for the Mn clusters of PSII and catalase. Such Mn dinuclear clusters give rise to textbook "exact cancellation" [14]N spectra, resulting from similar magnitudes of external magnetic field and internal hyperfine field that provide a near cancellation of total field for one of the electron spin manifolds (35), giving rise to spectral dominance of the ^{14}N nuclear quadrupolar interaction, the nuclear spin version of the ZFS interaction. A similar exact field cancellation spectrum is observed for Mn catalase, arising from histidine ligation to the dinuclear cluster in the superoxidized Mn(III)-Mn(IV) form (80; also see 52). However, the PSII cluster ESEEM spectrum is decidedly different (vide infra). ESEEM and ENDOR methods have also been used to study model Mn cluster interactions with protons of macrocyclic ligands (73, 79) and of protons and deuterons of ligated water and alcohol (74). The latter spectra serve as a basis for analysis of spectra probing water and alcohol coordination to the PSII Mn cluster.

Photosystem II Mn Cluster: the S_2 State

Cluster Structure   Because the S_2-state $g = 2$ multiline and $g = 4.1$ signals were first discovered a number of years ago (20, 31, 97), the magnetic properties of this intermediate state of the Mn cluster are the best characterized. Once it became clear that both signals arise from the S_2 state (98), a debate ensued concerning their relative origins. One possibility is that both signals arise from a common cluster, with a tetranuclear cluster the favored candidate because of the 4:1 Mn:PSII stoichiometry. For such a common cluster model, one must posit a spin conversion between an $S = 1/2$ form that gives rise to the $g = 2$ multiline and a higher-spin form (most likely $S = 5/2$) that gives rise to the $g = 4.1$ signal (25, 98). Another possibility is that the signals arise from two distinct centers. The original version of the separate-centers model pointed out that the $g = 4.1$ signal could arise from an isolated Mn(IV) ion (44), although the subsequent detection of ≥ 16 [55]Mn hyperfine features in the $g = 4.1$ spectra of oriented ammonia-treated PSII membranes made this unlikely (54). More recently the $g = 4.1$ signal has been proposed to arise from an Mn dimer exchange coupled to a radical species (3). The $g = 2$ multiline would then arise from a separate Mn(III)-Mn(IV) dinuclear center. Given the greater spectral line width for the PSII signal when compared with the Mn(III)-Mn(IV) model compounds, this model mandates very large hyperfine interactions for the PSII cluster (2). Based on our success with [55]Mn ENDOR of the model clusters, we set out to perform [55]Mn ENDOR on the PSII S_2-state multiline signal to accurately measure the [55]Mn hyperfine matrices, first to try to unambiguously assign the nuclearity and then to provide EPR/ENDOR-derived constraints to pare down the the covey of possible structural models.

Figure 12 shows our S_2-state EPR and [55]Mn ENDOR spectra, both on the $g = 2$ multiline signal of native PSII membranes and on an altered form of the

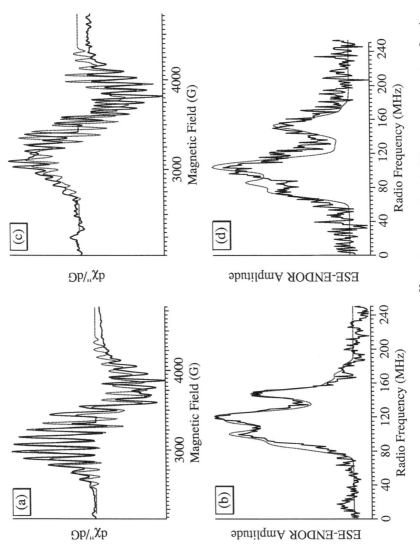

Figure 12 Electron paramagnetic resonance and ^{55}Mn electron nuclear double-resonance spectra of native (a, b) and ammonia-altered (c, d) S_2-state multiline signals. The *dashed lines* are simulations using parameters listed in Table 1. (Adapted from 70).

TABLE 1   Electron nuclear double resonance simulation parameters

Parameter	MeOH				Ammonia			
	Mn_A	Mn_B	Mn_C	Mn_D	Mn_A	Mn_B	Mn_C	Mn_D
A'_X (MHz)	−310	195	−255	240	−315	165	−225	210
A'_Y (MHz)	−310	195	−255	240	−315	165	−225	210
A'_Z (MHz)	−280	165	−185	210	−300	135	−165	180
$P'_\parallel$ (MHz)	6	1	5	5	6	1	5	5
η	0.1	0.1	0.1	0.1	0.1	0.1	0.1	0.1
g'_X	1.955				1.95			
g'_Y	1.955				1.95			
g'_Z	1.99				1.93			
Oxidation state	IV	IV	III	IV	IV	IV	III	IV

multiline signal produced on ammonia ligation (vide infra) (70; see also 69, 75). We observe ENDOR transitions only in the 100-MHz region; no reproducible peaks are observed above the noise floor in the higher-frequency region where the Mn(III) transitions occur in the model Mn(III)-Mn(IV) clusters. To obtain adequate simulations (Figure 12, *dashed lines*) of both the EPR and the ENDOR spectra, we must use four ^{55}Mn hyperfine interaction matrices; if we constrain the hyperfine couplings to the frequency range observed in the ENDOR spectra, EPR simulations with two or three ^{55}Mn couplings provide inadequate EPR simulations hallmarked by insufficient spectral line width. The parameters used to obtain the simultaneous EPR/ENDOR simulations of Figure 12 are listed in Table 1. It is interesting to compare our experimental ENDOR spectra and simulations with simulations generated with parameters used in previous simulations of the multiline EPR signal (Figure 13). Our own simulation (trace *a*) provides the best match to experimental data, but significant overlap of predicted and experimental transitions arises from other hyperfine sets based on tetranuclear assignments of the $g = 2$ multiline signal (45, 94) (traces *b, c*). However, the dinuclear model parameters (2) fail dramatically to match the experimental results (trace *d*).

We therefore assert that the constraints provided by the application of both EPR and ENDOR limit possible structures to those with four exchange-coupled Mn ions. These magnetic resonance techniques alone cannot provide a unique structure for the cluster. However, given additional structural information from EXAFS and XANES spectroscopies (71, 76, 90, 91), we can further limit possibilities to those structures that satisfy constraints provided by both the X-ray and magnetic resonance spectroscopies. The consensus S_2-oxidation state assignment from XANES analysis is 3 Mn(IV)-1 Mn(III). EXAFS reveals two 2.7-Å Mn-Mn vectors and an additional ≈ 3.3-Å vector that is thought to have an Mn-Mn component. There are a number of tetranuclear cluster arrangements allowed by these few EXAFS constraints (91).

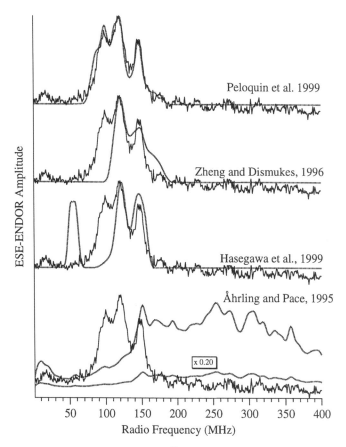

Figure 13 S_2-state multiline experimental ^{55}Mn electron nuclear double resonance, along with simulations based on tetranuclear (*a*, 70; *b*, 94; *c*, 45) and dinuclear (*d*, 2) parameter sets.

Our current approach towards defining possible structures is to take into account the set of possible structures suggested by EXAFS constraints, the favored XANES 3 Mn(IV)-1 Mn(III) oxidation state assignment, magnetic constraints from model Mn clusters [specifically, strong antiferromagnetic couplings for Mn ions separated by 2.7 Å, weaker couplings associated with the 3.3-Å distance, and well-defined ranges of hyperfine couplings for isolated Mn(III) and Mn(IV) ions], and the S_2-state magnetic constraints from our EPR/ENDOR, to find possible structures that are supported by all current spectroscopies. The often cited Berkeley "dimer-of-dimers" model (90, 91), with two 2.7-Å separation dimers linked by the 3.3-Å vector, is an example of a model that passes the EXAFS test but fails the EPR/ENDOR test; it is difficult to explain the origin of significant hyperfine couplings to the ^{55}Mn nuclei of the Mn(IV)-Mn(IV) dimer with its well-isolated diamagnetic ground state. On the other hand, successful magnetic properties arise from a family of

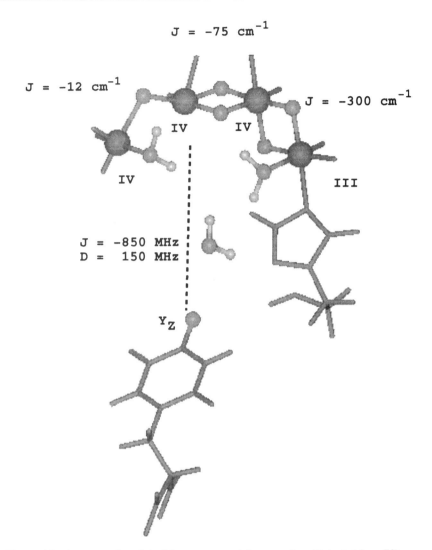

$$J = -75 \text{ cm}^{-1}$$

$$J = -12 \text{ cm}^{-1}$$

$$J = -300 \text{ cm}^{-1}$$

IV   IV

IV   III

J = -850 MHz
D = 150 MHz

Y$_Z$

Figure 14   A structural model of the oxygen-evolving complex. (Adapted from 70).

structures (91) in which three of the Mn ions are linked by strong antiferromagnetic interactions corresponding to the two 2.7-Å separation vectors, with the fourth Mn set off from the trinuclear core by the longer 3.3-Å distance. Such a "dangler" model is shown in Figure 14, along with the oxidation state arrangement and representative exchange couplings needed to give the proper hyperfine matrices for the net $S = 1/2$ ground state of the coupled spin system (70). This model also predicts excited spin states on the order of 36 cm^{-1} above the EPR-detected ground state, consistent with our Orbach relaxation results (59, vide infra). Moreover, if the weak exchange coupling associated with the 3.3-Å vector is changed from antiferromagnetic to ferromagnetic, an $S = 5/2$ ground state results, as required to produce the $g = 4.1$ signal. The tetranuclear model structure of Figure 14 has a similar overall geometry to the dimer-of-dimers structure, but by exchanging the 3.3-Å vector with one of the 2.7-Å vectors, one generates a model that nicely accounts for the known magnetic properties of the S_2-state cluster. In addition, because it still contains a pair of dimers at the core, albeit linked by a common Mn ion, this model is readily reconcilable with biochemical experiments showing that one Mn dimer remains after certain procedures that partially disrupt the cluster (77).

Histidine Ligation   Our most specific information concerning amino acid ligation to the cluster comes from ESEEM studies of PSII with specific ^{15}N labeling of histidine (85). This work followed up an earlier study (26) in which the PSII of cyanobacteria grown on ^{15}N loses a broad ESEEM peak at ≈ 5 MHz (15), showing that this feature indeed arises from [14]N. The nonquadrupolar $I = 1/2$ [15]N nucleus does not produce a detectable ESEEM feature in this case. The ^{14}N signature does not resemble the nicely resolved exact cancellation spectra observed in Mn model clusters and Mn catalase. Multifrequency ESEEM studies show that the feature tracks with field as a single quantum transition (37). Overall, the breadth of the ^{14}N feature and its lack of analogous detectable ^{15}N transitions are reminiscent of ^{14}N modulation in Cu amine oxidase attributed to a large and very anisotropic superhyperfine interaction (61). The specific histidine ^{15}N-labeling experiment (85) proves a histidine nitrogen origin of the feature; when only histidine is ^{15}N labeled, the ^{14}N modulation disappears. Thus we can argue that one or more histidine ligands are present; mutagenesis experiments suggest D1 histidine residues 190, 332, and 337 as likely candidates (24). Glutamates and aspartates are likely to complete the protein coordination.

Substrate and Inhibitor Binding   It is important to characterize the access of the water substrate molecules to the Mn cluster. First, it is necessary to either confirm or disprove the conventional model that the substrate waters bind directly to the Mn cluster. Second, if indeed direct substrate ligation occurs, it is crucial to determine at which S-state transition(s) the binding occurs. One limiting view would have two waters binding in Mn ligation sites cleared on the release of O_2 in the $S_4 \rightarrow S_0$ transition. In this case, the water ligands to Mn would be present in the most reduced state, S_0. Alternatively, the OEC may exclude water from the catalytic site during early S states to prevent formation of unwanted oxidation byproducts. Thus, the other limiting view would have waters bind to Mn only upon the $S_3 \rightarrow S_4$ transition, with an immediate, concerted four-electron oxidation to form O_2. Of course the binding can occur at one or two intermediate S-state transitions as well.

A number of S_2-state ENDOR and ESEEM studies have found no direct evidence for strongly dipolar-coupled exchangeable hydrogen nuclei such as expected from Mn-coordinated waters (34, 87, 89). However, we have had success with observing such strongly coupled hydrogen nuclei, both with [1]H-pulsed ENDOR and [2]H-pulsed ENDOR and ESEEM. For example, Figure 15 shows the Fourier

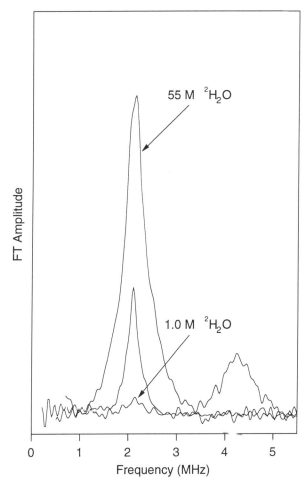

Figure 15 Fourier transform frequency domain spectra of the S_2-state Mn cluster electron spin echo envelope modulation with deuterated methanol or ^2H_2O. (Adapted from 36).

transforms of the multiline signal ^2H ESEEM for PSII samples incubated in ^2H_2O, compared with samples prepared with deuterated methanol (36). The methanol experiment is very clean because the methyl deuterons are nonexchangeable, unlike the deuterons from ^2H_2O. This methanol modulation has been modeled as caused by direct ligation of a single methanol ligand (36, but also see 33). Similar modulation is also observed from deuterated ethanol, but bulkier alcohols such as isopropanol cannot readily access the site (36). Deuterons from water give rise to much deeper modulation, with a much broader Fourier transform indicative of stronger dipolar couplings and shorter distances. We have modeled this modulation as arising from several deuterons at Mn-deuteron distances consistent with direct ^2H_2O or ^2HO ligation (39). For example, a good fit to the deep modulation and rapid damping of the time domain spectrum (not shown) arises from assigning

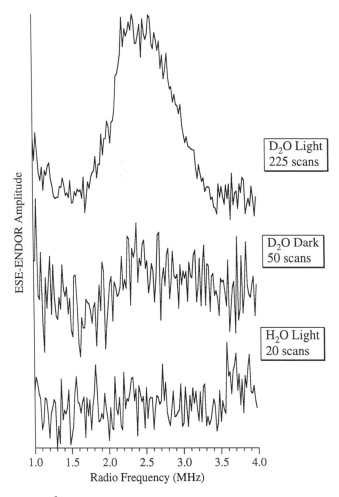

Figure 16   Mims ^{2}H electron nuclear double resonance spectra of the S_2-multiline signal after ^2H_2O exchange. (Adapted from 39).

one pair of deuterons at 2.5 Å, another pair at 3.1 Å, and three more at 3.3 Å. Such strongly coupled deuterons can also be directly detected with Mims ENDOR (Figure 16), and the complementary proton spectrum can be obtained before ^2H_2O exchange via Davies ENDOR (39).

As mentioned above, small alcohols appear to bind directly to the Mn cluster in the S_2 state (36). The binding occurs with a K_D of ≈80 mM, so at the S_2 state these water analog molecules bind at this site more tightly than water, which is present at ≈55 M. However, at this and appreciably higher concentration (to ≈ 1 M), there is absolutely no inhibition of oxygen evolution. Therefore, if these small alcohols bind at a substrate water site, they must be replaced by water or at least exchange with water on a fast timescale (≪1 ms), at the later S states.

ESEEM experiments have also demonstrated that ammonia binds directly to the Mn cluster in the S_2 state (15). This binding triggers the alteration of the multiline EPR spectrum shown in Figure 12c (7). From the highly rhombic nuclear quadrupolar coupling of the ammonia ^{14}N, we have argued against a simple NH_3 terminal ligation in favor of a less axial electronic structure around the nitrogen, such as would be found in an NH_2 bridge (15).

Given that small alcohols and ammonia each bind to the Mn cluster in the S_2 state, it is interesting whether these bind at separate sites or compete for a common binding site. Preliminary ESEEM experiments analyzing methanol for monitoring ^2H modulation and ammonia for monitoring ^{14}N modulation, indicate two separate binding sites (MJ Evanchik, KL Clemens, RD Britt, unpublished observation). It is appealing to speculate that these represent two S_2 state substrate water-binding sites in the absence of these added water analogs.

Proximity of Chloride Cl^- is a required cofactor for oxygen evolution. Arguments have been put forth for direct Cl^- ligation to the Mn cluster (78) or, alternatively, for an amino acid Cl^--binding site (51). The $I = 3/2$ ^{35}Cl, and ^{37}Cl nuclei are very difficult double-resonance targets because their large quadrupolar moments lead to very broad ENDOR spectra. However, possible Cl^- binding to the Mn cluster can be probed by inhibitors that have been demonstrated to be competitive with Cl^- (56, 78). We have recently targeted acetate as an inhibitor because we can use acetate deuterated at the nonexchangeable methyl positions in a fashion analogous to our previous use of deuterated alcohols (22). A complication is that one does not form a normal S_2-multiline signal under acetate inhibition conditions. However, one can form the S_2-$Y_Z^\bullet$ interaction spectrum (Figure 2d), and Szalai & Brudvig have demonstrated that, by using NO to quench the $Y_Z^\bullet$ component, one can recover the multiline EPR spectrum (83). ESEEM experiments of deuterated acetate/NO-treated PSII membranes show deuteron modulation comparable with the alcohol modulations previously described (22). This demonstrates that acetate binds in the vicinity of the Mn cluster, most likely as a direct ligand to the cluster. This in turn supports models of direct Cl^- ligation to the cluster (78).

Other Magnetic Properties   As mentioned earlier, the time domain nature of pulsed EPR lends itself to direct relaxation time measurments. We have exploited this to measure the temperature dependence of the spin lattice relaxation of the multiline signal (59). The relaxation rate shows an exponential temperature dependence such as predicted for Orbach relaxation via an excited spin state. The slope of a $\ln(1/T_1)$ vs T plot indicates a 36-cm^{-1} excitation of the relaxing spin manifold above the multiline ground state manifold.

The $g = 4.1$ signal is more difficult to study with pulsed EPR owing to relatively short "phase memory" ($\approx T_2$) even at low temperature. However, Astashkin et al (5) have investigated the pulse power dependence on the ESE amplitude and concluded that the $g = 4.1$ signal arises from an $S = 5/2$ state, consistent with earlier multifrequency EPR studies (40).

PSII Mn Cluster: S_2-$Y_Z^\bullet$

The S_2-$Y_Z^\bullet$ interaction spectrum was first reported in Ca^{2+}-depleted PSII membranes (9). An early assignment based on UV-difference spectra was that the radical component of this signal corresponds to an oxidized histidine (10). However, this was questioned by other workers, who posited a $Y_Z^\bullet$ origin (43). We were able to demonstrate that the split signal originates from $Y_Z^\bullet$, first with ^{1}H ENDOR (38), and most conclusively with ^{2}H ESEEM of PSII particles incorporating deuterated tyrosine (86). Other workers questioned the Mn component of the interaction spectrum (6). This led us to look for a ^{55}Mn contribution to the split-signal line shape, using ENDOR (69). The results, shown in Figure 17, are quite

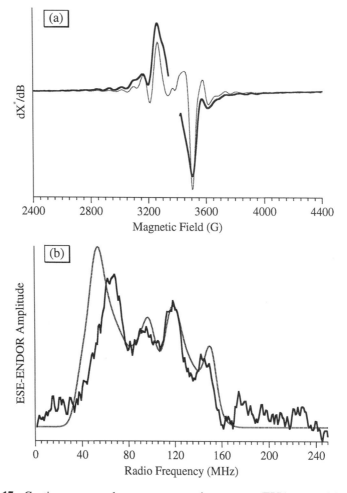

Figure 17 Continuous-wave electron paramagnetic resonance (EPR) spectra (*a*) and ^{55}Mn electron nuclear double resonance (*b*) and respective simulations of the "split" EPR signal assigned to an S_2-$Y_Z^\bullet$ interaction spectrum. (Adapted from 69).

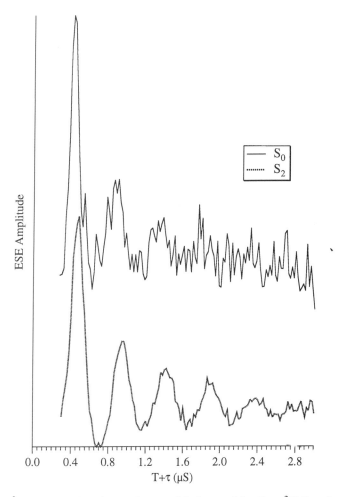

Figure 18 ^{2}H electron spin echo envelope modulation resulting from ^{2}H$_2$O exchange for the S$_0$ and S$_2$ states of the photosystem II Mn cluster.

interesting. The split-signal ENDOR spectrum shows ^{55}Mn ENDOR features very similar to the S$_2$ state multiline spectrum, with the addition of a new prominant feature at ≈75 MHz (69). Both ENDOR and EPR spectra are successfully simulated with S$_2$ state Mn cluster and Y$_Z^\bullet$ spectral parameters, but with the addition of exchange (-850-cm^{-1}) and dipolar ($+150$-cm^{-1}) couplings between the two spin centers [also see EPR simulations by Dorlet et al (32) and Lakshmi et al (57)]. The dipolar coupling gives a measure of a close Mn cluster-Y$_Z^\bullet$ radical distance, but the specifics are rather underdetermined owing to lack of a definitive structure for the cluster and the relative orientation of the tyrosine radical. Figure 14 shows a representative geometry based on our favored Mn cluster structure. Others have modeled Y$_Z^\bullet$ to be close enough for direct H-bonding of the tyrosine oxygen to hydrogens of Mn-bound water (58). Regardless of the details, pulsed EPR has provided definitive assignment of a Mn cluster-tyrosine radical interaction spectrum from the OEC, and this provides a key line of evidence for interesting new models invoking proton-coupled electron transfer in the mechanism of photosynthetic water splitting (38, 49, 50).

PSII Mn Cluster: S_0

Now that there is a new $S = 1/2$ EPR signal detected in the S_0 state (3, 63), pulsed EPR methods can be applied to the most reduced state of the Mn cluster. The issue of water access is particularly interesting for the S_0 state, given that this is the first state at which substrate waters could bind after O_2 release. Figure 18 shows preliminary time domain ESEEM traces comparing the modulation induced by exchangeable deuterons from ^2H_2O in the S_0 and S_2 states (J Messinger, JM Peloquin, J Roblee, KA Campbell, VK Yachandra, K Sauer, MP Klein, RD Britt, unpublished observation). The ^2H modulation patterns are clearly comparable, and, given our analysis of the S_2-state pulsed spectroscopies (39), this is strongly suggestive of water coordination from the earliest step in the cycle.

ACKNOWLEDGMENT

We acknowledge the National Institutes of Health (grant GM48242) for support of this work. A fellowship from the Department of Chemistry at University of California, Davis, is gratefully acknowledged by KAC.

Visit the Annual Reviews home page at www.AnnualReviews.org

LITERATURE CITED

1. Abragam A, Bleaney B. 1970. *Electron Paramagnetic Resonance of Transition Ions*: Section 3.14. Oxford, UK: Clarendon
2. Åhrling K, Pace RJ. 1995. Simulation of the S_2 state multiline electron paramagnetic resonance signal of photosystem II: a multifrequency approach. *Biophys. J.* 68:2081–90
3. Åhrling K, Smith PJ, Pace RJ. 1998. Nature of the Mn centers in photosystem II: modeling and behavior of the $g = 4$ resonances and related signals. *J. Am. Chem. Soc.* 120:13202–14
4. Åhrling KA, Peterson S, Styring S. 1998. An oscillating manganese electron paramagnetic resonance signal from the S_0 state of the oxygen evolving complex in photosystem II. *Biochemistry* 36:13148–52
5. Astashkin AV, Kodera Y, Kawamori A. 1994. Pulsed EPR study of manganese $g = 4.1$ signal in plant photosystem II. *J. Magn. Reson.* 105:113–19
6. Astashkin AV, Mino H, Kawamori A, Ono TA. 1997. Pulsed EPR study of the S'3 signal in the Ca^{2+}-depleted photosystem II. *Chem. Phys. Lett.* 272:506–16
7. Beck WF, de Paula JC, Brudvig GW. 1986. Ammonia binds to the manganese site of the O_2-evolving complex of photosystem II in the S_2 state. *J. Am. Chem. Soc.* 108:4018–22
8. Bencini A, Gatteschi D. 1989. *Electron Paramagnetic Resonance of Exchange Coupled System*. Berlin: Springer-Verlag
9. Boussac A, Zimmermann JL, Rutherford AW. 1989. EPR signals from modified charge accumulation states of the oxygen-

evolving enzyme in Ca^{2+}-deficient photosystem II. *Biochemistry* 28:8984–89

10. Boussac A, Zimmermann JL, Rutherford AW, Lavergne J. 1990. Histidine oxidation in the oxygen-evolving photosystem-II enzyme. *Nature* 347:303–6

11. Britt RD. 1988. Electron spin echo spectroscopy in photosynthesis. PhD thesis. Univ. Calif., Berkeley, Berkeley, Calif.

12. Britt RD. 1996. Oxygen evolution. In *Advances in Photosynthesis: Oxygenic Photosynthesis, The Light Reactions*, ed. CF Yocum, D Ort, pp. 137–64. Amsterdam: Kluwer

13. Britt RD. 1996. Electron spin echo methods in photosynthesis research. In *Biophysical Techniques in Photosynthesis*, ed. J Amesz, AJ Hoff, pp. 235–53. Dordrecht: Kluwer

14. Britt RD, Klein MP. 1992. Electron spin echo envelope modulation studies of mixed valence manganese complexes: applications to the catalytic manganese cluster of photosynthetic oxygen evolution. In *Pulsed Magnetic Resonance: NMR, ESR, and Optics, a Recognition of E. L. Hahn*, ed. DMS Bagguley, pp. 361–76, Oxford, UK: Clarendon

15. Britt RD, Zimmermann JL, Sauer K, Klein MP. 1989. Ammonia binds to the catalytic manganese of the oxygen-evolving complex of photosystem II. Evidence by electron spin-echo envelope modulation spectroscopy. *J. Am. Chem. Soc.* 111:3522–32

16. Campbell KA, Force DA, Nixon PJ, Dole F, Diner BA, Britt RD. 2000. Dual-mode EPR DETECTS the initial intermediate in photoassembly of the photosystem II Mn cluster: The influence of amino acid residue 170 of the DI polypeptide on M_n coordination. *J. Am. Chem. Soc.* in press

17. Campbell KA, Gregor W, Pham DP, Peloquin JM, Debus RJ, Britt RD. 1998. The 23 and 17 kDa extrinsic proteins of photosystem II modulate the magnetic properties of the S_1-state manganese cluster. *Biochem-istry* 37:5039–45

18. Campbell KA, Peloquin JM, Pham DP, Debus RJ, Britt RD. 1998. Parallel polarization EPR detection of an S_1-state "multiline" EPR signal in photosystem II particles from *Synechocystis* sp. PCC 6803. *J. Am. Chem. Soc.* 120:447–48

19. Campbell KA, Yikilmaz E, Grant CV, Gregor W, Miller AF, Britt RD. 1999. Parallel polarization EPR characterization of the Mn(III) center of oxidized manganese-superoxide dismutase. *J. Am. Chem. Soc.* 121:4714–15

20. Casey J, Sauer K. 1984. EPR detection of a cryogenically photogenerated intermediate in photosynthetic oxygen evolution. *Biochim. Biophys. Acta* 767:21–28

21. Chan MK, Armstrong WH. 1991. Support for a dimer of di-μ-oxo dimers model for the photosystem II manganese aggregate. *J. Am. Chem. Soc.* 113:5055–57

22. Clemens KL, Force DA, Britt RD. 2000. Acetate coordination to the manganese cluster of photosystem II: an ESEEM study. *Biochemistry*, submitted for publication

23. Davies ER. 1974. A new pulse ENDOR technique. *Physics Lett.* 47A:1–2

24. Debus RJ. 1992. The manganese and calcium ions of photosynthetic oxygen evolution. *Biochim. Biophys. Acta* 1102:269–352

25. de Paula JC, Beck WF, Brudvig GW. 1986. Magnetic properties of manganese in the photosynthetic O_2-evolving complex. 2. Evidence for a manganese tetramer. *J. Am. Chem. Soc.* 108:4002–9

26. DeRose VJ, Yachandra VK, McDermott AE, Britt RD, Sauer K, Klein MP. 1991. Nitrogen ligation to manganese in the photosynthetic oxygen-evolving complex: continuous wave and pulsed EPR studies of photosystem II particles enriched with ^{14}N and ^{15}N isotopes. *Biochemistry* 30:1335–41

27. Dexheimer SL, Gohdes JW, Chan MK, Hagen KS, Armstrong WH, Klein MP. 1989.

Detection of EPR spectra in $S = 2$ states of trivalent manganese complexes. *J. Am. Chem. Soc.* 111:8923–25

28. Dexheimer SL, Klein MP. 1992. Detection of a paramagnetic intermediate in the S_1 state of the photosynthetic oxygen-evolving complex. *J. Am. Chem. Soc.* 114:2821–26

29. Diner BA, Babcock GT. 1996. Structure, dynamics, and energy conversion efficiency in photosystem II. In *Advances in Photosynthesis: Oxygenic Photosynthesis, the Light Reactions*, ed. CF Yocum, D Ort, pp. 213–247. Amsterdam: Kluwer

30. Dismukes GC, Ferris K, Watnick P. 1982. EPR spectroscopic evidence for a tetranuclear manganese cluster as the site for photosynthetic oxygen evolution. *Photobio. Photobiophys.* 3:243–56

31. Dismukes GC, Siderer Y. 1981. Intermediates of a polynuclear manganese center involved in photosynthetic oxidation of water. *Proc. Natl. Acad. Sci. USA* 78:274–78

32. Dorlet P, DiValentin M, Babcock GT, McCracken JL. 1998. Interaction of $Y_Z^{\bullet}$ with its environment in acetate-treated photosystem II membranes and reaction center cores. *J. Phys. Chem. B* 102:8239–47

33. Evans MCW, Gourovskaya K, Nugent JHA. 1999. Investigation of the interaction of the water oxidising manganese complex of photosystem II with the aqueous solvent environment. *FEBS Lett.* 450:285–88

34. Fiege R, Zweygart W, Bittle R, Adir N, Renber G, Lubitz W. 1996. EPR and ENDOR studies of the water oxidizing complex of photosystem II. *Photosyn. Res.* 48:227–37

35. Flanagan HL, Singel DJ. 1987. Analysis of ^{14}N ESEEM patterns of randomly oriented solids. *J. Chem. Phys.* 87:5606–16

36. Force DA, Randall DW, Lorigan GA, Clemens KL, Britt RD. 1998. ESEEM studies of alcohol binding to the manganese cluster of the oxygen evolving complex of chotosystem II. *J. Am. Chem. Soc.* 120:13321–33

37. Gilchrist ML. 1996. Pulsed electron paramagnetic resonance investigations of photosynthetic oxygen evolution. *PhD thesis. Univ. Calif., Davis, Davis, CA*

38. Gilchrist ML, Ball JA, Randall DW, Britt RD. 1995. Proximity of the manganese cluster of photosystem II to the redox active tyrosine Y_Z. *Proc. Natl. Acad. Sci. USA* 92:9545–49

39. Gilchrist ML, Peloquin JM, Force DA, Randall DW, Kim SH, et al. 1999. Water ligation to the S_2-state Mn cluster of photosystem II investigated with pulsed ENDOR and ESEEM. *J. Am. Chem. Soc.* Submitted for publication

40. Haddy A, Dunham WR, Sands RH, Aasa R. 1992. Multifrequency EPR investigations into the origin of the S_2-state signal at $g = 4.1$ of the O_2-evolving complex. *Biochim. Biophys. Acta* 1099:25–34

41. Hagen WR. 1982. EPR of non-Kramers doublets in biological systems: characterization of an $S = 2$ system in oxidized cytochrome c oxidase. *Biochim. Biophys. Acta* 708:82–98

42. Hahn EL. 1950. Spin echoes. *Phys. Rev.* 80:580–94

43. Hallahan BJ, Nugent JHA, Warden JT, Evans MCW. 1992. Investigation of the origin of the "S_3" EPR signal from the oxygen-evolving complex of photosystem 2: the role of tyrosine Z. *Biochemistry* 31:4562–73

44. Hansson Ö, Aasa R, Vänngård T. 1987. The origin of the multiline and $g = 4.1$ electron paramagnetic resonance signals from the oxygen-evolving system of photosystem II. *Biophys. J.* 51:825–32

45. Hasegawa K, Ono TA, Inoue Y, Kusunoki M. 1999. Spin-exchange interactions in the S_2-state manganese tetramer in photosynthetic oxygen-evolving complex deduced from $g = 2$ multiline EPR signal. *Chem. Phys. Lett.* 300:9–19

46. Hendrich MP, Debrunner PG. 1989. Integer-spin electron paramagnetic resonance of iron proteins. *Biophys. J.* 56:489–506

47. Hendrich MP, Debrunner PG. 1998. EPR of non-Kramers systems in biology. In *Foundations of Modern EPR*, eds. GR Eaton, SS Eaton, KM Salikhov. pp. 530–47. Singapore: World Scientific

48. Hoffman BM, DeRose VJ, Doan PE, Gurbiel RJ, Houseman ALP, Telser J. 1993. Metalloenzyme active-site structure and function through multifrequency cw and pulsed ENDOR. In *Biological Magnetic Resonance*, eds. LJ Berliner, J Reuben, 13:151–218. New York: Plenum

49. Hoganson CW, Babcock GT. 1997. A metalloradical mechanism for the generation of oxygen from water in photosynthesis. *Science* 277:1953–56

50. Hoganson CW, Lydakis-Simantiris N, Tang XS, Tommos C, Warncke K, et al. 1995. A hydrogen-atom abstraction model for the function of Y_Z in photosynthetic oxygen-evolution. *Photosyn. Res.* 46:177–84

51. Homann PH. 1985. The association of functional anions with the oxygen-evolving center of chloroplasts. *Biochim. Biophys. Acta* 809:311–19

52. Invancich A, Barynin VV, Zimmermann JL. 1995. Pulsed EPR studies of the binuclear Mn(III)Mn(IV) center in catalase from *Thermus thermophilus*. *Biochemistry* 34:6628–39

53. Kevan L. 1979. Modulation of electron spin-echo decay in solids. In *Time Domain Electron Spin Resonance*, eds. L Kevan, RN Schwartz, pp. 279–341. New York: Wiley & Sons

54. Kim DH, Britt RD, Klein MP, Sauer K. 1990. The $g = 4.1$ EPR signal of the S_2 state of the photosynthetic oxygen evolving complex arises from a multinuclear Mn cluster. *J. Am. Chem. Soc.* 112:9389–91

55. Kok B, Forbush B, McGloin M. 1970. Cooperation of charges in photosynthetic O_2 evolution. I. A linear four step mechanism. *Photochem. Photobio.* 11:457–75

56. Kühne H, Szalai VA, Brudvig GW. 1999. Competitive binding of acetate and chloride in photosystem II. *Biochemistry* 38:6604–13

57. Lakshmi KV, Eaton SS, Eaton GR, Frank HA, Brudvig GW. 1998. Analysis of dipolar and exchange interactions between manganese and tyrosine Z in the S_2-$Y_Z^\bullet$ state of acetate-inhibited photosystem II via EPR spectral simulations at X-and Q-bands. *J. Phys. Chem. B* 102:8327–35

58. Limburg J, Szalai VA, Brudvig GW. 1999. A mechanistic and structural model for the formation and reactivity of a $Mn^V = O$ species in photosynthetic water oxidation. *J. Chem. Soc., Dalton Trans.* 1999:1353–61

59. Lorigan GA, Britt RD. 1994. Temperature dependent pulsed EPR relaxation studies of the S_2 state multiline signal of the photosynthetic oxygen-evolving complex. *Biochemistry* 33:12072–76

60. Matsukawa T, Mino H, Yoneda D, Kawamori A. 1999. Dual-mode EPR study of new signals from the S_3-state of oxygen-evolving complex in photosystem II. *Biochemistry* 38:4072–77

61. McCracken J, Peisach J, Cote CE, McGuirl MA, Dooley DM. 1992. Pulsed EPR studies of the semiquinone state of copper-containing amine oxidases. *J. Am. Chem. Soc.* 114:3715–20

62. Messinger J, Nugent JHA, Evans MCW. 1997. Detection of an EPR multiline signal for the S_0^* state in photosystem II. *Biochemistry* 36:11055–60

63. Messinger J, Robblee JH, Yu WO, Sauer K, Yachandra VK, Klein MP. 1997. The S_0 state of the oxygen-evolving complex in photosystem II is paramagnetic: detection of an EPR multiline signal. *J. Am. Chem. Soc.* 119:11349–50

64. Mims WB. 1965. Pulsed ENDOR experiments. *Proc. R. Soc. London Ser.* A283:452–57

65. Mims WB. 1972. Electron spin echoes. In *Electron Paramagnetic Resonance*, ed.

S Geschwind, pp. 263–351. New York: Plenum

66. Mims WB. 1972. Envelope modulation in spin-echo experiments. *Phys. Rev. B* 5:2409–19

67. Mims WB, Peisach J. 1981. Electron spin echo spectroscopy and the study of metalloproteins. In *Biological Magnetic Resonance*, eds. LJ Berliner, J Reuben, 3:213–63, New York: Plenum

68. Nixon PJ, Diner BA. 1992. Aspartate 170 of the photosystem II reaction center polypeptide D1 is involved in the assembly of the oxygen-evolving manganese cluster. *Biochemistry* 31:942–48

69. Peloquin JM, Campbell KA, Britt RD. 1998. ^{55}Mn pulsed ENDOR demonstrates that the photosystem II "split" EPR signal arises from a magnetically-coupled mangano-tyrosyl complex. *J. Am. Chem. Soc.* 120:6840–41

70. Peloquin JM, Campbell KA, Randall DW, Evanchik M, Britt RD. 2000. ^{55}Mn ENDOR of the S_2-state multiline EPR signal of photosystem II: implications on the structure of the tetranuclear Mn cluster. *J. Am. Chem. Soc.* Submitted for publication

71. Penner-Hahn JE, Fronko RM, Pecoraro VL, Yocum CF, Betts SD, Bowlby NR. 1990. Stuctural characterization of the manganese sites in the photosynthetic oxygen-evolving complex using X-ray absorption spectroscopy. *J. Am. Chem. Soc.* 112:2549–57

72. Randall DW. 1997. Pulsed EPR studies of tyrosine radicals and maganese complexes: insights into photosynthetic oxygen evolution. PhD thesis. Univ. Calif., Davis, CA

73. Randall DW, Chan MK, Armstrong WH, Britt RD. 1998. Pulsed ^{1}H and ^{55}Mn ENDOR studies of dinuclear Mn(III)Mn(IV) model complexes. *J. Mol. Phys.* 95:1283–94

74. Randall DW, Gelasco A, Pecoraro VL, Britt RD. 1997. ESE-ENDOR and ESEEM characterization of water and methanol ligation to a dinuclear Mn(III)Mn(IV) complex. *J. Am. Chem. Soc.* 119:4481–91

75. Randall DW, Sturgeon BE, Ball JA, Lorigan GA, Chan MK, et al. 1995. ^{55}Mn55 ESE-ENDOR of a mixed valence Mn(III)Mn(IV) complex: comparison with the Mn cluster of the photosynthetic oxygen-evolving complex. *J. Am. Chem. Soc.* 117:11780–89

76. Riggs PJ, Mei R, Yocum CF, Penner-Hahn JE. 1992. Reduced derivatives of the manganese cluster in the photosynthetic oxygen-evolving complex. *J. Am. Chem. Soc.* 114:10650–51

77. Riggs-Gelasco P, Mei R, Yocum DF, Penner-Hahn JE. 1996. Reduced derivatives of the Mn cluster in the oxygen-evolving complex of photosystem II: an EXAFS study. *J. Am. Chem. Soc.* 118:2387–99

78. Sandusky PO, Yocum CF. 1984. The mechanism of amine inhibition of the photosynthetic oxygen-evolving complex: amines displace functional chloride from a ligand site on manganese. *FEBS Lett.* 162:339–43

79. Schäfer KO, Bittl R, Zweygart W, Lendzian F, Haselhorst G, et al. 1998. Electronic structure of antiferromagnetically coupled dinuclear manganese ($Mn^{III}Mn^{IV}$) complexes studied by magnetic resonance techniques. *J. Am. Chem. Soc.* 120:13104–20

80. Stemmler TL, Sturgeon BE, Randall DW, Britt RD, Penner-Hahn JE. 1996. Spectroscopic characterization of inhibitor interactions with the Mn(III)/Mn(IV) core in *Lactobacillus plantarum* manganese catalase. *J. Am. Chem. Soc.* 119:9215–25

81. Sturgeon BE. 1994. Electron spin echo spectroscopy: techniques and applications to manganese systems. PhD thesis. Univ. Calif., Davis, Davis, CA

82. Sturgeon BE, Ball JA, Randall DW, Britt RD. 1994. ^{55}Mn electron spin echo ENDOR of Mn^{2+} complexes. *J. Phys. Chem.* 98:12871–83

83. Szalai VA, Brudvig GW. 1996. Reversible

binding of nitric oxide to tyrosyl radicals in photosystem II. Nitric oxide quenches formation of the S3 EPR signal species in acetate-inhibited photosystem II. *Biochemistry* 35:15080–87

84. Tamura N, Cheniae G. 1987. Photoactivation of the water-oxidizing complex in photosystem I membranes depleted of Mn and extrinsic proteins. I. Biochemical and kinetic characterization. *Biochim. Biophys. Acta* 890:179–94

85. Tang XS, Diner BA, Larsen BS, Gilchrist ML, Lorigan GA, Britt RD. 1994. Identification of histidine at the catalytic site of the photosynthetic oxygen-evolving complex. *Proc. Natl. Acad. Sci. USA* 91:704–8

86. Tang XS, Randall DW, Force DA, Diner BA, Britt RD. 1996. Manganese-tyrosine interaction in the photosystem II oxygen-evolving complex. *J. Am. Chem. Soc.* 118:7638–39

87. Tang XS, Sivaraja M, Dismukes GC. 1993. Protein and substrate coordination to the manganese cluster in the photosynthetic water oxidizing complex: ^{15}N and ^{1}H ENDOR spectroscopy of the S_2 state multiline signal in the thermophilic cyanobacterium *Synechococcus elongatus. J. Am. Chem. Soc.* 115:2382–89

88. Thomann H, Bernardo M. 1993. Pulsed electron nuclear double and multiple resonance spectroscopy of metals in proteins and enzymes. In *Biological Magnetic Resonance*, ed. LJ Berliner, J Reuben, 13:275–322. New York: Plenum

89. Turconi S, MacLachlan DJ, Bratt PJ, Nugent JHA, Evans MCW. 1997. Analysis of the interaction of water with the manganese cluster of photosystem II using isotopically labeled water. *Biochemistry* 36:879–85

90. Yachandra VK, DeRose VJ, Latimer MJ, Mukerji I, Sauer K, Klein MP. 1993. Where plants make oxygen: a structural model for the photosynthetic oxygen-evolving manganese cluster. *Science* 260:675–79

91. Yachandra VK, Sauer K, Klein MP. 1996. Manganese cluster in photosynthesis: where plants oxidize water to dioxygen. *Chem. Rev.* 96:2927–50

92. Yamauchi T, Mino H, Matsukawa T, Kawamori A, Ono T. 1997. Parallel polarization electron paramagnetic resonance studies of the S_1-state manganese cluster in the photosynthetic oxygen-evolving system. *Biochemistry* 36:7520–26

93. Zaltsman L, Ananyev GM, Bruntrage E, Dismukes GC. 1997. Quantitative kinetic model for photoassembly of the photosynthetic water oxidase from its inorganic constituents. *Biochemistry* 36:8914–22

94. Zheng M, Dismukes GC. 1996. Orbital configurations of the valence electrons, ligand field symmetry, and manganese oxidation states of the photosynthetic water oxidizing complex: analysis of the S_2 state multiline EPR signals. *Inorg. Chem.* 35:3307–19

95. Zheng M, Khangulov SV, Dismukes GC, Barynin VV. 1994. Electronic structure of dimanganese (II,III) and dimanganese (III,IV) complexes and dimanganese catalase enzyme—a general EPR spectral simulation approach. *Inorg. Chem.* 33:382–87

96. Zimmermann JL, Boussac A, Rutherford AW. 1993. The manganese center of oxygen-evolving and calcium-depleted photosystem II: a pulsed EPR spectroscopy study. *Biochemistry* 32:4831–41

97. Zimmermann JL, Rutherford AW. 1984. EPR studies of the oxygen-evolving enzyme of photosystem II. *Biochim. Biophys. Acta* 767:160–67

98. Zimmermann JL, Rutherford AW. 1986. Electron paramagnetic resonance properties of the S_2 state of the oxygen evolving complex of photosystem II. *Biochemistry* 25:4609–15

Annu. Rev. Biophys. Biomol. Struct. 2000. 29:497–521

ELECTROSTATIC MECHANISMS OF DNA DEFORMATION

Loren Dean Williams

School of Chemistry and Biochemistry, Georgia Institute of Technology, Atlanta, Georgia 30332-0400; e-mail: loren.williams@chemistry.gatech.edu

L. James Maher III[*]

Department of Biochemistry and Molecular Biology, Mayo Foundation, Rochester, Minnesota 55905; e-mail: maher@mayo.edu

Key Words   curvature, bending, counterion condensation, groove, collapse

■ **Abstract**   The genomes of higher cells consist of double-helical DNA, a densely charged polyelectrolyte of immense length. The intrinsic physical properties of DNA, as well as the properties of its complexes with proteins and ions, are therefore of fundamental interest in understanding the functions of DNA as an informational macromolecule. Because individual DNA molecules often exceed 1 cm in length, it is clear that DNA bending, folding, and interaction with nuclear proteins are necessary for packaging genomes in small volumes and for integrating the nucleotide sequence information that guides genetic readout. This review first focuses on recent experiments exploring how the shape of the densely charged DNA polymer and asymmetries in its surrounding counterion distribution mutually influence one another. Attention is then turned to experiments seeking to discover the degree to which asymmetric phosphate neutralization can lead to DNA bending in protein-DNA complexes. It is argued that electrostatic effects play crucial roles in the intrinsic, sequence-dependent shape of DNA and in DNA shapes induced by protein binding.

CONTENTS

---

*Corresponding author.

1056-8700/00/0610-0497$14.00   **497**

PERSPECTIVES AND OVERVIEW

In this review we discuss electrostatic forces that result in the local deformation of DNA. Four kinds of DNA deformation are considered here: curvature, bending, torsion, and stretching. DNA curvature and DNA bending (10, 25) refer to lateral deviations of the helix axis from a linear trajectory. Curvature refers to nonlinear geometries adopted by double-helical DNA fragments in a specified solvent and ion environment, but in the absence of bound proteins. The extent to which DNA curvature is a property intrinsic to the DNA sequence itself, rather than a response to the solvent and ion environment, is an important issue to be addressed here. DNA bending refers to nonlinear geometries induced in DNA upon binding to proteins. Of specific interest is the role of electrostatic forces in DNA bending and, in particular, how modulation of interphosphate repulsion forces might play a role in DNA bending by proteins. Besides DNA curvature and bending, DNA stretching along the helix axis and torsion about the helix axis are also of interest.

Local curvature and bending deformations of DNA are critical to three aspects of DNA function in cells. First, the extreme length of genomic DNA (∼2 m in the case of diploid human DNA) necessitates remarkable but reversible compaction for storage. The detailed basis of DNA compaction in nuclei and viruses is not fully understood but involves DNA wrapping or spooling on protein scaffolds or condensation with other oligocationic substances (5). Second, it appears likely that DNA sequence information is detected to some extent by "indirect readout," that is, sequence-specific DNA shapes that modulate interaction with DNA-binding proteins. Deformed (or deformable) DNA sequences may provide cues allowing the proper positioning of machinery that detects punctuation signals in genomes (62). Third, DNA deformation is required for the integration of DNA sequence information encoded at remote sites. Thus, DNA sequences specifying binding sites for regulatory proteins are frequently separated by relatively long distances, yet proteins bound to these sites often sense one another "at a distance," displaying cooperativity in function. Integration of remote sequence information is typically understood in terms of DNA bending and looping to bring remote binding sites into proximity. DNA deformation is particularly important because naked DNA behaves as a locally stiff polymer in aqueous solution.

MEASURES OF DNA STIFFNESS

Persistence Length

DNA stiffness can be described in terms of several measurable parameters (56). One measure of DNA stiffness is longitudinal persistence length P [$\sim$150 bp at 25°C, 0.2 M ionic strength (8, 35)], formally defined as the average projection of the molecular end-to-end distance vector on its initial path vector, in the limit of infinite chain length (8, 24). Persistence length is thus a measure of the resistance of a polymer to lateral bending. Various other interpretations of persistence length are also helpful. For example, as DNA length decreases below the persistence length, the molecular behavior approaches that of a rigid rod with elastic resilience (24). This rigid-rod approximation becomes particularly applicable to DNA fragments of $\sim P/2$ ($\sim$75 bp). Another useful interpretation of persistence length is the distance over which the root-mean-square (rms) bend angle in any particular direction is 1 rad ($\sim$60°). Thus, under the conditions specified above, the helix axis of an average DNA molecule changes direction by $\sim$60° over every 150-bp segment.

It should be noted that, although DNA is locally rather stiff, very long DNA molecules are globally flexible such that the average end-to-end molecular distance approximates $(PL)^{0.5}$, where L is the molecular contour length. Thus, the approximate end-to-end distance for a continuous DNA double helix encoding the human genome ($\sim 3 \times 10^9$ bp) would not be 1 m (its contour length), but rather 230 μm owing to global DNA flexibility. However, because animal cells have typical diameters of 10–30 μm and typical nuclear diameters of 5–7 μm, it is evident that random coiling provides insufficient compaction for DNA packaging. DNA spooling onto histones and subsequent higher-order interactions are therefore required.

Torsional Rigidity

DNA also displays local stiffness in torsion. This property can be expressed in terms of a "torsional" persistence length, that is, the length over which DNA tends to resist twisting about the helix axis. By analogy to longitudinal persistence length, the DNA length required to give an rms twist deviation of 1 rad ($\sim$60°) from the initial reference frame can be defined as the torsional persistence length T, which has a calculated value of $\sim$180 bp, a value similar to the longitudinal persistence length P (J Kahn, personal communication). Remarkably, the DNA distance required for two sites to become insensitive to torsional phasing (i.e. to obtain an rms torsional deviation of 180°) is ~2000 bp. Thus, over shorter distances, strong face-of-the-helix (phasing) effects can be reasonably expected for bound proteins.

The combination of lateral and torsional DNA stiffness has profound implications for three-dimensional nucleoprotein structures involving DNA. Because of this inherent stiffness, the biologically relevant bending and folding of DNA into compact nucleoprotein structures such as nucleosomes (53), recombination complexes (21), and transcription complexes (19, 35, 69) require energy if DNA is to be deformed more extremely than indicated by the persistence parameters described above. This energy is provided by favorable protein-DNA interactions involving van der Waals contacts, burial of hydrophobic surfaces, formation of hydrogen bonds, and ion pairings that release counterions. Many or all of these forces presumably play roles in the alteration of DNA shape by proteins.

A second key implication appears in calculations of the effective relative concentrations of DNA sites (or proteins bound to them) by virtue of their occurrence on the same DNA molecule. Such effective concentrations are equivalent to j factors (3, 74, 81) and reflect the frequency of intramolecular collisions between specified DNA sites. Model calculations accounting for DNA stiffness show that two sites on DNA collide most frequently when they are separated by ~500 bp, creating an effective concentration in excess of 1×10^{-7} M (74, 81). Under appropriate conditions, two proteins bound to such sites are held at higher local concentration via the DNA tether than when the proteins are free in solution. More closely spaced sites collide less frequently owing to the stiffness of the intervening DNA; at 150-bp separation, the effective concentration of one DNA site in the presence of another is only ~2×10^{-9} M (~50-fold lower than maximum). Sites separated by DNA lengths > ~500 bp also experience lower effective concentrations owing to dilution as each site samples a greater volume of space: at ~3000 bp of separation, the effective concentration of two tethered sites is reduced to ~2×10^{-8} M (~fivefold lower than maximum). These considerations emphasize the importance of local DNA curvature and/or bending in altering the degree to which proteins sense one another when bound to a common DNA molecule.

When two DNA sites are defined on specific faces of the double helix, effective concentrations also oscillate in a sinusoidal manner as a function of separation distance, reflecting the helical periodicity of the double helix. Optimal vs nonoptimal helical phasing may alter the effective concentration of two sites by five- to tenfold over separation distances of 60–200 bp because of torsional rigidity (74).

Young's Modulus

Besides resisting longitudinal and torsional deformation, DNA resists stretching beyond the contour length associated with its canonical B form. Resistance to such stretching is characterized by an elastic stretch modulus, S, which, when divided by the cross-sectional area of the polymer, gives the familiar Young's modulus, E. Recent innovative single-molecule stretching experiments with phage λ DNA have provided estimates for S (2). Interestingly, the measured longitudinal persistence length P was observed to be roughly constant between 10 mM and 600 mM ionic strength, whereas the elastic stretch modulus S increased dramatically: overstretching DNA was easier at low ionic strength. Interpreting the observed relationship between P and S will require additional studies.

CONTRIBUTIONS OF INTERPHOSPHATE REPULSIONS TO DNA STIFFNESS

What accounts for the stiffness of DNA? Surprisingly, the answer to this fundamental question remains unresolved. Various possibilities can be considered. In one view, the tendency to maximize base stacking is the dominant force resisting DNA deformations such as lateral bending, torsion, and stretching. On the other hand, mutual interphosphate repulsions (and their interactions with the local base-pair dipoles) might cause DNA rigidity by resisting deformed conformations, which crowd phosphate groups. In yet another view, DNA stiffness reflects an equilibrium between forces that tend to compress the DNA (such as base-pair stacking) and interphosphate repulsions (which tend to stretch it). Estimating the relative contributions of base stacking and electrostatic repulsions to DNA stiffness and deformation remains an important and active research area. This review considers the evidence that local electrostatic effects contribute substantially to intrinsic DNA curvature and to DNA bending induced by bound ligands and proteins.

Counterion Condensation Theory

Critical to a discussion of electrostatic effects in DNA is an appreciation for the counterion condensation phenomenon associated with densely charged polyelectrolytes. Many sophisticated analyses and simulations have been applied to understanding the distribution of counterions around DNA (27, 60, 61). The elegant theory of Manning (55) remains a useful framework for interpreting the thermodynamic behavior of DNA in solutions of ions. Manning proposed that the high negative charge density of DNA induces a concentrated cloud of mobile and hydrated counterions within ~ 7 Å of the DNA surface. For monovalent cations, the ionic concentration in this cloud approaches 1 M and is relatively independent of the bulk cation concentration. This "condensed" layer of counterions is sufficient to neutralize $\sim 76\%$ of the DNA charge, thereby reducing the charge of each phosphate (in a thermodynamic sense) to $-0.24\ e$. This model indicates that divalent and trivalent counterions reduce residual phosphate charge to $-0.12\ e$ and $-0.08\ e$, respectively (55). This analysis has two particularly important implications. First, the electrostatic contribution to DNA stiffness is reduced by phosphate screening owing to counterion condensation. Second, the binding of cationic ligands to

DNA is an ion-exchange reaction in which condensed counterions are released into bulk solvent, providing an important favorable entropic source of binding energy (70, 71).

DNA Persistence Length and Ionic Strength

Does the predicted residual phosphate charge of -0.24 (monovalent salt) contribute to polymer stiffness under physiological ionic conditions? Under such conditions, the Debye screening length, κ^{-1}, is ~ 10 Å (~ 3 bp), suggesting that, if interphosphate repulsions contribute substantially to stiffness, they must do so through local interactions (8, 57). A seemingly direct approach to estimating the electrostatic contribution to DNA stiffness has been to measure the longitudinal persistence length of DNA as a function of monovalent cation concentration (reviewed in 24). A particularly interesting recent example is the measurement of single-molecule DNA elasticity (related to persistence length) in the presence of different concentrations of counterions of different valences (2). For monovalent salt, these authors found:

$$P = P_0 + 0.324I^{-1} \qquad\qquad 1.$$

where P_0 (500 Å) is the nonelectrostatic contribution to longitudinal persistence length in Å and I is ionic strength in molar units. Thus, the stiffness of DNA as measured by persistence length in dilute solution appears to decrease dramatically as monovalent cations are added, reaching an invariant value of ~ 500 Å under physiological conditions.

The independence of longitudinal persistence length from cation concentration in the physiological range (as cited above) remains a subject of some dispute (24, 26, 55). If P achieves some constant "saturated" value above an ionic strength of 50 mM, it is tempting to conclude that interphosphate repulsions are completely screened under physiological conditions ($I \geq 140$ mM) and therefore make no contribution to DNA stiffness over this range of ion concentrations. In contrast, Manning's theory predicts that residual phosphate charges should make a constant local contribution to stiffness (55). That an electrostatic contribution to P persists above 100 mM ionic strength is suggested by the fact that multivalent cations such as Mg^{2+} [predicted to reduce residual phosphate charge from -0.24 to -0.12 (55)] drastically reduce persistence length (2). Persistence lengths below 300 Å were estimated for DNA in the presence of certain multivalent cations (2). The mechanism for this reduction in P is unknown. Bloomfield and coworkers suggest that transient and random multivalent cation binding and bending of DNA may be occurring (2, 76). An alternative interpretation is that counterions of higher valance lower residual phosphate charge in accord with counterion condensation theory (55), reducing interphosphate repulsions and decreasing DNA stiffness.

It is important, however, that P is not the only measure of DNA flexibility. For example, interphosphate repulsions may also contribute to the elastic stretch modulus of DNA, S (2). Thus, deducing the contribution of interphosphate repulsions to DNA stiffness from the dependence of P on I remains problematical.

Results of other recent experiments suggest that DNA-like molecules remain stiff even when their formal axial charge density is reduced by a factor of two. Hagerman & Hagerman allowed methylated monomeric adenosine nucleosides to spontaneously assemble into metastable "meroduplexes" on a complementary single-stranded poly(deoxythymidylate) (23). Using transient electric birefringence (TEB) analysis, these authors fit relaxation data to persistence length models and concluded that the hemi-charged meroduplex had a persistence length approaching that of duplex DNA. This intriguing result suggests that base stacking interactions predominate over interphosphate repulsions in determining P, although a role for local phosphate neutralization in modifying helix trajectory is not ruled out.

Interphosphate Repulsions and Persistence Length

Is it reasonable to expect that interphosphate repulsions should contribute strongly to persistence length? When DNA is laterally bent, phosphates on the inner face of the bend experience crowding. However, such a deformation simultaneously increases interphosphate distances on the opposite face of the site of bending, such that the costs associated with phosphate crowding on one face and the favorable energy of interphosphate stretching on the opposite face might tend to cancel. Compensation between phosphate crowding and stretching is observed when interphosphate distances are examined in bent DNA from the nucleosome crystal structure (53). Thus, the net electrostatic bending energy may be small in such cases, not because phosphate repulsions are fully screened but because they tend to cancel on opposite sides of the helix.

Manning Theory of Interphosphate Stretching Forces

Manning approached the problem of the electrostatic contribution to DNA rigidity by placing the focus on interphosphate stretching forces within the double helix (57). This theory proposes that the stable double-helix structure of DNA represents an equilibrium between stretching forces (caused by interphosphate repulsions) and compressive forces (caused by attractive interactions between nucleotides such as, but not necessarily limited to, stacking forces between base pairs). Manning estimated the stretching force as the partial derivative of DNA free energy as a function of length, thereby relating this force to the linear charge density and the Debye charge screening parameter. The theory requires no assumptions about the salt dependence of P, and a conventional value for P was used in calculations. The result of this analysis suggested that significant local interphosphate stretching forces balance compressive forces within DNA and that these stretching forces can drive DNA deformation when phosphate charges are locally neutralized. In particular, asymmetric phosphate neutralization (as might be induced by nonhomogeneous counterion density or the presence of a cationic protein bound to one DNA face) was predicted to result in significant asymmetric interphosphate stretching forces and DNA deformation. In the following discussion, we interpret electrostatic contributions to both DNA intrinsic curvature and induced bending in the context of this theory.

ELECTROSTATICS AND INTRINSIC DNA CURVATURE

Sequence-Dependent Shapes and Traditional Interpretations

Traditional analysis of high-resolution DNA structures, originating with "Calladine's Rules" (7), focuses on direct base-base interactions. Estimates of the relative importance of various types of base-base interactions and other conformational restraints have evolved over time, yet the essential heterocycle-centric, nonelectrostatic nature of the traditional paradigm has not. It has been proposed that direct base-base interactions vary with sequence and modulate relative orientations of bases and base pairs, thereby causing intrinsic curvature (11, 12). In these models, DNA can also be bent by external "leverage forces" exerted by proteins. These traditional models discount contributions from Manning's electrostatic stretching forces. Along with other deficiencies, traditional models deny the central role of electrostatics that is demanded by the effects of salt on intrinsic curvature of A-tracts (13, 48, 80) and G-tracts (6, 14, 89). By contrast, in electrostatic models DNA bends spontaneously when electrostatic forces are asymmetric. For example, an explicit treatment of dynamical characteristics of divalent cations described by Rouzina & Bloomfield (76) suggests that DNA curvature arises from short-range electrostatic interactions between phosphate groups and mobile divalent cations. An analogous conclusion was obtained by Stigter (86).

Role of Ions in Determining Intrinsic DNA Shape: Hybrid Solvent Model

History   We believe that an artifactual and unphysical charge imbalance in three-dimensional structures of DNA has contributed to the underestimation of the importance of electrostatics. The seminal "Dickerson dodecamer" [CGCGAATTCGCG, 2.5-Å resolution, Nucleic Acid Database (NDB) entry DBL001 (100)], which spawned the heterocycle-centric paradigm, contains DNA and site-bound water molecules, but no cationic counterions. Observation of monovalent cations such as sodium is particularly problematic. Even at very high resolution, Williams and coworkers directly observed only a magnesium ion and a partial spermine molecule among >150 water molecules [NDB entry BDL084, 1.4-Å resolution (82, 83)] associated with the Dickerson dodecamer. This charge imbalance is a general phenomenon that extends to essentially all nucleic acid structures. The 76 phosphates of the highest-resolution tRNA structure [NDB entry trna10, 2.5-Å resolution (32, 33)] are predominantly unneutralized. The tRNA structure contains only four magnesium ions and no monovalent cations. The apparent charge imbalance persists in complexes of nucleic acids with cationic proteins. In the nucleosome core particle [NDB entry pd0001, 2.8-Å resolution (53)], 290 phosphate groups are compensated for by only 162 cationic amino acids and 6 divalent cations. This count underestimates the imbalance by ignoring anionic amino acid residues.

Williams and coworkers have proposed a hybrid-solvent model (82, 83) that is consistent with the near invisibility of monovalent cations to X-ray diffraction. In this model, cations distribute asymmetrically around DNA, and solvent sites that were previously characterized as pure water are hybrids, which are partially occupied by monovalent cations (Figure 1; see color insert). The greater occupancies of water over monovalent cations in hybrid solvent sites present difficult analytical challenges during X-ray structure determination. However, these challenges are now being at least partially overcome with high-resolution data, ion substitution, and other techniques (82, 83, 96).

In purely polyelectrolyte solution models, cations around DNA are mobile and are distributed with radial dependence (70, 71). Several lines of evidence suggest that a modest modification of these powerful models may be in order. The mobile cation atmosphere, whether monovalent or divalent, appears to be perturbed by DNA functional groups and is sequence dependent. Crystallographic observations of monovalent cation-water hybrids within the minor groove of A-tracts (82, 83, 96) suggest selective partitioning into that region. In addition, fully hydrated magnesium ions have been shown to avoid DNA amino groups in X-ray structures (83), consistent with nuclear magnetic resonance (NMR) evidence for perturbations of divalent cations from purely radial distributions in solution (29). The influence of DNA functional groups on cation distribution appears to cause a superimposition of peaks and troughs on purely polyelectrolyte radial cation distributions.

Additional Evidence of Influence of DNA Functional Groups on Cation Distributions   The first observation of a cation within the minor groove of an AT-tract was made in 1973 by Rosenberg et al, who used single-crystal diffraction to identify a sodium ion near the floor of an abbreviated minor groove of a dinucleotide duplex (75). The relevance of that structure was discounted during initial interpretations of the Dickerson dodecamer. Those interpretations described a purely aqueous "spine of hydration" in the AT-tract minor groove (46). However, additional support for monovalent cations within the minor groove of AT-tracts was provided by Bartenev and coworkers, using fiber diffraction (1). The fiber and single-crystal data are supported by results obtained with DNA in solution. Hud et al demonstrated that ammonium binds preferentially in AT-tract minor grooves (31). These authors have established isotopically labeled ammonium as an excellent NMR probe for monovalent alkali ions in both B-DNA and quadruplex DNA (30). The combined experimental results are consistent with a series of nanosecond-level molecular dynamics simulations, by Young & Beveridge (101) and Young et al (102), of DNA fragments under various salt conditions. In those molecular dynamics simulations, monovalent cations bind preferentially in AT-tract minor grooves. Thus, a view emerges in which DNA curvature is not seen as intrinsic to the double helix in isolation but is the response of DNA to sequence-dependent asymmetries in the distribution of counterions.

ELECTROSTATICS AND DNA BENDING BY PROTEINS

Classes of DNA-Bending Proteins

High-resolution structural data reveal at least two motifs for DNA bending by proteins (Figure 2; see color insert). These two motifs suggest different underlying mechanisms. One class of DNA-bending proteins (class 1) contacts bent DNA on its convex surface, inducing the helical axis to curve away from the bound protein (54). Such proteins include the TATA-binding protein TBP (40, 42), high-mobility-group proteins such as the human male sex-determining factor SRY, and the lymphoid enhancer-binding protein 1 (68, 98), as well as other proteins that are often classified as "architectural" binding proteins (9, 98, 99). DNA bending by proteins in this group appears to involve intercalation of hydrophobic amino acids between base pairs in the minor groove of DNA, causing DNA unwinding to enlarge the minor groove and alter the helix axis (98, 99). It has been suggested that the relatively low dielectric character of the intercalated protein enhances specific interphosphate repulsions, contributing to DNA deformation (16).

A second class of DNA-bending proteins (which we have termed class 2) includes the *Escherichia coli* catabolite activator protein CAP (79), the histone octamer, responsible for the remarkable wrapping of ~150 bp of DNA by ~720° in nucleosomes (53), and the *E. coli* integration host factor IHF (72). Many other class-2 DNA-bending proteins have been described (43, 51, 67). Class-2 proteins contact bent DNA on its concave surface, curving the helical axis toward the bound protein. The engaged surfaces of class-2 proteins typically present cationic amino acids to the DNA, suggesting that electrostatic interactions are important for DNA binding by these proteins. How such electrostatic interactions contribute to DNA bending is an interesting question.

DNA Bending and Looping Energetics

Proteins that bend DNA do so because their binding free energy is sufficient to pay the energetic cost of deforming the relatively stiff double helix. Simplification of an expression for the free energy of DNA bending (35) leads to Equation 2:

$$\Delta G_{bend} = 0.0135 \frac{(\Delta\Theta_{deg})^2}{L_{bp}} \text{(kcal/mol)}, \qquad 2.$$

where the DNA-bending free energy at room temperature is expressed in kilocalories per mole, assuming a DNA persistence length of 150 bp. Equation 2 applies to the bending DNA by $\Delta\Theta$ degrees over a contour length of L_{bp}. When applied to

DNA bending on the scale of the nucleosome, this equation suggests that bending $\sim$75 bp of DNA into a circle requires >22 kcal/mol of energy. The equilibrium constant for spontaneous curvature of a 75-bp DNA segment into this shape is 3×10^{-18}, demonstrating that favorable protein-DNA interactions are essential to drive DNA bending in such a structure.

What are the probable sources of this bending energy, and what is the relative importance of each source? Unfavorable energetic contributions to DNA bending by histone binding include both electrostatic and nonelectrostatic costs of bending the DNA. Favorable contributions to DNA bending by proteins presumably arise from the formation of new hydrogen bonds, van der Waals contacts, release of water from interacting nonpolar surfaces, and electrostatic interactions including Coulombic attraction between cationic protein side chains and DNA phosphates and release of condensed counterions upon protein binding (70, 71).

Just as the case has been made for a dominant role of local electrostatics in determining DNA shape in the presence of small ions, a similar argument can be considered for DNA bending by proteins. Thus, the presence of a bound protein must alter the electrical potential experienced by the DNA and its associated ions. How the DNA relaxes in response to these changes is of interest.

The mechanism by which DNA collapses around a cationic protein can be conceptualized in several ways. For example, class-2 proteins often engage the double helix via a convex surface containing multiple cationic side chains. Coulombic attraction between these side chains and the negatively charged DNA surface provides an intuitive driving force favoring the bending of DNA to maximize favorable electrostatic interactions. Perhaps an equally valid view considers maximization of the favorable entropy of counterion release when DNA bends to enhance surface contact with the protein.

Rich-Mirzabekov-Manning Predictions

A related view of the DNA-bending process was originally suggested by Mirzabekov & Rich (59) and was subsequently addressed mathematically by Manning and coworkers as described above (57). This hypothesis grew from the observation that tRNA^{phe} appears to collapse around a groove-bound oligovalent cation (73). It was reasoned that the approach of a cationic protein side chain to a DNA phosphate is equivalent to canceling the residual negative charge of that phosphate: the fixed charges within the DNA experience pairwise electrostatic attractions (to the cation) and repulsions (from the phosphate). These attractive and repulsive forces cancel as the cation and phosphate are juxtaposed. Asymmetric neutralization of partial DNA phosphate charges by the cationic surface of a class-2 protein is thus predicted to alter the balance of electrostatic forces within the DNA double helix. Using an engineering analogy, Manning and coworkers calculated that modest asymmetric phosphate neutralization would create net local compressive forces within the double helix sufficient to account for the degree of DNA bending observed in the nucleosome (57).

Experiments to Isolate and Detect Collapse Forces

In their theory of DNA bending by asymmetric phosphate neutralization, Manning and coworkers introduced the concept of a phantom protein (57). This concept refers to a model in which the electrostatic consequences of protein binding to DNA are isolated from all other forces. Motivated by this idea, Strauss & Maher simulated the electrostatic consequences of protein binding by chemical synthesis of DNA duplexes in which the phosphate charge distribution was altered by partial substitution with neutral phosphate analogs (87). DNA shape was then indirectly monitored by electrophoresis experiments. Figure 3 depicts the molecular design of the original experiment (87) in which six phosphates flanking the DNA minor groove (oxygens are shown in white) were neutralized by methylphosphonate substitution in different phasings compared with an intrinsically curved

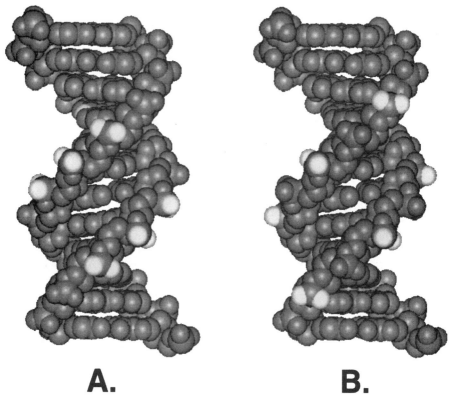

A.   **B.**

Figure 3   Phantom protein design. Synthetic DNA duplexes in which selected phosphates are chemically neutralized by substitution of methylphosphonate analogs. *White spheres* indicate positions of methyl groups in racemic mixtures. *A.* Neutralization of consecutive phosphates across the minor groove. *B.* Neutralization of alternating phosphates across the minor groove.

A_6 tract. Duplexes were ligated end-to-end for electrophoretic assays (10). In support of the model in question, these studies have consistently shown that asymmetric phosphate neutralization causes DNA bending in the predicted direction. DNA bending would not be anticipated in these model systems if the mechanism of class-2 proteins involved only maximization of favorable charge-charge interactions between protein and DNA, because no proteins were present in these experiments.

The initial study of DNA bending by asymmetric substitution of methylphosphonate linkages showed that $\sim20°$ of bending results when three phosphates on each side of one minor groove are neutralized (87). Realistic patterns of phosphate neutralization in protein-DNA complexes may be more diffuse. It was of interest to determine whether such a diffuse patch of neutralization (i.e. alternating neutralized and anionic phosphates) changes the extent of DNA bending compared with bending by consecutive neutralized phosphates. Synthetic duplexes were therefore created to measure DNA bending by alternating neutral methylphosphonate residues (racemic) and anionic phosphate diesters in a patch on one face of duplex DNA (91). Overall, the electrophoretic phasing data confirmed that the patch of alternating racemic methylphosphonate/diester linkages induced bending toward the minor groove, enhancing the A_6 tract bend. Calculations indicated that the magnitude of the bend angle caused by the patch of alternating racemic methylphosphonate/diester linkages was $\sim13°$ toward the minor groove. This result was in qualitative agreement with the previous observation that a patch of consecutive racemic methylphosphonate linkages induces an $\sim20°$ DNA bend toward the minor groove (87).

Analyses of DNA bending by methylphosphonate substitution assumed that electrostatic effects, rather than steric perturbations, are the major consequences of DNA modification. Methylphosphonate incorporation into synthetic oligomers converts the achiral diester to mixtures of diastereomers at each asymmetric phosphorus atom. Using the bending data obtained for alternating racemic methylphosphonate/diester linkages, Strauss and coworkers created synthetic DNA duplexes with purified dimer synthons of defined methylphosphonate stereochemistry to test effects on DNA bending. Results with chirally pure oligomers were qualitatively similar to those observed for duplexes with a patch of alternating racemic methylphosphonate/diester linkages groove (87). The patch of alternating R_P methylphosphonate/diester linkages induced $\sim9°$ of DNA bending. It was notable that DNA bending by pure R_P methylphosphonate isomers was somewhat reduced compared with racemic mixtures of methylphosphonates ($\sim9°$ versus $\sim13°$), although the predominant electrostatic effect was still clearly detectable. One interpretation of these data is that both R_P and S_P methylphosphonate isomers contribute to DNA bending by electrostatic mechanisms. In addition, however, S_P isomers may perturb DNA structure in a subtle manner through nonelectrostatic effects such as differential solvation or unfavorable steric contacts in the major groove. The latter class of contacts may then induce structural changes that tend to exaggerate modestly the electrostatic contribution to DNA bending.

Independent evidence that asymmetric phosphate neutralization can provide a theoretical force for DNA bending comes from a series of recent computer simulations. Sanghani and coworkers (78) used the JUMNA nucleic-acid-modeling program to predict DNA bending on asymmetric charge neutralization in simulated poly(dA)·poly(dT), poly(dG)·(dC), and poly(dTA)·poly(dTA) polymers. Base sequence had a minor effect on the observed bending. The degree of bending increased when neutralization was increased from 4 phosphates to 6 phosphates, remaining unchanged when 8 phosphates were neutralized and decreasing when the neutralization was increased to 10 phosphates. Earlier simulations by Swarnalatha & Yathindra showed no DNA bending when structures of short, uniformly neutralized DNA duplexes were simulated (94). This result would be expected, because it is the asymmetry in phosphate neutralization that is predicted to cause bending.

Gurlie and coworkers extended application of the JUMNA modeling program to the recognition sequence for the *E. coli* CAP protein (22). These authors made several interesting observations. (*a*) The CAP recognition sequence would possess intrinsic curvature (38°) that is amplified to 51° by CAP protein binding. (*b*) A subset of three neutralized phosphates was sufficient to generate much of this protein-induced bend. (*c*) There was an unexpected dependence of bending on sequence context; when the neutralized phosphates were shifted along the helix, induced bending was reduced. (*d*) Analysis of normal modes in the simulations suggested that phosphate neutralization reduced oligomer flexibility.

A subsequent simulation of asymmetric phosphate neutralization was used to study effects on DNA bending of neutralization pattern and explicit methylphosphonate stereochemistry in the context of a 12-bp alternating poly[d(CG)·d(CG)] duplex (47). Energy optimization of these B-like dodecamers with six phosphate neutralizations confirmed the induction of bending toward the neutralized DNA face. Detailed studies of the effects of stereochemistry showed that homogeneous R_P or S_P methylphosphonate substitutions gave somewhat different bend directions and magnitudes than those predicted by a "pure" mathematical neutralization of phosphate oxygens, a result consistent with previous studies (91). Interestingly, incorporation of racemic mixtures of R_P and S_P methylphosphonate stereoisomers resulted in DNA bending comparable with that predicted for "pure" phosphate neutralization. This important result supports the validity of experimental data obtained in such racemic systems (87, 92). In these simulations, however, the magnitude of DNA bending ($\sim 10°$) was somewhat smaller than had been estimated from electrophoretic experiments ($\sim 20°$).

The significance of DNA bending observed in computer simulations of asymmetric phosphate neutralization is largely dependent on the quality of the force fields used. To date, such simulations have not included explicit solvent or counterions. On one hand, this limitation exemplifies the rudimentary nature of these studies. On the other hand, DNA bending observed in these studies demonstrates that electrostatic collapse is predicted without invoking the redistribution of specific solvent and/or counterion molecules.

Strauss and coworkers reasoned that covalent tethering of ammonium ions to one face of the DNA double helix might provide an alternative method to simulate asymmetric phosphate neutralization caused by the cationic amino acids of a bound protein. Primary amines (positively charged at neutral pH) were attached via propyl (88) or hexyl (89) tethers to position 5 of pyrimidine residues in synthetic oligonucleotides. This design simulated the approach of six lysine residues near the phosphate backbone on one face of the double helix. As controls, neutral acetylated derivatives of these tethered amines were also analyzed. Appended cations were phased in relation to intrinsic curves caused by A_5-tracts in electrophoretic phasing assays. Quantitative data analysis demonstrated that the $5'$-A_3GT_3 sequence (studied for propylammonium substitutions) was intrinsically curved by $\sim 9°$ toward the minor groove. When supplemented with six tethered cations, bending toward the minor groove was enhanced to $\sim 17°$, suggesting that the appended positive charges induced $\sim 8°$ of bending. Acetylation of the tethered amines resulted in a DNA shape indistinguishable from the unmodified duplex, supporting the view that the ammonium cations, rather than the tethers, were responsible for DNA bending.

The $\sim 8°$ of bending induced by cations tethered via propyl groups was smaller than the $\sim 20°$ bend induced when a similar pattern of phosphates was completely neutralized by methylphosphonate substitution (87). However, this result was greater than the $\sim 4°$ bend induced in a different DNA sequence by ammonium ions on longer hexyl tethers (89). These results are summarized in Figure 4. Unlike methylphosphonate analogs, flexible tethers presumably allow some dispersion of appended cations over the DNA surface (52). Dispersion of tethered cations in these model duplexes may be greater than for cationic amino acid side chains in DNA-protein complexes, in which specific cation-phosphate interactions can be stabilized by networks of other contacts. These authors therefore speculated that the bending hierarchy methylphosphonate > propylamine > hexylamine reflected the decreasing extent of phosphate neutralization in this series. It will be interesting to explore DNA bending by cations on more rigid tethers (e.g. 3-aminopropyne) to explore these issues.

Experiments to Manipulate Electrostatic Effects in DNA Bending by Proteins

Strauss-Soukup & Maher also applied the phantom protein model to DNA sequences known to be bent by the binding of specific proteins (92). The PU.1 transcription factor is a member of the Ets family of DNA-binding proteins. PU.1 binds to DNA via a loop-helix-loop domain and functions in the differentiation of hematopoietic cells. The crystal structure of a PU.1-DNA complex has been reported (43). The DNA in this complex is bent by 8° as it engages the protein. The pattern of electrostatic contacts between PU.1 and its DNA-binding site suggested to Kodandapani and coworkers that laterally asymmetric phosphate neutralization accompanies PU.1 binding. Because of the previous studies showing that

Intrinsic Shape   Induced Shape

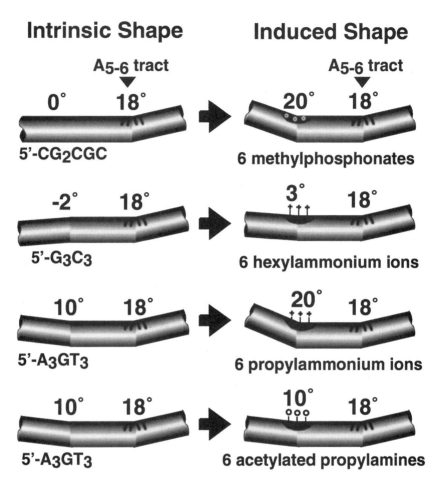

Figure 4 Summary of DNA bending observed by phantom proteins simulated by methylphosphonate substitution (87) or appending cations on propyl (88) or hexyl (89) tethers. Intrinsic DNA shapes of the indicated sequences are shown as cylinders at left, with the position of the reference A_{5-6}-tracts noted. Induced shapes are shown at right.

such neutralization can induce bending in naked DNA, the effect of phosphate neutralization by substituting neutral methylphosphonate internucleoside linkages at relevant positions within DNA containing the PU.1-binding sequence was explored. Duplex DNA oligonucleotides composing the PU.1 recognition sequence were synthesized with appropriate phosphates chemically neutralized. Consistent with the prediction that DNA will collapse toward its partially neutralized surface, DNA neutralized at these seven positions to simulate PU.1 binding was observed to bend by $28°$ (92). The directions of DNA curvature were slightly different in the cocrystal vs the partially neutralized duplexes. The electrostatic component of

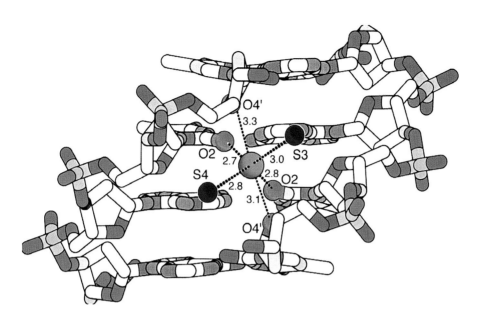

Figure 1 A view into the minor groove of [dCGCGAATTCGCG]2 showing the coordination geometry at the 5' ApT 3' step. The atoms are colored by type, with O, *orange*; P, *yellow*; N, *violet*; and C, *white*. The ligands of the water-cation hybrid, represented as spheres, are two O4' atoms, two thymine carbonyl oxygen atoms (O2), and two occupants of the secondary hydration layer (S, *magenta*). The sphere representing the water-cation hybrid (*blue*) is larger than the other six spheres. Distances indicated are in Å.

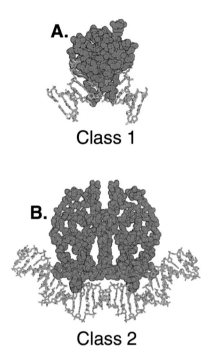

Figure 2 Classes of DNA-bending proteins. A. Class-1 bending proteins (TBP, *red*) bind the DNA minor groove, unwind DNA, and induce bending away from the protein-DNA interface by intercalation of hydrophobic-amino-acid side chains between base pairs. B. Class-2 bending proteins (CAP, *red*) form complexes in which DNA bends toward the protein-DNA interface.

the binding energy therefore appeared more than enough to account for the DNA bending observed in the PU.1-DNA complex.

The cases of dimeric basic-zipper (bZIP) DNA-binding proteins, including Fos/Jun (20), Jun/Jun, CREB (65), and GCN4 (17), are also particularly intriguing. Electrophoretic phasing experiments suggest that different members of this family affect DNA shape differently (36–39). The intrinsic shapes of the binding sites for these proteins in DNA have also been shown to differ (45, 65). Amino acids adjacent to the basic region of each bZIP monomer lie near the DNA double helix. It was noted that the pattern of charged amino acid residues in this region correlates with apparent DNA bending in the resulting complex (39, 65). This relationship has been subsequently demonstrated by showing that changing the charges of these residues induces apparent changes in the bend angle of bound DNA (50, 64, 90, 93).

For example, the yeast bZIP transcription factor GCN4 does not induce DNA bending in vitro. Strauss-Soukup and Maher substituted basic residues for three neutral amino acids in GCN4 to produce a GCN4 derivative that appears in electrophoretic phasing assays to bend DNA by $\sim 16°$ (90). This result is consistent with a model of induced DNA bending wherein excess positive charge in proximity to one face of the double helix neutralizes local phosphate diester anions resulting in a laterally asymmetric charge distribution along the DNA, causing collapse of the DNA toward the neutralized surface. When a wider range of charge substitutions was made, the direction and extent of apparent DNA bending by these derivatives were a roughly linear function of the charges of the amino acids adjacent to the basic domain of the protein (93). This relation held over the dimer charge range $+6$ (15.5° apparent bend toward the minor groove) to -6 (25.2° apparent bend toward the major groove). Independent data for mutants of Jun+Fos show similar, roughly linear relationships between peptide charge and DNA bending (50). These data suggest a model in which the trajectory of DNA responds to lateral asymmetries in charge density.

The observation that cationic amino acids positioned on one DNA face induce apparent DNA collapse toward that face suggests that such bZIP proteins can act as class-2 DNA-bending molecules. However, the underlying electrostatic mechanism of DNA bending is not revealed in such experiments. These data have been interpreted in terms of both direct Coulombic attraction (50) and asymmetric phosphate neutralization (64, 90). To directly test the hypothesis that asymmetric phosphate neutralization is responsible for DNA bending by cationic domains of these bZIP proteins, Tomky and coworkers applied the "phantom protein" strategy to measure the effect of partial phosphate neutralization on the shape of the AP-1 bZIP binding site in duplex DNA (97). DNA bending toward the neutralized face of DNA was again observed. The degree of DNA bending induced by methylphosphonate substitution ($\sim 3.5°$ per neutralized phosphate) was comparable with that induced by GCN4 variants carrying increasing numbers of additional basic amino acids. It is therefore plausible that asymmetric phosphate neutralization is the cause of DNA bending in such complexes. Confirmation of these results will require independent assays of DNA bending by other techniques owing to controversy about interpretation of electrophoretic-phasing experiments with bZIP proteins (50, 54, 84, 85).

FUTURE DIRECTIONS

Phantom Protein Models of Protein/DNA Complexes

It is important to determine the extent to which purely electrostatic effects can explain important biological examples of DNA bending by proteins. Two particularly well-studied cases involve the *E. coli* CAP protein (66, 79) and the nucleosome (53). High-resolution crystal structures now exist for both protein-DNA complexes. In both complexes DNA is highly bent toward the protein-DNA interface (90° over 18 bp in the nucleosome; 90° over 36 bp in the CAP complex). Based on the crystal structures, it is possible to identify cationic amino acid side chains that closely approach the DNA. In the future it may be possible to test the hypothesis that chemical neutralization of the corresponding phosphates will endow the corresponding naked DNA with an intrinsically curved geometry that mimics the shape of DNA in the complex. Quantitative comparison of DNA bending by the "phantom" protein vs bending in the crystal structures will help to estimate the extent to which asymmetric phosphate neutralization contributes to DNA bending in these cases. As described above, initial computer simulations have already addressed these questions for CAP (22).

All-Atom Simulations

An exciting opportunity in molecular mechanics and dynamics modeling is provided by the challenge of exploring DNA bending induced by asymmetries in local charge, whether caused by counterion distributions, bound ligands, bound proteins, or chemical modifications with charged adducts. As described above, important initial contributions have been made with all-atom models of DNA in which solvent and counterions are implicit (22, 47, 78). The development of more complete force fields for DNA and all-atom simulations with explicit solvent and ions has been impressive (34, 103). The availability of such tools leads to optimism that the basis for sequence-specific features of DNA structure may soon be understood at the level of steric and electrostatic factors and that the roles of solvent and ion distributions about the double helix may be elucidated with greater confidence (101, 102).

Effects of Asymmetrically Appended Ions

To date, phantom protein designs have involved chemically neutralizing phosphate diesters or appending monovalent cations asymmetrically about DNA to simulate the binding of class-2 proteins. The intriguing proposal that class-1 DNA-bending proteins (e.g. TBP) bend DNA away from the binding interface by asymmetrical enhancement of interphosphate repulsions extends the possible role of electrostatic effects (16). The apparent response of DNA shape to GCN4 variants substituted with multiple anionic residues supports the plausibility of this model (93). It is important to devise and study synthetic double helices wherein enhanced interphosphate repulsions are simulated by asymmetrically tethering additional anions.

Oligovalent cations such as Mg^{2+}, $Co(NH_3)_6^{3+}$, and spermidine^{3+} can dramatically alter the physical properties of double-helical DNA (2, 4, 5). A theory to explain reduced DNA longitudinal persistence lengths and, ultimately, DNA condensation has been presented (76). This model suggests that multivalent cations dispersed in the DNA grooves act to cause local DNA collapse, ultimately leading to DNA condensation. This process may be critical for DNA condensation during packaging and other phenomena in vivo. It has been impossible to directly measure bending caused by an isolated multivalent cation such as Co^{3+} bound to a single DNA. Perhaps synthetic strategies for tethering trivalent cations to DNA will allow analysis of their effects on local DNA bending.

DNA Rigidity In Vivo

Although simplified model systems provide tractable tools for measuring electrostatic effects on DNA stiffness, curvature, and bending, these issues are most significant in a cellular context. How important are intrinsic DNA longitudinal and torsional stiffness in the presence of the cellular machinery that handles, folds, unwinds, and reads DNA sequence information during gene expression?

Transcriptional regulation provides an important system for studying the importance of DNA curvature and bending because transcription activator proteins bound at a distance from promoters are thought to function through DNA looping to directly contact their targets (15, 28, 44, 63, 74). DNA looping plays a significant role in the regulation of certain prokaryotic genes including *gal, lac*, and *deo* in *E. coli* (3, 49, 58). Eukaryotic transcription activation is usually depicted such that the DNA intervening between the transcription start site and the sites of activator binding is bent to allow the activators to interact directly with the basal transcription apparatus (69).

Control of eukaryotic transcription initiation therefore involves regulating the affinity of a promoter for the transcription initiation machinery. Transcription activator proteins bound to DNA various distances from the TATA box contribute to promoter affinity. Because most eukaryotic transcription is thought to depend on favorable contributions of DNA-bound activator proteins, the local shape of the tethering DNA should constrain the spatial distribution of these proteins if they are to productively recruit RNA polymerase. Thus, DNA template bending (intrinsic or induced) is predicted to play a critical role in driving protein-protein interactions over the relatively short DNA separation distances commonly encountered for upstream activator-binding sites in promoters (74). The attractive hypothesis that the inherent physical properties of DNA constrain transcription activation from eukaryotic promoters has been examined in a few studies (18, 41, 77, 95) but should be subjected to systematic experimental verification.

CONCLUSION

Double-helical DNA is a locally stiff polymer in terms of longitudinal-persistence length, torsional rigidity, and resistance to stretching. The physical basis for DNA stiffness remains unresolved. A theoretical model predicts that unbalanced compressive and stretching forces will arise within the double helix upon asymmetric phosphate neutralization (57). We argue that lateral asymmetries in the distributions of counterions and protein cationic side chains both contribute to DNA deformation, based on these electrostatic principles.

ACKNOWLEDGMENTS

LJM expresses appreciation to present and past lab members, particularly A Rodrigues, J Strauss-Soukup, E Ross, P Hardwidge, L Cassiday, and R Den, and acknowledges funding support from NIH grant GM54411 and from the Mayo Foundation. LDW notes the contributions of L McFail-Isom, X Shui, C Sines, and D VanDerveer, and support from NSF grant MCB-9056300 and American Cancer Society grant RPG-95-116-03-GMC. Helpful discussions were provided by V Bloomfield, J Chaires, G Clark, D Crothers, J Feigon, B Gold, P Hagerman, N Hud, J Kahn, G Manning, Y-P Pang, T Record, I Rouzina, J Subirana, and C Switzer.

Visit the Annual Reviews home page at www.AnnualReviews.org

LITERATURE CITED

1. Bartenev VN, Golovamov EI, Kapitonova KA, Mokulskii MA, Volkova LI, Skuratovskii IY. 1983. Structure of the B DNA cationic shell as revealed by an X-ray diffraction study of CsDNA. Sequence-specific cationic stabilization of B form DNA. *J. Mol. Biol.* 169:217–34

2. Baumann C, Smith S, Bloomfield V, Bustamante C. 1997. Ionic effects on the elasticity of single DNA molecules. *Proc. Natl. Acad. Sci. USA* 94:6185–90

3. Bellomy G, Mossing M, Record M. 1988. Physical properties of DNA *in vivo* as probed by the length dependence of the *lac* operator

looping process. *Biochemistry* 27:3900–6

4. Bloomfield VA. 1996. DNA condensation. *Curr. Opin. Struct. Biol.* 6:334–41

5. Bloomfield VA. 1998. DNA condensation by multivalent cations. *Biopolymers* 44: 269–82

6. Brukner I, Susic S, Dlakic M, Savic A, Pongor S. 1994. Physiological concentration of magnesium ions induces a strong macroscopic curvature in GGGCCC-containing DNA. *J. Mol. Biol.* 236:26–32

7. Calladine CR. 1982. Mechanics of sequence-dependent stacking of bases in B-DNA. *J. Mol. Biol.* 161:343–52

8. Cantor CR, Schimmel PR. 1980. *Biophysical Chemistry. Part III: The Behavior of Biological Macromolecules*, pp. 979–1039, New York: WH Freeman

9. Crothers D. 1993. Architectural elements in nucleoprotein complexes. *Curr. Biol.* 3:675–76

10. Crothers DM, Drak J. 1992. Global features of DNA structure by comparative gel electrophoresis. *Meth. Enzymol.* 212:46–71

11. Dickerson RE. 1998. DNA bending: the prevalence of kinkiness and the virtues of normality. *Nucleic Acids Res.* 26:1906–26

12. Dickerson RE, Chiu TK. 1997. Helix bending as a factor in protein/DNA recognition. *Biopolymers* 44:361–403

13. Diekmann S, Wang JC. 1985. On the sequence determinants and flexibility of the kinetoplast DNA fragment with abnormal gel electrophoretic mobilities. *J. Mol. Biol.* 186:1–11

14. Dlakic M, Harrington RE. 1995. Bending and torsional flexibility of G/C-rich sequences as determined by cyclization assays. *J. Biol. Chem.* 270:29945–52

15. Dunaway M, Droge P. 1989. Transactivation of the *Xenopus* rRNA gene promoter by its enhancer. *Nature* 341:657–59

16. Elcock AH, McCammon JA. 1996. The low dielectric interior of proteins is sufficient to cause major structural changes in DNA on association. *J. Am. Chem. Soc.* 118:3787–88

17. Ellenberger TE, Brandl CJ, Struhl K, Harrison SC. 1992. The GCN4 basic region leucine zipper binds DNA as a dimer of uninterrupted alpha helices: Crystal structure of the protein-DNA complex. *Cell* 71:1223–37

18. Falvo JV, Thanos D, Maniatis T. 1995. Reversal of intrinsic DNA bends in the IFN beta gene enhancer by transcription factors and the architectural protein HMG1(Y). *Cell* 83:1101–11

19. Giese K, Kingsley C, Kirshner JR, Grosschedl R. 1995. Assembly and function of a TCRalpha enhancer complex is dependent on LEF-1-induced DNA bending and multiple protein-protein interactions. *Genes Dev.* 9:995–1008

20. Glover JNM, Harrison SC. 1995. Crystal structure of the heterodimeric bZIP transcription factor c-fos-c-jun bound to DNA. *Nature* 373:257–61

21. Goodman SD, Nash HA. 1989. Functional replacement of a protein-induced bend in a DNA recombination site. *Nature* 341:251–54

22. Gurlie R, Duong TH, Zakrzewska K. 1999. The role of DNA-protein salt bridges in molecular recognition: a model study. *Biopolymers* 49:313–27

23. Hagerman KR, Hagerman PJ. 1996. Helix rigidity of DNA: the meroduplex as an experimental paradigm. *J. Mol. Biol.* 260:207–23

24. Hagerman PJ. 1988. Flexibility of DNA. *Annu. Rev. Biophys. Biophys. Chem.* 17:265–86

25. Hagerman PJ, 1992. Straightening out the bends in curved DNA. *Biochim. Biophys. Acta* 1131:125–32

26. Harrington RE. 1978. The optico-hydrodynamic properties of high molecular weight DNA. III. The effects of NaCl concentration. *Biopolymers* 17:919–36

27. Honig B, Nicholls A. 1995. Classical electrostatics in biology and chemistry. *Science* 268:1144–49

28. Hori R, Carey M. 1994. The role of activators in assembly of RNA polymerase II transcription complexes. *Curr. Opin. Genet. Dev.* 4:236–44

29. Hud NV, Feigon J. 1997. Localization of divalent metal ions in the minor groove of DNA A-tracts. *J. Am. Chem. Soc.* 119:5756–57

30. Hud NV, Schultze P, Feigon J. 1998. Ammonium ion as an NMR probe for monovalent cation coordination sites of DNA quadruplexes. *J. Am. Chem. Soc.* 120:6403–4

31. Hud NV, Sklenar V, Feigon J. 1999. Localization of ammonium ions in the minor groove of DNA duplexes in solution and the origin of DNA A-tract bending. *J. Mol. Biol.* 286:651–60

32. Jack A, Ladner JE, Klug A. 1976. Crystallographic refinement of yeast phenylalanine transfer RNA at 2.5 Å resolution. *J. Mol. Biol.* 108:619–49

33. Jack A, Ladner JE, Rhodes D, Brown RS, Klug A. 1977. A crystallographic study of metal-binding to yeast phenylalanine transfer RNA. *J. Mol. Biol.* 111:315–28

34. Jayaram B, Beveridge DL. 1996. Modeling DNA in aqueous solutions. *Annu. Rev. Biophys. Biomol. Struct.* 25:367–94

35. Kahn JD, Crothers DM. 1993. DNA bending in transcription initiation, *Cold Spring Harbor Symposia Symp. on Quantitative Quant. Biology,* LVIII, 58:115–22. Cold Spring Harbor, NY; Cold Spring Harbor Lab. Press

36. Kerppola TK. 1994. DNA bending specificity among bZIP family proteins. In *Transcription: Mechanisms and Regulation,* ed. R.C. Conaway and, J.W. Conaway, pp. 387–424. New York: Raven

37. Kerppola TK, Curran T. 1991. DNA bending by Fos and Jun: The flexible hinge model. *Science* 254:1210–14

38. Kerppola TK, Curran T. 1991. Fos-Jun heterodimers and Jun homodimers bend DNA in opposite orientations: implications for transcription factor cooperativity. *Cell* 66:317–26

39. Kerppola TK, Curran T. 1993. Selective DNA bending by a variety of bZIP proteins. *Mol. Cell. Biol.* 13:5479–89

40. Kim JL, Nikilov DB, Burley SK. 1993. Cocrystal structure of TBP recognizing the groove of a TATA element. *Nature* 365:520–27

41. Kim TK, Maniatis T. 1997. The mechanism of transcriptional synergy of an in vitro assembled interferon-beta enhanceosome. *Mol. Cell* 1:119–29

42. Kim Y, Geiger JH, Hahn S, Sigler PB. 1993. Crystal structure of a yeast TBP/TATA-box complex. *Nature,* 365:512–20

43. Kodandapani R, Pio F, Ni C-Z, Piccialli G, Klemsz M, et al. 1996. A new pattern for helix-turn-helix recognition revealed by the PU.1 ets-domain-DNA complex. *Nature* 380:456–60

44. Koleske AJ, Young RA. 1995. The RNA polymerase II holoenzyme and its implications for gene regulation. *Trends Biochem. Sci.* 20:113–16

45. Konig P, Richmond TJ. 1993. The X-ray structure of the GCN4-bZIP bound to ATF/CREB site DNA shows the complex depends on DNA flexibility. *J. Mol. Biol.* 233:139–54

46. Kopka ML, Fratini AV, Drew HR, Dickerson RE. 1983. Ordered water structure around a B-DNA dodecamer. A quantitative study. *J. Mol. Biol.* 163:129–46

47. Kosikov K. 1998. *All-atom computer simulations of "activated" duplex DNA.* PhD thesis. Rutgers Univ., New Brunswick, NJ

48. Laundon CH, Griffith JD. 1987. Cationic metals promote sequence-directed DNA bending. *Biochemistry* 26:3759–62

49. Lee DH, Schleif RF. 1989. *In vivo* DNA loops in *araCBAD*: size limits and helical repeat. *Proc. Natl. Acad. Sci. USA* 86:476–80

50. Leonard DA, Rajaram N, Kerppola TK. 1997. Structural basis of DNA bending and oriented heterodimer binding by the basic leucine zipper domains of Fos and Jun. *Proc. Natl. Acad. Sci. USA* 94:4913–18

51. Li T, Stark MR, Johnson AD, Wolberger C. 1995. Crystal structure of the MATa1/MATa2 homeodomain heterodimer bound to DNA. *Science* 270:262–69

52. Liang G, Encell L, Nelson MG, Switzer C, Shuker DEG, Gold B. 1995. The role of electrostatics in the sequence selective reaction of charged alkylating agents with DNA. *J. Am. Chem. Soc.* 117:10135–36

53. Luger K, Mader AW, Richmond RK, Sargent DF, Richmond TJ. 1997. Crystal structure of the nucleosome core particle at

2.8 Å resolution. *Nature* 389:251–60

54. Maher LJ. 1998. Mechanisms of DNA bending. *Curr. Opin. Chem. Biol.* 2:688–94

55. Manning GS. 1978. The molecular theory of polyelectrolyte solutions with applications to the electrostatic properties of polynucleotides. *Q. Rev. Biophys.* 2:179–246

56. Manning GS. 1988. Three persistence lengths for a stiff polymer with an application to DNA B-Z junctions. *Biopolymers* 27:1529–42

57. Manning GS, Ebralidse KK, Mirzabekov AD, Rich A. 1989. An estimate of the extent of folding of nucleosomal DNA by laterally asymmetric neutralization of phosphate groups. *J. Biomol. Struct. Dyn.* 6: 877–89

58. Matthews KS. 1992. DNA looping. *Microbiol. Rev.* 56:123–36

59. Mirzabekov AD, Rich A. 1979. Asymmetric lateral distribution of unshielded phosphate groups in nucleosomal DNA and its role in DNA bending. *Proc. Natl. Acad. Sci. USA* 76:1118–21

60. Misra VK, Hecht JL, Sharp KA, Friedman RA, Honig B. 1994. Salt effects on protein-DNA interactions. *J. Mol. Biol.* 238:264–80

61. Misra VK, Hecht JL, Yang AS, Honig B. 1998. Electrostatic contributions to the binding free energy of the lambda c1 repressor to DNA. *Biophys. J.* 75:2262–73

62. Muller BC, Raphael AL, Barton JK. 1987. Evidence for altered DNA conformations in the simian virus 40 genome: site-specific DNA cleavage by the chiral complex lambda-tris(4,7-diphenyl-1,10- phenanthrolene)cobalt(III). *Proc. Natl. Acad. Sci. USA* 84:1764–68

63. Muller H-P, Sogo JM, Schaffner W. 1989. An enhancer stimulates transcription in trans when attached to the promoter via a protein bridge. *Cell* 58:767–77

64. Paolella DN, Liu Y, Schepartz A. 1997. Electrostatic mechanism for DNA bending by bZIP proteins. *Biochemistry* 36:10033–38

65. Paolella DN, Palmer CR, Schepartz A. 1994. DNA targets for certain bZIP proteins distinguished by an intrinsic bend. *Science* 264:1130–33

66. Parkinson G, Wilson C, Gunasekera A, Ebright YW, Ebright RE, Berman HM. 1996. Structure of the CAP-DNA complex at 2.5 Å resolution: a complete picture of the protein-DNA interface. *J. Mol. Biol.* 260:395–408

67. Pellegrini L, Tan S, Richmond TJ. 1995. Structure of serum response factor core bound to DNA. *Nature* 376:490–98

68. Pontiggia A, Rimini R, Harley VR, Good fellow PN, Lovell-Badge R, Bianchi ME. 1994. Sex-reversing mutations affect the architecture of SRY-DNA complexes. *EMBO J.* 13:6115–24

69. Ptashne M, Gann A. 1997. Transcriptional activation by recruitment. *Nature* 386:569–77

70. Record MT, Anderson CF, Lohman T. 1978. Thermodynamic analysis of ion effects on the binding and conformational equilibria of proteins and nucleic acids: the role of ion association and release, screening and ion effects on water activity. *Q. Rev. Biophys.* 11:103–78

71. Record MT, Zhang WT, Anderson CF. 1998. Analysis of effects of salts and uncharged solutes on protein and nucleic acid equilibria and processes: a practical guide to recognizing and interpreting polyelectrolyte effects, Hofmeister effects, and osmotic effects of salts. *Adv. Protein Chem.* 51:281–353

72. Rice PA, Yang SW, Mizuuchi K, Nash HA. 1996. Crystal structure of an IHF-DNA complex: A protein-induced DNA U-Turn. *Cell* 87:1295–1306

73. Rich A. 1978. Localized positive charges can bend double helical nucleic acids. *FEBS Lett.* 51:71–81

74. Rippe K, von Hippel PH, Langowski J. 1995. Action at a distance: DNA-looping

and initiation of transcription. *Trends Biol. Sci.* 20:500–6

75. Rosenberg JM, Seeman NC, Kim JJP, Suddath FL, Nicholas HB, Rich A. 1973. Double helix at atomic resolution. *Nature* 243:150–54

76. Rouzina I, Bloomfield A. 1998. DNA bending by small, mobile multivalent cations. *Biophys. J.* 74:3152–64

77. Ruden DM, Ma J, Ptashne M. 1988. No strict alignment is required between a transcriptional activator binding site and the "TATA box" of a yeast gene. *Proc. Natl. Acad. Sci. USA* 85:4262–66

78. Sanghani S, Zakrzewska K, Lavery R. 1996. Modeling DNA bending induced by phosphate neutralisation. In *Biological Structure and Dynamics*, ed. R Sarma, M Sarma, pp. 267–78. Schenectady, NY: Adenine

79. Schultz SC, Shields GC, Steitz TA. 1991. Crystal structure of a CAP-DNA complex: The DNA is bent by 90°. *Science* 253:1001–7

80. Shlyakhtenko LS, Lyububchenko YL, Chernov BK, Zhurkin VB. 1990. Influence of temperature and ionic strength on electrophoretic mobility of synthetic DNA fragments. *Mol. Biol. (Moscow)* 24:79– 95

81. Shore D, Langowski J, Baldwin RL. 1981. DNA flexibility studied by covalent closure of short fragments into circles. *Proc. Natl. Acad. Sci. USA* 78:4833–37

82. Shui X, McFail-Isom L, Hu GG, Williams LD. 1998. The B-DNA dodecamer at high resolution reveals a spine of water on sodium. *Biochemistry* 37:8341–55

83. Shui X, Sines C, McFail-Isom L, VanDerveer D, Williams LD. 1998. Structure of the potassium form of CGCGAATTCGCG: DNA deformation by electrostatic collapse around inorganic cations. *Biochemistry* 37:16877–87

84. Sitlani A, Crothers DM. 1998. DNA-binding domains of Fos and Jun do not induce DNA curvature: an investigation with solution and gel methods. *Proc. Natl.*

Acad. Sci. USA 95:1404–9

85. Sitlani A, Crothers DM. 1996. Fos and jun do not bend the AP-1 recognition site. *Proc. Natl. Acad. Sci. USA* 93:3248–52

86. Stigter D. 1998. An electrostatic model for the dielectric effects, the adsorption of multivalent ions, and the bending of B-DNA. *Biopolymers* 46:503–16

87. Strauss JK, Maher LJ. 1994. DNA bending by asymmetric phosphate neutralization. *Science* 266:1829–34

88. Strauss JK, Prakash TP, Roberts C, Switzer C, Maher LJ. 1996. DNA bending by a phantom protein. *Chem. Biol.* 3:671–78

89. Strauss JK, Roberts C, Nelson MG, Switzer C, Maher LJ. 1996. DNA bending by hexamethylene-tethered ammonium ions. *Proc. Natl. Acad. Sci. USA* 93:9515–20

90. Strauss-Soukup JK, Maher LJ. 1997. DNA bending by GCN4 mutants bearing cationic residues. *Biochemistry* 36:10026–32

91. Strauss-Soukup JK, Maher LJ. 1997. Effects of neutralization pattern and stereochemistry on DNA bending by methylphosphonate substitutions. *Biochemistry* 36:8692–98

92. Strauss-Soukup JK, Maher LJ. 1998. Electrostatic effects in DNA bending by GCN4 mutants. *Biochemistry* 37:1060–66

93. Strauss-Soukup JK, Maher LJ. 1997. Role of asymmetric phosphate neutralization in DNA bending by PU.1. *J. Biol. Chem.* 272:31570–75

94. Swarnalatha Y, Yathindra N. 1993. Stereochemical effects of methylphosphonate in B- and Z-DNA helices: variation in hydrophobicity and effective widths of grooves. *J. Biomol. Struct. Dyn.* 10:1023–45

95. Takahashi K, Vigneron M, Matthes H, Wildeman A, Zenke M, Chambon P. 1986. Requirement of stereospecific alignments for initiation from the simian virus 40 early promoter. *Nature* 319:121–26

96. Tereshko V, Minasov G, Egli M. 1999. A "hydrat-ion" spine in a B-DNA minor groove. *J. Am. Chem. Soc.* 121:3590–95

97. Tomky LA, Strauss-Soukup JK, Maher LJ. 1998. Effects of phosphate neutralization on the shape of the AP-1 transcription factor binding site in duplex DNA. *Nucleic Acids Res.* 26:2298–2305

98. Werner MH, Burley SK. 1997. Architectural transcription factors: Proteins that remodel DNA. *Cell* 88:733–36

99. Werner MH, Gronenborn AM, Clore GM. 1996. Intercalation, DNA kinking, and the control of transcription. *Science* 271:778–84

100. Wing R, Drew H, Takano T, Broka C, Takana S, et al. 1980. Crystal structure analysis of a complete turn of B-DNA. *Nature* 287:755–58

101. Young MA, Beveridge DL. 1998. Molecular dynamics simulations of an oligonucleotide duplex with adenine tracts phased by a full helix turn. *J. Mol. Biol.* 281:675–87

102. Young MA, Jayaram B, Beveridge DL. 1997. Intrusion of counterions into the spine of hydration in the minor groove of B-DNA: fractional occupancy of electronegative pockets. *J. Am. Chem. Soc.* 119:59–69

103. Young MA, Ravishanker G, Beveridge DL. 1997. A 5-nanosecond molecular dynamics trajectory for B-DNA: analysis of structure, motions, and solvation. *Biophys. J.* 73:2313–36

Annu. Rev. Biophys. Biomol. Struct. 2000. 29:523–43

STRESS-INDUCED STRUCTURAL TRANSITIONS IN DNA AND PROTEINS

T. R. Strick[*], J.-F. Allemand[*+], D. Bensimon[*] and V. Croquette[*]

[*]LPS, ENS, UMR 8550 CNRS, [+]PASTEUR, ENS, UMR 8640 CNRS, 24 rue Lhomond, 75231 Paris Cedex 05, France; e-mail:Vincent.Croquette@physique.ens.fr

Key Words single molecule manipulation, DNA unzipping, protein folding

■ **Abstract** The ability to manipulate, stretch and twist biomolecules opens the way to an understanding of their structural transitions. We review some of the recently discovered stress-induced structural transitions in DNA as well as the application of single molecule manipulation techniques to DNA unzipping and to the study of protein folding/unfolding transitions.

CONTENTS

INTRODUCTION

Phase transitions are very common in nature. As the temperature reaches a critical value many materials undergo a profound structural reorganization. Thus, water freezes at 0°C and boils at 100°C; magnetic materials lose their permanent magnetization above the Curie temperature; the two strands of DNA separate above ~90°C; and proteins denature as they are heated. In many cases an understanding of these transitions has been achieved thanks to the existence of a control parameter that could induce the transition at a fixed temperature. Thus, water can boil at T $<$ 100°C if the pressure is decreased below 1 atmosphere, and iron can remain magnetized above its Curie temperature if kept in a magnetic field.

Until recently no such easily tunable control parameter (as the pressure or magnetic field) existed to probe the structural phase space of DNA and proteins under physiological conditions. In the past four years, however, the ability to manipulate single molecules (DNA, proteins, polysaccharides, etc), to stretch and twist them, has added a new dimension to the study of the structural transitions of biomolecules. The purpose of this paper is to review the recent advances in this field and discuss its prospects. We first present the recently discovered stress-induced transitions in DNA observed when stretching or twisting the molecule. We then describe how one can open DNA as a zipper by pulling on its two strands. The fluctuations in the force needed to unzip the molecule are correlated with its sequence and may yield information on that sequence, provided some fundamental limitations are resolved. Similarly, one can denature a multidomain protein by pulling on it at a constant rate. In that case, the protein's extension displays a sawtooth pattern in time similar to the one observed in the DNA unzipping experiment. Although still at an early stage, these experiments suggest that by pulling on a single strand of DNA, an RNA, or a protein, one might be able to understand how these molecules fold into their secondary and tertiary structures. This problem is currently studied mostly through numerical and analytical modeling.

FORCES AT THE MOLECULAR SCALE

Let us first discuss the range of forces encountered at the molecular level. The smallest force on a molecule is set by the Langevin force f_n due to thermal agitation. It sets the lower limit to force measurements and is due to the Brownian fluctuations (of energy $k_B T = 4 \ 10^{-21}$ J $= 0.6$ kcal/mol—at room temperature) of the object of size d (sensor, cell, membrane) anchored by the molecule. For a d $= 2 \ \mu$m diameter bead or cell in water (viscosity $\eta = 10^{-3}$ poise), $f_n = (12\pi k_B T \eta d)^{1/2} \sim$ 10 fN/Hz$^{1/2}$ (notice that this is a noise density, i.e. the faster the measurement, the more noisy it is). This can be compared to the typical weight of a cell: $\sim$10 fN, i.e. every second a cell experiences a thermal knock equal to its weight!

Just above these forces lie the entropic forces that result from a reduction of the number of possible configurations of the system consisting of the molecule (e.g. protein, DNA) and its solvent (water, ions). As an example, a free DNA molecule in solution adopts a random coil configuration that maximizes its configurational entropy (1). Upon stretching, the molecular entropy is reduced so that at full extension there is but one configuration left: a straight polymer linking both ends. To reach that configuration, work against entropy has to be done, a force has to be applied. The entropic forces are rather weak. Since the typical energies involved are of order $k_B T$ and the typical lengths are of the order of a nanometer, entropic forces are of order k_BT/nm $= 4$ pN ($4\ 10^{-12}$ N). These are typically the forces exerted by molecular motors, such as myosin on actin (2), the force necessary to stretch a DNA molecule to its contour length (3) or to unzip the two strands of the molecule (44, 46).

Noncovalent (e.g. ligand/receptor) bonding forces are much stronger. They usually involve modifications of the molecular structure on a nanometer scale: breaking and rearrangement of *many* van der Waals, hydrogen, or ionic bonds and stretching of covalent bonds. The energies involved are typical bond energies, of the order of an electron-volt (1 eV $= 1.6\ 10^{-19}$ J $= 24$ kcal/mol). The elastic forces are thus of order eV/nm $= 160$ pN. These are typically the forces needed to break receptor/ligand bonds (4, 5, 6, 7, 8) or to deform the internal structure of a molecule (9, 10, 11).

Finally the strongest forces encountered at the molecular scale are those required to break a covalent bond of the order of 1 eV/Å ≈ 1600 pN.

FORCE-INDUCED TRANSITION TO S-DNA

The experiments we describe in the following were made possible by the development in the past decade of various techniques to apply and measure forces at the single molecule level, using mechanical springs [fibers (9, 12), cantilevers (4)], hydrodynamic drag (3), optical (10, 13, 14, 15, 2, 16) or magnetic (17, 18) tweezers]. These new techniques, allowing force measurements from a few femtoNewtons (10^{-15} N) to many nanoNewtons (10^{-9} N), cover the regime of molecularly relevant forces.

The first experiments on DNA involved a study of its mechanical response at low forces (<10 pN). In that regime DNA behaves as an ideal polymer of persistence length $\xi \sim 50$ nm (under physiological conditions), i.e. its elastic behavior is due purely to a reduction of its entropy upon stretching. As shown in Figure 1, the theoretical model describing such a system (the worm-like chain, or WLC, model (19–21)) provides an excellent description of the mechanical behavior of DNA at low forces and has since served as a benchmark, calibration, and framework for all single molecule work on DNA.

Above 10 pN and up to about 70 pN, DNA stretches elastically as does any material, i.e. following Hooke's law: $F \approx \Delta l/l_0$ (where $\Delta l = l - l_0$ is the increase in the extension l of the molecule of contour length l_0).

However, at about 70 pN a surprising transition has recently been discovered, where DNA stretches to about 1.7 times its crystallographic length (9, 10). As is characteristic of first-order transitions in nature (e.g. boiling), that transition is highly cooperative: A small change in force results in a large change in extension (see Figure 1). To address the possible structural modification in the molecule resulting from pulling on it, a numerical energy minimization of DNA under stress was performed by R. Lavery and collaborators (9, 11). Its results reveal the existence

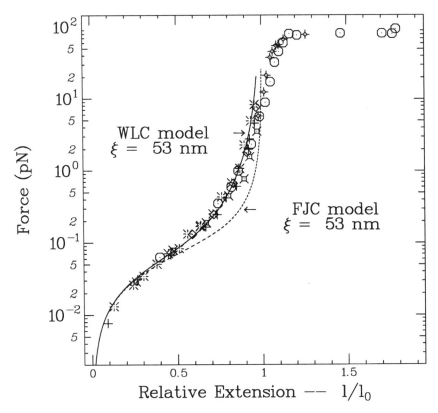

Figure 1 Force versus relative extension curves of single DNA molecules. The dots correspond to several experiments performed over a wide range of forces. The force was measured using the Brownian fluctuation technique (22). The full line curve is a best fit to the WLC model for forces smaller than 5 picoNewtons. The dashed curve is the result of the freely jointed chain (FJC) model with the same persistence length (it is clearly a worse description of the behavior of DNA under stress than the WLC model). At high forces, the molecule first elongates slightly, as would any material in its elastic regime. Above 70 pN, the length abruptly increases, corresponding to the appearance of a new structure called S-DNA.

of a conformational transition to a new form called S-DNA, indeed 70% longer than B-DNA, whose exact structure depends on which extremities of the DNA are being pulled ($3'$-$3'$ or $5'$-$5'$). If both $3'$ extremities are being pulled, the double helix unwinds upon stretching. The final structure resembles a ladder (Figure 2). If both $5'$ ends are pulled, a helical structure is preserved. It is characterized by a large base pair inclination, a narrow minor groove, and a diameter roughly 30% less than that of B-DNA (Figure 2). In both cases the rupture of the molecule (by unpairing of the bases) occurs as observed in other experiments when its extension is more than twice that of B-DNA (23, 24, 25).

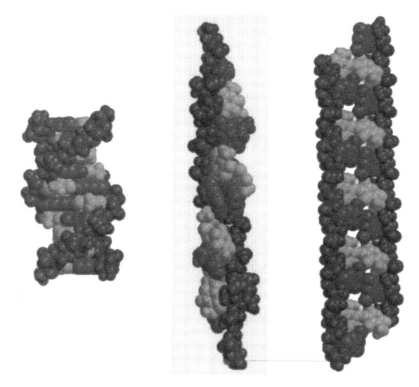

Figure 2   The new structures of DNA obtained in numerical simulations when pulling on the molecule (courtesy of R. Lavery–30). Left: usual B-DNA structure, middle: if the molecule is pulled by its 5′ ends, it keeps a double helical structure with inclined bases. Right: if the DNA is pulled by its 3′ extremities, the final structure resembles a ladder.

These numerical results are supported by experiments done almost fifty years ago by Wilkins et al (23), before the double helical structure of DNA was even proposed. These suggested that stretched DNA fibers indeed undergo a transition to a structure with inclined bases about two times longer than the relaxed molecule. However, recent experiments by J-F. Léger et al (26) in which single, torsionally constrained molecules are stretched have shown that the S-DNA phase has a helical pitch of 22 nm with 38 bases per right-handed turn, which would make it look more like a slightly twisted ladder.

The existence of a new stable form of DNA at high extension might have considerable interest for the study of DNA/protein interactions. Thus, RecA is known to induce a 60% extension of B-DNA and to facilitate the formation of a triple helix, a putative intermediate during recombination. Smith et al (10) calculated that the existence of an extended S-form of DNA reduced the energetics of RecA binding to DNA by as much as 15 k_BT (9 kcal/mol) per complex. Recent experiments (27–29) have indeed shown that the polymerization of RecA on double-stranded

DNA was facilitated by stretching the molecule. This implies that the barriers to nucleation and accretion of a RecA fiber on DNA is lowered by the presence of an S-DNA subphase. Numerical modeling further suggests that its structure is closer to the RecA/DNA complex than regular B-DNA (30).

DNA UNDER TORSION

Topological Properties of Coiled DNA

To describe DNA under torsional stress, we must introduce some topological concepts. The first is the twist (Tw), the number of helical turns along the molecule. For a torsionally unconstrained B-DNA, $Tw = Tw_0 = N/h$, where N is the number of bases and $h = 10.4$ is the number of bases per turn of the helix. The second topological quantity of interest is the writhe (Wr) of the molecule. Wr is a measure of the coiling of the DNA axis about itself, like a twisted phone cord that forms interwound structures in order to relieve its torque. If the DNA molecule is torsionally constrained, then the total number of times the two strands of the helix cross each other (either by twist or writhe) is a topological invariant of the system called the linking number $Lk = Tw + Wr$ (31). For relaxed linear DNA molecules, assuming the absence of any spontaneous local curvature, $Lk = Lk_0 = Tw_0$. The relative difference in linking number between the supercoiled and relaxed forms of DNA is called the degree of supercoiling, σ:

$$\sigma = (Lk - Lk_0)/Lk_0 = \Delta Lk/Lk_0 \tag{1}$$

The value of σ for most circular molecules isolated from cells or virions is roughly -0.06. In some of the experiments reviewed here (22, 32, 33), DNA is anchored at one end to a surface and at the other to a small magnetic bead held in the field of a pair of small magnets. A torsional constraint can be applied to the molecule by simply rotating the magnets. As one turn of the magnets implies a change of one turn of the molecule, one has $\Delta Lk = \pm n$, where $\pm n$ is the number of turns by which the magnets are rotated. Now at fixed Lk the ratio Tw/Wr will depend on the force stretching the molecule, the writhe being suppressed by high forces. As a consequence, pulling on a coiled molecule increases the torque twisting it until its writhe becomes nil.

The Mechanical Buckling Instability

Twisting DNA leads to a torsional buckling instability analogous to that observed on a coiled rubber tube. Let us therefore consider the torsional instability of such a tube of length l and bending and torsional moduli B and C, respectively. If we firmly hold one of its ends while simultaneously rotating and pulling on the other with a force F, we observe the following phenomenon (see Figure 3): When the twist constraint is small, the associated torque Γ increases linearly with the twist angle θ, $\Gamma = C\theta/l$ and the tube remains straight. As the tube is further twisted,

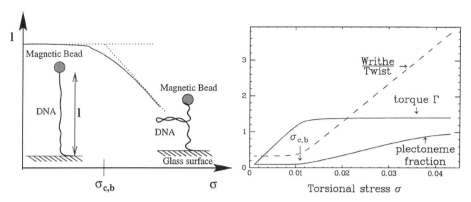

Figure 3 Left: Schematic view of the buckling transition for a twisted rubber tube (dotted line) or a DNA molecule (solid line). When $n_{c,b}$ turns have been added, the system abruptly exchanges twisting energy for bending energy and plectonemes begin to form. The plectonemes grow linearly with subsequent twisting, and the torque remains constant thereafter. In the case of DNA the same picture holds, except that thermal fluctuations round off the transition that takes place at $\sigma_{c,b}$. Right: The torque acting on the DNA (dashed curve) increases linearly until $\sigma_{c,b}$ and remains essentially constant thereafter. The short-dash curve represents the ratio of writhe to twist: note that the writhe is never zero and increases rapidly as $\sigma > \sigma_{c,b}$. Finally, the solid line measures the fraction of plectonemes in DNA; stable supercoiled structures only appear after the torsional buckling transition has been passed.

a critical torque $\Gamma_{c,b}$ is reached where the tube ceases to be straight; it locally buckles and forms a small loop. This critical torque is controlled by the stretching force: $\Gamma_{c,b} = (2B\ F)^{1/2}$. As we further twist the tube, we increase the length of the interwound structures (known as plectonemes or supercoils), but the torque in the tube remains basically fixed at its critical value $\Gamma_{c,b}$. In the case of the DNA experiment reviewed here, as the molecule is twisted and the length of its supercoils increases, the distance of the tethered bead to the surface decreases.

The torsional buckling instability just described treats DNA as a continuous elastic tube. It ignores the underlying double-helical structure of the molecule and is the same for overwinding or underwinding. Its relevance is limited to very low forces (F < 0.4 pN in 10 mM phosphate buffer) or low degrees of supercoiling ($-0.015 < \sigma < 0.037$). For higher forces and degrees of supercoiling, the buildup of torque in the molecule can be large enough to actually modify its internal structure before it reaches the threshold for buckling at $\Gamma_{c,b}$. This is evidenced by breaking of the σ to $-\sigma$ symmetry in the extension vs. supercoiling curves (see Figure 4). As a critical force is reached (ipso facto a critical torque), lower for an underwound than for an overwound DNA, the molecule undergoes a transition from a contracted state (plectonemic B-DNA) to a highly extended one. This state is characterized by the coexistence of B-DNA with denatured DNA (dDNA, for $\sigma < 0$) or with a new phase called P-DNA (for $\sigma > 0$) (32).

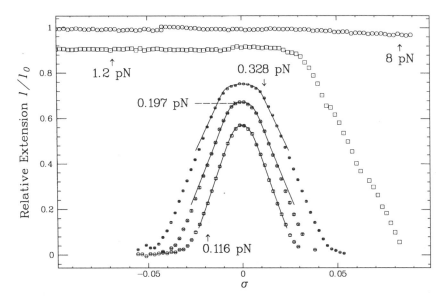

Figure 4 Relative extension of a DNA molecule versus the degree of supercoiling σ for various stretching forces. For the three curves obtained at low forces, the behavior is symmetrical under $\sigma \rightarrow -\sigma$. The shortening corresponds to the formation of plectonemes upon writhing. When the force is increased above 0.5 pN, the curve becomes asymmetric; supercoils still form for positive coiling while local denaturation relieves the torsional stress for negative σ. At forces larger than 3 pN, no plectonemes are observed even on positively supercoiled DNA: again, the torsional stress is absorbed not by writhe but in local structural changes of the molecule.

Force-Induced Denaturation of Unwound DNA

Let us first consider negative supercoiling ($\sigma < 0$). It is known (34) that for values of $|\sigma| > 0.06$, an unstretched DNA undergoes localized denaturation in AT rich regions. When stretched, similar local denaturation is expected to arise at smaller values of $|\sigma|$, due to the increased torque. If the twisted molecule phase separates into a pure B-DNA phase coexisting with denatured regions where the bases are exposed to the solvent, then every extra turn of the molecule should unpair about 10.5 nucleotides. This was checked by reacting twisted and stretched DNA with glyoxal, a reagent specific for exposed bases (35), and by hybridizing single-stranded DNA complementary to the most AT rich regions in the molecule (22). Striking, though less obvious, evidence for this phase separation can also be deduced from the extension versus force curves at various degrees of unwinding.

In general the free energy of a twisted DNA, $\mathcal{E}(\sigma, F)$ (and its extension $l = -\partial\mathcal{E}/\partial F$) is expected to be a complex function of both F and σ. However, if the twisted and stretched molecule partitions its twist between two pure phases [e.g. B-DNA with $\sigma_B = 0$ and denatured DNA (d-DNA) with $\sigma_d = -1$], then the energy and extension of the molecule become linear functions of σ:

$$l(F, \sigma) = (1 - \sigma/\sigma_d)l_B(F) + (\sigma/\sigma_d)l_d(F), \tag{2}$$

where $l_B(F)$ and $l_d(F)$ are respectively the extension (at a given force F) of the pure B-DNA and d-DNA phases. Thus, if one plots the extension of the molecule l as a function of σ at constant force F, one should observe a linear relation for $|\sigma| \leq |\sigma_d|$. For negative supercoiling, that is indeed the case when $\sigma \geq \sigma_d = -1$, see Figure 5. Moreover one can show that the measured extension versus force curves at different values of $\sigma > \sigma_d$ all collapse onto the same (σ independent) $l_d(F)$ curve (see Figure 5, in agreement with Equation 2).

Force-Induced Transition of an Overwound Molecule to P-DNA

Let us now consider the case for positive supercoiling ($\sigma > 0$). The elastic behavior of stretched, positively supercoiled DNA reveals the existence of a sharp transition at F $\sim$ 3 pN similar to the transition to denatured DNA observed in underwound DNA at a lower force (F $\sim$ 0.6 pN) (see Figure 4 and references 20, 22, 32).

As argued previously, if there is a phase separation, then the extension of the molecule $l(F)$ becomes a linear function of σ. As shown in Figure 6, the extension vs. σ curve at a fixed force is indeed a linearly decreasing function of σ for $\sigma < \sigma_p \sim 3$. Just as σ_d represented the degree of supercoiling of the denatured phase, the critical value σ_p represents the intrinsic degree of supercoiling of the new P-DNA phase, which thus corresponds to an overwound structure with 2.62 base pairs per turn! This is geometrically possible only if the bases are exposed to the solvent with the phosphate backbone allowed to wind at the center, a structure reminiscent of the one proposed by Pauling (36), but with two braided single strands instead of three (see Figure 7).

To demonstrate that the bases in this structure are indeed exposed to the solution, the positively twisted and stretched DNA was reacted with glyoxal. As for underwound DNA, the percentage of modified bases is equal to the fraction of P-DNA phase in the molecule σ/σ_p (32). Moreover, using the value of $\sigma_p = 3$ thus determined (in place of σ_d) in Equation 2, one can further show that the extension versus force curves measured for $3 > \sigma > 0.03$ collapse onto the same $l_p(F)$ curve (see Figure 6), in agreement with Equation 1. Here $l_p(F)$ is the extension at given force, F, of the pure P-DNA phase.

Biological Implications of the Torque-Induced Transitions

What is the possible biological significance of these torsionally induced structures? Many proteins interacting with DNA modify its twist (e.g. histones). In particular during transcription as the RNA polymerase progresses on its substrate, DNA overwinds downstream and underwinds upstream. Similarly, during replication, helicases unwind the molecule to make way for the replication complex. To

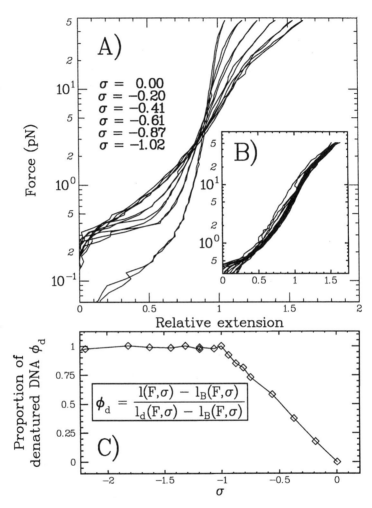

Figure 5 Experimental evidence for the coexistence in 10 mM phosphate buffer (PB) of B-DNA and denatured DNA at negative supercoiling: $-1 < \sigma < 0$. (A) Force (F) vs. extension (l) curves of a single DNA molecule obtained at different degrees of supercoiling. At $F = F_{c-} = 0.3$ pN, the extension of the molecule changes dramatically, pointing to the presence of a structural transition in DNA: denatured DNA appears. (B) The data from (A) are rescaled such that $l_d(F) = \sigma_d/\sigma[l(F,\sigma) - l(F,0)] + l(F,0)$, see Equation 2. All data collapse onto a single curve, validating our hypothesis that stretched, unwound DNA separates into pure B-DNA and dDNA phases. $l_d(F)$ is the extension vs. force curve for denatured DNA. (C) The fraction ϕ_d of dDNA is plotted as a function of the number of turns. As expected from Equation 2, $\phi_d = -\sigma$ and goes from 0 to 1. Beyond this value the points depart from linearity.

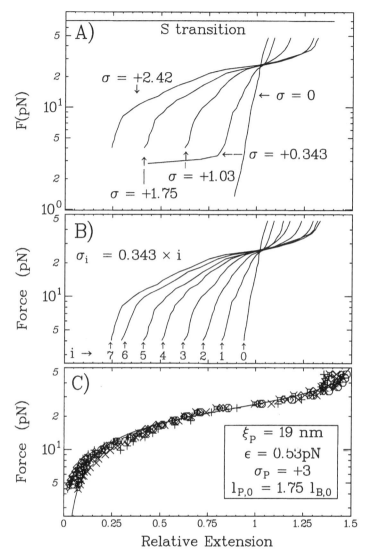

Figure 6 Mechanical characterization of P-DNA. (*A*) Elasticity curves showing two transitions at 3 pN and 25 pN. The first transition (not shown for all curves) is associated with the disappearance of plectonemes in B-DNA and the formation of P-DNA. The second transition, showing hysteresis, is attributed to the disappearance of plectonemes in the P-DNA subphase. At high force, these curves show that P-DNA is actually longer than B-DNA (at full extension by about 75%). (*B*) A detailed view of the curves from (*A*) for decreasing forces (each curve corresponds to $\sigma_i = i \times 0.343$). (*C*) Rescaling, following Equation 2, enables all the curves shown in (*B*) to be collapsed to the universal curve $l_p(F)$ represented here, which describes the extension vs. force behavior of a pure P-DNA. The solid line is a fit to a modified WLC model for P-DNA (32).

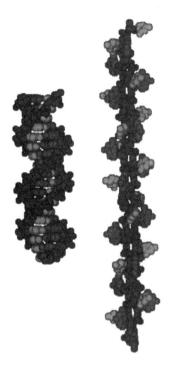

Figure 7 Structure of P-DNA deduced from molecular modeling (courtesy of R. Lavery). Space filling models of a $(dG)_{18}.(dC)_{18}$ fragment in B-DNA (left) and P-DNA (right) conformations. The backbones are colored purple and the bases blue (guanine) and yellow (cytosine). The anionic oxygens of the phosphate groups are shown in red. (colors not shown.) These models were created with the JUMNA program (40, 41), by imposing twisting constraints on helically symmetric DNA with regularly repeating base sequences.

control the degree of coiling of DNA, relax its torsional stress, and decatenate its chromosomes, the cell possesses a battery of enzymes: the topoisomerases. The torsional stress in the molecule thus depends on the balance between the generation of torsional stress (for example, during transcription or replication) and its relaxation by topoisomerases. It is also conceivable that the cell uses the torsional stress signal to control the expression of nearby genes. Some experiments indeed suggest that the wave of unwinding left behind the transcription complex may turn on other genes (37, 38). For positive coiling and the P-DNA structure associated with it, one may speculate that the possibility to expose the genetic message usually buried inside the double helix may have a useful role in various cellular processes (e.g. sister chromosome pairing). In any event a structure very similar to P-DNA has been reported for the packing of DNA in the Pf1 virus (39). There this unusual structure is stabilized by its interactions with the coat proteins of the virus.

ZIPPER-SEQUENCING OF DNA

Single molecule manipulation techniques have excited the imagination of many people. For example it has been suggested (42, 43) that one could sequence a DNA molecule by pulling apart its two strands (as in a zipper) and monitoring the force required for breaking each base pair as one progresses along the molecule.

Similarly, one could imagine following the 3D folding of an RNA molecule (or a protein) stretched between a surface and the tip of an AFM cantilever (43). However, the theoretical analysis (11, 42, 43) of these fascinating prospects reveals a number of conceptual difficulties, in particular a severe limitation on the stiffness of the measuring device.

This device consists typically of a macroscopic spring (e.g. cantilever, bead in an optical trap, microfiber) coupled to the stretched molecule via long polymers. Its effective stiffness ($k_{eff}^{-1} = \Sigma_i \, k_i^{-1}$) is dominated by its weakest, most flexible element. For example, when unzipping DNA, the double-stranded molecule is attached to the measuring device by flexible single-stranded DNA pieces, which get longer as the molecule is unzipped further. If one wants to observe the successive breaking of hydrogen bonds in the molecule as it unravels, the energy and spatial resolution should be respectively: $\delta\mathcal{E} \sim 10 \, k_B \, T \sim 4 \, 10^{-20}$ J and $\delta x \sim 3$Å. Between two successive measurements, the energy accumulated in the measurement chain is thus: $\delta\mathcal{E} = k_{eff} \, \delta x^2/2$, i.e. $k_{eff} \sim 1$ N/m. Whereas that value is not uncommon for AFM cantilevers, a polymer of reasonable size (>10 nm) is much less stiff. For example, when unzipping 1500 bps of DNA, typically at a force F of about 20 pN (44, 45), one ends up with two single-stranded DNA pieces (each about $l = 1 \, \mu$m in length) connecting the molecule to an anchoring surface and a sensor (see Figure 8). For such a single-stranded DNA, the elastic rigidity is $k_{WLC} \sim 10^{-4}$ N/m (10), which limits the spatial resolution of unzipping at that stage to $\sim$100 bps ($\delta x \sim 30$ nm). That resolution of course decreases as the length of the single-stranded DNA pieces increase.

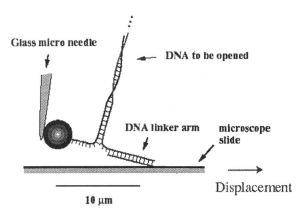

Figure 8   The set-up used by Heslot and coworkers (44) to unzip a λ-DNA molecule. A DNA construct was engineered such that one of its extremities had one strand anchored to a surface via a long DNA fragment, and the other strand was bound to a small bead, itself stuck to a flexible glass fiber used as a force sensor. As the surface is displaced, the molecule is unzipped and the force to unpair two bases measured by the force sensor (Courtesy of F. Heslot).

Force (pN)

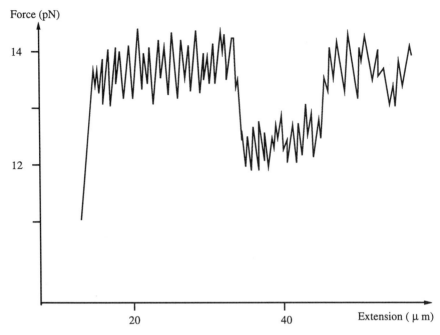

Figure 9 Sketch of the typical sawtooth pattern observed in the experiments of Helsot and coworkers (44) as the two strands of DNA are pulled apart. GC-rich regions yield at a higher force than AT-rich ones.

The experimental unzipping of a λ-DNA molecule has been performed by Heslot and coworkers (44, 46; see also Rief et al–45), first using a thin glass fiber as a sensor (of stiffness $k = 1.7 \ 10^{-6}$ N/m) attached to the DNA via a single-stranded piece, and more recently using an optical trap of higher stiffness. The unzipping signal displays a sawtooth pattern typical of a stick-slip process: As the molecule is stretched, energy accumulates in the measurement chain (see Figure 9). When the force reaches the threshold to unpair two bases (about 15 pN in GC rich regions and 12 pN in AT-rich ones), the bond yields and a stretch of n bases unbinds cooperatively. Because the loading rate in these experiments is much slower than the base pair binding/unbinding rates, unzipping occurs at thermal equilibrium. The role of the force is to shift this equilibrium (47, 48) from a configuration where n bases are paired to one where they are unpaired. Similar to the configurational changes described previously (e.g. B-DNA → S-DNA), the transition here is also first order, i.e. the behavior is cooperative, hence the "molecular stick-slip" signal observed. The spatial resolution observed in these experiments (about 500 bps) is in agreement with the theoretical limitations discussed above. To overcome those one would have to stiffen the single-strand pieces of DNA as the molecule unravels, for example by coating them with RecA (29).

However, even if one could completely freeze the thermal fluctuations of the measurement chain (thus stiffening it), zero temperature molecular modeling of DNA unzipping (11) reveals variations in the energy of the system that are not easily related to the sequence of the molecule. It is therefore not at all obvious that this ingenious technique could be used to read the sequence of a DNA molecule.

STRETCHING PROTEINS

In the past two years different groups have started to pull on proteins consisting of multiple domains, such as titin (49, 50, 51) (a giant 3.5 MD muscle protein) or tenascin (52, 53) (an extracellular matrix protein). The former consists of a linear chain of ∼300 immunoglobulin (Ig) and fibronectin III (Fn3) domains, which appear to undergo independent folding/unfolding transitions as the polypeptide is stretched. As with the DNA unzipping experiments, the high resolution protein experiments (50, 52) display a typical sawtooth pattern, due to the coexistence in the stretched protein of folded and unfolded domains. In these experiments, the protein is anchored to a surface at one end and to a stiff (∼0.1 N/m) AFM cantilever at the other. As the anchoring surface is displaced, the n unfolded domains are stretched. Although the discrete Kratky-Porod model (54) should be more appropriate to describe the response of the unfolded chain to stress, its continuous limit, the WLC model, often fits the data rather well (with a surprisingly short persistence length $\xi \sim 0.4$ nm, about the size of a single amino-acid). When the force reaches a critical value $F_u \sim 200$ pN, a single domain unfolds in an all-or-none event contributing an additional stretch of polypeptide (of length $l_d \sim 30$ nm) to the already unfolded chain, see Figure 10.

In contrast to the DNA unzipping experiments described previously, where the critical force for unzipping was insensitive to the pulling speed, in the case of protein unfolding the force required to unfold a domain depends on the loading rate. A simple two-level model was proposed (53) to explain these results.

Consider a transition between a folded and unfolded state: see Figure 11. The rate of unfolding is given by (47, 48, 53):

$$\alpha_0 = \omega e^{-\Delta G_u^*/k_B T}. \tag{3}$$

ΔG_u^* is the activation barrier for unfolding, and ω is the reciprocal of a diffusive relaxation time ($\omega \sim 10^8$ Hz) (47, 49). Similarly, the back reaction rate β_0 for folding is:

$$\beta_0 = \omega e^{-\Delta G_f^*/k_B T}. \tag{4}$$

ΔG_f^* is the activation barrier for folding. The equilibrium constant is of course $K_{eq} = \beta_0/\alpha_0 = \exp(\Delta G/k_B T)$, where ΔG is the free energy difference between folded and unfolded states (see Figure 11). When pulling a protein with force F, one increases the unfolding rate: $\alpha = \alpha_0 \exp(Fx_u/k_B T)$ and decreases the folding

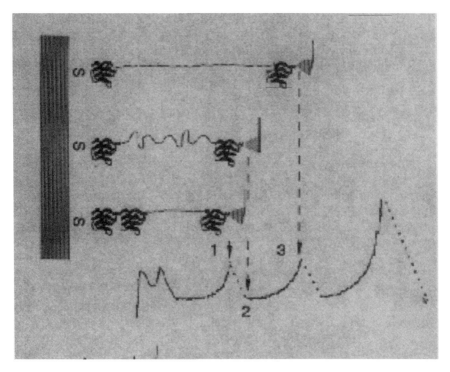

Figure 10 Typical sawtooth behavior of a multidomain protein, such as titin, under load (50). The protein exhibits a coexistence of folded and unfolded domains, whose extended fraction grows with the force until the whole protein has been denatured. At the force marked (1), the second domain on the left unfolds, resulting in a drop in the force to point (2). With further pulling on the protein, the unfolded domains are stretched to point (3) where another domain will unfold (Coutesy of H. Gaub).

rate: $\beta = \beta_0 \exp(-Fx_f/k_BT)$, where x_u and x_f are the typical widths associated with the activation barrier for unfolding and folding, respectively (see Figure 11). Now in the case of DNA unzipping, the typical size of the barrier widths is ~0.3 nm (the distance between successive base-pairs), and the force necessary to unzip is F ~ 20 pN. The folding/unfolding rates are thus modified only slightly ($F x_{u,f}/k_B T \sim 1.5$) and are still faster than the experimental pulling rates (<1000 bps/sec). In the case of protein unfolding, the width of the barrier to unfolding is similar to that for DNA unzipping, i.e. about 0.3 nm (50, 53, 55). However, because protein folding requires interactions between distant amino acids, the barrier width to refolding is much larger, typically the size of an unfolded domain. Even at the residual force after unfolding, $F \sim 10$ pN, that domain is already stretched to half its contour length: $x_f \sim 15$ nm for titin. Hence, the reduction in the back reaction rate is very large: $\exp(-F x_f/k_BT) \sim \exp(-35)$, and refolding is highly improbable (53). If the force is increased slowly, the protein has time to thermally hop over the barrier to

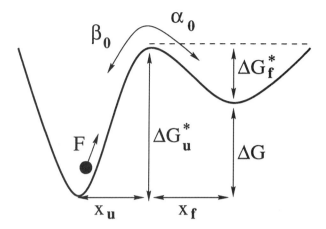

Figure 11 Two-level model for the unfolding of a protein domain (53). The domain in its native state (on the left) unfolds at a rate α_0 by hopping over the barrier (of energy difference ΔG_u^*) to unfolding. In the denatured state (on the right) the refolding rate β_0 is controlled by the energy difference with the transition state ΔG_f^*. When a force F is applied to the system, the free-energy difference ΔG between native and unfolded state is skewed toward unfolding by the work performed by the force: $F(x_u + x_f)$. (Courtesy of H. Gaub)

unfolding and will on the average do that at a lower force than when pulled faster. That explains the very different values reported in the literature (49, 50, 51) for the force F_u necessary to unfold titin. The laser tweezer experiments that deduced $F_u \sim 20$ pN were done at a pulling speed of 60 nm/sec, whereas the AFM experiments reached pulling speeds of 1000 nm/sec and measured $F_u \sim 150$ pN.

FUTURE PROSPECTS

The possibility of mechanically unfolding proteins opens the way to a better understanding of protein folding. A recent comparison (55) of mechanical and chemical unfolding of an engineered protein made of tandem repeats of identical Ig modules reveals equivalent pathways, similar transition rates, and same transition state. This suggests that a stretching force can be used as a "knob" to control and study the folding of proteins. Moreover, by varying the rate at which the force is applied, a dynamical force spectroscopy (56) of the reaction manifold for unfolding might be achieved. However, the spatial and temporal resolutions of these experiments need to be improved by at least an order of magnitude. That implies working with smaller and stiffer cantilevers and being able to observe the folding/unfolding of a single isolated domain (not a large multidomain protein). That might allow one to reduce the aforementioned limitations due to the elasticity of the anchoring polymeric chains.

On the theoretical side, the exploration of the folding of a protein under tension is at its very beginning (57, 58). Clearly more work is required to provide a framework for the conception and interpretation of future experiments.

It is quite interesting that the protein-folding experiments have already suggested some applications to the design of better glues (59) consisting of a chain of polymeric modules kept folded by weak bonds. As the adhesive is stretched, the modules unfold before the chain breaks, thus dissipating the tensional energy as heat. Such an adhesive would have both a high tensile strength and high toughness (59).

A further possible and instructive experiment would be to monitor the activity of a single enzyme under mild tension. How would it depend on the force? Would it vary continuously? Are there discrete states of activity? Is hysteresis observed when the force is varied cyclically? This is also a problem where a comparison with simulations might be fruitful. Whereas predicting the tertiary structure of a protein from its amino sequence is beyond today's computer power, looking for subtle conformational changes about a known native structure under stress might be within reach. Comparing the predicted enzymatic structure and activity with the measured one might help refine the modeling of protein structures.

Finally, though there are as yet no reports of stretching experiments on RNA molecules, this gap will certainly be closed soon. These molecules possess a very complex tertiary structure and a catalytic activity worthy of study. A further advantage of RNA molecules is the possibility to tag them with fluorescent probes at various positions and to monitor their conformational changes by fluorescent resonant energy transfer (FRET) (60). Although the two techniques (single molecule manipulation and FRET) have very different time scales, marrying the two might allow the study of stress-induced transitions at an unprecedented resolution, both spatial and temporal.

Visit the Annual Reviews home page at www.AnnualReviews.org

LITERATURE CITED

1. de Gennes PG. 1979. Scaling concepts in polymer physics. Ithaca, NY: Cornell Univ. Press
2. Finer JT, Simmons RM, Spudich JA. 1994. Single myosin molecule mechanics: piconewton forces and nanometre steps. *Nature* 368:113–119
3. Smith SB, Finzi L, Bustamante C. 1992. Direct mechanical measurements of the elasticity of single DNA molecules by using magnetic beads. *Science* 258:1122–26
4. Florin EL, Moy VT, Gaub HE. 1994. Adhesion force between individual lig-
and-receptor pairs. *Science* 264:415–17
5. Moy VT, Florin E-L, Gaub HE. 1994. Intermolecular forces and energies between ligands and receptors. *Science* 266:257–59
6. Hon T, Williams JM, Beebe TP Jr. 1996. Determination of single-bond forces from contact force variances in atomic force microscopy. *Langmuir* 12:1291–95
7. Dammer U, Popescu O, Wagner P, Anselmetti D, Günherodt H-J, Misevic GN. 1995. Binding strength between cell adhesion proteoglycans measured by atomic force microscopy. *Science* 267:1173–75

8. Lee GU, Chrisey LA, Colton RJ. 1994. Direct measurement of the forces between complementary strands of DNA. *Science* 266:771–73

9. Cluzel P, Lebrun A, Heller C, Lavery R, Viovy J-L, et al. 1996. DNA: an extensible molecule. *Science* 271:792–94

10. Smith SB, Cui Y, Bustamante C. 1996. Overstretching B-DNA: the elastic response of individual double-stranded and single-stranded DNA molecules. *Science* 271:795–99

11. Lebrun A, Lavery R. 1996. Modelling extreme deformations of DNA. *Nucl. Acids Res.* 24:2260

12. Ishijima A, Doi T, Sakurada K, Yanagida T. 1991. Sub-piconewton force fluctuations of actomyosin in vitro. *Nature* 352:301–306

13. Ashkin A. 1980. Applications of laser radiation pressure. *Science* 210:1081–88

14. Ashkin A, Schütze K, Dziedzic JM, Eutenauer U, Schliwa M. 1990. Force generation of organelle transport measured *in vivo* by an infrared laser trap. *Nature* 348:346–48

15. Perkins TT, Smith DE, Chu S. 1994. Direct observation of tube-like motion of a single polymer chain. *Science* 264:819–22

16. Yin H, Wang MD, Svoboda K, Landick R, Block S, Gelles J. 1995. Transcription against an applied force. *Science* 270:1653–57

17. Amblard F, Yurke B, Pargellis A, Leibler S. 1996. A magnetic manipulator for studying local rheology and micromechanical properties of biological system. *Rev. Sci. Instrum.* 67(2):1–10

18. Gosse C, Croquette V. 1999. Magnetic tweezers. *Rev. Sci. Instrum.* In preparation

19. Bustamante C, Marko JF, Siggia ED, Smith S. 1994. Entropic elasticity of lambda-phage DNA. *Science* 265:1599–1600

20. Marko JF, Siggia E. 1995. Statistical mechanics of supercoiled DNA. *Phys. Rev. E* 52(3):2912–38

21. Bouchiat C, Wang MD, Block SM, Allemand J-F, Croquette V. 1999. Estimating the persistence length of a worm-like chain molecule from force-extension measurements. *Biophys. J.* 76:409–13

22. Strick T, Allemand JF, Bensimon D, Bensimon A, Croquette V. 1996. The elasticity of a single supercoiled DNA molecule. *Science* 271:1835–37

23. Wilkins MHF, Gosling RG, Seeds WE. 1951. Nucleic acid: an extensible molecule? *Nature* 167:759–60

24. Bensimon A, Simon AJ, Chiffaudel A, Croquette V, Heslot F, Bensimon D. 1994. Alignment and sensitive detection of DNA by a moving interface. *Science* 265:2096–98

25. Bensimon D, Simon AJ, Croquette V, Bensimon A. 1995. Stretching DNA with a receding meniscus: Experiments and models. *Phys. Rev. Lett.* 74:4754–57

26. Léger JF, Romano G, Sarkar A, Robert J, Bourdieu L, et al. 1999. Structural transitions of a twisted and stretched DNA molecule. *Phys. Rev. Lett.* 83:1066–69

27. Léger JF, Robert J, Bourdieu L, Chatenay D, Marko JF. 1998. Binding to a single double-stranded DNA molecule: a possible role of DNA conformational fluctuations. *Proc. Natl. Acad. Sci. USA* 95:12295–96

28. Shivashankar GV, Feingold M, Kritchevsky O, Libchaber A. 1999. Polymerization on double-stranded DNA by using single-molecule manipulation: the role of ATP hydrolysis. *Proc. Natl. Acad. Sci. USA* 96:7916–921

29. Hegner M, Smith SB, Bustamante C. 1999. Polymerization and mechanical properties of single-DNA filaments. *Proc. Natl. Acad. Sci. USA* 96:10109–14

30. Lebrun A, Lavery R. 1997. Unusual DNA conformations. *Curr. Op. Struct. Biol.* 7:348–54

31. White JH. 1969. Self linking and the gauss integral in higher dimensions. *Am. J. Math.* 91:693–728

32. Allemand J-F, Bensimon D, Lavery R, Croquette V. 1998. Stretched and overwound DNA form a Pauling-like structure with exposed bases. *Proc. Natl. Acad. Sci. USA* 95:14152–57

33. Strick T, Allemand J-F, Bensimon D, Croquette V. 1998. The behavior of supercoiled DNA. *Biophys. J.* 74:2016–28

34. Kanaar R, Cozzarelli NR. 1992. Roles of supercoiled DNA structures in DNA transactions. *Curr. Op. Struct. Biol.* 2:369–79

35. Palacek E. 1991. Local supercoil-stabilized structures. *Crit. Rev. Biochem. Mol. Biol.* 26:151–226

36. Pauling L, Corey RB. 1953. A proposed structure for the nucleic acids. *Proc. Natl. Acad. Sci. USA* 39:84–97

37. Brahms JG, Dargouge O, Brahms S, Ohara Y, Vagner V. 1985. Activation and inhibition of transcription by supercoiling. *J. Mol. Biol.* 181:455–65

38. Lilley DMJ, Chen D, Bowater RP. 1996. DNA supercoiling and transcription: topological coupling of promoters. *Q. Rev. Biophys.* 29:203–25

39. Liu DJ, Day LA. 1994. Pf1 virus structure: helical coat protein and DNA with paraxial phosphates. *Science* 265:671–74

40. Lavery R. 1994. *Adv. Comput. Biol.* 1:69–145

41. Lavery R, Zakrzewska K, Sklenar H. 1995. *Comput. Phys. Commun.* 91:135–58

42. Viovy J-L, Heller C, Caron F, Cluzel P, Chatenay D. 1994. Ultrafast sequencing of DNA by mechanical opening of the double helix: a theoretical investigation. *C.R. Acad. Sci. Paris* 317:795–800

43. Thompson RE, Siggia ED. 1995. Physical limits on the mechanical measurement of the secondary structure of bio-molecules. *Europhys. Lett.* 31:335–40

44. Essevaz-Roulet B, Bockelmann U, Heslot F. 1997. Mechanical separation of the complementary strands of DNA. *Proc. Natl. Acad. Sci. USA* 94:11935–40

45. Rief M, Clausen-Schaumann H, Gaub HE. 1999. Sequence-dependent mechanics of single DNA molecules. *Nature Struct. Biol.* 6:346–49

46. Bockelmann U, Essevaz-Roulet B, Heslot F. 1997. Molecular stick-slip revealed by opening DNA with piconewton force. *Phys. Rev. Lett.* 79(22):4489–92

47. Bell GI. 1978. Models for the specific adhesion of cells to cells. *Science* 200:618–27

48. Evans E, Ritchie K. 1997. Dynamic strength of molecular adhesion bonds. *Biophys. J.* 72:1541–55

49. Kellermayer MSZ, Smith SB, Granzier HL, Bustamante C. 1997. Folding-unfolding transition in single titin molecules characterized with laser tweezers. *Science* 276:1112–16

50. Rief M, Gautel M, Oesterhelt F, Fernandez JM, Gaub HE. 1997. Reversible unfolding of individual titin immunoglobulin domains by afm. *Science* 276:1109–12

51. Tskhovrebova L, Trinic J, Sleep JA, Simmons RM. 1997. Elasticity and unfolding of single molecules of the giant muscle protein titin. *Nature* 387:308–12

52. Oberhauser AF, Marszalek PE, Erickson HP, Fernandez JM. 1998. The molecular elasticity of the extracellular matrix protein tenascin. *Nature* 393:181–85

53. Rief M, Gautel M, Schemmel A, Gaub HE. 1998. The mechanical stability of immunoglobulin and fibronectin III domains in the muscle protein titin measured by atomic force microscopy. *Biophys. J.* 75:3008–14

54. Cantor CR, Schimmel PR. 1980. *Biophysical Chemistry. Part III. The Behaviour of Biological Macromolecules.* San Francisco, CA: WH Freemann

55. Carrion-Vazquez M, Oberhauser AF, Fowler SB, Marszalek PE, Broedel SE, et al. 1999. Mechanical and chemical unfolding of a single protein: a comparison. *Proc. Natl. Acad. Sci. USA* 96:3694–99

56. Merkel R, Nassoy P, Leung A, Ritchie K,

Evans E. 1999. Energy landscapes of receptor-ligand bonds explored with dynamic force spectroscopy. *Nature* 397:50–53

57. Socci ND, Onuchic JN, Wolynes PG. 1999. Stretching lattice models of protein folding. *Proc. Natl. Acad. Sci. USA* 96:2031–35

58. Klimov DK, Thirumalai D. 1999. Stretching single-domain proteins: phase diagram and kinetics of force-induced unfolding.

Proc. Natl. Acad. Sci. USA 96:6166–70

59. Smith BL, Schäffer Viani M, Thompson JB, Frederick NA, et al. 1999. Molecular mechanistic origin of the toughness of natural adhesive, fibers and composites. *Nature* 399:761–63

60. Ha T, Zhuang X, Kim HD, Orr JW, Williamson JR, Chu S. 1999. Ligand-induced conformational changes observed in single RNA molecules. *Proc. Natl. Acad. Sci. USA* 96:9077–82

Annu. Rev. Biophys. Biomol. Struct. 2000. 29:545–76

MOLECULAR MECHANISMS CONTROLLING ACTIN FILAMENT DYNAMICS IN NONMUSCLE CELLS

Thomas D. Pollard,[1] Laurent Blanchoin,[1] and R. Dyche Mullins[2]

[1]*Structural Biology Laboratory, Salk Institute for Biological Studies, La Jolla, California 92037; e-mail: pollard@salk.edu;* [2]*Department of Cellular and Molecular Pharmacology, University of California, San Francisco, California 94143; e-mail: dyche@itsa.ucsf.edu*

Key Words cell motility, WASp, Arp2/3 complex, ADF/cofilins, profilin

■ **Abstract** We review how motile cells regulate actin filament assembly at their leading edge. Activation of cell surface receptors generates signals (including activated Rho family GTPases) that converge on integrating proteins of the WASp family (WASp, N-WASP, and Scar/WAVE). WASP family proteins stimulate Arp2/3 complex to nucleate actin filaments, which grow at a fixed 70° angle from the side of preexisting actin filaments. These filaments push the membrane forward as they grow at their barbed ends. Arp2/3 complex is incorporated into the network, and new filaments are capped rapidly, so that activated Arp2/3 complex must be supplied continuously to keep the network growing. Hydrolysis of ATP bound to polymerized actin followed by phosphate dissociation marks older filaments for depolymerization by ADF/cofilins. Profilin catalyzes exchange of ADP for ATP, recycling actin back to a pool of unpolymerized monomers bound to profilin and thymosin-β4 that is poised for rapid elongation of new barbed ends.

CONTENTS

INTRODUCTION

One important function of the actin cytoskeleton in eukaryotic cells is to drive locomotion by the extension of pseudopods. Unicellular organisms use pseudopods for directed motility to find and engulf food. In multicellular organisms, many different processes depend on cell locomotion, including morphogenetic movements during embryonic development, movement of neurites during development and remodeling of the nervous system, chemotactic movements of immune cells, and fibroblast migration during wound healing. Depending on their morphology and the cellular context, pseudopods, are called (rather loosely) lamellipods, leading lamellae, growth cones, or ruffles.

Pseudopod extension requires assembly of a specialized network of actin filaments at the forward or leading edge of the cell. Actin filaments are polarized. Based on the arrowhead pattern created when myosin binds actin filaments, the rapidly growing end of a filament is called the barbed end. The slowly growing end is called the pointed end. Elongation of the barbed end of actin filaments drives membrane protrusion (133). To generate directed motility in response to external cues like chemoattractants, cellular signaling pathways must control actin polymerization and depolymerization. Within seconds such stimuli can initiate directed movements from any site on the surface of a motile cell. When a stimulus ceases or changes direction, pseudopod extension stops just as quickly (41).

At first glance, the filament network underlying the leading edge of motile cells appears chaotic (Figure 1). Careful examination, however, reveals a remarkable degree of order and a number of important structural features that appear to be conserved across eukaryotic phyla. The best studied examples are the leading edges of the fish and amphibian keratocytes (126, 130, 128). These cells are ideal for both light and electron microscopy. They undergo rapid, constitutive motility and assemble a large, extremely thin lamellipod at the leading edge. The actin filament network in these lamellae is organized into two roughly orthogonal arrays, with the rapidly growing barbed ends pointing toward the membrane. The filament network is especially dense near the inner surface of the membrane, and the actin filaments are connected in a highly cross-linked, branching arbor with short filaments apparently growing from the sides of other filaments (130). These general features are conserved in vertebrate tissue culture cells (6, 130) and protozoans (28). The concentration of polymerized actin is about 1000 μM (1a).

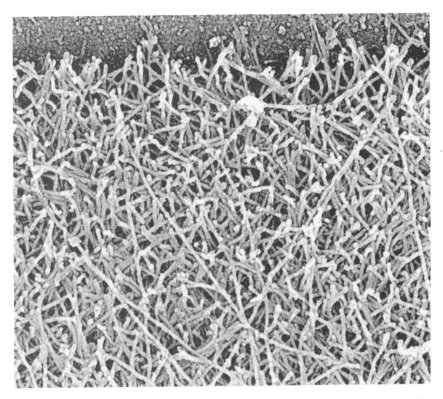

Figure 1   Electron micrograph of the leading edge of a migrating keratocyte prepared by detergent extraction and rotary shadowing. (Modified from 130.)

In a test tube, polymerizing actin with a cross-linking protein like α-actinin produces either an isotropic gel of filaments or parallel bundles (137), so how do cells use these proteins to assemble an ordered and polarized structure? The key to ordered network assembly is a cellular component that initiates polymerization and cross-linking in a highly localized manner. In the past 2 years, the Arp2/3 complex (65, 67, 142, 145) has emerged as the long sought cellular nucleator of actin filaments. This review focuses on a hypothesis that explains how Arp2/3 complex participates in the assembly and disassembly of the leading edge (Figure 2).

Arp2/3 complex is a stable complex of seven subunits—two actin-related proteins Arp2 and Arp3 with five novel proteins—p40 (ARPC1), p35 (ARPC2), p19 (ARPC3), p18 (ARPC4), and p14 (ARPC5) (Figure 3). The Arp2/3 complex was discovered in protozoans by affinity chromatography on the actin-binding protein profilin (67, 86). It is abundant (58), essential (124), and conserved (141) across eukaryotic phyla. In vitro, the complex also attaches the slowly growing pointed end of an actin filament to the side of another filament, producing a 70° branch exactly like those observed in cells (83). Immunoelectron microscopy has recently

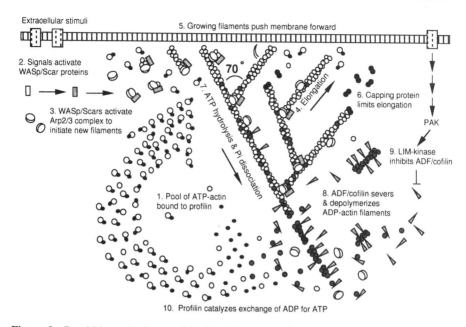

Extracellular stimuli

5. Growing filaments push membrane forward

2. Signals activate
WASp/Scar proteins

3. WASp/Scars activate
Arp2/3 complex to
initiate new filaments

7. ATP hydrolysis & Pi dissociation

70°

4. Elongation

6. Capping protein
limits elongation

PAK

9. LIM-kinase
inhibits ADF/cofilin

1. Pool of ATP-actin
bound to profilin •

8. ADF/cofilin severs
& depolymerizes
ADP-actin filaments

10. Profilin catalyzes exchange of ADP for ATP

Figure 2 Dendritic nucleation model. The 10 numbered steps correspond to the sections of this review. The location of step 3, actin filament nucleation by activated Arp2/3 complex, is not settled. In vitro, free Arp2/3 complex can nucleate polymerization, but secondary activation by filaments strongly favors nucleation on the sides of pre-existing filaments, coupling nucleation and branching. (Modified from 83.)

(128) localized Arp2/3 to filament branches at the leading edge. In 1999 several laboratories (70, 115, 144, 146) discovered that WASp/Scar proteins regulate the nucleation activity of Arp2/3 complex, providing for the first time a plausible link between many cell surface receptors and de novo actin assembly.

Based on these new discoveries, we postulate a concrete, quantitative mechanism for the assembly and disassembly of the leading edge (Figure 2), which we have called the dendritic-nucleation model (83). The model proposes that, in the absence of free barbed ends, cytoskeletal components are held in a metastable state, poised for assembly (step 1). Activation of WASp family proteins (step 2) activates Arp2/3 complex to create new barbed ends at a constant rate (step 3). These filaments grow rapidly (step 4) and push the membrane forward (step 5). After a short time, growth of barbed ends is terminated by capping (step 6). Consequently, the system requires continuous activation of new Arp2/3 complex, because it is consumed by incorporation into a network that grows for a limited time. If the rate of nucleation drops to zero, capping stops polymerization automatically (84). Constitutive ATP hydrolysis within actin filaments and dissociation of phosphate (step 7) trigger severing and depolymerization of older filaments by ADF/cofilins (step 9) at a rate that is controlled by some of the same signals that stimulate assembly. Nucleotide exchange catalyzed by profilin (step 10) recycles ADP-actin

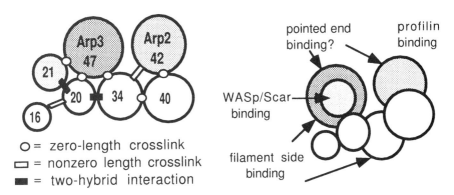

Figure 3 Subunit topology and binding partners of Arp2/3 complex. (Modified from 51.)

subunits back to the ATP-actin monomer pool. In a continuously moving cell, assembly and disassembly are balanced.

This is a minimal model with just 5 of the >60 families of actin-binding proteins (101). We focus on these proteins (profilin and thymosin-β4, Arp2/3 complex, capping protein, and ADF/cofilin), because they are highly conserved, well characterized, and sufficient to induce self-sustaining assembly of dynamic actin filament networks that drive motility of pathogenic, intracellular bacteria (63). Most eukaryotic cells use the same abundant set of cytoskeletal proteins to construct pseudopods (Table 1). Yeasts have similar proteins in dynamic actin patches. Because the building blocks, the overall structure, and (probably) the mechanism of assembly are so highly conserved, we regard the leading edge of a motile cell as a discrete cytoskeletal structure, one whose function and design principles were specified early in eukaryotic evolution.

TABLE 1 Cellular concentrations (μM) of key proteins in the actin system of diverse cells

Protein	Acanthamoeba	Dictyostellium	Neutrophil unactivated	Xenopus egg extract	Platelet unactivated	S. cerevisiae
Polymerized actin	100	90	100	4	330	2
Unpolymerized actin	100	160	300	12	220	0.01
Profilin	100			5		present
Thymosin-β4	? absent	? absent		20	550	absent
ADF/cofilin	20	<100		3	30	present
Arp2/3 complex	2–4	present	10		9	present
Capping protein	1	1	1–2		5	1
Gelsolin	? absent				5	
α-actinin	4	3				
Filamin	? absent				6	
ABP120	? absent	6				

References: *Acanthamoeba* (43, 134, 30, 58, 106); *Dictyostelium* (John Condeelis, Albert Einstein College of Medicine); neutrophil (32, Cano 91, 38, 50); platelet (John Hartwig, Harvard Medical School, 87, 9, 46); *S. cerevisiae* (John Cooper, Washington University).

This review evaluates each step in the proposed mechanism, emphasizing what is known and yet to be discovered about the molecular interactions. A number of recent reviews cover the organization of the leading-edge (129) structure of the key proteins in the system (102), the structure of the Arp2/3 complex (85), and activation of Arp2/3 complex by WASp/Scar (51, 69, 140). Earlier reviews of pseudopod extension (28, 29, 79) provide access to the older literature before the discovery of Arp2/3 complex and WASp/Scar proteins.

HOW DO CELLS MAINTAIN A POOL OF UNPOLYMERIZED ACTIN SUBUNITS?

Studies dating back 25 years (18, 43) documented that nonmuscle cells maintain a high concentration of unpolymerized actin, estimated to be ≤ 100 μM in some cells (Table 1). Most of this monomer pool has bound ATP (117) and is presumed to have bound Mg^{2+}, given the high physiological concentration of Mg^{2+} (millimolar) and the low concentration of Ca^{2+} (0.1 μM). This large pool of Mg-ATP-actin monomers is remarkable because, under physiological conditions, pure ATP-actin from muscle or nonmuscle cells has a critical concentration for polymerization (K_d) of 0.1 μM at the barbed end and 0.6 μM at the pointed end (Table 2). At 100 μM, pure actin in physiological concentrations of salt polymerizes in a few seconds, leaving only 0.1 μM monomer.

Elongation of an actin filament is a bimolecular reaction between monomers and filament ends. It can be regulated by controlling the ability of either monomers or filament ends to participate in the reaction. Cells evolved both mechanisms— proteins that bind monomeric actin and modify its polymerization properties and capping proteins that prevent monomers from adding to filament ends. Alone, neither mechanism is sufficient to account for the extremely large actin monomer pool in the cytoplasm. The combination creates a metastable state with a huge pool of unpolymerized actin, poised for explosive growth when a cell produces free barbed ends.

Monomer-Binding Proteins

The main actin monomer-binding proteins in vertebrate cells are thymosin-β4 and profilin. Thymosin-β4, a small peptide of 43 residues (118), competes with

TABLE 2   Actin filament elongation rate constants in 50 mM KCl, 1 mM MgCl$_2$, 1 mM EGTA, pH 7.0 (from 101)

	ATP-actin Barbed end	ATP-actin Pointed end	ATP-actin Barbed end	ATP-actin Pointed end
k_+ ($\mu M^{-1} s^{-1}$)	11.6	1.3	3.8	0.16
k_- (s^{-1})	1.4	0.8	7.2	0.27
K_d (μM)	0.12	0.62	1.9	1.7

profilin, a small globular protein of 125–139 residues, for binding to overlapping sites on actin (119, 123). Only profilin has been found in protozoa, slime molds, and fungi. (Budding yeasts have no thymosin gene.) Thymosin-β4 is a true sequestering protein that binds about 50-fold more strongly to ATP-actin (K_d, 1.2–1.6 μM) than to ADP-actin (22, 57a, 94, 136). The concentration of thymosin-β4 varies from 600 μM in platelets to 20 μM in *Xenopus* eggs (Table 1) and is thought to account for a large fraction of the unpolymerized actin in these cells. Actin bound to thymosin does not polymerize (22, 42, 57a), but profilin competes with thymosin-β4 for binding ATP-actin (22, 57a, 136) and can shuttle actin away from thymosin onto the barbed end of actin filaments (94, 103). Exchange is rapid, owing to the high dissociation rate constants (5 s^{-1} for profilin and 2.5 s^{-1} for thymosin-β4). ATP-actin partitions between profilin and thymosin-β4 based on the affinities and concentrations of the binding proteins (57a, 97, 136).

Profilin is the main protein that binds ATP-actin monomers in protozoa, slime molds, and fungi, and is present at concentrations of $\leq$100 μM (Table 1). Profilins bind cytoplasmic ATP-actin monomers ($K_d = 0.1$ μM) better than cytoplasmic ADP-actin monomers ($K_d = 0.5$ μM) and muscle ATP-actin monomers ($K_d = 0.5$ μM) (96, 136). The affinity of profilin for actin filaments is low, because the binding site on the barbed end of actin is buried in the filament structure (123).

Profilin-Mg-ATP-actin complexes elongate the barbed end of actin filaments nearly as quickly as free actin, but do not form nuclei or elongate the pointed end of actin filaments (94, 103, 109). High concentrations of profilin slow barbed-end elongation of Mg-ATP-actin $\sim$20% (44, 57), an effect that was originally attributed to rate limiting dissociation of profilin from the barbed end of actin filaments (103). On thermodynamic grounds, it has been argued that profilin should enhance the rate of ATP hydrolysis on the terminal subunit and that this should promote dissociation of profilin (44), but we have not been able to detect an effect of profilin on ATP hydrolysis (15). Thus the mechanism of the small effect of profilin on barbed-end elongation by Mg-ATP-actin is not yet understood. Similarly, we cannot explain how excess profilin completely inhibits elongation by Ca-ATP-actin (44, 57).

Because both free actin monomers and profilin-actin monomer complexes contribute equally to elongation of barbed ends (57a), the concentration of free actin required for growth is less in the presence of profilin than the critical concentration of free actin alone. Profilin is thus said to lower the critical concentration at the barbed end (94). In fact, the critical concentration is the same in the presence of profilin (57a), with both actin and actin-profilin contributing to the critical concentration.

Capping

Profilin (and thymosin-β4 when present) maintains a pool of Mg-ATP-actin that is ready to elongate any available actin filament barbed ends. If the barbed ends of cellular actin filaments were free, elongation would rapidly deplete this pool of actin monomers in a few seconds. Thus, the concentration of free barbed ends must be low. We do not know what fraction of cellular actin filaments has free barbed ends, but the micromolar concentration of capping protein (also called CapZ in muscle) and its affinity for barbed ends ($K_d = 0.1$ nM) are sufficient to cap most of the barbed ends (122). This is true in cellular extracts (32, 84) in which high concentrations of unpolymerized actin monomers are stable in the presence of actin filaments. The addition of uncapped filaments to such extracts results in the explosive polymerization of the actin pool. The rate and extent of growth of these new filaments are limited by capping, which follows a pseudo-first-order reaction (84).

Thus, both monomer binding by profilin and capping of barbed ends are required to maintain a pool of actin monomers. In cells with thymosin-β4, profilin serves as a carrier between the thymosin-ATP-actin pool and the barbed ends of actin filaments (94). Because neither actin-profilin nor actin-thymosin-β4 elongates pointed ends, pointed-end capping is not required to maintain a pool of unpolymerized subunits. Nevertheless, the micromolar concentration of Arp2/3 complex and its nanomolar affinity for pointed ends suggest that most pointed ends are also capped (83).

HOW ARE SIGNALS DIRECTED TO ARP2/3 COMPLEX?

External stimuli drive the assembly of the cortical actin filament network, acting through receptors and multiple signal transduction pathways, several of which converge on WASp/Scar proteins and Arp2/3 complex (Figure 4). The molecular pathways from receptors to WASp/Scar are not well established, but enough is known to postulate that WASp/Scar proteins integrate diverse signals, including those carried by Rho family GTPases, Rac, and Cdc42 (69). Downstream, the ability of active WASp/Scar to stimulate actin filament nucleation by Arp2/3 complex is firmly established (see below), so it is possible that Arp2/3 complex is the

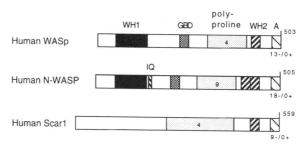

Figure 4 Domains of WASp/Scar proteins. Abbreviations: WH1, WASp homology domain 1, also called EVH1 domain; WH2, WASp homoloogy domain 2; GBD, GTPase-binding domain; A, acidic domain; IQ, IQ domain. The numbers within the polyproline domains indicate the number of polyproline sequences. The numbers below the A domains indicate the number of acidic (−) and basic (+) residues. (Modified from 51.)

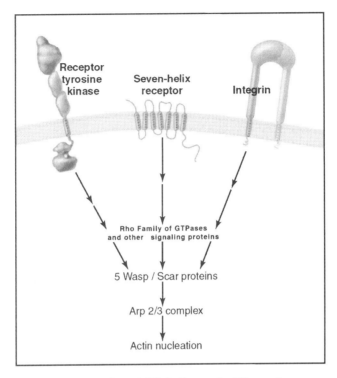

Figure 5   Signaling pathways through WASp/Scar to Arp2/3 complex.

final common effector for all of the signals that impinge on WASp/Scar. Intrinsic signals are also likely to exist for constitutive pseudopod formation but have not been identified.

WASp, the founding member of the WASp/Scar family (Figure 4), is the protein defective in Wiskott-Aldrich syndrome, a human genetic disease with deficiencies in the actin cytoskeleton of platelets and leukocytes (92). WASp is expressed in platelets and white blood cells. N-WASP is expressed in brain and many other tissues. Scar was discovered in *Dictyostelium discoideum* as a suppressor of a mutation in a seven-helix cyclic-AMP (cAMP)-receptor (11). The vertebrate homolog was discovered independently and named WAVE (78). In no case do we know the cellular concentration of a WASp/Scar protein, but anecdotal evidence suggests that the quantities are limiting compared with the abundant Arp2/3 complex. If so, activation of WASp/Scars is likely to be the limiting factor driving actin assembly.

WASp/Scar proteins share similar C-terminal WH2 and A domains and a proline-rich central region, but differ in the N-terminal third (Figure 5). The A domain consists of ~30 conserved residues, including a large fraction of acidic residues, and it interacts with the ARPC3 subunit of the Arp2/3 complex (68). The WH2 domain is a 30-residue motif first identified in verprolin (135). This domain binds actin monomers, blocking their addition to pointed ends but not barbed ends of filaments, similar to profilin (37, 51). Unlike profilin, the WH2 domain does not catalyze nucleotide exchange (50). Both the WH2 and A domains are required for efficient activation of the Arp2/3 complex and together they are sufficient. All WASp family proteins contain a conserved, proline-rich domain with four to nine clusters of polyproline. This domain binds SH3-containing proteins (127) and may bind multiple molecules of profilin. On the N-terminal side of the proline-rich domain, WASp and N-WASP have a GBD domain, a consensus sequence for binding the small G-protein Cdc42. Scar appears to be an effector for Rac but not Cdc42, although it lacks a recognizable GBD. The WH1 domain (also called the EVH1 domain) near the N-terminus is folded like a PH domain but binds polyproline-containing ligands. Crystal structures are available of an EVH1 domain (39, 108) and a GBD bound to Cdc42 (1). N-WASP also has a calmodulin-binding IQ motif. This domain structure gives WASp/Scar proteins the potential to integrate a wide variety of signals, but little is known about the conformation of the full-length proteins, not even an estimate of the native molecular weight. So, much is still to be learned about signal transduction at this level.

A strong case can be made for WASp and N-WASP as intermediaries between Rho family GTPases and Arp2/3 complex. In vertebrate cells, Rac is required for cell motility, and Cdc42 is required for chemotaxis (3, 45). WASp and N-WASP bind Cdc42 and are required for Cdc42-stimulated polymerization (115, 146). Cdc42-induced actin polymerization in cell extracts (84, 148, 149) depends on Arp2/3 complex (65, 84). A simple model, supported by cellular studies with dominant-active and dominant-negative Cdc42 (78), is that WASp/N-WASP is inactive until activated by GTP-Cdc42. Scar may be downstream of Rac (78), but because it lacks a binding site for Rho family GTPases, it may respond to different unidentified activators, perhaps downstream from the seven helix receptors.

HOW DO CELLS CREATE ACTIN FILAMENTS WITH FREE BARBED ENDS?

Profilin and thymosin-$\beta 4$ strongly inhibit spontaneous nucleation of unpolymerized actin, so the limiting factor in actin polymerization in vivo is the creation of free barbed ends. Cells could either initiate new filaments (the focus of this section) or uncap or sever existing filaments, allowing them to elongate.

Uncapping

The two most abundant barbed-end–capping proteins, gelsolin and capping protein, both cap filament ends with nanomolar affinity, and both can be removed by interacting with polyphosphoinositides [e.g. PI(4, 5)P$_2$ (56, 122)]. In platelets, uncapping of gelsolin-capped filaments appears to generate free barbed ends and contribute to actin polymerization (47). In other cells selective removal of capping protein from filaments may help filaments to grow persistently toward the membrane and to organize the three-dimensional structure of the actin network at the leading edge (see below). At least in filopodia growth of existing filaments persists at low rates for long times (74a).

Severing

Severing existing filaments into multiple smaller ones can generate new ends. Platelet activation is the best example, in which severing is a major mechanism of inducing actin polymerization (10). Platelet activation increases cytoplasmic Ca^{2+}, which activates gelsolin to sever actin filaments and tightly cap their barbed ends. Membrane PIP_2 can remove the gelsolin cap and contribute to the burst of polymerization (47). However, gelsolin is not absolutely required, because platelets from mice lacking gelsolin still polymerize and cap new actin filaments when activated. In fibroblasts the reactions mediated by gelsolin appear to be downstream of Rac (5). ADF/cofilins also sever actin filaments (discussed below), but most evidence suggests that this is associated with depolymerization rather than assembly (23, 61, 116). Nevertheless, cofilin-mediated severing has been proposed to generate short actin oligomers that are subsequently stabilized and cross-linked by Arp2/3 complex (35). This interesting possibility requires further study.

De Novo Filament Formation

In a many cell types, actin polymerization appears to be initiated de novo by assembly of nuclei from actin monomers and nucleation-promoting factors. Although this has long been considered, no barbed-end nucleating factor was known before Arp2/3 complex was shown to have this activity. The following section summarizes what has been learned about nucleation mediated by Arp2/3 complex, but we caution at the outset that an open mind is necessary about the possibility of other factors with such activity.

Spontaneous nucleation of actin alone is unfavorable because of the instability of actin dimers and trimers, which are obligate intermediates on the path to longer filaments. The details of these reactions are still murky, because no assays are available for dimers or trimers. Their properties have been inferred from complete polymerization time courses (reviewed in 104), using kinetic simulation to estimate equilibrium constants; $K_d = \sim 100,000$ μM for dimers and $\sim 10–100$ μM for trimers. Filament elongation is a rapid, diffusion-limited reaction (see below). If monomer association reactions are also diffusion limited, the lifetimes of dimers and trimers are exceedingly brief, in the submillisecond range. Nevertheless, under physiological salt conditions, pure actin does form nuclei spontaneously, if slowly, in a very concentration-dependent reaction. Nucleation reactions deserve new work with new approaches.

The term nucleation is sometimes used loosely and inappropriately in the primary literature. Nucleation is the initiation of a new actin filament by assembly from monomers. Accessory proteins can promote or inhibit these reactions. Addition of subunits to the ends of existing actin filaments, which are simply added to a reaction or are uncapped or severed to expose new ends, is elongation, not nucleation.

Highly purified Arp2/3 complex nucleates filaments with free barbed ends and capped pointed ends, but the mechanism is extremely inefficient, because it depends on the capture of spontaneously formed actin dimers (83). Cells use at least two synergistic regulatory mechanisms to turn on the intrinsically inactive Arp2/3 complex. WASp/Scar proteins are primary activators, and actin filaments are powerful secondary activators, an effect that promotes branching. Certain bacteria have evolved their own activators of Arp2/3 complex, such as *Listeria* ActA (143).

WASP-family proteins activate Arp2/3 complex to generate new actin filaments. Constructs consisting of the WH2 and A domains (WA) of all WASp/Scars activate actin filament nucleation by Arp2/3 complex, independently of the rest of the protein (70, 115, 144, 146). Under optimal conditions, each WA-activated Arp2/3 complex initiates a new filament (50). WA constructs from WASp and Scar interact with Arp2/3 subunits in affinity chromatography and yeast two-hybrid assays, and overexpression of WA peptides in vertebrate cells delocalizes Arp2/3 and inhibits actin reorganization (68).

The mechanism of nucleation by WA-activated Arp2/3 complex is being investigated. Activation may simply be allosteric—a conformational change induced in the complex by WA (85). WH2 domains also bind actin monomers (68) with submicromolar affinity, so they may actively recruit actin monomers to Arp2/3 complex to form a nucleus (37, 50). After nucleation, Arp2/3 complex remains attached to the pointed end of the filament, so it is incorporated into the growing actin filament network (83).

Actin filaments are powerful secondary activators of nucleation by Arp2/3 complex and WA. Inclusion of filaments with Arp2/3 complex and WA can eliminate the lag at the outset of an in vitro polymerization experiment (70). The synergism between WA and filaments biases the initiation of new filaments to the sides of existing actin filaments, where Arp2/3 complex anchors end-to-side branches at a fixed angle of 70° (12a, 83). Examination of the products by light microscopy revealed that branching occurs during rather than after nucleation (12a). This coupling between nucleation and branching explains the morphology of the leading edge. The situation must differ in filopodia, which depend on Cdc42 for initiation (78), but which consist of a parallel bundle of filaments rather than a branching network.

Full-length WASp/Scar proteins also activate Arp2/3 complex in vitro, but the details differ in the initial reports. Full-length Scar was as active as its WA domain (70), so the recombinant protein is constitutively active. Similarly, no GTPase was required for WASp to activate Arp2/3 complex (146). On the other hand, full-length N-WASP required both Cdc42 and lipid vesicles containing PI(4, 5)P$_2$ to stimulate maximal nucleation activity (115). Oddly, both GTP-Cdc42 and GDP-Cdc42 were active in these experiments, whereas Egile et al (37) found that GTP-Cdc42 was required for N-WASP to activate Arp2/3 complex.

Functional Implications

Nucleation in cells appears to require a continuous supply of activated Arp2/3 complex, because activated complex is physically consumed by incorporation into the filament network and because capping protein stops polymerization after a few seconds (see below). A supply of barbed ends will be maintained in the cytoplasm only if they are created at the same rate as they are capped. For this reason, any cellular mechanism that produces sustained actin polymerization must induce a constant rate of nucleation rather than produce a fixed number of nuclei all at once. Production of active Arp2/3 complex at a constant rate appears to be the function of WASP-family proteins and the *Listeria* ActA. This dependence on the rate of nucleation may explain why filament initiation stops abruptly when stimuli, such as chemotactic signals, turn off.

Two lines of evidence suggest that activators interact only transiently with Arp2/3 complex. *Listeria* ActA stimulates nucleation by Arp2/3 complex but remains attached to the bacterial surface, whereas Arp2/3 complex is incorporated into the actin comet tail behind the bacterium (143). Similarly, addition of WASp-coated beads to cytosolic extracts induces actin polymerization that is dependent on Arp2/3 complex, which is incorporated into the actin network leaving WASp behind on the beads (146). Thus each molecule of ActA or WASp/Scar may activate multiple Arp2/3 complexes. If true, the concentration of activated WASP family proteins will induce a constant rate of nucleation, but more work is required on the rates of the various reactions. The site of activation is unknown but has been suggested to be either on the inner surface of the plasma membrane (37, 115, 143) or in the cortical-filament network (70).

Polarity and Coincidence Detection

Although far from complete, current evidence suggests that multiple signals converge at the same place to maximally activate nucleation. Therefore, the combination of N-WASP and Arp2/3 complex may act as a coincidence detector that responds maximally to the combination of active GTPase, phospholipids, actin filaments, and other signals. In addition to making filament formation responsive to a signaling pathway, this mechanism prevents nucleation away from the membrane surface and causes filaments to feed back positively on their formation. The result is tightly localized filament formation that, once initiated, accelerates rapidly. This is probably critical for the cell's ability to polarize rapidly in response to external signals and to maintain polarity during movement.

HOW DO NEW FILAMENTS ELONGATE?

Elongation of purified actin is the best characterized part of this system (Table 2), because robust assays are available to measure the elongation rates at both ends of filaments. The ratio of the dissociation rate constant to the association rate constant for each reaction gives the dissociation equilibrium constant, also known as the critical concentration. The critical concentrations for ADP-actin are the same at both ends. (The apparent difference in Table 2 represents experimental error.) For Mg-ATP-actin, the critical concentration is considerably lower at the barbed end than at the pointed end, whether measured kinetically during rapid elongation or at steady state. This difference in critical concentrations at the two ends in ATP must be from ATP hydrolysis and/or phosphate dissociation, but the mechanism is not understood. It is not caused by different rates of ATP hydrolysis at the two ends (15).

Elongation of ATP-actin at the barbed end is diffusion limited by accepted physical-chemical criteria, namely that the reciprocal of the rate constant is proportional to the viscosity of the solution and extrapolates to an infinite rate constant at zero viscosity (33). Elongation at the pointed end is slower and not diffusion limited. Molecular dynamics simulations (125) revealed why the rate constants differ at the two ends; without taking electrostatics into consideration, elongation is favored at the pointed end, but electrostatic effects enhance elongation rates at the barbed end and inhibit elongation at the pointed end, as observed. Through electrostatic effects, proteins such as ADF/cofilins bound to actin monomers may accelerate elongation modestly [20%–50% (125)], but suggestions that other proteins enhance elongation by 10- or 20-fold (23) may not be physically possible.

Two opposing factors influence diffusion-limited reactions in cytoplasm. The high concentration of macromolecules slows diffusion of proteins the size of actin by a factor of about 3 (64), but this is compensated for by an excluded volume effect that increases reaction rates, including actin filament elongation (33). At the concentrations of unpolymerized actin found in cells (10–100 μM), elongation rates of barbed ends in dilute buffers are exceptionally fast, $\sim$100–1000 subunits/s, that is, $\sim$0.3–3 μm/s. In cytoplasm the rate may be lower, but even if twofold lower, the rate is adequate to account for the rate of pseudopod formation in rapidly moving cells, and it is much faster than required for slow cells like epithelial cells in tissue culture. Some authors argue that diffusion of actin to sites of elongation is rate limiting, but this is unlikely to be true in cells with a large pool of unpolymerized, freely diffusible actin.

In the foregoing, it was assumed that all of the unpolymerized actin is bound to profilin (Figure 6). This is true in amoebae, but part of the unpolymerized actin pool is bound to thymosin in vertebrate cells. This lowers the available monomer concentration and the rate of elongation. If the concentration of unpolymerized actin really varies as much as reported (Table 1), the rate of elongation will vary considerably.

HOW DO GROWING FILAMENTS PUSH THE MEMBRANE FORWARD?

The network of actin filaments at the leading edge of a motile cell is uniquely adapted to convert the free energy of monomer binding into mechanical energy. The idea that polymerization itself generates force to deform the plasma membrane

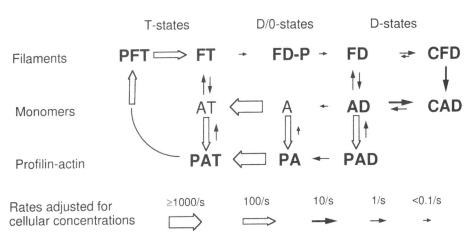

Figure 6 Actin monomer economy. A, actin monomer; F, actin filament; P, profilin; C, ADF/cofilin; T, ATP; D, ADP; D-P, ADP-P$_i$. The *arrows* indicate the approximate reaction rates based on rate constants and cytoplasmic concentrations of proteins.

was proposed by Tilney et al (133). It is consistent with most observations of living cells but has never been demonstrated experimentally to be the mechanism of membrane protrusion in vivo. The best experimental evidence for this mechanism comes from two sources: (*a*) studies in which monomeric actin encapsulated in giant liposomes is induced to polymerize (80) and (*b*) reconstitution of bacterial motility from purified components. In giant liposomes the polymerization of pure actin is sufficient to deform the membrane and, in the presence of actin cross-linking proteins, the deformation is quite severe (81). *Listeria* motility requires, in addition to actin, only three proteins (Arp2/3 complex, ADF/cofilin, and capping protein), none of which is a force-generating motor protein (63). Assembly and turnover of the actin comet tail appear to be sufficient to propel the bacterium forward.

The microscopic details of polymerization-driven motility are not immediately obvious. Peskin et al (98) proposed that, when the end of an actin filament contacts a load, elongation of the filament could act as a ratchet to rectify the thermal motions of the load. That is, if thermal motions cause the load to fluctuate away from the end of the filament, elongation of the filament into the gap will prevent the load from returning to its original position. This might apply to membranes, but not to bacteria, which are too large to undergo appropriate Brownian motions. Mogilner & Oster (82) combined this idea of a thermal ratchet with the elastic properties of an actin filament and proposed an "elastic Brownian ratchet" model. In this model, filaments behave like elastic springs with properties determined by the bending modulus of the filament and the angle it makes with the load. According to Mogilner & Oster, the thermal fluctuations of actin filaments are the most important. Thermal motion can displace a filament from the membrane, allowing room for additional monomers to add to the end of the filament. The elastic restoring force of the filament tries to return the longer filament to its original position and results in deformation of the membrane. One important prediction of this model is that there is an optimal angle to transmit force from an actin filament to a load. In the force regime of the leading edge (~45 pN), this angle is ~45° as observed in cells (130; Figure 1). The branches formed by Arp2/3 complex are quite stiff (12a), in keeping with this model. The actin filament concentration is also consistent with protrusion being driven by polymerization (1a).

WHAT LIMITS THE GROWTH OF FILAMENTS?

Our dominant theme is that control of actin polymerization takes place at the barbed end of the filament; to make new filaments, cells create new barbed ends; and to limit filament growth, cells cap barbed ends rapidly (Figure 2). The supporting evidence is that most cells maintain a large pool of polymerizable actin that would disappear if ends were allowed to grow indefinitely; filaments injected into living cells do not elongate detectably (120), and actin seeds added to cell extracts grow for only a short time and do not deplete the pool of monomeric actin (53, 84, 149).

The factor thought to cap barbed ends in most cells is a ubiquitous heterodimeric protein called capping protein, discovered in amoebae (55). Capping protein is abundant in most cell types, with cytoplasmic concentrations in the micromolar range (Table 1). The muscle isoform of capping protein (CapZ) caps the barbed ends of the actin filaments at the Z-disk (26). Injection of function-blocking anti-CapZ antibodies into developing muscle cells profoundly disrupts sarcomere formation (121). Genetic deletion of capping protein in nonmuscle cells alters the balance between polymerized and unpolymerized actin (4, 54) and immunodepletion of capping protein from nonmuscle cell extracts removes almost all of the barbed-end capping activity (32).

Capping protein binds the barbed end of actin filaments very tightly [$K_d = 0.1$ nM (122)] and prevents both association and dissociation of monomers (55). Capping protein binds barbed ends with an association rate constant of 3 μM s^{-1}. At cellular concentrations of capping protein, a free barbed end will have a half-life of about a quarter of a second before it is capped, but, because of the high cellular concentration of monomeric actin, the filament will have elongated by >200 monomers during this time. The high affinity of capping protein for barbed ends is a consequence of its extremely slow dissociation rate [5×10^{-4} s^{-1} (122)]. The half-time for uncapping is >1000 s, much longer than the lifetime of dynamic actin filaments in cells (27, 132), so, unless it is actively uncapped or severed, a capped filament probably never elongates again.

If a new filament is cross-linked into the network with its barbed end pointing away from the membrane, it will probably remain capped until it is disassembled by ADF/cofilin. If, however, a capped barbed end collides with a membrane, interaction with poly phosphoinositides like PIP$_2$ and PIP$_3$ may remove capping protein and allow one or more additional rounds of growth and capping. In this way, localized uncapping may bias the growth of filaments and produce more long filaments with barbed ends oriented toward the leading edge. This might explain why the barbed ends of all long filaments in the keratocyte leading edge point forward. New experiments are required to test this idea. Another area for research is to learn how activated Cdc42 protects growing actin filaments from capping in leukocyte extracts (53). Elsewhere in this review, we consider further consequences of uncapping.

HOW ARE FILAMENTS MARKED FOR DEPOLYMERIZATION?

Hydrolysis of ATP bound to actin subunits, subsequent to their incorporation into filaments, and the dissociation of the gamma-phosphate are postulated to mark filaments for depolymerization by ADF/cofilin proteins (74; Figure 2). New actin filaments at the leading edge of a cell are built with ATP actin subunits, because ATP-actin is the predominate form of unpolymerized actin (117). Phosphate dissociation is an effective timer for destruction, because the depolymerizing proteins, ADF/cofilins (next section), bind polymerized ADP-actin subunits more strongly than ATP-actin or ADP-P_i actin subunits (Table 3). This explains why BeF_3 (14, 23) or millimolar concentrations of phosphate (14, 23, 72, 74) protect ADP-actin filaments from ADF/cofilins in binding, low-shear-viscosity, and depolymerization experiments.

ATP hydrolysis by polymerized actin is irreversible (24), but phosphate dissociates slowly. By several criteria including critical concentration, ADP-P_i actin is very similar to ATP-actin (113). ADP-actin is distinctly different. The dissociation equilibrium constant for P_i from polymerized ADP-P_i subunits is in the low millimolar range (19), so some ADP-actin subunits may retain the gamma-phosphate in vivo. The nucleotide bound to polymerized actin subunits is not exchangeable along the length of the filament (105), but ATP does exchange rapidly with ADP on the terminal subunits at the barbed ends of filaments, possibly contributing to the stability of barbed ends (131). By inhibiting this exchange ADF/cofilin might destabilize barbed ends in cells. Nothing is known about nucleotide exchange on pointed ends.

TABLE 3   Dissociation equilibrium constants (μM) for ADF/cofilins binding actin monomers and filaments

ADF/cofilin	Mg-ATP-monomer	Mg-ADP-monomer	Mg-ADP-P-filament	Mg-ADP-filament
Actophorin, amoeba actin[a]	5.9	0.15		5.6
Actophorin, muscle actin[b]	4.5	0.14	$\approx$20	0.49
Plant ADF, muscle actin[c]	8	0.1		0.3
Human ADF, muscle actin[d]		0.09		

References: a. 14, b. 15, c. 23, d. 112.

TABLE 4 ATP hydrolysis rate constants (s^{-1}) by polymorized actin calculated assuming random hydrolysis

Report	Mg-ATP-actin	Ca-ATP-actin	Li-ATP-actin
Pardee & Spudich, 1982 (95)		~0.0005 $(t_{1/2} = 30$ min.)	
Pollard & Weeds, 1984 (107)	0.07^*	0.08	
Carlier et al, 1986 (25)	0.08	0.02	
Pieper & Wegner, 1996 (99)	0.02	0.01	
Blanchoin & Pollard, 2000 (13)	0.10	0.06	0.10

*This was Ca-ATP-actin polymerized in 50 mM KCl, 1 mM MgCl$_2$, 1 mM EGTA. We now know that much of the actin incorporated into polymer was Ca-ATP-actin.

ATP hydrolysis and gamma-phosphate dissociation are both first-order reactions. The simplest model for these reactions is that each subunit in a polymer acts independently (52), so that all have an equal probability of hydrolyzing ATP and dissociating phosphate. The time courses of hydrolysis and phosphate dissociation are consistent with but do not prove this model. Alternatively, it is reasonable to think that the local environment in the polymer might influence either or both reactions. The most extreme version of such thinking is a vectorial hydrolysis model in which ATP hydrolysis occurs only at the interface between the central core of ADP-P$_i$-actin subunits and ATP-actin subunits at either end of a growing filament (25). If this mechanism is correct, the hydrolysis rate at the interface of ADP- and ATP-subunits would have to be very high to account for the observed hydrolysis rates, because so few subunits would be eligible for hydrolysis. Kinetics experiments cannot prove or disprove this hypothesis, but an experiment of Pieper & Wegner (99) argues against vectorial hydrolysis. They found that copolymerization of ATP-actin with a range of ADP-actin concentrations did not affect the rate of ATP hydrolysis by the polymerized actin.

The range of ATP hydrolysis rates reported over the years is wide (Table 4). Some differences are caused by technical limitations of the early work, because the experiments were done before we knew how to make good Mg-ATP-actin. The most recent work with quench-flow methods shows that Mg-ATP-actin (and Li-ATP-actin) hydrolyzed ATP about twice as quickly as Ca-ATP-actin. Atomic structures explain the different rates, because Mg^{2+} and Li^+ position the attacking water more favorably than Ca^{2+} (S Almo, personal communication).

Both groups reporting on the rate of gamma-phosphate dissociation from Mg-ADP-P$_i$-actin subunits agree that the rate constant is about $0.002\,s^{-1}$ (14, 20, 77), but this half time of >5 min is too slow to account for the fastest turnover of actin filaments in vivo $[t_{1/2} = 23\,s$ (132)]. One resolution of this difference is that ADF/cofilin increases the rate of phosphate release by a factor of >10, although ADF/cofilins bind only weakly to ADP-P$_i$-actin subunits (14). This is reasonable thermodynamically, because, if phosphate reduces the affinity of ADF/cofilin for actin, ADF/cofilin must reduce the affinity of phosphate for actin.

Thus phosphate dissociation is the most plausible timer for actin polymer destruction by ADF/cofilin. If true, the lag between rapid actin polymerization in vivo and the enhanced rate of phosphate release by ADF/cofilin should influence the thickness of the network of ATP-actin filaments near the membrane. Careful observations of ADF/cofilin localization revealed differences between highly motile keratocytes and slower fibroblasts (128). Keratocytes exclude ADF/cofilin from a zone near the membrane, whereas in fibroblasts ADF/cofilin is present throughout the cortex, up to the front of the leading edge. This difference may reflect more rapid growth of the actin network or a longer lag between actin polymerization and phosphate release in keratocytes than fibroblasts.

What about long-lived actin filaments? The best example is striated muscle, in which ADP-actin filaments are stable for hours to days. These filaments are protected from depolymerization by tropomyosin, which inhibits ADF/cofilin binding and depolymerization (12, 91). Some stable actin filaments in nonmuscle cells, including stress fibers, are also protected by tropomyosin (62). The brush border of intestinal epithelial cells is another example, with two populations of stable actin filaments (49). Those in the terminal web are probably stabilized by tropomyosin. Those in the microvilli lack tropomyosin, so they must be stabilized by the other associated proteins.

HOW DO FILAMENTS DEPOLYMERIZE?

Filaments turn over rapidly during pseudopod extension (27, 132) and during the centripetal flow of the cortical actin filament network in some stationary cells (40, 138). How fast must subunits dissociate from individual filaments to account for these rates of polymer turnover? If all depolymerization were in one zone at a fixed distance from the front of the cell, the rates would have to be very fast, hundreds of subunits per second, because lamellipodia move up to 1 μm s^{-1} (370 subunits/μm) and centripetal flow can be $\leq$0.8 μm s^{-1}. However, depolymerization takes place across a broad zone (132), so no one knows how quickly individual filaments shorten.

The situation is more complicated than usually acknowledged. Making the reasonable assumption that subunit dissociation is restricted to the ends of filaments, the rate of depolymerization of a population of polymerized actin depends directly on the intrinsic rate of subunit dissociation (k_-) and the concentration of free ends minus the rate of subunit association:

$$\text{Depolymerization rate} = k_-(\text{ends}) - k_+(\text{ends})(\text{actin monomer}).$$

Dissociation rate constants for Mg-ADP-actin are 7 s^{-1} at the barbed end and a very slow 0.3 s^{-1} at the pointed end (Table 2). For a given mass of polymer, the concentration of ends depends inversely on their lengths, so the bulk depolymerization rate is inversely proportional to polymer length. This is why severing is so important to consider as part of the depolymerization mechanism. In a cell, some barbed ends and some pointed ends will be free and others capped. All of these parameters appear to be subject to control in cells. In no live cell are all of these parameters known.

Proteins of the ADF/cofilin family are thought to promote recycling of actin (for review, see 21), because they enhance the dynamics of actin filaments in *Listeria* comet tails (23, 116) and promote depolymerization of pure actin filaments (7, 14, 23, 30, 34, 66, 72, 74, 90). A major point of disagreement is whether ADF/cofilin proteins enhance depolymerization by severing actin filaments and creating more ends, by increasing the rate of subunit dissociation from one or both ends, or by both severing and rapid subunit dissociation (for review, see 71).

As explained in the following paragraphs, most investigators favor a dual mechanism with ADF/cofilins severing filaments to increase the number of ends and also increasing the rate constant for subunit dissociation at one or both ends (Figure 6, large vertical arrow at the top right). Carlier et al (23) and Ressad et al (112) have argued that the effects of ADF/cofilin on actin filaments might be explained entirely by a 30-fold-higher rate of subunit dissociation at the pointed ends of filaments. Much remains to be learned about the depolymerization mechanism.

Binding of ADF/cofilins to ADP-actin filaments is still incompletely understood. One basic uncertainty is whether association is cooperative as observed for all ADF/cofilins tested (including amoeba-actophorin) binding to muscle actin filaments or not cooperative as observed for amoeba-actophorin binding to amoeba-actin filaments, the only homogeneous system tested to date. Resolving this question is important for understanding cells, because polymerized actin exceeds the concentration of ADF/cofilins, and cooperativity would focus this limited ADF/cofilin locally on filaments and might promote subsequent reactions. For the homogeneous, noncooperative amoeba system, the association rate constant is exceptionally slow, $0.03 \ \mu M^{-1} \ s^{-1}$, but, for the cooperative system of actophorin and muscle actin, the rate constant increases with saturation from $0.008 \ \mu M^{-1} \ s^{-1}$ to $>0.075 \ \mu M^{-1} \ s^{-1}$ (14). The rates of cooperative binding of plant ADF to muscle actin are orders of magnitude faster (111). Both the very slow binding in the homogeneous system and the cooperative binding suggest that few subunits in bare filaments are in a conformation that favors binding.

Saturating concentrations of ADF/cofilins change the twist of the long pitch helix of muscle actin filaments by $5°$ per subunit (75), a structural change that is suggested to promote severing and subunit dissociation. Binding of ADF/cofilins to pyrene-labeled actin filaments quenches the fluorescence down to the low level of actin monomers (14, 23), a valuable signal to measure binding that does not yet have a structural interpretation. Both tropomyosin (12, 74) and phalloidin (14, 74) inhibit the binding of ADF/cofilins to actin filaments.

A variety of evidence suggests that ADF/cofilin proteins sever actin filaments: direct visualization by fluorescence microscopy (48, 74), electron microscopy (30, 72), viscometry (30, 73), kinetics of spontaneous polymerization (34, 74, 110), measurement of ends by elongation assays (14, 72), and fluorescence recovery after photobleaching (34). The extent of severing depends on the concentration of ADF/cofilin and time, but the number of breaks is much lower than the number of

ADF/cofilins bound. For example, mixing 4 μM actophorin with 2 μM polymerized actin severs each filament of ~2000 subunits into ~10 shorter filaments (14). In contrast, gelsolin severs actin filaments with high efficiency, with one break per binding event (139), so ADF/cofilins are said to sever weakly.

Other experiments show that ADF/cofilins promote the dissociation of subunits from the ends of actin filaments. The most extensive study (23) showed that filaments depolymerize about 30-fold more quickly from their pointed ends in the presence of plant ADF, assuming that ADF had no effect on the number of ends. The same study found a 20-fold increase in the rate of elongation at the barbed end of actin filaments, a result that can be explained only by an increase in the concentration of barbed ends (125). Thus the higher rate of dissociation at the pointed end may be explained in part by a higher concentration of ends produced by severing.

One unresolved issue is how filaments can depolymerize in the presence of high concentrations of unpolymerized actin and proteins that cap both ends with high affinity. Why do bare filament ends created by severing or uncapping become shorter rather than growing or being capped? How is depolymerization made processive enough that an entire filament can disappear on a time scale of tens of seconds?

Binding most unpolymerized ATP-actin monomers to profilin (and thymosin-β4 when present) allows depolymerization of pointed ends, but strongly favors elongation at free barbed ends. This argues that depolymerization is most likely at pointed ends. However, the rate of ADP-actin dissociation from pointed ends is so slow (Table 2) that even a 30-fold increase in this rate (23) may not explain the high in vivo rates of turnover inferred from leukocyte or keratocyte movement (27, 132). ATP exchange on subunits at barbed ends of ADP-actin filaments makes depolymerization even less favorable (131) and may influence pointed-end depolymerization as well.

Thus, other cellular factors may be required to enhance actin filament turnover. One candidate is actin-interacting protein 1 (Aip1), a conserved 64-kDa protein that interacts with actin and cofilin. Aip1 localizes to dynamic regions of the cell cortex such as lamellipodia in *Dictyostelium discoideum* (60). This protein enhances the filament disassembly activity of ADF/cofilin (93, 114), but the published work has not revealed the mechanism. One hypothesis is that, at any given time, few subunits in actin filaments are in the conformation required to bind ADF/cofilin. By interacting with both actin filaments and ADF/cofilin, Aip1 may enhance the binding of ADF/cofilin to actin filaments.

Capping poses theoretical difficulties for depolymerization at both ends. All of the actin filaments in the dendritic arbor at the leading edge are associated at their pointed ends with the side of other filaments, presumably capped by Arp2/3 complex (128). Therefore, how does depolymerization get started? One answer is that ADF/cofilins sever filaments between the caps, as shown by experiments with filaments of pure actin capped on both ends with gelsolin and Arp2/3 complex. Such double capping does not inhibit depolymerization by ADF/cofilin (16, 111). A more difficult question is what prevents capping of free ends during depolymerization? The micromolar cytoplasmic concentrations and nanomolar affinities of capping protein and Arp2/3 complex are theoretically sufficient to cap all ends (83, 122). The rate of capping protein binding to barbed ends is expected to leave them free only for brief intervals. Nothing is known about the rate of Arp2/3 complex binding to pointed ends, and in principle the large complex may bind so slowly that free pointed ends are left open for longer times. In addition, three potentially synergistic mechanisms might favor processive depolymerization of dendritic actin filament networks: (*a*) ADF/cofilin binding to Arp2/3 complex (16) may inhibit binding to pointed ends; (*b*) the conformational change induced in actin filaments by ADF/cofilin (75) may promote dissociation of cappers from one or both ends, particularly if it is cooperative; or (*c*) ATP hydrolysis and phosphate dissociation from terminal subunits may reduce the affinity of one or both cappers (12a). To account for the rapid turnover in vivo, it would be helpful if one or more of these mechanisms made depolymerization processive, because rapid recapping appears to have the potential to stop disassembly soon after an end is exposed.

HOW DO STABLE FILAMENTS SURVIVE IN CYTOPLASM?

In addition to the intrinsic ATP timer built into actin filaments, at least two mechanisms control the stability of actin filaments in cytoplasm: regulation of severing proteins, including both gelsolin and ADF/cofilins, and binding of stabilizing proteins like tropomyosin.

Phosphorylation of ADF/cofilins provides a mechanism for signaling pathways to regulate the stability of actin filaments. PAK (a kinase regulated by Rho family GTPases) activates LIM-kinase (36) to phosphorylate a serine near the N terminus of ADF/cofilins (2, 88). Phosphorylation has no effect on the atomic structure, but reduces the affinity of ADF/cofilins for actin monomers and filaments by about 2 orders of magnitude, presumably by steric and electrostatic effects (17). Substitution of an acidic residue for this serine has a much smaller effect (112). The extent of ADF/cofilin phosphorylation and rate of phosphate turnover depend on agonist stimulation (8, 76). This mechanism may allow signals flowing through Rho family GTPases to coordinate the initiation of new filaments (through WASp and Arp2/3 complex) with their rate of turnover (through PAK, LIM-kinase, and ADF/cofilins). It is not known whether this regulation of ADF/cofilins is global or local in cells.

Calcium regulates actin filament binding and severing by gelsolin (147). Free Ca^{2+} affects the rate but not the extent of actin filament severing by gelsolin (59). Significant binding of gelsolin to actin filaments is possible at physiological concentrations of free Ca^{2+} (0.1–1 μM) (59). In resting cells, the low concentration of free calcium may allow very slow severing and contribute to filament turnover. Transient increases in intracellular free calcium will promote both gelsolin binding and actin filament severing.

One unsolved mystery is how a population of filaments in lamellapodia survives to become very long. Behind the dense arbor of short filaments at the leading edge, the actin network is composed exclusively of long filaments that extend for several micrometers toward the nucleus (126, 128, 130). Tropomyosin or other stabilizing proteins seem likely, but they have not been shown to be present.

HOW ARE SUBUNITS RECYCLED TO THE ATP-ACTIN-PROFILIN POOL?

Acting together, profilin and ADF/cofilin enhance the turnover of actin filaments to a time scale nearly compatible with the one observed in vivo (13, 23, 31). Regardless of the mechanism, the species dissociating from filaments is likely to be Mg-ADP-actin, either free or bound to ADF/cofilin. Most unpolymerized actin has bound ATP (117), so nucleotide exchange is required (Figure 6). The rate-limiting step is dissociation of ADP ($k = 0.08$ s^{-1} for Mg-ADP-actin). However, in physiological salt, ADF/cofilins bind ADP-actin monomers with high affinity ($K_d = 0.15\ \mu$M) and slow ADP dissociation by >10-fold to 0.006 s^{-1} (13, 23, 89). In the absence of other actin-binding proteins, a pool of ADF/cofilin-Mg-ADP-actin monomers would tend to accumulate. However, profilin competes with ADF/cofilin for binding ADP-actin and catalyzes the exchange of ADP for ATP (13). This process works, because both profilin and ADF/cofilins exchange rapidly with ADP-actin. When profilin binds, ADP dissociates rapidly, and the excess of ATP over ADP in cytoplasm favors rebinding of ATP. Mg-ATP-actin binds tightly to profilin and (when present) to thymosin-β4, restocking the pool of subunits ready to elongate uncapped barbed ends and releasing ADF/cofilins to recycle back to ADP-actin filaments for another round of severing and depolymerization.

CONCLUSIONS

Exciting new experimental results summarized in the dendritic-nucleation hypothesis have opened the way toward a molecular explanation for pseudopod extension. We have described what amounts to an enzymatic cycle that converts the energy of ATP hydrolysis into mechanical force through the polymerization and depolymerization of actin filaments. In the inactivated state, the system is poised for assembly, with a large supply of actin monomers ready for rapid elongation when new filaments are created by the activation of Arp2/3 complex. WASp/Scar proteins control the activity of Arp2/3 complex, which is consumed by incorporation into a branching network of filaments. Growth of each filament is transient, owing to rapid capping, so signaling pathways must supply active Arp2/3 complex at a constant rate to maintain polymerization and pseudopod extension. The system tends automatically toward depolymerization, so that, when assembly stops, the balance is shifted to disassembly by ADF/cofilins. The direction of subunit flow through the system is created by irreversible hydrolysis of ATP bound to polymerized actin (and P_i release) and is driven by the higher concentration of ATP than ADP in the cytoplasm. Thus ATP hydrolysis is necessary to return polymerized actin back to the unpolymerized monomeric pool. The rates of the reactions explain why cells can change direction so quickly in response to chemotactic signals and why, in the absence of signals, pseudopods tend to collapse. The pace of these events can vary between cell types and in a single cell, depending on the rate of signal input and the concentrations and activities of a few key proteins.

Although attractive as an initial attempt at a mechanism, most of the ideas in the dendritic-nucleation hypothesis still require rigorous testing, especially in live cells. In particular, we lack essential information about signaling pathways, signal integration, WASp/Scar activation, nucleation mechanisms, and depolymerization mechanisms.

ACKNOWLEDGMENTS

The authors thank Graham Johnson for Figure 5. NIH research grant GM-26338 supported our research on this topic. We thank Dr. Harry Higgs for his thoughtful suggestions on the manuscript.

Visit the Annual Reviews home page at www.AnnualReviews.org

LITERATURE CITED

1. Abdul-Manan N, Aghazadeh B, Liu GA, Majumdar A, Ouerfelli O, et al. 1999. Structure of Cdc42 in complex with the GTPase-binding domain of the 'Wiskott-Aldrich syndrome' protein. *Nature* 399:379–83

1a. Abraham VC, Krishnamurthi V, Taylor DL, Lanni F. 1999. The actin-based nanomachine at the leading edge of micrating cells. *Biophys. J.* 77:1721–32

2. Agnew BJ, Minamide LS, Bamburg JR. 1995. Reactivation of phosphorylated actin depolymerizing factor and identification of the regulatory site. *J. Biol. Chem.* 270:17582–87

3. Allen WE, Zicha D, Ridley AJ, Jones GE. 1998. A role for Cdc42 in macrophage chemotaxis. *J. Cell Biol.* 141:1147–57

4. Amatruda JF, Cannon JF, Tatchell K, Hug

C, Cooper JA. 1990. Disruption of the actin cytoskeleton in yeast capping protein mutants. *Nature* 344:352–54

5. Azuma T, Witke W, Stossel TP, Hartwig JH, Kwiatkowski DJ. 1998. Gelsolin is a downstream effector of rac for fibroblast motility. *EMBO J.* 17:1362–70

6. Bailly M, Macaluso F, Cammer M, Chan A, Segall JE, Condeelis JS. 1999. Relationship between Arp2/3 complex and the barbed ends of actin filaments at the leading edge of carcinoma cells after epidermal growth factor stimulation. *J. Cell Biol.* 145:331–45

7. Bamburg JR, Harris HE, Weeds AG. 1980. Partial purification and characterization of an actin depolymerizing factor from brain. *FEBS Lett.* 121:178–82

8. Bamburg JR, McGough A, Ono S. 1999.

Putting a new twist on actin: ADF/cofilins modulate actin dynamics. *Trends Cell Biol.* 9:364–70

9. Barkalow K, Hartwig JH. 1995. The role of filament barbed-end exposure in cytoskeletal dynamics and cell motility. *Biochem. Soc. Trans.* 23:451–56

10. Barkalow K, Witke W, Kwiatkowski DJ, Hartwig JH. 1996. Coordinated regulation of platelet actin filament barbed ends by gelsolin and capping protein. *J. Cell Biol.* 134:389–99

11. Bear JE, Rawls JF, Saxe CL. 1998. SCAR, a WASP-related protein, isolated as a suppressor of receptor defects in late Dictyostelium development. *J. Cell Biol.* 142:1325–35

12. Bernstein BW, Bamburg JR. 1982. Tropomyosin binding to F-actin protects the F-actin from disassembly by brain actin-depolymerizing factor (ADF). *Cell Motil.* 2:1–8

12a. Blanchoin L, Amann Kj, Higgs HN, Marchand J-B, Kaiser DA, Pollard TD. 2000. Direct observation of dendritic actin filament networks nucleated by Arp2/3 complex and WASp/Scar proteins. *Nature.* In press

13. Blanchoin L, Pollard TD. 1998. Interaction of actin monomers with Acanthamoeba actophorin (ADF/cofilin) and profilin. *J. Biol. Chem.* 273:25106–11

14. Blanchoin L, Pollard TD. 1999. Mechanism of interaction of Acanthamoeba actophorin (ADF/cofilin) with actin filaments. *J. Biol. Chem.* 274:15538–46

15. Blanchoin L, Pollard TD. 2000. Effect of actin binding proteins on ATP hydrolysis by polymerized actin.

16. Blanchoin L, Pollard TD, Mullins RD. 2000. Disassembly of dendritic networks of capped actin filaments by ADF/cofilin. Submitted

17. Blanchoin L, Robinson RC, Choe S, Pollard TD. 2000. Phosphorylation of Acanthamoeba actophorin (ADF/cofilin) blocks interaction with actin without a

change in atomic structure. *J. Mol. Biol.* 295:203–11

18. Bray D, Thomas C. 1976. Unpolymerized actin in fibroblasts and brain. *J. Mol. Biol.* 105:527–44

19. Carlier M-F, Pantaloni D. 1988. Binding of phosphate to F-ADP-actin and role of F-ADP-Pi-actin in ATP-actin polymerization. *J. Biol. Chem.* 263:817–25

20. Carlier MF. 1987. Measurement of Pi dissociation from actin-filaments following ATP hydrolysis using a linked enzyme assay. *Biochem. Biophys. Res. Commun.* 143:1069–75

21. Carlier MF. 1998. Control of actin dynamics. *Curr. Opin. Cell Biol.* 10:45–51

22. Carlier MF, Jean C, Rieger KJ, Lenfant M, Pantaloni D. 1993. Modulation of the interaction between G-actin and thymosin $\beta4$ by the ATP/ADP ratio : possible implication in the regulation of actin dynamics. *Proc. Natl. Acad. Sci. USA* 90:5034–38

23. Carlier MF, Laurent V, Santolini J, Melki R, Didry D, et al. 1997. Actin depolymerizing factor (ADF/cofilin) enhances the rate of filament turnover: implication in actin-based motility *J. Cell Biol.* 136:1307–22

24. Carlier MF, Pantaloni D, Evans JA, Lambooy PK, Korn ED, Webb MR. 1988. The hydrolysis of ATP that accompanies actin polymerization is essentially irreversible. *FEBS Lett.* 235:211–14

25. Carlier MF, Pantaloni D, Korn ED. 1986. The effects of Mg^{2+} at the high-affinity sites on the polymerization of actin and associated ATP hydrolysis. *J. Biol. Chem.* 261:10785–92.

26. Casella JF, Maack DJ, Lin S. 1986. Purification and initial characterization of a protein from skeletal muscle that caps the barbed ends of actin filaments. *J. Biol. Chem.* 261:10915–21

27. Cassimeris L, McNeill H, Zigmond SH. 1990. Chemoattractant-stimulated polymorphonuclear leukocytes contain two

populations of actin filaments that differ in their spatial distributions and relative stabilities. *J. Cell Biol.* 110:1067–75

28. Condeelis J. 1993. Life at the leading edge: the formation of cell protrusions. *Annu. Rev. Cell Biol.* 9:411–44

29. Cooper JA. 1991. The role of actin polymerization in cell motility. *Annu. Rev. Physiol.* 53:585–605

30. Cooper JA, Blum JD, Williams RC Jr, Pollard TD. 1986. Purification and characterization of actophorin, a new 15,000 dalton actin binding protein from *Acanthamoeba castellanii*. *J. Biol. Chem.* 261:477–85

31. Didry D, Carlier M-F, Pantaloni D. 1998. Synergy between actin depolymerizing factor/cofilin and profilin in increasing actin filament turnover. *J. Biol. Chem.* 273:25602–11

32. DiNubile MJ, Cassimeris L, Joyce M, Zigmond SH. 1995. Actin filament barbed-end capping activity in neutrophil lysates: the role of capping protein-β2. *Mol. Biol. Cell* 6:1659–71

33. Drenckhahn D, Pollard TD. 1986. Elongation of actin filaments is a diffusion-limited reaction at the barbed end and is accelerated by inert macromolecules. *J. Biol. Chem.* 261:12754–58

34. Du J, Frieden C. 1998. Kinetics studies on the effect of yeast cofilin on yeast actin polymerization. *Biochemistry* 37:13276–84

35. Eddy RJ, Han J, Condeelis JS. 1997. Capping protein terminates but does not initiate chemoattractant-induced actin assembly in *Dictyostelium*. *J. Cell Biol.* 139:1243–53

36. Edwards DC, Sanders LC, Bokoch GM, Gill GN. 1999. Activation of LIM-kinase by Pak1 couples Rac/Cdc4242 GTPase signalling to actin cytoskeletal dynamics. *Nat. Cell Biol.* 1:253–59

37. Egile C, Loisel TP, Laurent V, Li R, Pantaloni D, et al. 1999. Activation of the Cdc42 effector N-WASP by the *Shigella flexneri* IcsA protein promotes actin nu-

cleation by Arp2/3 complex and bacterial actin-based motility. *J. Cell Biol.* 146:1319–32

38. Fechheimer M, Zigmond SD. 1983. Changes in cytoskeletal proteins of polymorphonuclear leukocytes induced by chemotactic peptides. *Cell Motil.* 3:349–61

39. Fedorov AA, Fedorov E, Gertler F, Almo SC. 1999. Structure of EVH1, a novel proline-rich ligand-binding module involved in cytoskeletal dynamics and neural function. *Nat. Struct. Biol.* 6:661–65

40. Forscher P, Smith SJ. 1988. Actions of cytochalasins on the organization of actin filaments and microtubules in a neuronal growth cone. *J. Cell Biol.* 107:1505–16

41. Gerisch G. 1982. Chemotaxis in *Dictyostelium*. *Annu. Rev. Physiol.* 44:535–52

42. Goldschmidt-Clermont PJ, Furman MI, Wachsstock D, Safer D, Nachmias VT, Pollard TD. 1992. The control of actin nucleotide exchange by thymosinβ4 and profilin: a potential regulatory mechanism for actin polymerization in cells. *Mol. Biol. Cell* 3:1015–24

43. Gordon DJ, Eisenberg E, Korn ED. 1976. Characterization of a cytoplasmic actin isolated from *Acanthamoeba castellanii* by a new method. *J. Biol. Chem.* 251:4778–86

44. Gutsche-Perelroizen I, Lepault J, Ott A, Carlier MF. 1999. Filament assembly from profilin-actin. *J. Biol. Chem.* 274:6234–43

45. Hall A. 1998. Rho GTPases and the actin cytoskeleton. *Science* 279:509–14

46. Hartwig JH. 1992. Mechanisms of actin rearrangements mediating platelet activation. *J. Cell Biol.* 118:1421–42

47. Hartwig JH, Bokoch GM, Carpenter CL, Janmey PA, Taylor LA, et al. 1995. Thrombin receptor ligation and activated Rac uncap actin filament barbed ends through phosphoinositide synthesis in permeabilized human platelets. *Cell* 82:643–53

48. Hawkins M, Pope B, Maciver SK, Weeds AG. 1993. Human actin depolymerizing

factor mediates a pH-sensitive destruction of actin filaments. *Biochemistry* 32:9985–93

49. Heintzelman MB, Mooseker MS. 1992. Assembly of the intestinal brush border cytoskeleton. *Curr. Top. Dev. Biol.* 26:93–122

50. Higgs HN, Blanchoin L, Pollard TD. 1999. Influence of the C terminus of Wiskott-Aldrich syndrome protein (WASp) the Arp2/3 complex on actin polymerization. *Biochemistry* 38:15212–22

51. Higgs HN, Pollard TD. 1999. Regulation of actin polymerization by Arp2/3 complex and WASp/Scar proteins. *J. Biol. Chem.* 274:32531–34

52. Hill TL, Kirschner MW. 1982. Bioenergetics and kinetics of microtubule and actin filament assembly-disassembly. *Int. Rev. Cytol.* 78:1–125

53. Huang M, Yang C, Schafer DA, Cooper JA, Higgs HN, Zigmond SH. 1999. Cdc42-induced actin filaments are protected from capping protein. *Curr. Biol.* 9:979–82

54. Hug C, Jay PY, Reddy I, McNally JG, Bridgman PC, et al. 1995. Capping protein levels influence actin assembly and cell motility in Dictyostelium. *Cell* 81:591–600

55. Isenberg GH, Aebi U, Pollard TD. 1980. An actin binding protein from *Acanthamoeba* regulates actin filament polymerization and interactions. *Nature* 288:455–59

56. Janmey PA. 1994. Phosphoinositides and calcium as regulators of cellular actin assembly and disassembly. *Annu. Rev. Physiol.* 56:169–91

57. Kaiser DA, Vinson VK, Murphy DB, Pollard TD. 1999. Profilin is predominantly associated with monomeric actin in Acanthamoeba. *J. Cell Sci.* 112:3779–90

57a. Kang F, Purich DL, Southwick FS. 1999. Profilin promotes barbed-end actin filament assembly without lowering the critical concentration. *J. Biol. Chem.* 274:36963–72

58. Kelleher JF, Atkinson SJ, Pollard. TD. 1995. Sequences, structural models, and cellular localization of the actin-related proteins Arp2 and Arp3 from *Acanthamoeba*. *J. Cell Biol.* 131:385–97

59. Kinosian HJ, Newman J, Lincoln B, Selden LA, Gershman LC, Estes JE. 1998. Ca^{2+} regulation of gelsolin activity: binding and severing of F-actin. *Biophys. J.* 75:3101–9

60. Konzok A, Weber I, Simmeth E, Hacker U, Maniak M, Muller-Taubenberger A. 1999. DAip1, a Dictyostelium homologue of the yeast actin-interacting protein 1, is involved in endocytosis, cytokinesis, and motility. *J. Cell Biol.* 146:453–64

61. Lappalainen P, Drubin DG. 1997. Cofilin promotes rapid actin filament turnover in vivo. *Nature* 388:78–82. Erratum. 1997. *Nature* 389:211

62. Lazarides E. 1976. Actin, alpha-actinin and tropomyosin interaction in the structural organization of actin filaments in nonmuscle cells. *J. Cell Biol.* 68:202–19

63. Loisel TP, Boujemaa R, Pantaloni D, Carlier MF. 1999. Reconstitution of actin-based motility of Listeria and Shigella using pure proteins. *Nature* 401:613–16

64. Luby-Phelps K. 1994. Physical properties of cytoplasm. *Curr. Opin. Cell Biol.* 6:3–9

65. Ma L, Rohatgi R, Kirschner MW. 1998. The Arp2/3 complex mediates actin polymerization induced by the small GTP-binding protein Cdc42. *Proc. Natl. Acad. Sci. USA* 95:15362–67

66. Mabuchi I. 1983. An actin depolymerizing protein (depactin) from starfish oocytes: properties and interactions with actin. *J. Cell Biol.* 97:1612–21

67. Machesky LM, Atkinson SJ, Ampe C, Vandekerckhove J, Pollard TD. 1994. Purification of a cortical complex containing two unconventional actins from *Acanthamoeba* by affinity chromatography on

profilin agarose. *J. Cell Biol.* 127:107–15

68. Machesky LM, Insall RH. 1998. Scar1 and the related Wiskott-Aldrich syndrome protein WASP regulate the actin cytoskeleton through the Arp2/3 complex. *Curr. Biol.* 8:1347–56

69. Machesky LM, Insall RH. 1999. Signaling to actin dynamics. *J. Cell Biol.* 146:267–72

70. Machesky LM, Mullins DM, Higgs HN, Kaiser DA, Blanchoin L, et al. 1999. Scar, a WASp-related protein, activates nucleation of actin filaments by the Arp2/3 complex. *Proc. Natl. Acad. Sci. USA* 96:3739–44

71. Maciver SK. 1998. How ADF/cofilin depolymerizes actin filaments. *Curr. Opin. Cell Biol.* 10:140–44

72. Maciver SK, Pope BJ, Whytock S, Weeds AG. 1998. The effect of two actin depolymerizing factors (ADF/cofilins) on actin filament turnover: pH sensitivity of F-actin binding by human ADF, but not of Acanthamoeba actophorin. *Eur. J. Biochem.* 256:388–97

73. Maciver SK, Wachsstock DH, Schwarz WH, Pollard TD. 1991. The actin filament severing protein actophorin promotes the formation of rigid bundles of actin filaments crosslinked with alpha-actinin. *J. Cell Biol.* 115:1621–28

74. Maciver SK, Zot HG, Pollard TD. 1991. Characterization of actin filament severing by actophorin from *Acanthamoeba castellanii. J. Cell Biol.* 115:611–20

74a. Mallavarapu A, Mitchison T. 1999. Regulated actin cytoskeleton assembly at filopodium tips controls their extension and retraction. *J. Cell. Biol.* 146:1097–1106

75. McGough A, Pope B, Chiu W, Weeds A. 1997. Cofilin changes the twist of F-actin: implications for actin filament dynamics and cellular function. *J. Cell. Biol.* 138:771–81

76. Meberg PJ, Ono S, Minamide LS, Takahashi M, Bamburg JR. 1998. Actin depolymerizing factor and cofilin phosphorylation dynamics: response to signals that regulate neurite extension. *Cell Motil. Cytoskelet.* 39:172–90

77. Melki R, Fievez S, Carlier M-F. 1996. Continuous monitoring of Pi release following nucleotide hydrolysis in actin or tubulin assembly using 2-amino-6mercapto-7-methylpurine ribonucleoside and purine-nucleoside phosphorylase as an enzyme-linked assay. *Biochemistry* 35:12038–45

78. Miki H, Suetsugu S, Takenawa T. 1998. WAVE, a novel WASP-family protein involved in actin reorganization induced by Rac. *EMBO J.* 17:6932–41

79. Mitchison TJ, Cramer LP. 1996. Actin-based cell motility and cell locomotion. *Cell* 84:371–79

80. Miyata H, Hotani H. 1992. Morphological changes in liposomes caused by polymerization of encapsulated actin and spontaneous formation of actin bundles. *Proc. Natl. Acad. Sci. USA* 89:11547–51

81. Miyata H, Nishiyama S, Akashi K, Kinosita K Jr. 1999. Protrusive growth from giant liposomes driven by actin polymerization. *Proc. Natl. Acad. Sci. USA* 96:2048–53

82. Mogilner A, Oster G. 1996. Cell motility driven by actin polymerization. *Biophys. J.* 71:3030–3045

83. Mullins RD, Heuser JA, Pollard TD. 1998. The interaction of Arp2/3 complex with actin: nucleation, high-affinity pointed end capping, and formation of branching networks of filaments. *Proc. Natl. Acad. Sci. USA* 95:6181–86

84. Mullins RD, Pollard TD. 1999. Rho-family GTPases require the Arp2/3 complex to stimulate actin polymerization in Acanthamoeba extracts. *Curr. Biol.* 9:405–15

85. Mullins RD, Pollard TD. 1999. Structure and function of the Arp2/3 complex. *Curr. Opin. Struct. Biol.* 9:244–49

86. Mullins RD, Stafford WF, Pollard TD. 1997. Structure, subunit topology, and actin-binding activity of the Arp2/3 complex from *Acanthamoeba*. *J. Cell Biol.* 136:331–43

87. Nachmias VT, Yoshida K-L. 1988. The cytoskeleton of the blood platelet: a dynamic structure. *Adv. Cell Biol.* 2:181–211

88. Nebl G, Meuer SC, Samstag Y. 1996. Dephosphorylation of serine 3 regulates nuclear translocation of cofilin. *J. Biol. Chem.* 271:26276–80

89. Nishida E. 1985. Opposite effects of cofilin and profilin from porcine brain on rate of exchange of actin-bound adenosine 5′-triphosphate. *Biochemistry* 24:1160–64

90. Nishida E, Maekawa S, Muneyuki E, Sakai H. 1984. Action of a 19K protein from porcine brain on actin polymerization: a new functional class of actin-binding proteins. *J. Biochem.* 95:387–98

91. Nishida E, Muneyuki E, Maekawa S, Ohta Y, Sakai H. 1985. An actin-depolymerizing protein (destrin) from porcine kidney: its action on F-actin containing or lacking tropomyosin. *Biochemistry* 24:6624–30

92. Ochs HD. 1998. The Wiskott-Aldrich syndrome. *Semin. Hematol.* 35:332–45

93. Okada K, Obinata T, Abe H. 1999. XAIP1: a Xenopus homologue of yeast actin interacting protein 1 (AIP1), which induces disassembly of actin filaments cooperatively with ADF/cofilin family proteins. *J. Cell Sci.* 112:1553–65

94. Pantaloni D, Carlier MF. 1993. How profilin promotes actin filament assembly in the presence of thymosin β4. *Cell* 75:1007–14

95. Pardee JD, Simpson PA, Stryer L, Spudich JA. 1982. Actin-filaments undergo limited subunit exchange in physiological salt conditions. *J. Cell Biol.* 94:316–24

96. Perelroizen I, Didry D, Christensen H, Chua NH, Carlier MF. 1996. Role of nucleotide exchange and hydrolysis in the function of profilin in actin assembly. *J. Biol. Chem.* 271:12302–9

97. Perelroizen I, Marchand JB, Blanchoin L, Didry D, Carlier MF. 1994. Interaction of profilin with G-actin and poly(L-proline). *Biochemistry* 33:8472–78

98. Peskin CS, Odell GM, Oster GF. 1993. Cellular motions and thermal fluctuations: the Brownian ratchet. *Biophys. J.* 65:316–24

99. Pieper U, Wegner A. 1996. The end of a polymerizing actin filament contains numerous ATP-subunit segments that are disconnected by ADP-subunits resulting from ATP hydrolysis. *Biochemistry* 35:4396–402

100. Pollard TD. 1986. Rate constants for the reactions of ATP- and ADP-actin with the ends of actin filaments. *J. Cell Biol.* 103:2747–54

101. Pollard TD. 1999. Introduction to actin and actin-binding proteins. In *Guidebook to the Cytoskeletal and Motor Proteins*, ed. T Kreis, R. Vale, pp. 3–11. Oxford, UK: Oxford Univ. Press. 2nd ed.

102. Pollard TD, Almo SC, Quirk S, Vinson V, Lattman EE. 1994. Structure of actin binding proteins: insights about function at atomic resolution. *Annu. Rev. Cell Biol.* 10:207–49

103. Pollard TD, Cooper JA. 1984. Quantitative analysis of the effect of *Acanthamoeba* profilin on actin filament nucleation and elongation. *Biochemistry* 23:6631–41

104. Pollard TD, Cooper JA. 1986. Actin and actin-binding proteins. a critical evaluation of mechanisms and functions. *Annu. Rev. Biochem.* 55:987–1035

105. Pollard TD, Goldberg I, Schwarz WH. 1992. Nucleotide exchange, structure and mechanical properties of filaments assembled from the ATP-actin and ADP-actin. *J. Biol. Chem.* 267:20339–45

106. Pollard TD, Tseng PC-H, Rimm DL, Bichell DP, Williams RC, Sinard J. 1986. Characterization of alpha-actinin

from *Acanthamoeba. Cell Motil.* 6:649–61

107. Pollard TD, Weeds AG. 1984. The rate constant for ATP hydrolysis by polymerized actin. *FEBS Lett.* 170:94–98

108. Prehoda KE, Lee DJ, Lim WA. 1999. Structure of the enabled/VASP homology 1 domain-peptide complex: a key component in the spatial control of actin assembly. *Cell* 97:471–80

109. Pring M, Weber A, Bubb M. 1992. Profilin-actin complexes directly elongate actin filaments at the barbed end. *Biochemistry* 31:1827–36

110. Quirk S, Maciver SK, Ampe C, Doberstein SK, Kaiser DA, et al. 1993. Primary structure and studies of Acanthamoeba actophorin. *Biochemistry* 32:8525–33

111. Ressad F, Didry D, Egile C, Pantaloni D, Carlier MF. 1999. Control of actin filament length and turnover by actin depolymerizing factor (ADF/cofilin) in the presence of capping proteins and Arp2/3 complex. *J. Biol. Chem.* 274:20970–6

112. Ressad F, Didry D, Xia G-X, Hong Y, Chua N-H, et al. 1998. Kinetics analysis of the interaction of actin-depolymerizing factor ADF/cofilin with G- and F-actins. *J. Biol. Chem.* 273:20894–902

113. Rickard JE, Sheterline P. 1986. Cytoplasmic concentrations of inorganic phosphate affect the critical concentration for assembly of actin in the presence of cytochalasin D or ADP. *J. Mol. Biol.* 80:273–79

114. Rodal AA, Tetreault JW, Lappalainen P, Drubin DG, Amberg DC. 1999. Aip1p interacts with cofilin to disassemble actin filaments. *J. Cell Biol.* 145:1251–64

115. Rohatgi R, Ma L, Miki H, Lopez M, Kirchhausen T, et al. 1999. The interaction between N-WASP and the Arp2/3 complex links Cdc42-dependent signals to actin assembly. *Cell* 97:221–31

116. Rosenblatt J, Agnew BJ, Abe H, Bamburg

JR, Mitchison TJ. 1997. Xenopus actin depolymerizing factor/cofilin (XAC) is responsible for the turnover of actin filaments in Listeria monocytogenes tails. *J. Cell Biol.* 136:1323–32

117. Rosenblatt J, Peluso P, Mitchison TJ. 1995. The bulk of unpolymerized actin in Xenopus egg extracts is ATP-bound. *Mol. Biol. Cell* 6:227–36

118. Safer D, Nachmias VT. 1994. Beta thymosins as actin binding peptides. *Bioessays* 16:473–79

119. Safer D, Sosnick TR, Elzinga M. 1997. Thymosin beta 4 binds actin in an extended conformation and contacts both the barbed and pointed ends. *Biochemistry* 36:5806–16

120. Sanders MC, Wang YL. 1990. Exogenous nucleation sites fail to induce detectable polymerization of actin in living cells. *J. Cell Biol.* 110:359–65

121. Schafer DA, Hug C, Cooper JA. 1995. Inhibition of CapZ during myofibrillogenesis alters assembly of actin filaments. *J. Cell Biol.* 128:61–70

122. Schafer DA, Jennings PB, Cooper JA. 1996. Dynamics of capping protein and actin assembly in vitro: uncapping barbed ends by polyphosphoinositides. *J. Cell Biol.* 135:169–79

123. Schutt C, Myslik JC, Rozychi MD, Goonesekere NCW, Lindberg U. 1993. The structure of crystalline profilin-β-actin. *Nature* 365:810–16

124. Schwob E, Martin RP. 1992. New yeast actin-like gene required late in the cell cycle. *Nature* 355:179–82

125. Sept D, Elcock AH, McCammon JA. 1999. Computer simulations of actin polymerization can explain barbed-pointed end asymmetry. *J. Mol. Biol.* 294:1181–89

126. Small JV, Herzog M, Anderson K. 1995. Actin filament organization in the fish keratocyte lamellipodium. *J. Cell Biol.* 129:1275–86

127. Suetsugu S, Miki H, Takenawa T. 1998.

The essential role of profilin in the assembly of actin for microspike formation. *EMBO J.* 17:6516–26

128. Svitkina TM, Borisy GG. 1999. Arp2/3 complex and actin depolymerizing factor/cofilin in dendritic organization and treadmilling of actin filament array in Lamellipodia. *J. Cell Biol.* 145:1009–26

129. Svitkina TM, Borisy GG. 1999. Progress in protrusion: the tell-tale scar. *Trends Biochem. Sci.* 24:432–36

130. Svitkina TM, Verkhovsky AB, McQuade KM, Borisy GG. 1997. Analysis of the actin-myosin II system in fish epidermal keratocytes: mechanism of cell body translocation. *J. Cell Biol.* 139:397–415

131. Teubner A, Wegner A. 1998. Kinetic evidence for a readily exchangeable nucleotide at the terminal subunit of the barbed ends of actin filaments. *Biochemistry* 37:7532–38

132. Theriot JA, Mitchison TJ. 1991. Actin microfilament dynamics in locomoting cells. *Nature* 352:126–31

133. Tilney LG, Bonder EM, DeRosier DJ. 1981. Actin filaments elongate from their membrane-associated ends. *J. Cell Biol.* 90:485–94

134. Tseng PCH, Runge MS, Cooper JA, Williams RC Jr, Pollard TD. 1984. Physical, immunochemical, and functional properties of *Acanthamoeba* profilin. *J. Cell Biol.* 98:214–21

135. Vaduva G, Martin NC, Hopper AK. 1997. Actin-binding verprolin is a polarity development protein required for the morphogenesis and function of the yeast actin cytoskeleton. *J. Cell Biol.* 139:1821–33

136. Vinson VK, De La Cruz EM, Higgs HN, Pollard TD. 1998. Interactions of Acanthamoeba profilin with actin and nucleotides bound to actin. *Biochemistry* 37:10871–80

137. Wachsstock DH, Schwarz WH, Pollard TD. 1993. Structure and mechanical-properties of actin filament gels. *Biophys. J.* 65:205–14

138. Wang Y. 1985. Exchange of actin subunits at the leading edge of living fibroblasts: possible role of treadmilling. *J. Cell Biol.* 101:597–602

139. Way M, Gooch J, Pope B, Weeds AG. 1989. Expression of human plasma gelsolin in Escherichia coli and dissection of actin binding sites by segmental deletion mutagenesis. *J. Cell Biol.* 109:593–605

140. Welch MD. 1999. The world according to Arp: regulation of actin nucleation by the Arp2/3 complex. *Trends Cell Biol.* 9:423–27

141. Welch MD, DePace AH, Verma S, Iwamatsu A, Mitchison TJ. 1997. The human Arp2/3 complex is composed of evolutionarily conserved subunits and is localized to cellular regions of dynamic actin filament assembly. *J. Cell Biol.* 138:375–84

142. Welch MD, Iwamatsu A, Mitchison TJ. 1997. Actin polymerization is induced by Arp2/3 protein complex at the surface of *Listeria monocytogenes. Nature* 385:265–69

143. Welch MD, Rosenblatt J, Skoble J, Portnoy DA, Mitchison TJ. 1998. Interaction of human Arp2/3 complex and the Listeria monocytogenes ActA protein in actin filament nucleation. *Science* 281:105–8

144. Winter D, Lechler T, Li R. 1999. Activation of the yeast Arp2/3 complex by Bee1p, a WASP-family protein. *Curr. Biol.* 9:501–4

145. Winter D, Podtelejnikov AV, Mann M, Li R. 1997. The complex containing actin-related proteins Arp2 and Arp3 is required for the motility and integrity of yeast actin patches. *Curr. Biol.* 7:519–29

146. Yarar D, To W, Abo A, Welch MD. 1999. The Wiskott-Aldrich syndrome protein directs actin-based motility by

stimulating actin nucleation with the Arp2/3 complex. *Curr. Biol.* 9:555–58

147. Yin HL, Stossel TP. 1979. Control of cytoplasmic actin gel-sol transformation by gelsolin, a calcium-dependent regulatory protein. *Nature* 281:583–86

148. Zigmond SH, Joyce M, Borleis J, Bokoch GM, Devreotes PN. 1997. Regulation of actin polymerization in cell-free systems by GTPγS and Cdc42. *J. Cell Biol.* 138:363–74

149. Zigmond SH, Joyce M, Yang C, Brown K, Huang M, Pring M. 1998. Mechanism of Cdc42-induced actin polymerization in neutrophil extracts. *J. Cell Biol.* 142:1001–12

Annu. Rev. Biophys. Biomol. Struct. 2000. 29:577–606

UNNATURAL LIGANDS FOR ENGINEERED PROTEINS: New Tools for Chemical Genetics

Anthony Bishop, Oleksandr Buzko*, Stephanie Heyeck-Dumas, Ilyoung Jung*, Brian Kraybill*, Yi Liu, Kavita Shah, Scott Ulrich*, Laurie Witucki, Feng Yang, Chao Zhang*, and Kevan M. Shokat*†

Department of Chemistry, Princeton University, Princeton, New Jersey 08544; e-mail: shokat@cmp.ucsf.edu

Key Words   protein engineering, orthogonal ligands, signal transduction, protein design

■ **Abstract** Small molecules that modulate the activity of biological signaling molecules can be powerful probes of signal transduction pathways. Highly specific molecules with high affinity are difficult to identify because of the conserved nature of many protein active sites. A newly developed approach to discovery of such small molecules that relies on protein engineering and chemical synthesis has yielded powerful tools for the study of a wide variety of proteins involved in signal transduction (G-proteins, protein kinases, 7-transmembrane receptors, nuclear hormone receptors, and others). Such chemical genetic tools combine the advantages of traditional genetics and the unparalleled temporal control over protein function afforded by small molecule inhibitors/activators that act at diffusion controlled rates with targets.

CONTENTS

---

*Current address: Department of Cellular and Molecular Pharmacology, University of California, San Francisco, CA.

†Current address: Department of Chemistry, University of California, Berkeley, Berkeley, CA.

1056-8700/00/0610-0577$14.00

INTRODUCTION

The power of genetic approaches to the study of protein function is the ability to affect the activity of a single protein in a whole organism; yet the use of genetics to alter protein function is not an ideal process, because protein levels respond very slowly to changes at the gene level. In contrast, the use of small synthetic molecules or natural products to alter protein activity elicit extremely rapid results, because these agents act at diffusion-controlled rates with their targets and do not require operation of cellular transcriptional machinery. The small-molecule approach, however, suffers from problems of specificity, because enzyme inhibitors are often not specific for just one protein in the organism of interest. Furthermore, it is often difficult to determine the true spectrum of action of such small molecules. As tools for studying protein functions, small molecules require extensive characterization before their effects on a complex biological system can be interpreted.

On one hand, genetics offers unprecedented target specificity. On the other hand, the chemical approach offers unprecedented temporal control over the function of target proteins. Experimental systems that incorporate the advantages of both of these approaches are powerful tools for studying protein function in the postgenomic era.

Recently, the benefits of combining these two approaches have been demonstrated through a number of studies in diverse areas of cell biology and chemistry. All of these studies have used the same fundamental approach. First, a small molecule that binds to the protein of interest is modified in a manner that eliminates its ability to bind to its target. This modified ligand is said to be "orthogonal" in normal cells because it is completely silent (noninteracting with the natural system), in contrast to its unmodified counterpart (Scheme A). Second, the individual protein of interest is engineered to accept the orthogonal ligand (substrate, inhibitor, activator, etc). It is important that the mutation to the protein must affect only binding to the orthogonal ligand and not introduce any other modification to protein function. In some situations the engineered protein may not accept the natural ligand, thus creating a protein that itself is orthogonal. (In this situation, the protein functions as a conditional allele).

This simultaneous engineering of the target of interest and derivatization of the small molecule are similar in genetic terms to a suppressor screen, which can reveal obligate interactions between two proteins. The unprecedented specificity of such systems arises because the degeneracy of the natural system (multiple proteins that use the same substrate) is broken down to create the ideal "one-ligand/one-protein" system.

This review focuses on the use of small molecules to elucidate gene function, using engineered proteins and unnatural ligands. Several excellent recent reviews have described analogous approaches to engineering protein-protein interactions (1–3).

ENGINEERING UNNATURAL CELL-SIGNALING PATHWAYS WITH CHEMICAL GENETICS

Switching a GTPase into an XTPase

The first engineered protein in a signal transduction pathway to accept an unnatural substrate was a member of the GTPase family of enzymes (4). GTPases control many biological processes, including translation, protein translocation, vesicle transport, nuclear import, and signal transduction. GTPases typically exist in both GTP- and GDP-bound states. The enzymes interchange between these two states by hydrolyzing bound GTP to GDP + P_i, followed by binding of GTP. Several different effector proteins can accelerate the interchange between the two states either by acceleration of GTP hydrolysis (GTPase-activating proteins) or by the exchange of GTP for GDP (guanine nucleotide exchange factors).

One of the best characterized roles of GTPases is in protein biosynthesis. EF-Tu is a GTPase that is responsible for loading amino-acyl transfer RNAs onto the ribosome during protein biosynthesis. EF-Tu not only loads the amino-acyl transfer RNA but is also responsible for hydrolyzing the amino acid from the transfer RNA if it is not the amino acid coded for by the messenger RNA.

What is the energy cost (i.e. number of GTPs hydrolyzed per amino acid loading step) involved in this process? The problem with making this measurement is that another GTPase (EF-G) is intimately coupled to EF-Tu's function during ribosomal protein synthesis. EF-G is responsible for translocation of the ribosome after each successive peptide bond formation step. Hwang & Miller (4) proposed that the role of EF-Tu could be distinguished from that of EF-G by engineering EF-Tu to accept a nucleotide other than GTP.

Analysis of the highly conserved GTP-binding motif revealed several hydrogen bonds between amino-acid side chains in EF-Tu and the guanine base of GTP (Figure 1A, see color insert). Hwang & Miller (4) used site-directed mutagenesis to disrupt one key H bond, between Asp-138 and the C^2 exocyclic amine of GTP. Mutation of Asp-138 → Asn disrupted the H-bond acceptor function of Asp-138, and replaced it with an H-bond donor. The presence of an H-bond donor opposite the exocyclic amine of GTP produces a repulsive (donor-donor) interaction that Hwang & Miller (4) accurately predicted would lead to the inability of Asp-138–Asn–EF-Tu to accept GTP as a substrate.

A surrogate for GTP was chosen that contains an H-bond acceptor at the C2 position, XTP (Figure 1B). The xanthine base perfectly complements the mutation in EF-Tu by providing an H-bond acceptor functionality (carbonyl) to the new H-bond donor residue (Asn-135). The mutation of Asp-138 → Asn produces an XTP-dependent allele of EF-Tu. This elegantly designed mutation and chemical

TABLE 1   Consensus sequences in the GTPase super family

	Phosphate and Mg^{2+} binding			Guanine ring binding	
	G1	G2	G3	G4	G5
Consensus sequence	GXXXXGK (S/T)	D(X)$_n$T	DXXG	NKXD	TXAX
H/K/N-Ras human	GAGGVGKS$_{17}$	DEYDPTI$_{36}$	DTAG$_{60}$	NKCD$_{119}$	TSAK$_{147}$
G proteins mammalian	GAGESGKS	D(X)$_7$TT	DVGG	NKKD	TCAT
Transposase P element	GLKKSWKO$_{268}$	DPDTL$_{283}$	DVDSG$_{355}$	NKSD$_{396}$	TTAS$_{414}$

complementation work surprisingly well, in that the kinetic constants of the mutant with the designed substrate (XTP) are indistinguishable from those of the wild-type enzyme with the natural substrate, GTP (5). Hwang & Miller (4) suggested that, because the motif NKXD (G4 consensus region) is conserved in all known GTPases, the mutation of Asp → Asn should convert any GTPase into an XTPase (Table 1). This in fact has been the case, as evidenced by the use of this particular strategy to elegantly decouple single GTPases in many complex pathways (Table 2).

With the (D138N) EF-Tu XTPase in hand, Weijland & Parmengiani (5) determined the energy cost of nucleotide hydrolysis by EF-Tu. Poly(U)-directed poly (phenylalanine) synthesis was carried out in an in vitro translation experiment in the presence of the XTPase (D138N–EF-Tu), the GTPase–EF-G, ribosomes, and all necessary components of ribosomal protein biosynthesis, including GTP and [γ-^{32}P]XTP (Figure 2, see color insert). By careful quantitation of the ^{32}PO$_4^{2-}$ produced during each amino acid-coupling cycle, these authors were able to determine that two cycles of EF-Tu–mediated nucleotide hydrolysis occurred during each amino acid coupling. Previously it had been impossible to determine

TABLE 2   GTPases that have been successfully engineered to accept XTP

GTPase	XTPase	Function	References
EF-Tu	D138N	Protein biosynthesis	4, 5
Adenylosuccinate	D333N	Purine nucleotide metabolism	74
FtsY	D441N	Signal recognition particle receptor	6
Ypt1	D124N	Regulation of endoplasmic reticulum to Golgi vesicle trafficking	7, 15
HypB	D241N	Nickel insertion into hydrogenases	75
Ran	D125N	Nuclear protein import	9
p21Ras	D119N	Control of MAPK pathway	13
Rab5	D136N	Endo- and exocytic pathways	76
Gα_o	D273N/Q205	G protein-coupled receptor pathway	15
P element transposase	D379N	DNA transposition	16

whether the amino-acyl–loading step (EF-Tu) or the translocation step (EF-G) was more energy demanding. This finding suggests that, in an as-yet-undefined way, two different GTP-loaded EF-Tu molecules interact with the ribosome during each amino acid-loading cycle.

The Specificity Switch from GTP to XTP Is Generalizable

Mutation of the conserved aspartate to asparagine in the highly conserved GTP-binding consensus motif (NKX<u>D</u>) has been exploited to probe the function of individual GTPases in complex cell lysates as well as in whole cells (Table 2).

Powers & Walter investigated the *Escherichia coli* GTPases Ffh and FtsY, which are homologs of essential components of the eukaryotic signal recognition particle and its receptor, respectively (6). Ffh and FtsY are GTPases that catalyze the cotranslational targeting of proteins to the bacterial plasma membrane. To understand the role of each GTP-binding site and GTP/GDP-binding cycle, the FtsY (D441N) mutant was created, which accepted only XTP as a substrate and did not accept GTP. After measurement of the GTPase and XTPase activities of Ffh, and FtsY (D441N), respectively, at different nucleotide concentrations, Powers & Walter (6) showed that Ffh stimulated XTP hydrolysis by FtsY (D441N) in the presence of 4.5S RNA and that Fts (D441N) similarly stimulated GTP hydrolysis by Ffh in a reaction that required XTP. Thus, nucleotide hydrolysis by Ffh and FtsY appears to occur by a reciprocally coupled reaction in which each GTPase acts as a <u>G</u>TPase-<u>a</u>ctivating protein for the other GTPase; therefore, Powers & Walters (6) used the XTPase mutation in this system to uncover a novel way in which GTPases themselves can regulate the GTPase activity of their associated proteins.

The XTPase mutation has been used to create selectively inhibitable mutants of the GTPase of interest. Jones et al (7) engineered the yeast Rab family member Ypt1 to accept XTP rather than GTP, by mutation of aspartate-124 to asparagine, producing the Ypt1 mutant D124N, which was expressed in yeast and acted in a dominant fashion to confer growth inhibition and block protein secretion. Because D124N does not bind GTP or GDP, the dominant inhibitory function of this mutant can be ascribed to the nucleotide-free form of the enzyme. Because function of the Ypt1 mutant (D124N) is dominant negative only in the absence of a competent nucleotide, the inhibition can be relieved by the addition of XTP in an in vitro-reconstituted system. Jones et al (7) proposed that the nucleotide-free form of Ypt1 (D124N) acted dominantly by sequestering the GTP exchange factor from wild-type Ypt1, thus inhibiting the vesicular transport pathway.

Another elegant use of the XTPase mutation has been in combination with nonhydrolyzable GTP analogs. Because the only active site inhibitors of GTPases are nonhydrolyzable analogs of GTP, such as GTP(γ)S, such reagents inhibit all GTPases in a cell or cell lysate. The lack of selective inhibitors has made answering even the simple question of whether one or more GTPases are required for a given cell-signaling pathway very difficult. Signal-dependent transport of proteins into the nucleus was known to involve at least one cytosolic GTPase protein, Ran (8). To investigate whether other GTPases were also involved, the XTPase mutation in

Ran (D125N) was made by two laboratories (9, 10). As expected, the Ran (D125N) mutation was not inhibitable by GTPγS, thus providing a tool for carrying out an elegant screen for GTPases other than Ran that are important for nuclear import of proteins. Indeed, in an in vitro assay, nuclear import can be reconstituted by Ran (D125N)-XTP, yet this pathway remains sensitive to GTPγS, implicating another unidentified GTPase for the first time. Sweet & Gerace (9) suggest that the unidentified GTPase could be a component of the nuclear pore complex. In principle, candidate GTPases could be turned into XTPases by similar mutagenesis, and their involvement in the nuclear transport pathway could be tested.

The best characterized GTPase, p21Ras, has also been studied by using the XTPase mutational approach (11). It is interesting that, unlike the previous examples of GTPases engineered to accept XTP, the corresponding D119N mutation in p21Ras was originally identified by a random screen for mutants with poor GTP-binding activity (12). These authors characterized the D119N p21Ras mutant in terms of its inability to bind GTP but did not use XTP as a surrogate nucleotide for this mutant. The XTPase activity of p21Ras (D119N) has been characterized in great detail by Schmidt et al (13), especially for the effects of Ras regulators such as GTPase-activating proteins, the guanine nucleotide exchange factor Cdc25^{Mm}, and others. The kinetic constants k_{on} and k_{off} for GDP and XDP for both wild type and the D119N mutant of p21Ras were determined in a fluorescence assay with methylanthraniloyl-substituted nucleotides (Table 3).

The D119N p21Ras exhibits a 10^3-fold loss in binding affinity for GDP in comparison with wild-type p21Ras. The kinetic constants reveal that the k_{on} for GDP binding to both proteins is almost unchanged, yet the k_{off} has increased by $\sim 10^3$ for D119N p21Ras. This rapid dissociation rate for GDP from D119N closely mirrors the fast dissociation of XDP from the wild-type protein, 1150×10^5/s vs 440×10^5/s, respectively (13). This again demonstrates the extremely well-behaved nature of the D-to-N mutation in GTPases and their faithful recapitulation of function, which is dependent on XTP rather than GTP. The remaining kinetic comparisons between the wild type and the D119N mutant of Ras are also quite well matched (Table 3).

Schmidt et al (13) were particularly interested in using the XTP-engineered p21Ras protein to probe Ras signaling in whole cells by altering the cellular pool of XTP-XDP. Previously it was shown that D119N p21Ras is an oncoprotein even though it does not appreciably bind GTP. As a test of whether XTP concentrations in cells could be increased, Wittinghofer and colleagues (14) measured the inhibition of transforming activity of D119N Ras after microinjection of millimolar concentrations of XTP and XDP, as well as exogenously provided xanthine. Over the 6-h time course of the experiment, no inhibition of the transformed phenotype was observed. This suggests that the intracellular pools of XTP or XDP are not manipulatable, owing to the presence of numerous metabolic enzymes, which interconvert XTP- and GTP-based nucleotides. By a clever strategy, the authors coinjected a preloaded D119N p21Ras protein with XDP and, using a rapid assay for induction of DNA synthesis, showed that the XDP-loaded protein in cells was

TABLE 3   Nucleotide binding of wild-type p21 and p21(D119N) with guanosine and xanthosine nucleotides

Nucleotide	k_{on} $(10^6$ M s$^{-1})$	k_{off} $(10^{-5}$ s$^{-1})$	$K_A = k_{on}/k_{off}$ $(10^{10}$ M$^{-1})$
p21 wild type			
$_m$GDP	1.5	2.0	7.5
$_m$G$_{pp}$N$_p$	1.8	36	0.5
$_m$XDP	1.2	440	0.027
$_m$X$_{pp}$N$_p$	0.4	⟨1200⟩	0.003
GTP$_\gamma$S	3.3	9.4	3.5
p21(D119N)			
$_m$GDP	⟨0.45⟩	1150	⟨0.0039⟩
$_m$XDP	0.51	6.5	0.78
$_n$X$_{pp}$N$_p$	1.0	18	0.55

nontransforming for a period of time. After the D119N Ras mutant releases XDP, it regains its transforming activity. Thus, the mutant protein behaves like the wild-type Ras initially after injection and later as an oncogenic protein. These same authors have also recently characterized further mutations to the D119N p21Ras to produce severely dominant negative alleles of this protein (14).

One class of GTPases required additional mutagenesis to the well-described D-to-N mutation. The heterotrimeric G proteins are composed of α, β, and γ subunits. On ligand activation of the seven transmembrane classes of receptor proteins, Gα components are induced to exchange GTP for GDP. When Gα_o was engineered by Yu and colleagues (15) to accept XTP by mutation of D273N, the protein lost all ability to bind nucleotides. In a search for second site revertants, these authors used the previously described mutation of Q205L in conjunction with the D273N mutation. Although the glutamine residue at position 205 is at the opposite end of the nucleotide-binding site from aspartate-273, the double mutant was able to accept XTP in the expected fashion. The authors went on to reconstitute G protein-coupled signaling in Gα_o (D273N/Q205L)-transfected COS cells after cell wall permeabilization and the addition of XDP. Thus, the large family of Gα GTPases can also be engineered to accept XTP, albeit in the context of an additional mutation in the active site. The structural basis for the ability of the Q205L mutation to rescue XTP binding in the context of the D273N mutation is not known.

In the preceding discussion of the use of GTPase-to-XTPase engineering, the GTPase in question adhered to the well-described consensus sequence shown in Table 1. For the *Drosophila*-encoded P element transposase protein, it was known that GTP was essential for optimal in vitro transposition reactions. However, the classic GTP-binding cassette (Table 1) was not present in the transposase, indicating that GTP hydrolysis may or may not be involved in the complex DNA transposition reaction. To investigate the relationship between GTP-binding activity and in vivo transposition of *Drosophila* P elements, Mul & Rio engineered the D379N mutation in P-element transposase (16).

Mul & Rio (16) used an elegant genetic screen involving excision of a P element from a reporter plasmid, which creates a functional kanamycin resistance gene to follow the activity of the transposase. With this cellular assay, many mutations affecting GTP binding were studied. Even though the P-element transposase does not contain the canonical GTP-binding motif, the D379N, which corresponds to the residues that can be mutated in the canonical GTPase sequences described above, somewhat surprisingly produced a transposase that accepts XTP rather than GTP. The D379N transposase mutant was then studied in insect cells, where transposition reactions could be scored by using the kanamycin resistance-based reporter assay. Strikingly, insect cells transfected with D279N transposase showed a 50-fold increase in DNA transposition when the cells were incubated with exogenous xanthosine. Xanthine could also be added extracellularly to induce transposition but afforded only one-half of the induction provided by xanthosine.

This elegant study demonstrated that the noncanonical GTP-binding motif of P-element transposase was quite similar, in terms of structure-function relationships, to other GTPases. Furthermore, Mul & Rio (16) used the XTPase mutation in transposase to demonstrate that nucleotide hydrolysis activity of this complex protein is essential for DNA transposition, through selective rescue of the cellular transposition function of D379N transposase by the addition of extracellular xanthosine to increase the intracellular concentration of XTP. It is important that Mul & Rio have shown that the addition of xanthosine in the medium of *Drosophila* Schneider L2 cells leads to an appreciable increase in intracellular XTP. This is in distinct contrast to the work of Yu et al (15), in which xanthosine treatment of COS cells did not produce a concentration of XTP to support G protein-coupled signaling. Either the $G\alpha_o$ (mutant) signaling apparatus requires a higher concentration of XTP or the *Drosophila* cells possess a different balance of metabolic enzymes for controlling the GTP-GDP-XTP-XDP pools. In any case, this study demonstrates that not all in vivo cellular systems will react similarly to attempts at manipulation of intracellular nucleotide pools.

Because the GTPase family of enzymes represents one of the largest protein superfamilies in the genome, the XTPase mutation strategy promises to be a very valuable strategy for selectively manipulating one particular GTPase family in a complex mixture to carry out functional genomics studies of GTPases.

Seven-Transmembrane Receptors Activated Solely by Synthetic Ligands

The seven-transmembrane (7-TM) family of receptors is the largest family of transmembrane receptors in the human genome (17). They respond to photons, odorants, biogenic amines, lipids, peptide hormones, and other ligands. The 7-TM receptors control many physiological processes, including heart rate, proliferation, chemotaxis, neurotransmission, and hormone secretion (18). Ligand binding

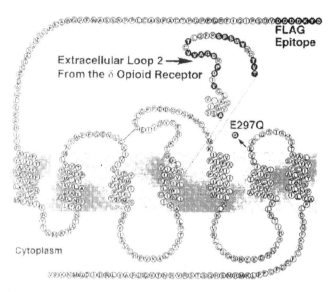

Figure 3 Topology of seven-transmembrane G protein-coupled receptor engineered to respond only to a synthetic ligand. The κ-opioid receptor is shown with a second extracellular loop transferred from the δ-opioid receptor to eliminate binding of endogenous ligands of the κ-opioid receptor.

induces dissociation of heterotrimeric (α, β, γ) G proteins, which are associated at the cytoplasmic side of the 7-TM receptors. As discussed above, Gαs are induced to bind GTP rather than GDP when ligands bind to the receptor.

The 7-TM receptors represent the targets of an estimated 75% of current pharmaceuticals. Thus the repertoire of specific ligands for individual receptors is enormous and should allow for simple chemical control of any 7-TM receptor of interest. However, animal studies are complicated by the presence of endogenous peptide ligands, which can activate or inhibit signaling events. To get around the problem of endogenous activation of 7-TM receptors, Coward et al (19) have engineered receptors that respond only to synthetic ligands and not to their endogenous ligands.

The topology of 7-TM receptors is shown in Figure 3. The ligand-binding site is composed of contacts from the extracellular loops. Coward et al (19) capitalized on the fact that peptide hormone-binding contacts are distinct from the contacts made by small-molecule ligands. Specifically, peptides typically interact with the extracellular loops of the receptor, whereas small-molecule binding determinants are closer to the transmembrane domains.

Coward et al (19) engineered the well-characterized κ-opioid receptor to be unresponsive to endogenous ligands by swapping an extracellular loop from the δ-opioid receptor Ro1 (Figure 3). In addition, a point mutation was made in the first extracellular loop (E297Q). This site was known to contribute to specific peptide binding, because the cognate residue in the δ receptor is tryptophan (19). Furthermore, the E297A mutant in the κ-opioid receptor was known to disrupt

TABLE 4 κ-Opioid receptor and engineered RASSL (Ro2) affinity for the endogenous ligand dynorphin A and for two synthetic ligands, bremazocine and spiradoline[a]

	Receptor	
Ligand	k-WT	Ro2
Dyn A(YGGFLRRIRPKLK)	0.06 ± 0.04	124.52 ± 19.38 (1946)
Bremazocine	0.04 ± 0.401	0.05 ± 0.02 (1.2)
Spiradoline	1.32 ± 0.38	5.65 ± 1.19 (4.3)

[a]Data are from 19. Data are expressed in nanomolar as mean $\pm$ SD. Fold differences from k-WT are shown in parentheses.

binding of κ-selective small-molecule agonists. To disrupt the essential chemical nature of the wild-type residue (Glu) to interfere with peptide hormone binding, without disruption of small-molecule binding, the conservative E297Q mutation was made, resulting in receptor Ro2. This engineered receptor displayed >2000-fold–lower binding affinity for the natural ligand dynorphin A (Table 4). Remarkably, however, the binding affinity for the synthetic ligand bremazocine was unchanged.

To test whether the engineered receptors could activate the expected downstream signaling pathways in cells, Ro1 and Ro2 were transfected into cells. Rat 1a cells proliferate in response to G_i signaling, which can be monitored easily as an increase in DNA synthesis (20). Wild-type κ–opioid receptor-transfected cells showed robust proliferation in response to the peptide hormone dynorphin A [50% effective concentration (EC_{50}) = 10 nM], whereas the engineered Ro1 induced no detectable proliferation, even at 100-fold-higher dynorphin A concentrations. The wild-type κ–opioid receptor and Ro1 showed the same levels of proliferation when stimulated with the synthetic ligand spiradoline [4.4 nM vs 5.5 nM, respectively (Figure 4A)]. Thus, the synthetic receptor Ro1 is insensitive to its natural ligand, yet can activate cellular responses when stimulated with synthetic agonists. Cell culture systems can demonstrate the feasibility of animal studies, yet many parameters that can be tightly controlled in cell culture are not manipulatable in an animal.

In an animal, it is difficult to determine a priori whether the receptors that are activated solely by synthetic ligands (RASSLs) will remain unstimulated, because of the many complicating factors in the in vivo production of peptide hormones. Redfern et al (21) directly addressed this question by engineering an Ro1-expressing transgenic mouse line.

To measure the effect of Ro1 expression in a whole animal, Redfern et al (21) used heart rate (HR) as a sensitive readout of RASSL responses. G_i signaling in the heart leads to a dramatic decrease in HR (bradycardia), which can be easily monitored (21). These authors engineered conditional and tissue-specific expression of Ro1 in mice. When Ro1 was expressed in the heart, where κ–opioid receptors are not expressed, the basal HR was 660, compared with a normal mouse HR of 650

A.

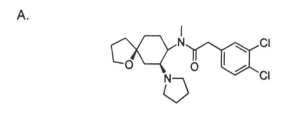

B.

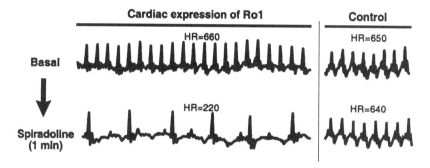

Figure 4   *A*. Chemical structure of spiradoline, a selective agonist of the κ-opioid receptor. *B*. Effect of spiradoline injection on heart rate of Ro1-expressing mouse vs control littermate that does not express Ro1 in the heart.

(Figure 4*B*). Thus, the 200-fold lowering of dynorphin A-binding affinity for Ro1 is sufficient to eliminate all stimulation of Ro1 by endogenous ligands.

When the synthetic ligand spiradoline was injected into the Ro1-transgenic mice, their HRs instantaneously (within <1 min) decreased to 220 (Figure 4*B*). The control mice that do not express Ro1 in the heart showed no bradycardia in response to spiradoline (HR, 640). Thus the RASSL engineered by Redfern et al (21) functioned perfectly in the whole-animal system, allowing for future investigations of a number of physiological and disease-related phenomena that are controlled by G_i-signaling pathways, including olfaction, taste transduction, weight control, memory, and locomotion.

In addition to the use of RASSLs to uncover the physiology of G protein-coupled receptors, Redfern et al (21) propose that RASSLs could be used to control physiologic responses with exogenously added ligands. The advantage to using RASSLs to control physiology is the rapidity of the G_i-coupled signal transduction cascade, allowing for induction of responses (<1 min) in contrast to other systems, which rely on dimerization (see below) or activation of transcription factors, which takes minutes or days, respectively.

Because spiradoline activates endogenous κ–opioid receptors, which are primarily expressed in the brain, the Ro1 transgenic system may be most useful when used in conjunction with the recently produced κ–opioid receptor knockout mouse (22). This would allow the use of spiradoline to activate only the introduced Ro1 receptors and would be predicted to have no effect on G_i signaling in any tissue.

An alternative approach would be to further engineer RASSLs to respond to synthetic ligands, which are orthogonal to all endogenous G protein-coupled receptors. As pointed out by Redfern et al (21), such ligands have been developed, yet currently they are not sufficiently potent to use in animals. Perhaps the success of RASSLs in transgenic mice will encourage chemists to address this deficiency, allowing for RASSLs to be used ubiquitously without the need to knock out the endogenous κ–opioid receptors. The RASSL system not only is a success in terms of protein engineering but is also an extremely powerful method for deciphering the physiological consequences of stimulation of the >1000 predicted G protein-coupled receptors in the mouse genome.

Protein Kinases with Specificity for Unnatural Nucleotides

Protein kinases play a central role in controlling many diverse signal transduction pathways in all cells (24–26). These enzymes catalyze the phosphorylation of tyrosine, serine, or threonine residues on proteins by using ATP as the phosphodonor. The identification of the cellular substrates of individual protein kinases remains one of the central challenges in the field. We have recently developed a chemical method to tag the direct substrates of two Src family kinases, v-Src and Fyn (27, 28). To distinguish the substrates of v-Src from all other kinase substrates, we used structure-based design and site-directed mutagenesis to make v-Src catalyze a unique phosphotransfer reaction not catalyzed by any other protein kinase in the cell. We engineered the ATP-binding site of v-Src to uniquely accept an ATP analog (A*TP) as the phosphodonor substrate. The engineering of the active site of v-Src to accept $[\gamma\text{-}^{32}P]A^*TP$ provides a method by which the direct substrates of v-Src can be specifically radiolabeled in the presence of any number of cellular kinases (Figure 5, see color insert).

We have extended this strategy to a number of tyrosine and serine/threonine kinases to accept unnatural ATP analogs (28; Bishop AC, Shah K, Blethrow J, Ubersax J, Morgan DO, Shokat KM, unpublished data). This was accomplished by using a semirational design approach. To create an orthogonal ligand, we synthesized N^6-substituted derivatives of ATP (27). We then mutated a bulky residue in the active site of the kinase v-Src, Ile-338, to a smaller group, Ala or Gly. Ile-338 was chosen because it appeared to be in close contact with the N^6 amine of ATP (Figure 6, see color insert). By screening a large panel of N^6-substituted ATP analogs containing aliphatic or aromatic substituents, we identified the optimal A*TP substrates for the *I338A* and *I338G* mutated v-Src kinases.

Initially only the crystal structures of Ser/Thr kinases, protein kinase A (PKA), and cyclin dependent kinase 2 (CDK2) (29, 30) were available to guide our engineering of the tyrosine kinase v-Src. Crystal structures of PKA and CDK2, which share only ~50% homology to v-Src, served as a limited guide to our design efforts. Based only on these structures, however, we introduced two mutations (*V323A* and *I338A*) into v-Src, affording a kinase with good specificity for N^6 (cyclopentyl) ATP (27).

In the design of second-generation v-Src mutants, we were guided by newly solved structures of three tyrosine kinases—c-Src, Hck, and Lck (31–33). Relying heavily on the Hck-AMP-PNP cocrystal structure and kinase sequence alignments, we found that a single bulky residue at the position corresponding to Ile-338 in v-Src is primarily responsible for restricting the ability of wild-type kinases to accept N^6-substituted ATP analogs. To our surprise, N^6-(benzyl) ATP was the best substrate for the v-Src single mutation (*I338A* or *I338G*), based on screening a panel of >35 unique A*TP analogs (28; Shah K, Shokat KM, unpublished data). We had initially expected that an A*TP with a smaller substituent attached at the N^6 position would better complement the small pocket engineered (Ile → Ala/Gly) into the kinase.

Although no crystal structure of the engineered v-Src kinase is yet available, several ligands bound to wild-type Src family kinases have been used to predict the binding mode of the orthogonal ATP analog, N^6-(benzyl) ATP, to the engineered v-Src (34). From modeling studies, we conclude that, for the N^6-substituted benzyl group to gain access to the existing pocket adjacent to N^7, the side chain of residue 338 (a "molecular gate") must be shortened (i.e. *I338A* or *G*). This analysis predicts that the benzyl ring of N^6-(benzyl) ATP partially occupies a pocket already present in v-Src after the molecular gate, which normally restricts access to this pocket in all wild-type kinases, is removed by our mutation. This would explain why a larger than expected A*TP (>80 Å^3) is the optimal analog identified in a screen of >35 A*TPs against *I338G* v-Src (28).

Further study of the binding mode suggested that more flexible links between the phenyl ring and the N^6 amino group of ATP would allow better van der Waals packing of the added bump on the ligand into the engineered hole in the protein. It was suggested that one more methylene group could be added to the linker to allow the aromatic ring more flexibility to reach the existing pocket near the N^7 atom of ATP.

In fact, the analog designed with an extra methylene group, N^6-(2-phenethyl) ATP, is a better substrate ($k_{cat} = 0.6$ min^{-1}; $K_m = 8$ μM with I338A v-Src) than the previous optimal analog, N^6-(benzyl) ATP [$k_{cat} = 0.5$ min^{-1}; $K_m = 20$ μM with the I338A mutant (28)]. For comparison, the kinetic constants for the I338A mutant with ATP are $k_{cat} = 1.0$ min^{-1} and $K_m = 70$ μM (28). This confirms the prediction that adding extra flexibility into the substrate serves to orient the orthogonal substrate into the existing pocket above the N^7 nitrogen.

To summarize, the binding site for orthogonal N^6-substituted A*TP substrates of mutant v-Src proteins containing *I338A* or *I338G* mutations has been functionally probed with a wide variety of A*TPs. The pocket in the v-Src tyrosine kinase that accommodates the added substituents at the N^6 position of ATP is actually present in the wild-type v-Src kinase. It is *access* to the existing pocket that is controlled by Ile-338 in v-Src. Rather than engineering a new pocket by mutation of Ile to the smaller Ala or Gly residues, we believe that the *I338G* and *I338A* mutations provide a path for the N^6 substituent on the ATP analog to gain access to an existing pocket in the ATP-binding site. Our laboratory has demonstrated that non-Src family tyrosine kinases, as well as many Ser/Thr-specific kinases, can be similarly engineered to accept N^6-substituted ATP analogs including N^6-(benzyl) ATP (Bishop AC, Blethrow J, Ubersax J, Morgan DO, Shokat KM, unpublished data).

Uniquely Inhibitable Protein Kinases

The ability to dissect signaling pathways by kinase substrate identification will certainly allow for more direct analysis of the roles of kinases in many diverse signaling environments. However, signaling pathways are not simply a summation of enzyme-substrate interactions. These pathways are highly interconnected, nonlinear, and exquisitely sensitive. Thus, in addition to biochemical mapping of pathways, genetic analyses of a pathway's organization provide important information about the key nodes of signal processing, by testing the functional importance of individual kinases. Unfortunately, because signaling cascades are responsible for ultrafast regulation of responses to light, oxygen, toxins, etc, genetic methods often fail to reveal the role of individual kinases because they are slow (days to weeks) at perturbing the system under study.

Regulation of kinase activity by homologous recombination in a mammalian genome requires at least 1–2 weeks even using the most sophisticated recombinase-mediated methods. During these 2 weeks, the signaling pathway of interest typically responds to the missing kinase by transcriptional up-regulation of a closely related kinase, which masks the real effect of missing the kinase of interest. A chemical method of inhibiting any kinase of interest would not suffer from such limitations, because small molecules can be added to the cell culture medium or the whole animal and in seconds bind to and inhibit the target.

Truly specific inhibitors for kinases and other members of large-protein super families are extremely difficult to identify. The stunning size and conserved active site fold of the protein kinase super family present two serious problems. First, the simple generation of a small-molecule inhibitor, which is unique for a single-family member out of a group of >2000 highly homologous proteins, is a daunting problem.

To rapidly develop uniquely specific inhibitors of any protein kinase in the genome, we have designed protein kinase inhibitors that inhibit only specifically mutated kinases. We have termed this approach the design of chemically sensitive alleles of protein kinases (35). To identify a cell-permeable small molecule that uniquely inhibits Ile-338–Gly v-Src, Bishop et al (35) tethered bulky chemical groups to the previously described Src family inhibitor, PP1 (36). Through modeling of the Src family-selective inhibitor PP1 (Figure 7, structure 1) in the active site of the Src family kinase Hck, it was predicted that PP1 would bind in an orientation analogous to that of ATP, therefore presenting its exocyclic amine (N^4) to the space surrounding residue 338 (32). Thus, the amine was used as a chemical

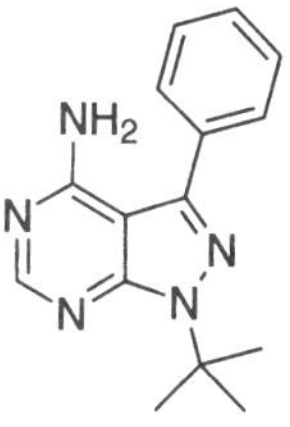

Figure 7 Chemical structures of PP-1, and its analogs which contain additional substituents (highlighted in blue bonds) designed to complement the additional space in appropriately mutated kinases.

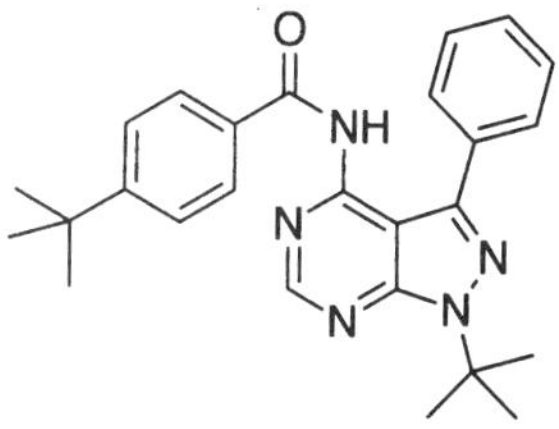

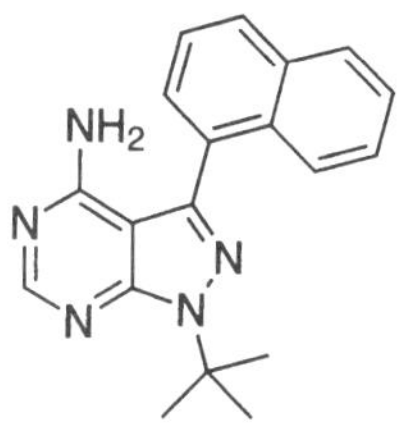

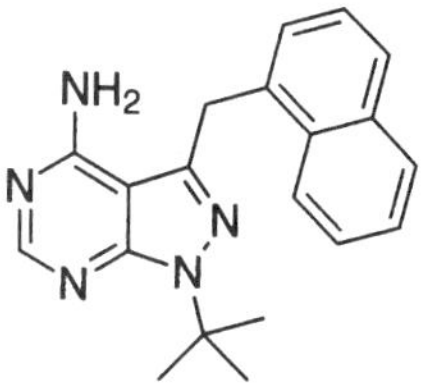

hook to attach hydrophobic moieties that would prevent binding of the derivatized molecules to wild-type protein kinases. The same hook would concurrently generate novel van der Waals interactions with the engineered v-Src.

From a panel of 10 PP1 analogs, the most potent inhibitor of Ile-338–Gly was (4-[p-*tert*-butyl]benzamido-1–*tert*-butyl-3-phenylpyrazolo[3,4-*d*]pyrimidine) [50% inhibitory concentration (IC$_{50}$) = 430 nM; Figure 7, structure 2]. The selectivity of PP1 analog 2 was confirmed against wild-type v-Src, Fyn, Abl, PKA, and PKC-δ, all of which were inhibited $\geq$700-fold less effectively than the target kinase. Bishop et al (35) also showed that the equivalent mutation in Fyn also made it sensitive to inhibition by PPI analog 2 (IC$_{50}$ = 830 nM), showing that a chemical genetic approach to protein–small-molecule recognition can rapidly circumvent the selectivity problem inherent in the structural degeneracy of homologous protein families.

The use of kinase inhibitors, which are competitive with ATP, is complicated by the high intracellular concentrations of ATP (1–5 mM in most cell types). Pyrazolopyrimidine-based inhibitor 2 is highly selective for appropriately mutated kinases, yet lacks high potency. Typically 100- to 1000-fold increases in cellular EC$_{50}$ values are found, compared with in vitro IC$_{50}$ values for ATP-competitive kinase inhibitors. Thus, an inhibitor with an IC$_{50}$ value of 400 nM will require 40–400 μM in whole-cell assays, which is a concentration range in which general cytotoxicity can be induced.

To increase the potency of the pyrazolopyrimidine-based inhibitors, the binding mode of PP1 in the active site of the Src family kinase. Hck was investigated by molecular modeling (32, 34). From this model, it was deduced that derivatization of N^4 was not the only means of generating complementary van der Waals interactions with the unique binding pocket of *I338G* v-Src. It was predicted that derivatization of the C^3 phenyl ring of PP1 [e.g. a phenyl ring replaced with a naphthyl ring system (Figure 7, PP1 analog 3)] with a bulky group leads to a steric clash between the derivatized inhibitor and the molecular surface created by Thr-338 (Figure 8, see color insert). Mutation of residue 338 to glycine generates a unique binding pocket, which is predicted to be large enough to accept the naphthyl analog of PP1. It was reasoned that derivatization of the phenyl group in PP1 with hydrophobic substituents should afford compounds that complement the corresponding I338G v-Src–active site, without disrupting any potential hydrogen-bonding interactions at N^4. In addition, this added bulk at the C^3 moiety should cause these molecules to be sterically incompatible with the active sites of wild-type tyrosine kinases, affording high specificity for the suitably engineered v-Src.

The group of modified inhibitors was screened against the catalytic domain of the target kinase, I338G v-Src, which was expressed in bacteria and purified as a glutathione-*S*-transferase (GST) fusion protein. All of the C^3-derivatized analogs are more potent inhibitors of I338G v-Src than the most potent molecule (2, IC_{50} = 430 nM) identified from the first-generation panel of N^4 derivatized compounds (35). Two naphthyl analogs of PP1 (analogs 3 and 4) exhibited the greatest potency (IC_{50} = 1.5 nM). Under the assay conditions, the parent molecule, PP1, inhibited its optimal target, Fyn, at only IC_{50} = 30 nM. These data show that an inhibitor design strategy combining enzyme engineering with directed small-molecule synthesis could match the potency of molecules identified through screening of large libraries. Furthermore, this strategy can lead to a significant increase (20-fold analogs 3 and 4) in affinity over previously optimized inhibitors of wild-type kinases.

Identification of a selective enzyme inhibitor through chemical genetic design is useful only if the inhibitor can be used in a relevant cellular context to probe the target's function inside the cell. To demonstrate cellular inhibition of the target kinase by analog 3, Bishop et al (35) treated NIH 3T3 fibroblasts, which expressed either wild-type or Ile-338–Gly v-Src with the mutant-specific inhibitor (35). The mutant-selective inhibitor, PP1 analog 3, at 100 μM had no effect on the phosphotyrosine level of cells expressing wild-type v-Src, whereas the phosphotyrosine levels of cells that expressed the target kinase were moderately reduced. It is more striking that, under prolonged drug treatment, it was found that the Ile-338–Gly–expressing cells selectively reverted to the flattened morphology of nontransformed fibroblasts. This phenotype was confirmed by staining the actin stress fibers that are characteristic of normal fibroblasts (Figure 9, see color insert). No change in the morphology or actin organization was observed for the wild-type v-Src–expressing cells. Thus it was demonstrated that a small-molecule inhibitor, which is uniquely selective for a tyrosine kinase oncogene product, could revert the morphological changes associated with cellular transformation.

Only through chemical genetic design coupled with the built-in control of the wild-type target homolog could such a determination of cellular specificity be

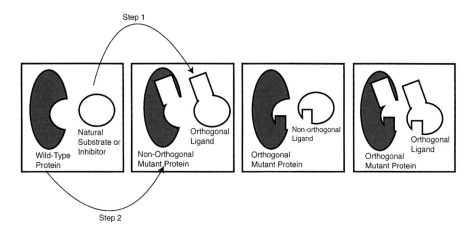

Scheme A Operational definition of orthogonal ligands and orthogonal proteins.

A.

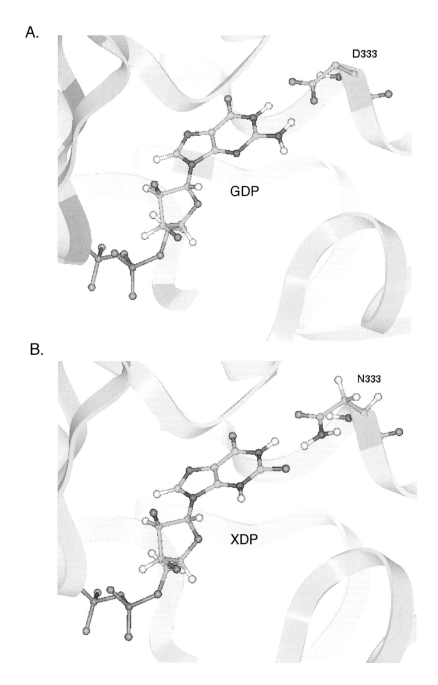

B.

Figure 1 caption appears at right, on following page.

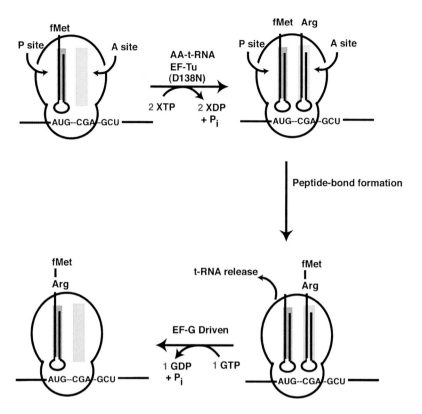

Figure 2 Use of XTP dependent D138N EF-Tu to measure number of XTP hydrolyses per amino acid coupling step in ribosomal protein syntheses. Figure derived from data in reference 5.

Figure 1 (from page 2) A. Ribbon diagram of GDP bound to Elongation Factor Tu (EF-Tu). GDP is shown in ball-and-stick representation, with a bifurcated H-bond to aspartate 138 (D138) also shown in ball-and-stick representation. Atom colors are: *green*=carbon, *red*=oxygen, *blue*=nitrogen, *white*=hydrogen, *purple*=phosphorous. B. Hypothetical structure the orthogonal ligand, xanthine diphosphate (XPD), bound to the orthogonal EF-Tu mutant (D138N EF-Tu).

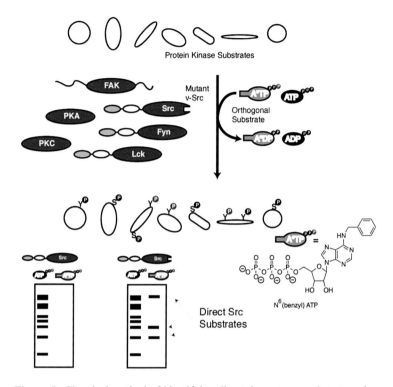

Figure 5 Chemical method of identifying direct downstream substrates of v-Src kinase. *Red ovals* represent the conserved kinase domain in different members of the protein kinase superfamily. *Other ovals* represent protein-protein association domains. *Empty ovals* represent cellular proteins which become phosphorylated by a variety of kinases. *Ovals with a segment missing* represent mutant kinases which accept "bumped" substrates such as N^6(benzyl) ATP, as shown. *Bottom rectangles* represent hypothetical autoradiograms of protein gels to identify specific substrates of v-Src.

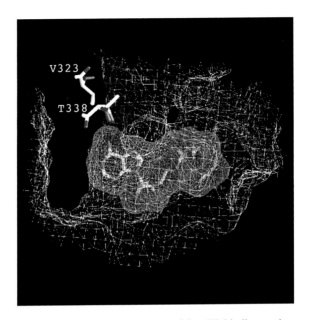

Figure 6 Surface representation of the ATP binding pocket in Hck, a Src-family tyrosine kinase. The solvent accessible surface of Hck within 7 Å of ATP is shown in *white* mesh, the surface of ATP is shown in *blue* mesh. The portion of Hck's solvent accessible surface area (A) formed by T338 (corresponding to I338 in v-Src) is colored *red* (mesh) and the portion of the surface formed by V323 is shown in *green* (mesh). ATP and residues T338 and V323 are shown in stick representation with the following atom coloring: O—*red*, N—*blue*, C=*white*, P=*yellow*. This figure was created using GRASP.

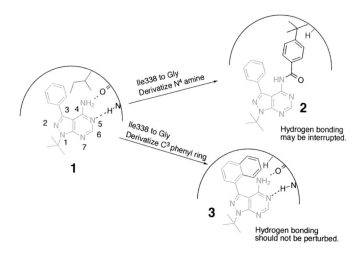

Figure 8 Schematic representation of the predicted binding orientation of two classes of derivatized prazolo[3,4-*d*]pyramidines. Analogues that were derivatized at N⁴ may have lost potency due to an interruption of the ATP-like hydrogen bonding network. This network is presumably intact in the C³ derivatized inhibitors.

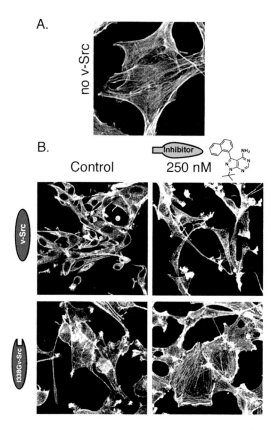

Figure 9 I338G v-Src transformed fibroblasts selectively acquire a flattened morphology and selectively regain actin stress fibers upon incubation with **3**. (A)Non-transformed NIH3T3 cells. (B) Cells transformed by either wild-type v-Src or I338G v-Src were treated with 0.5% DMSO or 250 nM **3** in 0.5% DMSO for 16 hours. All cells were fixed, stained, with phalloidin-rhodamine, and visualized by confocal microscopy.

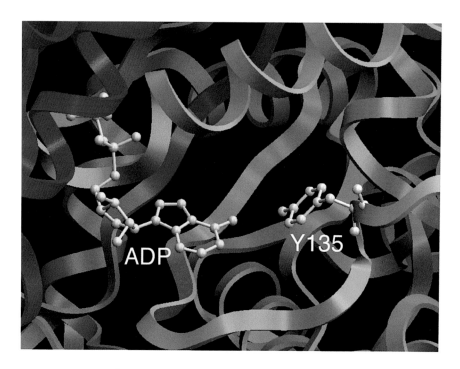

Figure 10 Myosin-Iβ Tyr-61 is a suitable residue for substitution. Ribbon representation of the Dictyostelium myosin-II motor domain complexed to ADP and aluminum fluoride. Note the close contact between adenine ring of ADP, shown in *yellow,* and Tyr-135 (Y135) equivalent to tyrosine-61 of rat or mouse myosin-Iβ, shown in *white*. The NH2-terminal domain (25 kDa) is shown in *green*, the central domain (50kDa) is shown in *red*, and the COOH-terminal domain (20 kDa in chicken skeletal muscle myosin) is shown in *blue*.

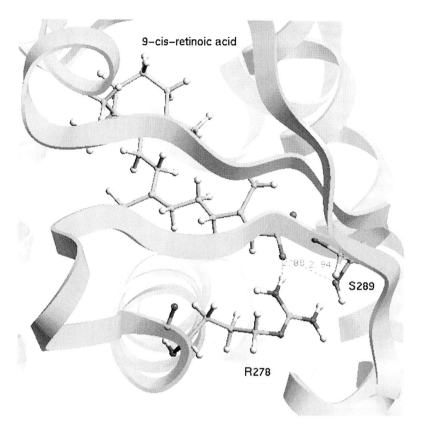

Figure 12 Ribbon diagram of 9-cis-retinotic acid bound to RARγ. 9-cis-retinotic acid is shown in ball-and-stick representation as are the two key residues in RARγ which form important contacts with the carboxylic acid of 9-cis-retinotic acid. Atom colors are the same as in Figure 1.

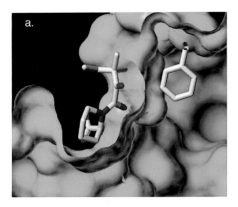
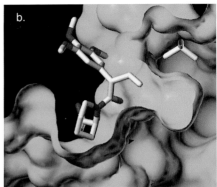
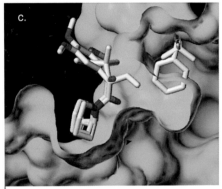

Figure 15 Crystal structure of a remodeled interface between the FK506-binding protein (FKPB) and a synthetic ligand. A cutaway through the solvent-accessible area is shown (green); carbon atoms of the original complex are shown in white and those of the modified complex are in yellow. (a) The complex between wild-type FKBP and a synthetic ligand, showing the tight complementarity around the C9 carbonyl group. The sidechain of Phe36 is shown. This interaction has a K_d of 10nM. (b) Complex of a ligand with a designed C9 S-ethyl bump with F36V FDBP. Apart from the removal of the Phe36 sidechain, the protein structure is essentially identical to that of the wild type. Note that the bumped ligand also has a second difference compared to the ligand in (a); a C9 trimethoxy substitent was substituted in place of tert-pentyl to improve affinity. This interaction has a K_d of 0.1 nM. (c) Overlay of (a) and (b). For further details see (1, 73).

made. We have recently shown that PP1 analogs 2 and 3 are potent inhibitors of protein kinases in the Ser/Thr kinase super family, which are engineered to contain the same pocket, above the N^6 position of ATP. This genome-wide approach to rapidly identifying potent small-molecule inhibitors of protein kinases will be useful for target validation of protein kinases as well as for generating adult knock-out-like phenotypes in transgenic animals.

Conditional Alleles of Kinesin and Myosin Motors

Another widely distributed family of ATP-utilizing enzymes is the motor protein family, including myosins and kinesins. Many different cellular processes are controlled by these force-generating enzymes, including muscle contraction, vesicle trafficking, cell motility, and axon guidance. To clarify the specific role of individual members of these families, two laboratories have developed mutant motors capable of interacting with unnatural ATP analogs to gain chemical control over individual motors in cells.

By making a space-creating mutation within the ATP-binding pocket of myosin 1β, Gillespie et al have produced a mutant that is potently inhibited by particular bulky N^6-substituted ADP analogs (37).

The actin-based myosin motor plays a crucial role in many specialized cellular events including extension of cellular processes (axonal outgrowth), cell division (cytokinesis), phagocytosis, signal transduction, cell movement, changes in cell shape during development, hearing, and muscle contraction (38). As many as 18 different myosin isozymes have been identified to date (Table 5). The myosin super family is divided into the conventional or type II myosins (those involved in muscle contraction) and the unconventional myosins (types I and III–XV+, as well as all other myosins). Features common to all myosin isozymes are a conserved

TABLE 5 Alignment of representative sequences from different classes of the myosin family (Genbank ID)

Class	Genbank ID	Sequence
RAT MYOSIN 1β	(A45439):	49 GSVVISVNPYRSLP.I**Y**SPEKVEDYRNRN 77
Class I:	P22467:	46 GPVLVSMNPYKQLG.I**Y**GNDQINLYKGKH 74
Class II:	P08964:	109 GLSLVAINPYHNLN.L**Y**SEDHINLYHNKH 136
Class III:	P10676:	365 GDILLSLNSNEIKQ.EFPQEFHAKYRFKS 384
Class V:	Q99104:	104 GIVLVAINPYEQLP.I**Y**GEDIINAYSGQN 132
Class VI:	U49739:	91 ANILIAVNPYFDIPKI**Y**SSDTIKSYQGKS 120
Class VII:	U81453:	99 GSILVAVNPYQLLS.I**Y**SPEHIRQYTNKK 127
Class VIII:	U94781:	151 GPVLVAINPFKKIP.L**Y**GSDYIEAYKRKS 178
Class IX:	S54307:	180 GSILVAINPFKFLP.I**Y**NPKYVKMYENQQ 208
Class X:	U55042:	97 GSIIASVNPYKTITGL**Y**SRDAVDRYSRCH 126
Class XI:	U94785	96 GNILIAINPFQRLPHL**Y**DTHMMEQYKGAG 125

[a]Conserved tyrosine in rat myosin 1β is highlighted. This residue can be mutated to glycine, allowing N^6 substituted ATP analogs to be accepted as alternative substrates for mutant mysosin 1β.

head group that encompasses the actin-binding ATP-driven motor region, less-conserved domains involved in binding regulatory light-chain molecules, and divergent tail structures that likely provide specificity of function (e.g. binding of a particular cargo) (38).

Myosin binds to and moves along actin filaments in an ATP-dependent process. The hydrolysis of ATP within the myosin head group leads to the "ratcheting" of the head group, which charges it energetically to produce force upon return to the unratcheted state. It is in this bent state, bound to ADP and P_i, that myosin is capable of binding actin. Release of P_i leads to the unracheting of the actin-bound head group and the coincident movement of the myosin tail and its attached cargo towards the positive end of the actin filament. The release of ADP sets the stage for another cycle of ATP binding and hydrolysis. The binding of ATP releases the head group from actin. Release and rebinding of multiple myosin head groups provide the machinery by which myosin motors can move along an actin filament.

Several myosin isozymes have been implicated in the hearing process in mammals. MYO15, myosin VIIA, and myosin VI mutations all lead to apparent hearing loss in mice. Mutations in MYO15 and myosin VIIA have been mapped in deaf patients (39). Myosin isozyme expression studies (immunohistochemical techniques and in situ hybridization experiments) have provided insight into the potential players in certain aspects of hearing. However, given that multiple myosin isozymes are expressed in the auditory hair cells of the ear, direct proof of the role of a particular isozyme has been difficult. Developmental stresses put in place by the lack of one isozyme (as in knock-out mice) may result in the use of alternative isozymes, making genetic studies difficult to interpret.

Gillespie et al designed a system to probe the involvement of myosin 1β in the hearing process. Making use of the knowledge that ADP release from myosin is the rate-limiting step in myosin movement along actin (i.e. in the presence of high concentrations of ADP, movement can be stalled), they have successfully designed isozyme-specific inhibitors of mutant myosin 1β. Complementary space-creating and space-filling alterations in the conserved nucleotide-binding site of myosin 1β and the nucleotide, respectively, have allowed allele-specific inhibition. Mutation of rat myosin 1β tyrosine 61 (Figure 10) to glycine creates an enlarged binding pocket capable of uniquely accepting N^6-substituted adenosine analogs. In vitro motility assays show that the mutant myosin is capable of functioning at or near wild-type levels in the presence of ATP and that its movement was inhibited robustly in the presence of N^6-substituted ADP analogs. It is interesting that the mutant myosin motor actually moves more quickly (0.12 μm s^{-1}) than the wild-type motor (0.03 μm s^{-1}). This is caused by the lower ADP affinity of the Y61G mutant ($K_d = 74 \pm 19$ μM) compared with wild-type myosin ($K_d = 20 \pm 2$ μM). Because release of ADP is rate limiting for cycling of myosin (40), it is reasonable that the mutant with a space creating mutation in the adenine-binding site would move more quickly. The force generated by the mutant myosin would be predicted to be lower than that of the wild-type protein, but this has not been determined. It is important that the tyrosine mutated in myosin 1β is conserved across the myosin family, suggesting that the same strategy could be applied to other myosin family members.

The large kinesin super family of ATP-driven molecular motors have also proven amenable to a similar strategy for generating allele-specific inhibitors. Kinesin and kinesin-like proteins are responsible for movement of organelles along microtubules (MT), spindle formation, and the segregation of chromosomes at cell division (41). Kinesin super family members have a conserved MT-binding ATPase head group with structural similarities to the myosin head group (42). Kapoor and Mitchison examined of the amino acid residues within 5 Å of the ADP-N^6 atom in the X-ray crystal structure of human kinesin (42) and noticed the presence of two conserved charged groups (Arg-14 and Arg-16).

Kapoor & Mitchison (43) have, in fact, recently reported the use of just such an approach to produce kinesin allele-specific activators and inhibitors. Mutation of Arg-14 to alanine does indeed provide a binding pocket, which is capable of using N^6-cyclopentyl ATP. Not surprisingly, however, the removal of the charged group in the binding pocket disrupts the ability of the molecule to function with endogenous ATP, making the mutant kinesin reliant on the N^6-substituted analog for its function (Table 6). Because hydrolysis of ATP, not release of ADP as in myosin, is the rate-limiting step in the kinesin system, Kapoor & Mitchison made use of a nonhydrolyzable form of the analog to specifically inhibit the mutant kinesin. Such allele-specific activators and inhibitors should allow the

TABLE 6   Engineered motor proteins kinesin and myosin, kinetic constants with ATP, and orthogonal nucleotides[a]

	ATP				K_i
	K_m	V_{max}	K_m	V_{max}	
kinesin	60 μM	0.6 μm/s	*	*	b
kinesin*	*	*	1200 μM	0.2 μm/s	
myosin1β	9–6 μM	0.5–0.3/s			230 μM
myosin1β*	10–2 μM	0.5–0.3/s			2.4 μM

*Very little activity.

[a]V_{max} for kinesin is in microtubule movement (micrometers/second), whereas myosin results are given as ATP hydrolysis (1/s).

[b]In the presence of 25 μM actin and 10 μM ATP.

clarification of the role of individual kinesin family members in various cellular processes.

Conditional Alleles of Nuclear Hormone Receptors

The super family of nuclear hormone receptors is a unique family of transcriptional regulators. This group of receptors has both DNA-binding and ligand-dependent transactivation abilities. On selective binding of small-ligand molecules, this family of receptors can single-handedly provide a transcriptional signal to specific target genes (44).

The retinoid X receptor (RXR) activates the transcription of genes in response to 9-*cis*-retinoic acid (RA) or 9cRA, its natural ligand. Nuclear receptors such as RXR are a super family of ligand-inducible transcription factors that, along with RA receptors (RARs), play a role in the control of cellular differentiation and vertebrate development through their interaction with RAs. RAs are natural derivatives of vitamin A (retinol). The RXRs show a binding preference for 9-*cis*-RA whereas the RARs bind with equal affinity to 9-*cis* RA as well as to the stereoisomer, all-*trans*-RA (t-RA) (Figure 11).

RXR functions as a ligand-binding homodimer, but it is also able to function as a silent non–ligand-binding partner in a heterodimer with other nuclear receptors. Altered activation of nuclear hormone receptors in response to ligand binding occurs in natural and directed mutants and results in responses ultimately leading to diseased states. For example, a Thr-877 $\to$ Ala mutation in the androgen receptor results in the inability to bind and activate in response to progesterone, estradiol, and antiandrogens (45). This mutation is associated with pharmacoresistant prostate cancer.

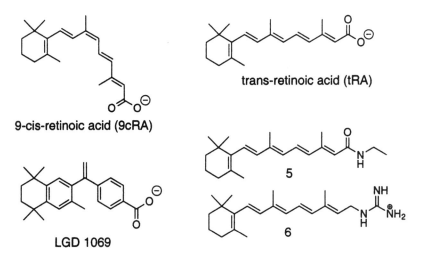

Figure 11   Chemical structures of 9-*cis*-retinoic acid (9cRA) and *trans*-retinoic acid (tRA) along with orthogonal ligands for engineered retinoic-acid receptors.

The development of receptors that could be activated by selected ligands would expand the applications for metabolic and genetic control, as well as provide insights into the structural specificity and origin of disease states. The ability to activate or repress transcription of specific genes by selective or "designer" ligands would provide a tool that is useful for the control of genetic and metabolic pathways.

Peet et al (46) tested a number of RXR synthetic ligands with a variety of RXR mutants, and this structure-based mutagenesis was used to change the ligand specificity of RXR. The amino acid residues Phe-313 and Leu-436 were found to be crucial in determining ligand specificity. The first class shows decreased activation by the natural ligand 9cRA and increased affinity for synthetic ligands. The second class continues to be activated by 9cRA but no longer responds to synthetic ligands (narrower specificity). Two new classes of mutant RXR proteins were developed.

Single and double mutants were tested in which Phe-313 and Leu-436 of RXR were changed to various uncharged amino acids. The Phe-313 $\rightarrow$ Ile mutation produced a dramatic shift in specificity—a 40-fold change in favor of the synthetic ligand LGD 1069 over the natural ligand 9cRA, as compared with the EC_{50}s of the wild-type RXR (Figure 11). The Phe-313$\rightarrow$Ala mutant also displayed a similar shift in specificity towards the synthetic ligands.

The only Leu-436 substitution to show any change in specificity was L436F. In contrast to the Phe-313 mutants, L436F shows a ninefold increase (less potent) in EC_{50} for the natural ligand 9cRA, and a shift away from the synthetic ligands.

Koh and colleagues (47) investigated another member of the nuclear hormone receptor family (RARγ) to selectively activate genes with small molecules designed to bind to engineered receptors. Specifically, the RARγ was rationally reengineered to respond to novel synthetic ligands.

The crystal structure of t-RA in a complex with RARγ was used for the design of the engineered receptor synthetic and ligand pair (Figure 12, see color insert). Two residues were shown to interact directly with the carboxylic acid moiety of t-RA through site-directed-mutagenesis studies (48). These two residues (Ser-289 and Arg-278) possess the critical electrostatic and size recognition elements necessary for ligand binding. Mutation of one or both of these residues to glycine or to a negatively charged residue (Asp or Glu) results in receptors that prefer neutral or positively charged RA analogs such as ligands 5 and 6 (Figure 11). The synthetic analogs contain sterically larger groups or cationic groups in place of the carboxylic-acid moeity of t-RA. These ligand modifications complement the engineered receptors and are preferentially accepted by the mutants, compared with the wild type, with selectivities of >threefold between wild-type and mutant receptors (6) and 14.4-fold induction of the mutant receptor with ligand 5.

The ability to design and synthesize ligands for engineered nuclear hormone receptors opens up many exciting opportunities to study these complex transcription factors with small molecules. Examples of future directions may include the study of orphan nuclear hormone receptors, in which the natural ligand has not been identified, or activation (agonist) of engineered receptors in transgenic animals.

ENGINEERING SIGNALING PATHWAYS FOR HUMAN THERAPY

Antibody-Directed Enzyme Prodrug Therapy

One of the major limitations of research strategies that use orthogonal-pair design is that they generally have little or no direct medicinally relevant applications in humans. Whereas the introduction of engineered proteins into a variety of lower organisms is now commonplace, modern medicine is still many years removed (technologically and ethically) from the generation of transgenic humans. However, Smith and co-workers (49) and Wolfe et al (50) have recently devised an elegant approach for using orthogonal enzyme/substrate pairs to selectively deliver potent cytotoxic agents to tumor cells in vivo.

It had previously been shown that antibody-directed enzyme prodrug therapy (ADEPT) can be used to deliver chemotherapeutic agents to tumors (51, 52). ADEPT is used to selectively target an enzyme of interest to a tumor by coupling the enzyme to a tumor-specific antibody. Generally, the selected enzyme catalyzes the cleavage of a prodrug to release the active drug in the vicinity of the tumor mass. Thus, a twofold treatment of the antibody-enzyme conjugate, followed by the small-molecule prodrug, could lead to potent cytotoxicity directed to tumor cells. Although such approaches to cancer therapy have great promise, they also face formidable hurdles. The introduction of foreign enzymes into the human bloodstream can be highly immunogenic. In addition, ADEPT therapies often show weak tumor cell selectivity because the prodrugs can be hydrolyzed by any number of wild-type enzymes in the patient.

Previous to the studies by Smith et al (49), Vitols et al (53) had developed an ADEPT system by using bovine carboxypeptidase A and prodrugs of the potent cytotoxic drug methotrexate (MTX). Smith et al set out to lower the immunogenicity and improve the target specificity of this system through orthogonal-pair design (49). Initially, the authors chose to use human carboxypeptidase A1 (hCPA1) to minimize the immune response from the introduction of a bovine enzyme. More importantly, they engineered hCPA1 so that it would be capable of hydrolyzing MTX prodrugs that were not substrates for either wild-type hCPA1 or hCPA2. To suitably engineer hCPA1, Christianson & Lipscomb used a model of the protein that had been generated by using the crystal structure of bovine carboxypeptidase A [CPA (54)]. To this protein they docked a model substrate and found that the side chain of Thr-268 of hCPA1 was in close contact with the 2 and 3 positions of the phenyl ring of substrates containing phenylalanine or tyrosine. Because it had been previously shown that MTX-Phe (7) was an excellent substrate for hCPA1 (53), the authors reasoned that derivatives of MTX-Phe with bulky substituents at the 2 or 3 positions should be uniquely accepted by mutants of hCPA1 that have smaller amino acids (glycine or alanine) at position 268.

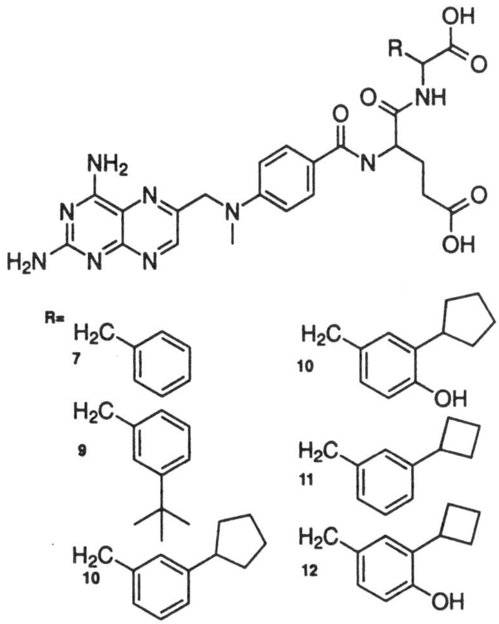

Figure 13 Chemical structures of orthogonal substrates for engineered carboxypeptidaseA designed to facilitate ADEPT (49).

Smith et al (49) synthesized a series of bulky aromatic MTX prodrugs, and, as would be expected, many of these molecules were extremely poor substrates for wild-type hCPA1 and hCPA2 (Figure 13) (49). In addition, these molecules were shown to possess far greater stability than MTX-Phe in pancreatic juice. The derivatized MTX prodrugs were then screened for their ability to act as substrates in hCPA1-T268G and hCPA1-T268A. The authors discovered that hCPA1-T268G was able to efficiently catalyze the hydrolysis of several of the bulky prodrugs (MTX-3-t-butyl-Phe-8, MTX-3-cyclopentyl-Phe-9, MTX-3-cyclopentyl-Tyr-10, MTX-3-cyclobutyl-Phe-11, and MTX-3-cyclobutyl-Tyr-12). Using the best substrate of the panel, MTX-3-cyclobutyl-Phe, hCPA1-T268G had a catalytic efficiency (k_{cat}/K_m) that was roughly fourfold higher than that of the wild-type enzyme with MTX-Phe and $>4 \times 10^5$ higher than MTX-3-cyclobutyl-Phe with wild-type hCPA1.

Smith et al (49) proceeded to demonstrate the utility of this system in a cell culture system by conjugating hCPA1-T268G to two separate antibodies. The enzyme was linked to ING-1, which recognizes Epcam, a protein expressed on many epithelial tumors, and to Campath-1H, which recognizes CDw52, which is expressed on the surface of lymphocytes (but not in epithelial cells). The antibody conjugates were incubated with the epithelial tumor cell line HT-29 at various concentrations to test for selective sensitization of the cells to the designed prodrug. It was found that preincubation with 10 μg/ml of the ING-1–hCPA1-T268G conjugate strongly sensitized HT-29 cells to growth inhibition by

MTX-3-cyclobutyl-Phe and MTX-3-cyclopentyl-Tyr. At this conjugate concentration, the EC_{50} was ~ 10 nM, which is roughly the same as with free MTX. In the absence of the antibody conjugate, the derivatized prodrugs were $\sim 10^3$ less potent. As expected, in the presence of the Campath-1H–hCPA1-T268G conjugate, the sensitivity of HT-29 cells to the derivatized prodrugs was unchanged, demonstrating the immunospecificity of the ING-1–hCPA1-T268G ADEPT strategy.

In further studies, Wolfe et al (50) have investigated the in vivo efficacy of this orthogonal-pair ADEPT strategy in mouse models. Primary-toxicity studies showed that 8, 9, and 10 were highly stable in vivo and could be tolerated at doses 10- to 20-fold higher than free MTX. It was also shown that the ING-1–hCPA1-T268G conjugate localizes to tumor cells in Swiss nude mice bearing LS174T tumors. Over 144 h after injection, the tumor-to-blood ratio of the conjugate steadily grew to a maximum of 19.6. Despite these promising signs, however, treatment of the mice with the conjugate/prodrug therapy did not lead to a reduction of in vivo tumor growth for reasons that are to this point unclear.

Although, to date, it has not been shown that orthogonal MTX prodrugs will have an impact on the clinical treatment of cancer, the concept of heightening the specificity of ADEPT through orthogonal-pair design holds great promise. There are countless current and future prodrugs for which the general strategy of using a human enzyme to catalyze a "nonhuman" reaction could potentially prove applicable. The work of Smith and coworkers has demonstrated that medicinally important orthogonal pairs can possess enzymatic efficiencies that equal and surpass those of wild-type enzyme/substrate pairs. Ideally, in future approaches that combine ADEPT with orthogonal pairs, the oncology will correlate more strongly with the enzymology.

Initiation of Signals with Chemical Inducers of Dimerization

Because protein-protein interactions are key to almost all biological processes, a novel method for inducing intracellular protein dimerization was developed by Spencer et al (55). This method makes use of small, cell-permeable organic molecules called chemical inducers of dimerization (CIDs). CIDs have two binding surfaces that recognize one or more dimerization domains fused to target proteins. CID treatment causes the desired proteins to become cross-linked and initiate signaling. The protein complex can also be rapidly dissociated with the addition of a modified "CID," having only one of the two binding surfaces. The dimerization domains were derived from immunophilins FKBP12, cyclophilin (CyP), and the FKBP12–rapamycin-binding domain of FKBP-rapamycin–associated protein (FRAP). Various CIDs have been used to initiate a wide array of signaling pathways by dimerizing receptors at the cell surface [e.g. insulin (56), platelet-derived growth factor (56), Fas (57, 58), erythropoietin (59), transforming growth factor (60), and T-cell antigen (61, 62)], to inducibly translocate cytosolic proteins to the plasma membrane [e.g. the GTP exchange factor Sos (61) and kinases such as Src (63), Lck, Zap70 (62), and Raf (64)], to import various proteins to (65) and export (66) them from the nucleus, to regulate gene transcription (67), to induce cell-specific apoptosis, and to achieve regulated synthesis of human growth hormone in mice (68). CIDs have also been used to induce frog mesoderm in animal pole explants.

Initially, CIDs were either homodimers linked by a covalent tether of FK506 (FK1012) or cyclosporin $(CsA)_2$ or a heterodimer of FK506 and cyclosporin (FK-CsA). Complicating matters, FKBP12-FK506 complex binds to and inactivates calcineurin, a calcium-calmodulin–dependent protein phosphatase (69). This binding causes impaired signaling of the T-cell receptor followed by immunosuppression and toxicity. Therefore, these CIDs were modified synthetically to counteract their intrinsic biological activities.

Although the control of various signal transduction events with the CIDs has proven to be versatile, a significant shortcoming of this approach is the poor specificity of CIDs towards the wild-type immunophilins. The high expression of immunophilins in cells reduces the potency of CID ligands toward immunophilin fusion proteins by forming nonspecific receptor-ligand complexes. In transgenic animals, where there may be few cells expressing the desired fusion protein, the abundance of natural immunophilin could mask the biological response to CIDs. To improve the specificity of these CIDs, the orthogonal-pair or "bump-hole" strategy was developed.

The CIDs were modified to contain bulky substituents that clash with the amino acid side chains in the receptor, thereby abolishing its binding with wild-type receptors. Complementary mutations were made in the receptor that restores binding to these modified CIDs. Initially, cyclophilin-cyclosporin (CyP-CsA) was used as a model system to make this unique receptor-ligand pair (70). The crystal structure of the CyP-CsA complex revealed a hydrophobic interaction between the side chain of MeVal11 of CsA and a pocket of the CyP receptor. A modified CsA ligand was synthesized, in which the addition of only a methyl group to MeVal11 was enough to reduce the binding affinity from K_d from 5 nM to >3 mM with the wild type (Figure 14). As such, four different complementary mutations were rationally designed in the immunophilin receptor. The double mutant CyP(S99T, F113A) with modified CsA (MeIle11) showed >1000-fold selectivity $(K_d \sim 2$ nM). Although in the NFAT-signaling assay, MeIle11-CsA potently inhibited NFAT signaling in cells expressing CyP(S99T, F113A), MeIle11-CsA also caused the same inhibition in the cells expressing wild-type CyP ($IC_{50} \sim 300$ nM). To further improve this specificity, a more orthogonal CsA analog (CsA*) was synthesized that substituted a cyclopentylsarcosine (Figure 14) for the MeVal11 side chain. This compound does not bind CyP ($K_d > 15$ μM) and thus does not inhibit calcineurin in the wild-type cells. However, CsA* binds to triple-mutant CyP (F113G, C115M, S99T; CyP*) with very high affinity ($K_d \sim 9$ nM). Thus, this orthogonal receptor-ligand pair provides a potent tool for calcineurin inhibition in a cell- or tissue-specific manner.

The orthogonal design strategy was also extended to the rapamycin-FRAP system. Rapamycin binds to both FKBP12 and the FKBP12–rapamycin-binding domain of FRAP simultaneously to inhibit the activation of p70 S6 kinase and cyclin-dependent kinases (71). To study the role of FRAP in this pathway, a bump

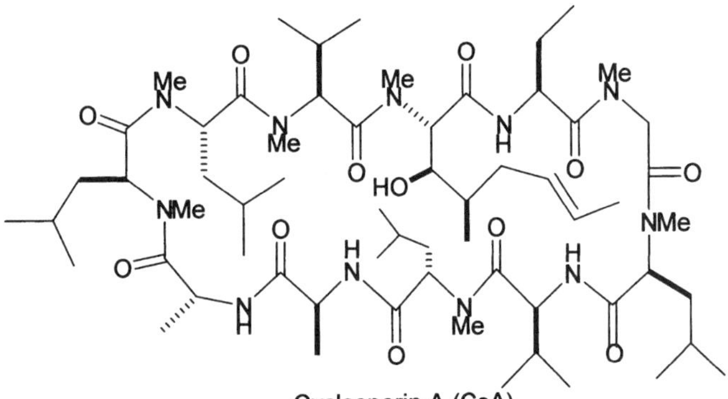

Cyclosporin A (CsA)

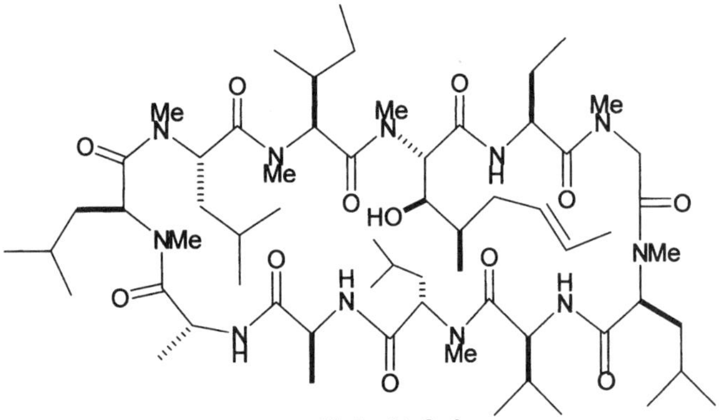

MeIle 11 CsA

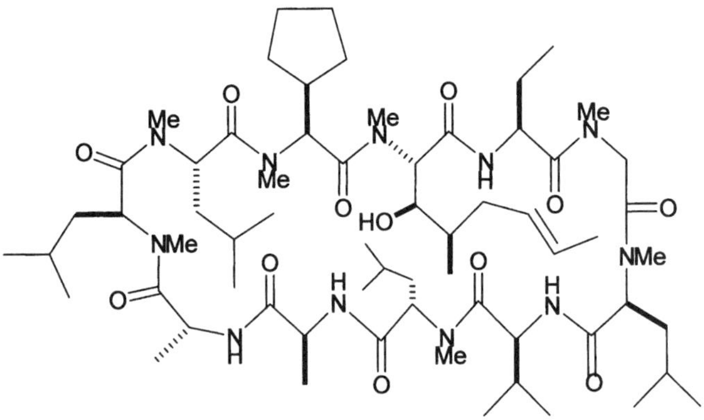

α-cyclopentylsarcosine 11-CsA

Figure 14 Chemical structures of cyclosporin A (CsA) and two analogs of CsA: MeIle 11 CsA, *α*-cyclopentylsarcosine 11-CsA, designed to complement specifically engineered cyclophilin proteins. Atoms which were added to CsA to precluded binding to wild-type cyclophilin are highlighted.

was added to the FRAP protein by mutating Ser-2035 to either threonine or an isoleucine. The orthogonal FRAP mutants did not bind the FKBP12-rapamycin complex and were used to explore its cellular function after inhibiting the endogenous FRAP with rapamycin. This system revealed that inhibition of FRAP blocks signaling to p70 S6 kinase and 4E-BP, thereby interfering with the translation of specific messenger RNA transcripts and G1 cell cycle progression.

To prevent rapamycin from inhibiting cell proliferation, nontoxic dimerizers (rapamycin*) were synthesized with a bulky substituent at the C16 position. Both methallyl and isopropoxy substituents at this position abrogated rapamycin* binding to FRAP and allowed T-cell proliferation (72). To identify compensating holes, a triple mutant of FRAP was tested that restored its ability to bind one of the rapamycin* ligands (from 500 to 10 nM). As a result, Liberles et al (72) were able to induce targeted gene expression in Jurkat T cells with an EC_{50} of <10 nM, by using this orthogonal pair.

Clackson et al redesigned the FKBP-ligand interface to introduce a novel specificity-binding pocket (73). The crystal structure of a high-affinity synthetic ligand of FK506 (FKBP ligand 1) with FKBP revealed that the C9 carbonyl group packs tightly against Tyr-26 and Phe-36 of FKBP (Figure 15a, see color insert). Therefore C9 carbonyl was replaced by larger ethoxy or ethyl group that selectively abrogated its binding to the wild-type protein ($K_d > 10$ μM). To rescue the binding of the orthogonal ligand with FKBP, four different mutants were tested containing different point mutations at Phe-36. All of these mutants restored binding and preferred S stereoisomers over R at the C9 position. To further improve the specificity of the S-ethyl–modified ligand, a trimethoxyphenyl group was used to replace the branched aliphatic side chains at this position. This resulted in a highly specific ligand ($K_d \sim 0.1$ nM), which is 1000-fold more specific for FKBP (F36V) than the wild-type protein.

Clackson and coworkers (73) have studied the interaction between engineered (F36V) FKBP and the orthogonal ligands with high resolution by using X-ray crystallography. The crystal structure, solved at 1.9-Å resolution (Figure 15b), is the first crystal structure of an engineered receptor ligand pair, and it provides tremendous insight into the critical design considerations necessary to achieve high-selectivity ligands for engineered receptors.

The first question answered by this structure relates to the compensatory changes in the protein that occur in response to the space-creating mutation. The structure of F36V shows that there are essentially no compensatory structural adjustments to the rest of FKBP. Furthermore, the F36V mutation opens up an additional 90 Å^3 of volume in the active site (Figure 15b).

Analysis of the binding conformation of the engineered ligand exactly agreed with the predictions in terms of the stereochemical preference for attachment of the ethyl group to FK506. The most interesting feature of the cocrystal structure is the failure of the ethyl bump to completely fill the introduced hole in the kinase. A completely enclosed cavity of $\sim$60 Å^3 is left unoccupied in the cocrystal structure.

Furthermore, no ordered water molecules were visible in the structure, suggesting that the remaining void is not occupied by solvent.

The remaining space in the cocrystal structure actually suggests something more broadly for engineering of orthogonal-receptor ligand pairs. Even with imperfect filling of the engineered pocket, it appears that high-affinity interactions can be recapitulated. One way to interpret this result is to realize that the way in which such ligands are discovered is first by discovery of an optimal "unbumped" ligand. This unbumped ligand provides many highly specific H-bond and van derWaals interactions with the protein target. The addition of a bump to this ligand can easily remove its ability to bind the protein (orthogonality). However, when a compensating hole is introduced into the protein, all of the formerly optimized interactions of the ligand with the protein can be regained by simply removing the steric insult of the added bump. In addition, the added bump and hole can create a greater surface area for interaction, which allows for even tighter binding than the original optimized situation.

The engineered FKBP (F36V) has been used in a wide variety of cell contexts to control diverse signaling pathways. A chimeric protein, FKBP (F36V) fused to the intracellular domain of the Fas receptor was expressed both in cells and in mice. Treatment of the modified ligand AP1903 caused rapid apoptosis of the engineered cells and in a mouse model, independently of endogenous FKBP.

Thus, the reengineering of the protein-ligand interface allows unparalleled temporal control of gene expression and protein subcellular localization that can be used for therapeutic purposes in the presence of endogenous proteins

CONCLUSIONS AND FUTURE DIRECTIONS

The ability to genetically program individual proteins in cells or whole organisms for inhibition by small organic molecules should continue to provide highly specific information about the role of key proteins in complex signal transduction pathways. The rapid increase in the number of drug targets identified through genomic approaches could be validated by using such combined chemical and genetic techniques.

Further structural studies of engineered receptors and orthogonal ligands also promise to provide interesting insights into the key design features required of such engineered interfaces.

ACKNOWLEDGMENTS

We thank the following funding agencies for supporting our early work on engineered kinases:National Science Foundation MCB-9874587, National Institutes of Health (R01 CA70331-04, IROIAI/CA44009-01), Pew Charitable Trust, Searle Foundation, Cottrell Scholars Program, and GlaxoWellcome. We are also especially grateful to Tim Clackson and Bruce Conklin for providing Figures 3, 4, and 14, describing their work.

Visit the Annual Reviews home page at www.AnnualReviews.org

LITERATURE CITED

1. Clackson T. 1998. *Curr. Opin. Struct. Biol.* 8:451–458
2. Crews CM, Splittgerber U. 1999. *Trends Biochem. Sci.* 24:317–20
3. Schreiber SL. 1998. *Bioorg. Med. Chem.* 6:1127–52
4. Hwang Y-W, Miller DL. 1987. *J. Biol. Chem.* 262:13081–85
5. Weijland A, Parlato G, Parmeggiani A. 1994. *Biochemistry* 33:10711–17
6. Powers T, Walter P. 1995. *Science* 269 (5229):1422–24
7. Jones S, Litt RJ, Richardson CJ, Segev N. 1995. *J. Cell Biol.* 130:1051–61
8. Weis K. 1998. *Trends Biochem. Sci.* 23:185–89
9. Sweet DJ, Gerace L. 1996. *J. Cell Biol.* 133:971–83
10. Weis K, Dingwall C, Lamond AI. 1996. *EMBO J.* 15:7120–28
11. Zhong JM, Chen-Hwang MC, Hwang YW. 1995. *J. Biol. Chem.* 270:10002–7
12. Feig LA, Pan BT, Roberts TM, Cooper GM. 1986. *Proc. Natl. Acad. Sci. USA* 83:4607–11
13. Schmidt G, Lenzen C, Simon I, Deuter R, Cool RII, et al. 1996. *Oncogene* 12:87–96
14. Cool RH, Schmidt G, Lenzen CU, Prinz H, Vogt D, Wittinghofer A. 1999. *Mol. Cell Biol.* 19:6297–305
15. Yu B, Slepak VZ, Simon MI. 1997. *J. Biol. Chem.* 272:18015–19
16. Mul YM, Rio DC. 1997. *EMBO J.* 16:4441–47
17. Strader CD, Fong TM, Tota MR, Underwood D, Dixon RA. 1994. *Annu. Rev. Biochem.* 63:101–32
18. Spiegel AM, Shenker A, Weinstein LS. 1992. *Endocrinol. Rev.* 13:536–65
19. Coward P, Wada HG, Falk MS, Chan SD, Meng F, et al. 1998. *Proc. Natl. Acad. Sci. USA* 95:352–57
20. Pace AM, Wong YH, Bourne HR. 1991. *Proc. Natl. Acad. Sci. USA* 88:7031–35
21. Redfern CH, Coward P, Degtyarev MY, Lee EK, Kwa AT, et al. 1999. *Nat. Biotechnol.* 17:165–69
22. Simonin F, Valverde O, Smadja C, Slowe S, Kitchen I, et al. 1998. *EMBO J.* 17:886–97
23. Strader CD, Gaffney T, Sugg EE, Candelore MR, Keys R, et al. 1991. *J. Biol. Chem.* 266:5–8
24. Pawson T. 1995. *Nature* 373:573–80
25. Cohen GB, Ren R, Baltimore D. 1995. *Cell* 80:237–48
26. Hunter T. 1995. *Cell* 80:225–36
27. Shah K, Liu Y, Deirmengian C. Shokat KM. 1997. *Proc. Natl. Acad. Sci. USA* 94:3565–70
28. Liu Y, Shah K, Yang F, Witucki L, Shokat KM. 1998. *Chem. Biol.* 5:91–101
29. Zheng J, Knighton DR, Ten Eyck LF, Karlsson R, Zuong N-H, et al. 1993. *Biochemistry* 32:2154–61
30. Jeffrey PD, Russo AA, Polyak K, Gibbs E, Hurwitz J, et al. 1995. *Nature* 376:313–20
31. Xu W, Harrison SC, Eck MJ. 1997. *Nature* 385:595–602
32. Sicheri F, Moarefi I, Kuriyan J. 1997. *Nature* 385:602–9
33. Yamaguchi H, Hendrickson WA. 1996. *Nature* 384:484–89
34. Liu Y, Shah K, Yang F, Witucki L, Shokat KM. 1998. *Bioorg. Med. Chem.* 6:1219–26
35. Bishop AC, Shah K, Liu Y, Witucki L, Kung C, Shokat KM. 1998. *Curr. Biol.* 8:257–66
36. Hanke JH, Gardner JP, Dow RL, Changelian PS, Brissette WH, et al. 1996. *J. Biol. Chem.* 271:695–701
37. Gillespie PG, Gillespie SKH, Mercer JA, Shah K, Shokat KM. 1999. *J. Biol. Chem.* 274:31378–81
38. Karp G. 1996. *Cell and Molecular Biology: Concepts and Experiments.* New York: John Wiley & Sons

39. Redowicz M. 1999. *J. Muscle Res. Cell Motil.* 20:241–48
40. Spudich JA. 1994. *Nature* 372:515–18
41. Hirokawa N. 1998. *Science* 279:519–26
42. Kull FEA. 1996. *Nature* 380:550–55
43. Kapoor T, Mitchison T. 1999. *Proc. Natl. Acad. Sci. USA* 96:9106–11
44. Weatherman R, Fletterick R, Scanlan T. 1999. *Annu. Rev. Biochem.* 68:559–81
45. Veldscholte J, Ris-Stalpers C, Kuiper GG, Jenster G, Berrevoets C, et al. 1990. *Biochem. Biophys. Res. Commun.* 173:534–40
46. Peet DJ, Doyle DF, Corey DR, Mangelsdorf DJ. 1998. *Chem. Biol.* 5:13–21
47. Koh J, Putnam M, Tomic-Canic M, McDaniel C. 1999. *J. Am. Chem. Soc.* 121:1984–85
48. Tairis N, Gabriel JL, Soprano KJ, Soprano DR. 1995. *J. Biol. Chem.* 270:18380–87
49. Smith GK, Banks S, Blumenkopf TA, Cory M, Humphreys J, et al. 1997. *J. Biol. Chem.* 272:15804–16
50. Wolfe LA, Mullin RJ, Laethem R, Blumenkopf TA, Cory M, et al. 1999. *Bioconjug. Chem.* 10:38–48
51. Sell S, Reisfeld RA. 1985. *Monoclonal Antibodies in Cancer.* Clifton, N.J.:Humana Press
52. Huennekens FM. 1994. *Adv. Enzyme Enzym. Regul.* 34:397–419
53. Vitols KS, Haag-Zeino B, Baer T, Montejano YD, Huennekens FM. 1995. *Cancer Res.* 55:478–81
54. Christianson DW, Lipscomb WN. 1989. *Acc. Chem. Res.* 22:22–69
55. Spencer DM, Wandless TJ, Schreiber SL, Crabtree GR. 1993. *Science* 262:1019–24
56. Yang J, Symes K, Mercola M, Schreiber SL. 1998. *Curr. Biol.* 8:11–18
57. Spencer DM, Belshaw PJ, Chen L, Ho SN, Randazzo F, et al. 1996. *Curr. Biol.* 6:839–47
58. Belshaw PJ, Spencer DM, Crabtree GR, Schreiber SL. 1996. *Chem. Biol.* 3:731–38
59. Blau CA, Peterson KR, Drachman JG, Spencer DM. 1997. *Proc. Natl. Acad. Sci. USA* 94:3076–81
60. Stockwell BR, Schreiber SL. 1998. *Chem. Biol.* 5:385–95
61. Holsinger LJ, Spencer DM, Austin DJ, Schreiber SL, Crabtree GR. 1995. *Proc. Natl. Acad. Sci. USA* 92:9810–14
62. Graef IA, Holsinger LJ, Diver S, Schreiber SL, Crabtree GR. 1997. *EMBO J.* 16:5618–28
63. Spencer DM, Graef I, Austin DJ, Schreiber SL, Crabtree GR. 1995. *Proc. Natl. Acad. Sci. USA* 92:9805–9
64. Farrar MA, Alberol I, Perlmutter RM. 1996. *Nature* 383:178–81
65. Belshaw PJ, Ho SN, Crabtree GR, Schreiber SL. 1996. *Proc. Natl. Acad. Sci. USA* 93:4604–7
66. Klemm JD, Beals CR, Crabtree GR. 1997. *Curr. Biol.* 7:638–44
67. Ho SN, Biggar SR, Spencer DM, Schreiber SL, Crabtree GR. 1996. *Nature* 382:822–26
68. Rivera VM, Clackson T, Natesan S, Pollock R, Amara JF, et al. 1996. *Nat. Med.* 2:1028–32
69. Liu J, Farmer JD Jr, Lane WS, Friedman J, Weissman I, Schreiber SL. 1991. *Cell* 66:807–15
70. Belshaw PJ, Schoepfer JG, Liu K-Q, Morrison KL, Schreiber SL. 1995. *Angew. Chem. Int. Ed. Engl.* 34:2129–2132
71. Brown EJ, Beal PA, Keith CT, Chen J, Shin TB, Schreiber SL. 1995. *Nature* 377:441–46
72. Liberles SD, Diver ST, Austin DJ, Schreiber SL. 1997. *Proc. Natl. Acad. Sci. USA* 94:7825–30
73. Clackson T, Yang W, Rozamus LW, Hatada M, Amara JF, et al. 1998. *Proc. Natl. Acad. Sci. USA* 95:10437–42
74. Kang C, Sun N, Honzatko RB, Fromm HJ. 1994. *J. Biol. Chem.* 269:24046–24049
75. Maier T, Lottspeich F, Bock A. 1995. *Eur. J. Biochem.* 230:133–38
76. Barbieri MA, Hoffenberg S, Roberts R, Mukhopadhyay A, Pomrehn A, et al. 1998. *J. Biol. Chem.* 273:25850–55

SUBJECT INDEX

A

A-40, 926
  vancomycin structural
    biology and, 271, 275
Acanthamoeba spp.
  actin filament dynamics
    and, 549
Acceptor substrate binding
  GCN5-related
    N-acetyltransferases and,
    95–96
Accumulation
  intermediate
    protein folding and
      hydrogen exchange,
      213–31
Acetylation
  GCN5-related
    N-acetyltransferases and,
    81–100
Acid molten globule state
  fast protein-folding
    kinetics and, 347
Actin filament dynamics
  in nonmuscle cells
    Arp2/3 complex, 552–54
    capping, 551–52
    coincidence detection,
    557
    conclusions, 567–68
    de novo filament
      formation, 555–56
    depolymerization,
    561–66
    elongation of new
      filaments, 557–58
    free barbed ends, 554–57
    functional implications,
    557
    introduction, 546–50
    limitations on filament

growth, 560–61
    monomer-binding
      proteins, 550–51
    polarity, 557
    pushing forward of
      membrane by growing
      filaments, 558–60
    recycling to
      ATP-actin-profilin pool,
      567
    severing, 555
    signal transduction,
    552–54
    survival in cytoplasm,
    566–67
    uncapping, 554–55
    unpolymerized actin
      subunit pool, 550–52
Activation
  actin filament dynamics
    and, 545–68
  molecular forces in protein
    interactions and, 16–17
  orthogonal ligands for
    engineered proteins and,
    577–604
  voltage-dependent
    ClC-type chloride
    channels and, 421–22
Acyl phosphatase
  fast protein-folding
    kinetics and, 348, 350
Adenosine triphosphate
  (ATP)
  actin filament dynamics
    and, 545–68
ADF/cofilins
  actin filament dynamics
    and, 545–68
Adhesion proteins
  molecular forces in protein

interactions and, 12–13,
    16
Aesthetics
  structural symmetry and
    protein function, 148–49
Affinity
  designed DNA ligands and,
    439–56
AGADIR program
  fast protein-folding
    kinetics and, 339
Alanine
  designed DNA ligands and,
    450
  fast protein-folding
    kinetics and, 334–35, 337,
    341, 345
  GCN5-related
    N-acetyltransferases and,
    90, 92
  quantitative chemical
    analysis of single cells
    and, 249
  vancomycin structural
    biology and, 266, 269–78,
    282–83
Alignment
  comparative structure
    protein modeling and,
    291–314
All-atom simulations
  electrostatic mechanisms
    of DNA deformation and,
    514
Allosterism
  membrane-binding
    domains and, 51, 70
  structural symmetry and
    protein function, 105,
    120–22
  vancomycin structural

CUMULATIVE INDEXES

CONTRIBUTING AUTHORS, VOLUMES 25–29